Carol A. Januska
6630 State Rd. #129
Parma, Ohio 44134
845-7861

Akt. 301
Tues. + Thurs.

MARKETING

FUNDAMENTALS

The Dun-Donnelley Publishing Corporation's
Series in Marketing □ Ralph L. Day, Consulting Editor

MARKETING

FUNDAMENTALS

FOR RESPONSIVE MANAGEMENT

Robert F. Hartley

Cleveland State University

Dun-Donnelley Publishing Corporation
A Dun & Bradstreet Company, New York

Library of Congress Cataloging in Publication Data

Hartley, Robert F.
    Marketing fundamentals for responsive management.

    (The Dun-Donnelley Publishing Corporation's
series in marketing)
    Edition for 1972 published under title: Marketing:
management and social change.
    Includes bibliographical references and index.
    1. Marketing.   2. Marketing management.
3. Marketing—Social aspects.   I. Title.
HF5415.H243   1976   658.8   75-35562
ISBN 0-912212-05-5

Dun-Donnelley Publishing Corporation
666 Fifth Avenue
New York, New York 10019

Design by A Good Thing

Manufactured in the United States of America

For Dorothy

CONTENTS

Part IV☐SOCIAL AND ENVIRONMENTAL ISSUES

Cases

PREFACE

I have always felt that the first course in marketing should be presented from a somewhat broader perspective than a strictly micro approach to an individual firm. Today the problems and goals of marketing are not dictated solely by the actions of competitors, but are affected by society and, increasingly, by government. The marketer must respond to all of these pressures—as must an author.

This new edition (the 1972 edition was titled *Marketing: Management and Social Change*) takes these issues into account, but it differs from the first in a number of significant ways. The material has been rearranged so that the environmental aspects of marketing are treated in Parts I and IV, the micro aspects—cast in a managerial framework—in Parts II and III. Chapters on marketing theory, comparative marketing, and marketing to the government have been dropped, the book being in consequence shorter. A better developed theme, responsive marketing, has been added. The text now focuses on answering the question: What is a responsive marketing strategy and how is it developed? It is assumed that if marketing is responsive to the needs and demands of consumers, its results will be profit for the firm.

The text is designed to be teachable and interesting to students. Questions for discussion are found at the ends of each chapter, along with an "exercise in creativity," a project, and a "role-playing case."

The ideas and techniques described in the text are illustrated by numerous vignettes (boxed material) entitled Marketing In Action, Marketing Mistakes, or Marketing Tools. These are either short cases or details of techniques and are usually accompanied by discussion questions. For example, "Marketing in Action" boxes include Frank Perdue's achievement in differentiating brands of chickens, Arm and Hammer's successful remarketing of baking soda, Midas Muffler's attention to marketing a service, and STP's use of reference groups to sell oil additives. "Marketing Mistakes" include, of course, the Edsel, but also the failure of Du Pont's Corfam artificial leather and Gillette's delay in bringing out a stainless steel razor blade to compete with Wilkinson and Schick. Examples of "Marketing Tools" are brainstorming, using the Survey of Purchasing Power to develop market potential, designing the semantic differential attitudinal scale, and using zip codes to aid in market segmentation.

As in the first edition, there are twenty-five cases at the end of the book, of which one third are new. These have been class tested and are open to both analytical and creative solution. The cases deal with current problems and follow the organization of the book.

They are easily adaptable to classroom presentation or to written assignments.

Many have contributed to this book: students, colleagues, and individuals from business and government. I particularly want to acknowledge the help of Donald W. Scotton of Cleveland State University, Ralph L. Day of Indiana University, Anthony F. McGann of The University of Wyoming, Joan Mizis of Florissant Valley Community College, and James U. McNeal of Texas A & M.

Jean L. Woy of Dun-Donnelley Corporation has been most constructive at the latter stages of the manuscript's development. Any errors or omissions are of course mine.

MARKETING

FUNDAMENTALS

PART I

OVERVIEW

OF

MARKETING

CHAPTER 1

INTRODUCTION: THE ROLE OF MARKETING

Marketing is one of the most characteristic activities of modern industrial society. In this first chapter we seek to define marketing and to describe its role. The visibility of marketing and the implications of this visibility are also discussed, and finally we look at the variety of careers in marketing, including some salary ranges. In this chapter you will encounter these terms:

marketing	caveat emptor
service marketing	consumerism
return on investment	merchandise turnover
after-sales aspects of marketing	activities of marketing
product differentiation	exchange

WHAT IS MARKETING?

Marketing is an exchange—as simple as a boy trading a pocket knife for a frog or as complicated and exciting as trying to choose the right product features, price, and promotional approaches for a new product, such as the Polaroid SX-70 camera. Marketing is the glamor part of business. Imaginative marketing actions can lead to business success. Even a dull product, if skillfully marketed, can find eager and appreciative customers. And what could be more prosaic than chicken?

3

MARKETING
IN
ACTION

Chicken Marketing

A chicken had always been viewed as a homogeneous product, a commodity that could not really be differentiated from other chickens in the supermarket or butcher shop. But Frank Perdue was audacious enough to try to turn his chickens into brand-name delicacies. In trying to do this he spent $1,000,000 a year on advertising.

To make his chickens different from other chickens, he feeds them "stuff" that turns them yellow: xanthophyll, a chemical naturally occurring in corn, egg yolk, and marigold petals goes into their feed. Mr. Perdue himself appears in TV commercials, as the "head of the company, asking for your gripes, promising your money back if you don't like the chickens." "With a face that's so plain it's got to be honest, you can't help but believe in the guy and his product," as an ad executive says. Perdue also is appearing on U. S. Spanish television to tell the Latin market (some 11 million people total in the U. S.) the merits of his chickens.

And Perdue chickens dominate the New York City area. The aggressive marketing efforts which started in 1971 have built up a family business to sales of $120 million.

SOURCE: "It Isn't Chicken Feed to Put Your Brand on 78 Million Birds," *Wall Street Journal,* May 13, 1974, pp. 1 and 17; "A Spanish Accent Is Very 'In' These Days on Madison Avenue," *Wall Street Journal,* January 24, 1975, pp. 1 and 17.

For thought and discussion:

Perdue's efforts represent successful *product differentiation* for a commodity product difficult to distinguish or differentiate from other similar products (in this case, chickens). How would you market innovatively other products difficult to brand, such as coal, corn, oranges, and pork?

Marketing is a basic part of our society. We are all exposed to it as consumers; many of us are or will soon be employed in marketing jobs. As consumers we are interested in marketing performance and responsiveness to our needs and wants. The quality of our life, or our life style, is vitally affected by marketing because marketing provides both the products and the services of a life style. As present or prospective marketers, we are concerned with what it offers in job satisfaction, advancement, and, for some of us perhaps, contribution to society.

Marketing has been defined as "the performance of business activities that direct the flow of goods and services from producer to consumer or user."[1] But this is an old and narrow definition of mar-

[1] Committee on Definitions, *Marketing Definitions: A Glossary of Marketing Terms* (Chicago: American Marketing Association, 1960), p. 15.

keting. It does not give us a true picture of marketing in today's society. First, it would be disastrous for any firm to consider marketing as being involved only after goods have been produced and are ready to leave the warehouse. Marketing should have been brought in long before this, in the product-planning stages and the assessment of consumer needs and wants. Furthermore, a firm is shortsighted indeed if it thinks it can repudiate any responsibility for its goods after they get into consumers' hands. Problems of after-sales servicing, of warranties and guarantees, even of product safety and expected performance, cannot be ignored. Marketing should even be concerned with some products—especially durable goods such as autos, washers, dryers, and refrigerators—after the product ceases to function and is worn out, in order to lessen the environmental problems of scrap, waste, and pollution.[2]

Consequently, we will define marketing as:

> Performance of activities involved in planning and facilitating the exchange of goods and services as well as other things of value.

This definition points to marketing involvement both before the sale or exchange, and after. It also suggests that not only goods and services can be exchanged (as is the common conception of marketing), but also other things such as a person's time, energy, or vote. Thus, the political candidate may use marketing in seeking the exchange of his or her energies and talents for the votes of others. Likewise a city may seek to market itself as a good place to live and work, offering to exchange its services and amenities for the social and economic energies of its residents. Figure 1-1 depicts the old and newer conceptions of marketing.

Activities in Marketing

It has long been said that if you build a better mousetrap the world will beat a path to your door, but today this may not be true. Unless effective marketing takes place, no one will know about the better mousetrap. Marketing is needed to distribute the product, inform people about it, and persuade them to try it—only in this way will the better product be recognized and sought.

Major activities involved in marketing are:

> Research on markets and how best to reach them
> Product planning
> Pricing
> Promotional communication via advertising and salespeople
> Packaging

[2] "Lazer Asks, 'Can Marketing Survive?' Replies, 'Yes, but . . .'," *Marketing News,* June 1, 1974, pp. 1, 5, and 11.

Physical distribution from the manufacturer, perhaps through various wholesalers and retailers, to the final consumer or user

We will examine each of these marketing activities in detail in later chapters.

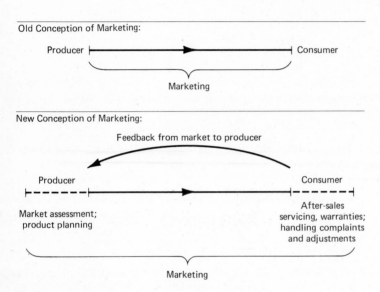

Figure 1-1. Changing conceptions of marketing.

What Can Be Marketed?

When we think of marketing, we tend to think of products, ranging from aspirins and deodorants to TVs and cars. The so-called soap operas that have been with us for decades on radio and TV are thus named because of their sponsorship predominantly by soap companies such as Procter & Gamble and Lever Bros.; they dominate the networks during those times of the day when housewives are the principal audience. In addition to consumer goods, industrial goods bought by other firms and by the government need to be marketed, with, of course, different marketing methods (for example, mass-media TV would seldom be an effective way of reaching such customers, since there would be too much wasted coverage).

But marketing is not limited to products. Services such as insurance, health care, investment opportunities, repair and maintenance, and even education can use the tools and techniques originally developed to sell products. All sorts of things and organizations can better promote themselves, perhaps improve a public image, or create new sources of customers or clients. Police departments, hospitals, schools, charitable drives, zoos, museums, causes—even political

When you grow up in Cleveland, you never stop growing.

Growing up in Cleveland means growing up with the best in music, art and theater. And there is no better way for a child to grow. But then, there is no better way for an adult to keep on growing.

It's good to know, for example, that the Cleveland Orchestra has free children's concerts. But it's better knowing that you can hear a symphony orchestra that is second to none as often as you like.

The same holds for our Museum of Art. Your child's class may tour there. But in Cleveland the whole family may tour one of the world's great art museums anytime. Together. Just as you can visit our Natural History Museum, Health Museum, Crawford Auto-Aviation Museum, or any of the 23 other cultural institutions at University Circle Complex. It's the only center of its kind in the country, providing experiences that can't be duplicated anywhere else in the country.

But so much in Cleveland can't be duplicated. The Salvador Dali Museum. The Great Lakes Shakespeare Festival. Cleveland Playhouse. Blossom Music Center. Karamu House, a unique inter-racial center that brings black culture and history alive.

If you think that art, music and theater are part of the better things in life, you couldn't choose a better place to live than Cleveland.

CLEVELAND
The best things in life are here.

For further information write or phone Richard L. DeChant, Vice President, Greater Cleveland Growth Association, 690 Union Commerce Building, Cleveland, Ohio, 44115. (216) 621-3300.

Service institutions and even cities are finding it desirable to use marketing techniques such as this ad for Cleveland. *Greater Cleveland Growth Association.*

Table 1-1.
Employment in Marketing Sectors:
Retail, Wholesale, Services, 1965–1972

Sector	Number of Persons Employed (millions)		
	1965	1970	1972
Retail	9,813	11,387	11,930
Wholesale	3,358	3,838	3,989
Services	11,763	14,033	14,760

Source: U. S. Department of Commerce, Bureau of the Census, *Statistical Abstract of the United States 1973*, pp. 741–42.

candidates—can use marketing. So can cities. The advertisement reproduced here is an effort to upgrade Cleveland's image, for both residents and nonresidents, as a desirable place to work and live.

PROMINENCE OF MARKETING

However we look at marketing, its size and importance strike us. We are never far from exposure to marketing efforts, through billboards, magazine, radio, newspaper, and TV commercials, shopping centers, and door-to-door salespeople, as well as through the acquisitions of our neighbors.

The sheer scope of marketing may be better realized by examining some statistics. Between one fourth and one third of the civilian labor force is engaged in marketing activities such as retailing, wholesaling, warehousing, transportation, communication and advertising, as well as employment in marketing departments of manufacturers. Table 1-1 shows the number of persons employed in retailing, wholesaling, and the service industry (such as hotels and motels, repair services, motion pictures and other recreational services). But the substantial employment in marketing is not limited to these three broad sectors; manufacturers, while not classified as being engaged in marketing, still employ many persons in marketing departments.

Another indicator of the importance of marketing in our economy is the expenditure for advertising and the sharp trend upward since 1950, shown in Table 1-2.

The overwhelming use of advertising in the United States, as compared to other countries of the world, can be seen in Table 1-3. This table shows per capita advertising expenditures, thereby eliminating the distortion in comparing smaller countries to bigger ones based on their total advertising expenditures. The much greater use of advertising in the United States partly reflects less tolerance for

Table 1-2.
Trend of Advertising
Expenditures in the
United States

Year	Expenditures (billions of dollars)
1900	$ 0.5
1919	2.0
1929	3.0
1946	3.0
1950	5.9
1956	9.7
1960	11.9
1966	16.8
1970	19.6
1973	25.1

Source: *Advertising Age*, September 18, 1967, p. 2; and U. S. Department of Commerce, Bureau of the Census, *Statistical Abstract of the United States 1974*, p. 771.

Table 1-3.
Advertising Expenditures
per Person in Major Nations
for 1973*

Country	Expenditures in Dollars
Austria	13
Belgium	30
Denmark	30
Finland	19
France	20
Ireland	12
Italy	12
Japan	31
Netherlands	14
Norway	25
Portugal	3
Spain	6
Sweden	43
United Kingdom	29
USA	120
West Germany	45

* Includes radio, TV, newspaper, magazine, and billboard advertising.
Source: *Vision: The European Business Magazine*, July/August 1974, p. 78.

Table 1-4.
Trend of Production
of Selected Packaging Materials, 1960–1972

Type of Package	1960	1970	1972
Tinplate cans (thousands of tons)	4,801	5,970	5,748
Aluminum cans (thousands of tons)	—	365	478
Aerosol containers (millions of units)	730	2,600	2,681
Plastic bottles (millions of pounds)	65	491	545
Glass containers (per 1,000 gross)	156,799	265,000	267,000

Source: *Modern Packaging Encyclopedia and Planning Guide*, 1972–1973, pp. 43–46.

and more restrictions on advertising in many countries. See chapter 16 for more detail on such constraints.

Table 1-4 shows the increasing production and use of certain selected packaging materials since 1960. The quantity produced in one year almost staggers the imagination. Yet, we take for granted and expect easy availability of all kinds of goods conveniently packaged. The increased use of such containers as aerosols and plastics indicates how marketers seek to provide better service to consumers. However, another aspect of these statistics also deserves attention: the contribution of solid waste and fluorocarbon to the pollution of our environment. We will examine this problem more specifically in a later chapter.

VISIBLE AND NONVISIBLE ASPECTS OF MARKETING

Marketing by its very nature is a visible and conspicuous activity, in contrast to other business functions such as finance, production, research, and, most of the time, labor relations and personnel policies.

Retailers of course are exposed to public scrutiny. Their stores, shopping centers, displays, merchandise carried, services offered, caliber and effectiveness of the salespeople, can add to our enjoyment and satisfaction in shopping, or can make a negative impression.

Although manufacturers' sales representatives usually do not come in direct contact with ultimate consumers (unless the manufacturer distributes directly, without middlemen, as do Avon and Fuller Brush), the advertising, packaging, pricing, quality of product, after-sales guarantees and servicing are fully visible. Numerous products enhance the quality of our lives; some, such as TV, have made major changes in our life style. Unfortunately, the plastic toy that falls apart after a few minutes of play, or the advertising message with exaggerated claims or poor taste, are visible activities that give marketing a negative image. We will examine some implications of this visibility shortly.

Some aspects of marketing, however, are far from visible. The ordinary consumer has difficulty assessing the quality of many products, for example. Definition of quality often is subjective—the subtlety of taste of a fine Scotch, dependability of an appliance, the smooth fit and drape of an expensive suit, the assurance of a reputable drug.

Another ingredient of confusion is the esoteric nature of profitability. While most publicly owned firms are required to publish the statistics of their sales and profits, sometimes this can be misleading. The ratio of net profit to sales is a widely used standard of business success. Yet when different types of businesses are compared according to this standard, measures of profitability may be deceiving. Let us examine such an instance.

Food prices tend to provoke criticism, and from time to time demands arise that supermarket pricing practices be investigated. Thereupon the supermarket chains quickly offer convincing statistics to prove that their prices are not too high, but that indeed supermarket net profits are often lower than those of other retailers, averaging little more than one penny on every dollar of sales.

These are not fictitious or unrepresentative figures: supermarket profits do range from 0.9 to 2.7 percent of sales, compared with 5 percent and better for many other retailers, such as department stores. However, a more revealing statistic—and this is seldom mentioned—is the return on investment, that is, profits as a percentage of investment. This ranges from 9.2 to 17.6 percent for supermarkets, higher than for most other retailers, indicating rather conclusively that supermarkets are indeed quite profitable.

The explanation is that the supermarket operates a plant that is rather inexpensive, at least in comparison with the facilities of most department stores. Furthermore, a supermarket has a low investment in inventory. Food is sold and replenished often. It has a high turnover. Dresses, furniture, and jewelry turn over slowly and much more investment is needed to maintain an adequate stock. Therefore, while profit on sales (net profit) may be low for grocery stores, the real measure of profitability—the return on investment—is high. Table 1-5 compares the profitability of a supermarket and a department store.

IMPLICATIONS OF THE VISIBILITY OF MARKETING

Being so visible, marketing presents an inviting target to criticism both at home and abroad. Indeed, our entire economic system is often judged on the basis of impressions left by marketing techniques. When our economy is characterized as one of planned

Table 1-5.
Supermarket and Department Store Profitability

	Supermarket	Department Store
Annual sales	$1,000,000	$1,000,000
Net profit (percent of sales)	1%	5%
Net profit (dollars)	$10,000	$50,000
	(1% × 1,000,000)	(5% × 1,000,000)
Merchandise turnover (number of times average stock is sold in one year)	25	4
Average stock at selling price	$40,000	$250,000
	(1,000,000 ÷ 25)	(1,000,000 ÷ 4)
Average gross margin (markup percentage)*	25%	40%
Investment in inventory (average stock at cost)	$30,000	$150,000
	[40,000−(40,000 × 25%)]	[250,000−(250,000 × 40%)]
Return on investment† (net profit ÷ investment)	33%	33%
	(10,000 ÷ 30,000)	(50,000 ÷ 150,000)

* Gross margin percentage is the money left after cost of goods sold have been deducted from sales, or to put it another way, it is the amount that goods are marked up. Expenses of operating the business are deducted from gross margin to (hopefully) provide a net profit.

† Exclusive of building and fixtures, which would reduce this return on investment. The department store, having a more elaborate store and fixtures, would have a higher investment and a consequently lower percentage return on investment than would the more sparsely furnished supermarket.

obsolescence, creating and encouraging waste, directing national goals in selfish, materialistic directions, when much of our television programming and the ever-present commercials are called the Great Wasteland, marketing gets the blame. Similarly, when consumer credit commitments reach dangerous levels the responsibility is laid to the overzealousness of advertising and the doctrine of conspicuous consumption that it fosters.

The public tends to focus on the less flattering image of marketing. We remember our bad experiences; we relish the reports on marketing deception or abuses. We take for granted the inspired and selfless. Consider:

In the mid-1950s, Campbell Soup Company found itself in a quandary familiar to many large corporations: its headquarters and principal plant were located in a decaying industrial community, one experiencing exodus of its middle class, the boarding up of stores, and an increasing burden of unemployment and poverty. Reaction of most firms in such a situation is to move to the suburbs and thereby escape the deteriorating environment—and consequently hasten its deterioration by removing jobs and a tax base.

Campbell refused to do this. Instead it directed money and manpower to rehabilitating its hometown, Camden, N.J. Efforts included: building parks, setting up day-care centers, underwriting a summer job program, arranging loans and management aid for black businessmen, and furnishing major support for large-scale downtown and port renewal. It even set up a housing rehabilitation plan whereby low-income families have been helped to buy their own homes.[3]

Consider:

The Federal Trade Commission has shown increasing concern about television commercials which use misleading or deceptive mockups or demonstrations. In 1969 a complaint was issued against Campbell Soup Company for using marbles in the bottom of a bowl of soup which was depicted in a ready-to-eat situation. Of course, the marbles prevented the ingredients from sinking to the bottom, thereby giving the illusion of more heavy solid ingredients than actually contained. The Commission accepted a consent order by which Campbell agreed to cease such misrepresentation.

However, SOUP, Inc., an organization created by members of the public to "Stamp Out Unfair Practices," sought to have the FTC withdraw its acceptance of the consent order and that, furthermore, Campbell's future advertising be required to disclose this "deception." The major argument for such stigmatizing was that consumers' buying habits can be influenced by past advertising claims; only by requiring deceptive advertisers to publicize their deception in future advertising can this effect be dissipated. Barely by a split vote of the Commission was the petition of SOUP denied.[4]

Our attention—and that of the press and government—was riveted on the latter "misconduct" of Campbell, but the altruistic actions of the first example received scant national attention. This has serious implications for marketing, in that a small number of less-than-desirable practices are sufficient to create a totally negative image.

Public opinion of marketing has become increasingly negative in recent years. Criticisms have been reflected in such books as *The*

[3] "Business Rights the Social Ills—In a Recession," *Business Week*, March 6, 1971, p. 60.
[4] "Legal Developments in Marketing," *Journal of Marketing*, January 1971, p. 82, and October 1969, pp. 84–85.

Consumerism — promotion of consumers' interest

Innocent Consumer vs. the Exploiters,[5] Let the Seller Beware,[6] and, written by a U. S. Senator, The Dark Side of the Marketplace,[7] now in its second edition. The popular term for consumer dissatisfaction is consumerism, which we will examine in considerable detail later in the book.

A critical evaluation of marketing stems in part from older practices. Not too many decades ago the marketing philosophy was stated as caveat emptor—"let the buyer beware." In those days the shrewder purchaser might drive a good bargain; the less sophisticated would probably be victimized. The Yankee horse trader symbolized this era. In an age when a man's livelihood, and even his life, might depend on his horse, this aspect of marketing was not a matter of light concern.

Today the doctrine of caveat emptor has been put aside by reputable business firms. Most marketers are now concerned with fair treatment of their customers if for no other reason than to maintain their position in a competitive environment. If customers are to be retained, then customer satisfaction must be sought.

Our advertising and marketing efforts may be described as our picture window to the world. They display the good life to be sought by all, or are the shallow veneer of a decadent society, depending on the perspective of the evaluator. Aspiration for the products of an affluent age can stimulate the upward mobility of society. It has been established that aspirations are not static, that they rise with success;[8] people move to better homes, seek ever higher positions and incomes, a better neighborhood, a higher education. Marketing stimulates this upward drive by publicizing the products that make up the higher standard.

The visibility of marketing has other implications. Marketing mistakes of a firm can hardly be hidden—they are visible not only to other firms and competitors but to the public as well.

---

[5] Sidney Margolius, The Innocent Consumer vs. the Exploiters (New York: Trident Press, 1967).

[6] James Bishop, Jr., and Henry Hubbard, Let the Seller Beware (Washington, D. C.: National Press, 1969).

[7] Warren G. Magnuson and Jean Carper, The Dark Side of the Marketplace, 2d ed. (Englewood Cliffs, N.J.: Prentice-Hall, 1972).

[8] George Katona, "Economic Psychology," Scientific American, October 1954, p. 35.

MARKETING MISTAKES

The Failure of "Dry, White" Whiskey

In February 1971, with much hoopla, Brown-Forman Distillers Corporation brought out Frost 8/80, a unique "dry, white" whiskey. "Our research pointed to widespread acceptance of the product and its introduction was all we could have hoped for," Brown-Forman's president noted. "It was greeted with great applause by our people and a gnashing of teeth by our competitors." The timing did indeed seem right since traditional spirits (bourbons) had been faltering, wherein other "white goods" (gin, vodka) had been growing at a rapid rate.

But 22 months later the company admitted defeat and stopped production because sales were "too small to continue any further investment." It had spent about $6.5 million on the product, including $500,000 on consumer research (it had employed eight ouside research or packaging firms for this). It introduced the product with heavy advertising; when first year sales proved disappointing, Brown-Forman switched ad agencies—but to no avail.

With the benefit of hindsight, company executives believe they misinterpreted the results of the market research. They also think switching ad agencies may have confused people: "the switch of ads in midstream wasn't too good . . . we should have stuck with one approach or the other."

One competitor (with tongue in cheek) says Brown-Forman "pulled out too soon." "You can't establish anything as different as Frost 8/80 in just two years. It took vodka about 10 years to really get a foothold in this country." Mr. Lucas, president of Brown-Forman, rejects this charge. "We don't believe in perpetuating our failures. A lot of companies won't recognize a mistake and just let it go ahead, draining their resources and demoralizing their people. We took a risk, and we lost."

SOURCE: "How a New Product Was Brought to Market Only to Flop Miserably," *Wall Street Journal,* January 5, 1973, pp. 1 and 11.

For thought and discussion:
Does this example suggest that consumer research before introducing a new product is wasted? Why or why not?

Why do you think the white whiskey did not sell?

If you were the brand manager for Frost 8/80, what arguments would you offer for continuing it for another 1-2 years?

CAREERS IN MARKETING

Marketing employs many people in diversified positions. For a sampling of the variety of job opportunities, and of salary levels, see Figure 1-2. This is from the "Positions Available" section of the *Wall Street Journal* in the summer of 1975.

Attractive Aspects of Marketing Careers

One's Job Ability is Easily Measured. Marketing is the sales-generating aspect of any business. Other activities, such as production,

Figure 1-2.

finance, personnel, accounting, are really sales-supporting—the operations that facilitate the performance of the marketing function. Regardless of size, the success of a firm depends on the primacy of the marketing division as the income-producing segment of the operation.

For the person reasonably confident of his or her abilities, many aspects of marketing hold unusual attractiveness relative to other positions in government or industry. A person's effectiveness can often be more tangibly measured in dollar sales and profits earned, and earnings and promotions are frequently matched with performance. This is in contrast with accounting, personnel, or finance executives who often find it difficult to prove their actual contribution to a firm's profits.

**MARKETING
IN
ACTION**

Marketing the American Hamburger in Europe

Peter Morton was 24 years old and had just graduated from the University of Denver. Now he was wandering around London, and "I couldn't find a decent hamburger." Since millions of Americans visit London every year, he figured that a restaurant offering good quality hamburgers would be a natural. He was able to raise $50,000 through family and friends, and he opened a restaurant in April 1970. It had seating for 52 people, and he called it The Great American Disaster.

Soon he began serving 5,000 customers a week: "Even on rainy nights we had waiting lines a quarter-mile long. We became the in place not only for Americans in London but for Londoners as well." In one year, the restaurant grossed $500,000. Now a chain of Great American Disasters is franchised all over Europe.

SOURCE: Connecticut Walker, "What Europe Needs Is the American Hamburger," *Parade,* September 26, 1971, p. 20.

Opportunity for Creativity and Innovative Thinking. Marketing needs creative individuals, people with imagination, seeking freedom from routinization (which is coming to plague more and more occupations). This is true at all levels, from top management to the lowest echelon, and in almost all aspects, from advertising to retailing to selling to researching. The advertiser, in creating a new theme, seeking the most effective copy, administering an entire advertising campaign, needs creative ability as well as a thorough knowledge of business and marketing operations; in addition, creative insight into the consumer decision-making process, its complexities and patterns, is needed. The retailer, at almost any level in the organization, can use imagination to turn customer interest into sales. The researcher frequently must use ingenuity to develop new approaches to better understand the capricious consumer. And marketing executives are continually faced with these questions: Is there a better marketing strategy to use? How can the consumer be reached more efficiently? What innovations are necessary or desirable? Sometimes imagination can reveal a latent opportunity in a commonplace setting.

Opportunities for Women in Marketing. Marketing offers many opportunities for women. In retailing, for example, women in many department and specialty stores fill one third to one half of the buying and executive positions. Women are particularly prominent as publicity and fashion directors and in personnel and training positions. Women reach major executive levels: for example, Macy's New York promoted five women to vice presidential rank.[9] There are now opportunities for women in most areas of business—retailing, advertising, marketing research, package design, and sales. In advertising there is the story of the account executive of an advertising agency who almost single-handedly provided the inspiration for transforming a mediocre airline into the talk of the transportation industry.

---

[9] Samuel Feinberg, "From Where I Sit," *Women's Wear Daily,* November 27, 1970, p. 11.

**MARKETING
IN
ACTION**

Overcoming Mediocrity: Mary Wells and Braniff Airline
Surveys had shown that the chief characteristic of Braniff Airline was its lack of character; it was neither liked nor disliked, but just ignored by most people. The new president of Braniff gave his advertising agency one year to build up a national awareness of Braniff.

Mary Wells, working with interior designer and color specialist Alexander Birard, and Italian couturier Pucci, recommended a startling transformation: a marketing theme for the airline built around color. The key elements were new aircraft interiors, solid-color fuselages, robes for stewardesses. Seven "shocking" colors were used for the planes, ranging from ochre to carrot orange. This was heralded as the end of the "plain plane." Rather than the traditional tailored suits for stewardesses, Pucci's concept was several changes of costume—promoted as the "air strip"—ranging from apricot-colored outercoats to brightly patterned stretch pants.

Did such "hoopla" fill the jets? In 1964 Braniff had a net profit of $5.9 million on revenues of $109 million. After the change, in just 9 months (through September 1966) it earned $15 million on income of $138 million.

SOURCE: "More Blue in Braniff's Yonder," *Business Week,* January 21, 1967, pp. 102–110.

For thought and discussion:
As with Perdue chickens, the intent with Braniff was to find some way to differentiate its airline from its competitors. Can you think of other ways in which Braniff might have achieved product differentiation?

Opportunities for social betterment. You may think that marketing is so firmly wedded to making a profit that there is no room for making any contribution to society (except for advancing a materialistic standard of living). This is not necessarily true. Consider the following two examples:

Gulf Oil and Reston. Reston was a highly-touted "new town" in northern Virginia about twenty miles from Washington, D. C. Amid urban sprawl—usually unplanned and often chaotic, ugly, inefficient—the possibilities of planned communities seem most desirable. Reston was planned to be eventually a small city of 75,000 people and it was hailed by sociologists and city planners as the prototype for cities of the future. But it was undercapitalized and poorly managed by its visionary founder, Robert Simon. The ambitious new community was rescued from the brink of collapse by Gulf Oil Company in 1967; Gulf stepped in with millions of dollars and assumed active management from the reeling founder.

And Reston survived and began to prosper, with the original ideal mostly untarnished. Population in 1968 jumped from 2,800 to 5,000 with improved marketing efforts and more efficient management. By 1970, population had reached over 10,000, and finally Reston was beginning to make money for Gulf Oil.[10]

Pier I Imports. After five years of operation, by 1971 Pier I had grown to the largest chain of import stores in the United States. The strategy that made all this possible also brought new—even undreamed—prosperity to scores of tiny villages in remote, undeveloped corners of the world. Cottage industries have been organized to mass-produce handcrafted items such as cricket cages and carved elephants from Kenya, dried blowfish from Taiwan, Mexican piñatas, brass pots, wicker tables and chairs, and wooden bowls from the Philippines. One small farming community in Rumania supplies 10,000 wicker chairs a year made in the winter when the fields cannot be worked. One supplier in Mexico transformed a small shop in the back of

[10] *Reston Quarterly Fact Sheet,* publication of Gulf-Reston, Fall 1970.

his house into a factory employing more than fifty workers; an entire village in Kenya carves wooden animals for Pier I.[11]

As these examples show, profitability need not be sacrificed for social causes, although, as in the case of Reston, profits may have to be deferred temporarily in order to make a new sociological concept viable.

DESIGN OF THIS BOOK

This book combines a marketing management approach with a social or environmental approach and merges them into a perspective we can call responsive marketing. We will be concerned with marketing's role in society and the shortcomings and challenges arising from that role. Marketing in our age of affluence and mass-promotional techniques has an increasingly important part to play. It is a powerful tool that either can yield mediocrity and shallow materialism or, conversely, can make a significant social contribution. It touches on some controversial issues: consumerism, ethics, social responsibility, the environment. With this in mind we will examine how well marketing is fulfilling its role, what pressures marketers may need to anticipate, and what can be done to be more responsive.

At the same time, marketing will be considered from a practical perspective. We will describe tools and techniques needed for effective management. Scattered throughout are examples of marketing successes and marketing failures or omissions; these suggest the opportunities in marketing.

QUESTIONS AND PROBLEMS

1. We are currently seeing a tide of marketing-related legislation. To a great extent this is the result of the poor public image of marketing coupled with today's more militant consumer. Should government through its laws and regulations assume a larger role in the functioning of marketing? Discuss.

2. The author has contended that marketing offers more opportunity and reward for the creative and imaginative person than most other fields of business endeavor. How would you defend this assertion to the student majoring in accounting, finance, personnel, or production management?

3. The number of workers engaged in wholesaling and retailing increased twelvefold between 1870 and 1950, as contrasted with only a threefold

[11] "Pier I: A Retailer for Cottage Industries," Business Week, October 2, 1971, pp. 58–59.

increase in production workers during the same period. Does this indicate growing wastes and inefficiencies in marketing? What factors do you think might account for this disproportionate increase?

4. What explanations can you give for the much greater use of advertising in the United States relative to the rest of the world (see Table 1-3)? Is this an indication of the greater sophistication and efficiency of U. S. marketing compared to that of other nations?

5. We have discussed the visibility of marketing and some of the implications of this visibility. On balance, what is the effect of this visibility on marketing efficiency? on society? on consumer satisfaction?

6. "In the national arena of public policy and in the arena of international economics, marketing is becoming more crucial as a component in the total social system; its impact on national well-being and on international dynamics is much larger than in earlier days." Evaluate this statement (from Michael Halbert, *The Meaning and Sources of Marketing Theory,* New York: McGraw-Hill, 1965, p. xxii). Why do you think the impact of marketing is much larger than in earlier days?

7. Discuss some of the more important reasons that might justify a study of marketing, even by those who do not intend to find employment in marketing-related activities.

Project

Find as many specific examples as you can of nonproducts which are being marketed (nonproducts such as a city, a museum, a police department, a school bond issue, a political candidate, and the like). What marketing efforts are being used? How successful would you judge these efforts to be?

Exercise in Creativity

Develop a list of nonproducts which you think could benefit from marketing efforts, but which are apparently receiving no attention in your community. What specific recommendations would you make for marketing these nonproducts?

Role-playing Case

You have just finished college. Rather than touring Europe (as Peter Morton of the "Great American Disaster" did), you decide to spend a few months traveling around the United States before settling down to a job. You find that taco restaurants which are very popular in your part of the country are nonexistent in certain metropolitan areas around the Great Lakes. You believe you have stumbled onto a significant marketing opportunity.

You seek out some of your friends in order to raise the $35,000 you estimate will be necessary to get started. "This is a great chance to get into a market before competition. We know that tacos can be very popular—they are already big sellers in most parts of the country. We can't miss on this, but we'll have to act fast," you enthusiastically tell them.

What objections would you anticipate? How would you answer them?

CHAPTER 2

INNOVATION IN MARKETING AND THE MARKETING CONCEPT

Mass marketing is a fairly recent phenomenon, and it is still changing. In this chapter we discuss the development of marketing in the United States and the mass marketing we know today; milestones in the development of advertising are also described. We will consider change or innovation in marketing, how it serves society, and how it can be encouraged in an organization. Short biographies of four marketing innovators, two of whom have had major impact on our society, illustrate the opportunities for fresh, innovative thinking and give some of the flavor of our development toward mass marketing. Finally, the marketing concept, a major marketing philosophy, is discussed along with its limitations. Key terms in this chapter are:

institutional convenience
mass marketing
merchandise diversification
brainstorming
product-use innovation

marketing concept
customer or consumer
   orientation
responsive marketing

HISTORICAL DEVELOPMENT

The first marketing probably took place near the beginning of civilization, perhaps as some caveman exchanged an extra club for an animal skin that his neighbor didn't need. As you can imagine, some degree of specialization is needed if marketing is to take place regularly—because specialization leads to surpluses, and surpluses lead to trade. For example, the hunter traded with the arrow maker; each did what he best could do, and primitive marketing took place.

Now of course as sophisticated production leads to greater specialization, the marketing process becomes more highly formed. Middlemen—persons and/or firms between the producer and the consumer—emerge, as well as such techniques as advertising, personal selling, and marketing research.

Let us now look briefly at the historical development of marketing in the United States. During colonial times, especially in rural America, food, clothing, and shelter for the most part were home-grown, homespun, and constructed from materials on the land. Until the Civil War, small businesses—shopkeepers, metalsmiths, peddlers —dominated the economic scene. Probably the first retail selling in most of America was done by peddlers:

> At the outset they walked. Those of more stature rode horseback and the even more prosperous rode in wagons or carriages. . . . The peddler's life was strenuous, lonely, and hazardous. When the opportunity developed or when they found the right place or the right girl, many were happy to settle down as storekeepers.[1]

The Civil War required a major commitment of resources for a sustained period of time. Thus, it hastened mass production, fostered large-scale enterprises, and laid the groundwork for the surge to come.

Transportation, especially rail, had been developing rapidly prior to 1860 and was critically important in the growth of a mass-production economy—both for obtaining raw materials as well as for distributing finished products. During the 1850s, 21,000 miles of new track were laid—more than twice that existing prior to 1850. The total more than tripled again between 1860 and 1880, becoming, by 1914, more than that for all Europe.

Increasing population meant growth in markets. To this was added advances in technology and mechanization, and greater availability of power. As an example of how production increased, 11,000 tons of steel were produced in 1860; by 1914 this had skyrocketed to 23 million tons. With mass production and the eventual possibility of overcapacity, marketing became more important: either more goods had to be sold, or plants would shut down.

INGREDIENTS OF MASS MARKETING

We can recognize certain ingredients or attributes of mass marketing:

Mass production
Brand names
Lower prices and per unit profits than without mass marketing
Selling—both through salespeople and through mass-media advertising
Institutional convenience

[1] Tom Mahoney and Leonard Sloane, *The Great Merchants* (New York: Harper & Row, 1966), p. 5.

Mass production (providing a large volume of rather standardized goods) is essential because it requires marketing efforts to dispose of such goods. Brand names identify manufacturers and give the consumer some assurance of quality while motivating the manufacturer to give fair value under his brand in order to get repeat business.

Prices and margins (markups) tend to be lower in a mass-marketing situation because more total profits usually result from the greater volume of business generated by lower prices, due to economies of scale. Selling is needed to move the output of mass production and also to open new markets and expand over-all demand. Therefore, personal selling and mass promotion (advertising) become necessary to inform consumers of the goods available, and also to persuade them to buy.

Another attribute of mass-marketing is *institutional convenience*. By this we mean that the institutions of marketing (retailers and the various kinds of wholesalers) proliferate, become larger, more efficient, more able to cope with the diverse needs of consumers and the heterogeneity of products. Transportation and storage facilities also develop to expedite the physical handling of goods.

The end result, ideally, is mass consumption, more or less balancing the ever-increasing products of mass production.

An important part of mass marketing is mass promotion or advertising. In the next section we briefly trace the early development of advertising as it paves the way for expansion of markets.

DEVELOPMENT OF ADVERTISING

Advertising has been a major ingredient in the mass marketing of the United States, with over $25 billion spent on it in 1973. The great expansion of advertising occurred in the last several decades, but even at the turn of the century over half a billion dollars was spent. Advertising is no new thing.

Efforts to persuade people to buy can be traced back thousands of years. The streets of ancient Greece, Rome, and Carthage were filled with "barkers." Brands and trademark differentiation began in the Middle Ages, with marks used to identify guilds and thereby assure the quality of goods from a reputable guild. In the early seventeenth century, the first English newspaper was published and furnished a significant new advertising medium. Benjamin Franklin is sometimes regarded as the father of American advertising; the first issue of his *Pennsylvania Gazette* contained a soap advertisement. The newspaper soon included ads for wine, tea, chocolate, books, quills, and many other products.

Newspaper advertising dominated in early nineteenth-century America; some newspapers even devoted all or most of the front

Advertising as we know it appeared near the turn of the century. This ad is from *Judges* magazine, 1902. *Library of Congress.*

page to advertising. Many of these early ads were classified ads, although tobacco products were being advertised even before the beginning of the nineteenth century. Patent medicine advertising became widespread. Without a Federal Trade Commission to restrain fraudulent practices, wild claims abounded. Although magazine publishing began in the early eighteenth century, this medium was little used for advertising until much later.

Up to 1880 most advertising was done by retailers, but as national

This example of the very successful advertising campaign promoting smoking to women focused on the nonfattening characteristics of cigarettes. The ad is from *Life* magazine, 1929. *Library of Congress.*

markets developed, aided by a transcontinental railroad and growing urban concentration, this changed. In the 1880s, four manufacturers began large-scale advertising. Three of these products were soaps, of which one, Ivory, is still on the market today. The fourth product was Royal Baking Powder. The first national advertising plan is believed to be one developed by Gillette Safety Razor Company, about 1905.[2]

With the excesses of the laissez-faire era finally resulting in trust-busting and a reform movement against certain business practices, advertising came under attack. Newspaper and magazine publishers began to scrutinize advertising copy. *Printers' Ink,* the magazine of the advertising industry, drew up a model state law that would penalize false advertising.

The 1920s were years of great growth in advertising, and high-pressure selling became accepted. The most notable accomplishment of advertising persuasion during the 1920s was the promotion of smoking among women. Lucky Strike sales boomed and advertising expenditures by the American Tobacco Company rose to $19 million in 1931. It was found that movie star testimonials helped to sell Lux soap, and promotion of products by movie stars and athletes became commonplace, as it still is.

Another advertising medium, radio, came in the 1920s and, with over 50 percent of the homes in the United States having radios by 1930, became a major medium for mass advertising. Television added its massive thrust beginning in the late 1940s, and has grown faster than any other advertising medium with its potent ability to transmit messages by sight and by sound.

INNOVATION IN MARKETING

Sometimes marketing has led change; more often it has reacted or adjusted to changes in the economy and society. There is no reason now to think that change is slowing down. On the contrary, it may even be occurring more rapidly than in the past, with technology, consumer tastes, and the economic and political environment sometimes in dramatic flux. (For example, consider the impact of an energy shortage and petroleum price hikes on world economies and standards of living.) Figure 2-1 shows various directions of change or innovation in marketing during the last few decades.

New types of retail institutions include the various kinds of discount stores (from catalog stores to sprawling general-merchandise stores), convenience food stores, vending machines, and more recently, small boutiques. Even traditional retail firms have undergone

[2] Paul D. Converse, *The Beginning of Marketing Thought in the United States* (Austin: University of Texas, 1959), p. 30.

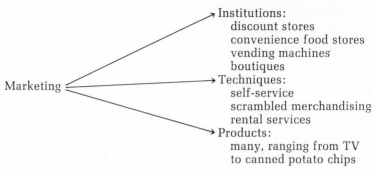

Marketing

Institutions:
  discount stores
  convenience food stores
  vending machines
  boutiques
Techniques:
  self-service
  scrambled merchandising
  rental services
Products:
  many, ranging from TV
  to canned potato chips

Figure 2-1. Innovations in marketing

changes in techniques. Self-service is no longer limited to super-markets and discount stores but has spread to variety stores, drug-stores, and even certain sections in department stores. *Merchandise diversification* is occurring, with supermarkets selling nonfood items, drugstores expanding to carry hardware, housewares, gifts, some grocery products, and even small appliances, while variety stores (the former "dime stores") now carry TV sets costing several hun-dred dollars and 10-speed bicycles. Not even the gasoline station has ignored the tempting potential of nontraditional merchandise. This phenomenon is known as *scrambled merchandising,* and will be dis-cussed in the next chapter.

Other marketing techniques that have become popular in the last decade include auto-rental firms and the expansion of other rental services; home-cleaning services offered by some department stores; the selling format of the Book-of-the-Month now expanded to records and other merchandise; and use of premium methods of promotion, such as games and contests.

Product innovations cover a wide range, from canned potato chips to digital watches and pocket calculators, from "earth" shoes to computers and color TVs. Admittedly, many product changes are superficial: a different color package, a new flavored toothpaste, a model change, some unknown "Extra" ingredient.

Product changes usually come about through systematic plan-ning and effort; the major innovations of computers and television resulted from years of patient, tedious technological development. But sometimes a new use can be found for an existing product, and it can become a successful "innovation" rather quickly.

Presumably, the more innovative an action is the better it satis-fies the present and potential needs of consumers. However, an innovation can be so far ahead of its time that public acceptance is not forthcoming, and failure results. Modular housing may be an ex-ample of this.

MARKETING
IN
ACTION

Product-Use Innovation: Arm & Hammer Baking Soda
Church and Dwight is a small, family-owned firm that makes Arm &
Hammer baking soda. It had the dubious distinction of being a 125-year-old
one-product company. Though its baking soda had almost 100% market
dominance, sales were declining.

Then in 1970 the company conceived the idea of using Arm & Hammer
to eliminate foul odors—and it really does absorb them. So Church and
Dwight went on TV touting the benefits of using it inside refrigerators.
Today over 70 percent of the nation's refrigerators contain the opened
yellow package. Result: in four years sales doubled and profits tripled. Now
the latest marketing idea is the use of Arm & Hammer as an additive to cat
sand, where it can also cut odors.

SOURCE: "A Smell-Less Story," *Forbes,* August 15, 1974, p. 29.

For thought and discussion:
Do you know of any other products that have found new uses?
What is the attractiveness of this type of innovation from the firm's
    viewpoint?

Lapses in innovative thinking and adaptability. Large, well-established
firms have sometimes lagged seriously in adjusting to changing conditions and opportunities. Significant breakthroughs have often come
not from the large and well-financed firms, but from either outside
the industry or else from a few small interlopers. For example:

The air-brake, automatic coupling, the refrigerator car, and
    the streamlined train—none of these important railroad
    innovations were invented by a railroad man.
Development of tetraethyl lead came from outside the petroleum
    industry.
The motel was not originated by traditional hotel-keepers; the
    success of motels forced hotels to enter the field.
Drive-in movies were not pioneered by the great movie chains.
Paperback books were not initiated by the big publishers, who
    entered the field only later when it was already thriving.[3]
Two major retailing institutional "revolutions"—supermarkets
    and discount stores—rose and flourished while traditional
    retailers, until too late, were complacent and scornful.

Fostering innovation. Most of us can improve our creative talents and
flow of unique ideas, given some instruction and encouragement. In

[3] Above examples taken from Leo Burnett, "Marketing Snags and Fallacies,"
Journal of Marketing, July 1966, p. 2.

one experiment, 140 business students generated over 2,100 new product ideas as a part of their course work.[4] Of course, some people are more creative than others; one study of creative workers found that the top 10 percent produced approximately 50 percent of the total output of new ideas.[5]

**MARKETING
IN
ACTION**

Railroads: Innovative Passenger Service

Railroads have long shunned passenger service to the point of alienating all rail passengers; even major cities like Dallas and Cleveland lost rail passenger service. But in the winter of 1971-72 an innovation was introduced: the Auto-Train.

An auto-bearing passenger train, it leaves a suburb of Washington, D. C. (now it also leaves from Louisville, Kentucky) at 8 p.m. and arrives in central Florida at 11 a.m. En route the passengers are feted with food, drinks, and entertainment. The car and four passengers ride for a price not far out of line with the costs of making the tiresome 1,200-1,300 mile trip by car.

Did the railroads conceive of this? No indeed. While the Seaboard Coast Line provided the crews, maintenance, and track for this lavish overland cruise, a 35-year-old attorney floated a public stock issue to buy equipment for the new venture (even bankers refused to provide investment capital). How successful? After just one ad (on October 4, 1971) in selected Northeastern newspapers, the Auto-Train was booked for all of December and part of January. Three years later, in 1974, the Auto-Train is still filled to capacity.

SOURCE : "Overland Cruise to Florida," *Time,* November 8, 1971, p. 91; and "Auto-Train to Florida Is On the Right Track," *Cleveland Plain Dealer,* September 8, 1974, pp. 9H and 13H.

For thought and discussion:

What rationale did the railroad industry have for spurning passenger business?

While most railroads today have shifted their passenger service to government-operated Amtrack, what conditions do you think are needed to make rail passenger service profitable?

The organization seeking creativity must provide a hospitable climate for it. Receptivity to new ideas, rewarding and publicly acknowledging significant ideas, fostering good communication

[4] Roman R. Andrus, "Creativity: A Function for Computers or Executives?" *Journal of Marketing,* April 1968, p. 3.

[5] Wayne Dennis, "Variations in Productivity Among Creative Workers," *Scientific Monthly,* April 1955, pp. 277–78.

throughout the organization—these are some of the ingredients of a creative environment. A rapidly growing organization induces a sense of unlimited possibilities, which moderates resistance to change. There is a tendency for innovation to beget more innovation; creative people are attracted to a fast-growing and receptive firm.

MARKETING TOOL

Fostering Creativity—Brainstorming

Brainstorming is a technique to stimulate group creativity. A group of persons (5 to 8 people seem to be the best size group) are brought together for the sole purpose of producing ideas, the more the better, regardless of the quality or the practicality of the ideas. Under a conducive environment, one idea tends to spark other ideas. Only after the brainstorming session is over should any efforts be made to cull, evaluate, and select those most acceptable. Alex Osborn, the father of brainstorming, and probably the foremost authority on developing creativity, lists these four rules for effective brainstorming:

1. Criticism is ruled out.
2. Free-wheeling is welcomed—the wilder the idea, the better.
3. Quantity is wanted—the greater the number of ideas, the more likely some useful ones will be found.
4. Combination and improvement are sought—participants are encouraged to build or modify the ideas of others.

Brainstorming can be useful, even with participants who are unskilled in creativity, in producing useful ideas. It can also be a training device in developing the creative juices of the individual participants.

SOURCE: Alex F. Osborn, *Applied Imagination,* 3d rev. ed. (New York: Scribner's, 1963).

For thought and discussion:

For which of the following situations would you expect brainstorming to be most effective, and why?

1. Sales in a particular territory are drastically down from last year.
2. Your firm is ready to introduce a new product and is planning its promotional campaign.
3. Your firm wishes to open a new retail outlet and wonders where best to locate it.

Innovation in customer relations. A major change in consumer thinking regarding the marketplace, *consumerism,*[6] is taking place. Some firms have not reacted until forced to by governmental intervention

[6] We will discuss consumerism in considerable detail in chapter 18. The term refers to consumer dissatisfaction with products and practices in the marketplace.

responding to consumer and voter complaints. Other firms have found that consumerism stimulated them to better satisfy customers, with, for example, improved product and usage information, beefed-up warranties and guarantees, tighter product quality control, and quicker and more liberal handling of customer complaints.

There is always a need for innovative thinking, not only regarding different products, institutions, and selling techniques, but also directed to new perspectives about consumers and the role of business in society. We will turn to this discussion again later.

FOUR MARKETING INNOVATORS

Men of great accomplishment and vision can be both inspired and blinded. In the following four examples of innovators, we will consider their contribution to society, and in the case of three of them, some crucial flaws that placed the viability of their enterprises in jeopardy.

Henry Ford

Henry Ford's greatest accomplishment rested somewhat outside the realm of marketing—he originated mass production for automobiles via the assembly line—but certainly the marketing ramifications were profound.

Henry Ford was born on a farm in frontier Michigan in the 1860s. His interest in mechanics led him away from the horse-driven world of his father's farm, and he eventually became a master mechanic and developed an interest in self-propelled vehicles. He laboriously began making a motor car in a woodshed behind his house and in 1896, when he was thirty-three, successfully made a trial run in the first Ford automobile.

But it was one thing to make an automobile in one's spare time and quite another to raise the money to make cars and then attempt to displace the horse, especially when no known market existed for such a contraption. At the age of thirty-six, with a family to support, with only modest means and little education, he gained some backers and established the Detroit Automobile Company. Soon he needed new backing, and to get it he won a race from the man who then held the American speed record. After several false starts, the present Ford Motor Company was incorporated in 1903, founded with $28,000 in cash. The company became successful. In 1904–1905 Ford sold 1,745 cars and in 1906–1907, 8,423. Then in 1909 Ford introduced the Model T, a light, strong, efficient, and cheap

($850) car, available only in one color, black, and the Model T quickly became a way of life. Sales in 1913–1914 topped 245,000, and in 1920–1921, 933,000.

Ford conducted mass production on a scale never before seen, introducing and perfecting the moving assembly line so that the work moved to the worker. At the maximum daily rate, one Model T came out of the Ford factory every 15 seconds. Ford sold half the new cars made in this country up to 1926 and had more than double the output of his nearest competitor, General Motors. Price by 1926 had fallen to $263. For seventeen years the Model T had remained dominant in the industry, with neither model changes nor significant improvement, except for a lower selling price as more production economies were realized.

But ignoring changing consumer tastes as well as competition almost demolished the Ford Company. By the mid–1920s, there were millions of Americans who wanted something a bit fancier, more convenient, than the Model T with its mechanical brakes, its crank, its austerity. General Motors brought out Chevrolet and in 1923 sold 465,000 cars by featuring color, comfort, styling, safety, modernity—a showy appearance. The Model T was doomed.

In desperation, the Model T was painted attractive colors, fenders were rounded, the body lengthened and lowered, the windshield slanted; but still sales declined. And in May 1927, Ford stopped production altogether for nearly a year while 60,000 workers in Detroit alone were laid off, and a new car, the Model A, slowly took shape with the vast problem of designing machine tools and new dies, a changeover estimated to have cost Ford $100 million. While the Model A was successful and the V-8 engine introduced in 1932 was a technological breakthrough at the time, the Depression was making its impact on the whole economy and the Ford Motor Company lost, apparently irretrievably, the commanding position it had held in the auto industry.[7]

Henry Ford presents a classic example of one of the ultimate achievements of marketing, that of giving the common man the opportunity to enjoy products that formerly were luxury goods, attainable only by the wealthy. Ford with his Model T transformed a rich man's plaything into the basic mode of American transportation. But he later ignored some basic requirements of sound marketing—changing consumer demand, actions of competitors, long-range planning.

[7] From Jonathan Hughes, *The Vital Few* (Boston: Houghton Mifflin, 1966), pp. 274–356.

J. C. Penney

The personal accomplishment of James Cash Penney in developing in his lifetime a chain of retail stores—starting with his first in a little mining town in Wyoming in 1902 and ending as a nationwide chain of over 1,600 stores—is not atypical of the vision and accomplishments of other pioneer retail entrepreneurs such as Woolworth, Kresge, Walgreen, and Montgomery Ward.

Penney was born on a farm in Missouri in 1875, one of a large family of a poor Baptist minister. After graduating from high school he went to work as a clerk in a small-town dry goods store for $2.27 a month. Poor health forced him to resign and move west. Buying a butcher shop, he soon lost it along with most of his savings. Finally he opened a dry goods store (calling it the Golden Rule Store) in Kemmerer, Wyoming, in the face of the virtual monopoly of a company-owned store. The mining company issued scrip; the company store sold on credit and accepted scrip. Penney bucked the local monopoly with values so much better that customers were willing to pay cash and carry home their purchases; that store became the seed of the J. C. Penney Company.

Between 1912 and 1926—fourteen years—the Penney Company grew from 34 stores to 747; in seven more years it had 1,466 stores. Two things accounted for the early success. First there was the enlightened self-interest of the managers, since each manager was given the chance to finance a one-third interest in a new store—in other words, become a partner of the company—provided he had trained a new man capable of managing the new link in the chain. Second, the policy of cash, lowest possible prices, and moneyback privileges if customers were dissatisfied built strong customer loyalty, while confining efforts to smaller communities promoted friendliness and respectability in these communities.

Significant as the achievement of Penney was, in later years growth slowed appreciably. While "cash and carry" was a policy compatible with the time and with the needs of a population dissatisfied with the lethargic inefficiencies of many independent stores and their high prices, four decades later a reevaluation was sorely needed. *Merchandise diversification* was also long delayed: Penney's until the 1960s had remained only a dry goods and clothing operation. Appliances, furniture and carpeting, sporting goods, auto supplies—merchandise categories long carried by other general-merchandise chains, such as Sears and Ward, and by department stores—were ignored by Penney's.

Therefore, as in the case of Ford, imaginative, innovative ideas and a fresh and timely approach to marketing were forgotten as the company and the organization became older.

In the next example we see a marketing innovator who also was flawed, as it took only a decade and a half to discover.

Eugene Ferkauf—Founder of Korvette

Eugene Ferkauf began the Korvette operation in 1948, selling luggage and appliances at less than list price in an upstairs loft on New York's East Forty-Sixth Street. The success of this venture convinced him that the same low-margin, low-service, high-turnover techniques that sold appliances could sell many other kinds of goods also. He opened his first department store in a suburb of New York in 1954: the nation's first full-line discount store. By 1961, he had eleven discount department stores and two supermarkets; the next year five discount stores were opened; then eight more in 1963, eight again in 1965, and seven in 1966, all bigger than any existing ones—in four years store space and sales volume tripled. By 1965, sales had risen to $800 million. During this time a cluster strategy was used: four major stores were opened at about the same time around Chicago, three around Detroit, two in suburban St. Louis. In such a cluster strategy, promotion takes on a multiplying effect, since advertising impact and expenses can be spread among all the stores in the area.

While discounting was sweeping the United States, Ferkauf was the leader and for a time the biggest and most successful. Malcolm McNair, Professor Emeritus of Retailing at Harvard, had nominated him as one of the six greatest merchants in U. S. history.

But "confusion caught up with Korvette," as one *Fortune* article in 1966 announced.[8] Heavy losses were incurred and the internal problems of Korvette began to emerge: an ill-defined management structure, a lack of sophisticated controls and systems, and poor morale. The company's image was muddled by efforts to change from a discounter to a more conventional department store. Ferkauf could not run forty stores through personal observation—he had failed to delegate and to develop a strong management team. In December 1965, McNair changed his mind about Ferkauf.

By late 1966, a merger was consummated with Spartan Industries, a smaller firm of only $375 million in sales, but one with top-notch management and inventory-control techniques.

[8] Lawrence A. Mayer, "How Confusion Caught Up with Korvette," *Fortune*, February 1966, p. 153ff.

Spartan became the surviving corporation and Ferkauf was eased out of active management.

Ferkauf made a significant contribution to the marketing environment. He was the forerunner of the "retailing revolution," as some called it, that swept the marketplace and furnished strong evidence that a vast reservoir of consumer wants was untapped by traditional retailers. As a relative newcomer, Ferkauf, not the established retailers, provided this innovative thinking.

Colonel Harland Sanders and Kentucky Fried Chicken

Our last example shows that innovative thinking can come at any age. Sanders had had a varied career as a railroader, a ferry-boat operator, and a justice of the peace. At age 65 he was operating a moderately successful Southern fried chicken restaurant on a main highway from Detroit to Miami. But a new highway was built in 1955, bypassing his place by seven miles, and he was forced to close; all he had left was a sixth-grade education and $105, his first social security payment.

On a hunch, he took five frozen frying chickens and a special cooker, some flour and spices, and began calling on restaurants in Indiana and Ohio. His method was to cook chickens at high temperatures for less than eight minutes. After three years he finally made some headway. He gave franchises away; he leased cookers or converted their stoves for high temperature; he supplied at cost paper, napkins, and buckets with his image and the Kentucky Fried Chicken name—and he received 5 cents for each chicken sold by these restaurants.

Customers liked the product. In eight years he had granted over 500 franchises and his revenues were over $2.3 million. He was his own sales force and he never had more than 18 employees. In 1962, then 72 years of age, he expanded the business to include take-home sales. In 1964 he sold the entire business, including patents, to a group for $2 million, retaining for himself the lifetime job of goodwill ambassador. The new management concentrated on take-home sales. By 1968, sales were over $250 million and there were more than 1,500 outlets.

Again we see an example of a marketing innovator appealing to hitherto untapped consumer wants. While the physical product did not differ greatly from that of other fried chickens (except for the subtleties of eleven unknown spices to tempt the imagination), the image of a colorful Kentucky colonel was a natural. But perhaps more important to the success was the take-home dinner quickly prepared at reasonable prices; this adroitly appealed to the consumer desire for convenience.

As mass marketing became necessary for mass production, it was only natural that marketing began to be viewed by some firms and by marketing scholars as something more than merely disposing of the "fruits of production." In the marketing literature of the late 1950s and early 1960s, the terms *marketing concept, marketing orientation,* or *marketing management philosophy* began increasingly to be found.

During World War II and the Korean War the general tone of the environment favored sellers. With the return to a buyer's market, a gap began to develop between the ability of firms to produce quantities of goods and their ability to dispose of such goods. An aggressive hard-sell approach which had been effective in earlier periods was less effective as consumers became better educated and more affluent. A growing recognition developed that the marketing person, who was closer to the "firing line," needed to have a voice in what was produced and how it was offered for sale.

The marketing concept or orientation then can be defined as follows:

> An integration of marketing activities directed toward customer satisfaction.

Components of the Marketing Concept

Essentially what this idea or concept signified was a change in emphasis within a firm. Attention became focused on producing goods wanted by consumers, rather than selling whatever might have been heedlessly produced. Representative of this changed viewpoint was the pronouncement of the president of General Foods Corporation:

> Instead of trying to market what is easiest for us to make, we must find out much more about what the consumer is willing to buy. In other words, we must apply our creativeness more intelligently to people, and their wants and needs, rather than to products.[9]

Descriptions and definitions of this intangible concept have been numerous. Most of the definitions suggest a customer-oriented type of thinking. We have seen how, in the case of Henry Ford and J. C. Penney, this type of thinking prevailed during the early and growth stages of their firms, but was somehow forgotten as the businesses matured. In the case of Ferkauf this philosophy was evident, but poor management lessened its effectiveness and its profitability.

[9] Charles G. Mortimer, "The Creative Factor in Marketing," Fifteenth Annual Parlin Memorial Lecture, Philadelphia Chapter, American Marketing Association, May 13, 1959.

Colonel Sanders, whether by accident or keen foresight, found a combination of product and service which led to a high degree of customer satisfaction.

The marketing concept demands these basic components:

1. Customer orientation
2. Integrated marketing
3. Marketing research
4. Long-range planning and new-product development

Organizational realignment has sometimes been the most tangible evidence that a firm has adopted the concept. All business functions related to marketing are integrated for coordination and a unified objective. The position of the top marketing executive is generally upgraded, perhaps to a vice president, and responsibility given for such diverse functions as sales, advertising, marketing research, product planning, physical distribution, after-sales servicing, and sometimes even credit and public relations, with at least partial responsibility given for pricing and new product development.

A consumer orientation demands continuous market research in order to keep up with customers' needs and preferences. Henry Ford and J. C. Penney assumed that consumer wants, attitudes, and buying patterns were static, unchanging. A more formal role for long-range planning is also needed to coordinate a firm's efforts as well as to pursue a vigorous program of new-product development.

Problems in Implementing the Marketing Concept

It is one thing to accept the idea of the marketing concept; it is another to implement it. The concept embraces a very diversified group of activities, such as sales, advertising and promotion, product planning, marketing research, traffic management, pricing, and packaging. Certain aspects may be neglected or underemphasized despite the integration on paper.

Gearing all products and their development to defined wants of consumers—with technology becoming the servant of marketing—may not always be best. Nor of course should technological research take place in a vacuum, far from the clamoring need of the marketplace. Neither approach seems advisable. Judgment is needed regarding the role of the marketing concept in new-product development: it should not be disregarded, but should not be the supreme dictator either.

For example, nylon was developed not because marketing people were clamoring for a synthetic fiber but because of fundamental research on polyamide resins. The plastics industry grew out of exploratory research on high polymers, not out of particular market needs. The airplane hardly came about because of consumer demand. On the other hand, many profitable new products have been developed because of clearly defined consumer wants.

Another problem which has limited the full acceptance of the marketing concept in some firms has been an ingrained production orientation; old customs are not easily put aside. Furthermore, there is the difficulty of correctly interpreting consumer sentiments.

The Marketing Concept in Foreign Markets

The marketing concept has been slow to spread to the rest of the world. Until recently, this has given American firms an advantage in penetrating foreign markets. For example, marketing research is a ". . . relatively untilled field in Britain. Know-how spread through firms of consultants, journal articles, formal teaching of the subject, is almost entirely absent."[10] A study of Brazilian consumer goods manufacturers showed that sales policies of two thirds of the companies were determined by the production department, and more surprising, only 46 percent of the firms even had a sales department.[11] Clearly, of course, the marketing concept may be irrelevant in those parts of the world where per capita income is pitifully low and innovations are not well received because of deeply entrenched traditions and customs.

A Faltering Marketing Concept Today?

Surveys have indicated that the majority of large American firms believe they have adopted the marketing concept.[12] Unfortunately some executives delude themselves; they pay pious lip service to the consumer orientation (which is the crux of it), and perhaps even organize some marketing functions so as to present an integrated marketing operation, and perhaps establish a marketing research department —but the philosophy is not wholeheartedly embraced and does not permeate the organization. And critics note that the consumer orientation is really self-serving, that profits are expected to be enhanced by such an orientation, and every policy that does not produce immediate profits is given short shrift.[13]

We have to realize, of course, that not all firms, especially smaller ones, have understood, much less implemented, the market-

[10] W. G. McClelland, "Some Management Problems Now Facing British Retailers," *Journal of Retailing,* Spring 1965, p. 10.

[11] Leo G. Erickson, "Analyzing Brazilian Consumer Markets," *Business Topics,* Summer 1963, p. 13.

[12] Hector Lazo, "Big Business Gives Big O.K. to Marketing Management," *Sales Management,* November 21, 1958; Richard T. Hise, "Have Manufacturing Firms Adopted the Marketing Concept?" *Journal of Marketing,* July 1965, pp. 9–12.

[13] Hiram C. Barksdale and Bill Darden, "Marketers' Attitudes Toward the Marketing Concept," *Journal of Marketing,* October 1971, pp. 29–36; Martin L. Bell and C. William Emory, "The Faltering Marketing Concept," *Journal of Marketing,* October 1971, pp. 37–42.

ing concept. Other firms—such as transportation companies and utilities—have been constrained by governmental regulations so that their freedom of action has been limited and their ability to compete aggressively been reduced; or they have been protected from competition, so that the incentive of consumer satisfaction is watered down.

Therefore, while the philosophy represented by the marketing concept is positive and desirable, its operational effectiveness in really meeting the needs and desires of consumers can sometimes be questioned. Proclamations of consumer orientation and "We Aim to Satisfy You" make good public relations gestures but may have less real substance. Consumer dissatisfaction is still an issue.

Responsive Marketing

In light of these difficulties in applying the marketing concept, researchers have suggested modifications of it. One expert calls for the replacement of the marketing concept with the "human concept," which would systematically seek to consider human and environmental aspects of marketing decisions.[14] Another advocates a "customer concept," with the major functions of organizations being to serve people, their "customers."[15] In both cases, the idea takes the marketing concept a step further, introducing a more complete and systematic consideration of consumer needs.

Responsive marketing is a similar approach, a deeper commitment to customer satisfaction than some firms have actually given. Such a philosophy would involve greater responsiveness to the social and cultural environment. It would seek harmony with consumer wants, feelings, and aspirations, not only in products, but in performance, in service, in shopping satisfaction, as well as in buying confidence. (We will discuss responsive marketing and the broader context of social responsiveness of marketing in much more detail in chapter 4.)

What would likely be the effects on profits of such a modified marketing concept? To answer this question we have to define what profits we are talking about: short-run or long-range profits? As marketing becomes more responsive to the wants, and even demands, of increasingly vocal consumers, it is probable that immediate profits would not be given quite the number-one priority they presently are given in many firms. However, long-range profits have often been achieved through better-satisfied and more loyal customers and the favorable public image of a company.

[14] Leslie M. Dawson, "The Human Concept, New Philosophy for Business," *Business Horizons,* December 1969, pp. 29–38.
[15] Robert J. Lavidge, "The Growing Responsibility of Marketing," *Journal of Marketing,* January 1970, p. 27.

Customer satisfaction disregarded, but might be coincidentally provided

Customer satisfaction considered, but only when not incompatible with profit

Full commitment to customer satisfaction through service as well as products

Short-run profits maximized

Long-range profits maximized

Figure 2-2. Extent of customer satisfaction provided by marketers, and probable effect on profits

The efforts marketers have made to provide customer satisfaction, as well as the probable effect on profits, can be viewed along a scale or continuum, as shown in Figure 2-2.

Before the marketing concept as a philosophy became popular, customer wants were satisfied by coincidence if at all (although in a less sophisticated time, customers were less demanding than today). The marketing concept itself aimed to satisfy customers, but only where increased profits could be expected, and this often meant short-term profits. A responsive marketing approach would be fully committed to customer satisfaction.

QUESTIONS AND PROBLEMS

1. Define in your own words the term *marketing concept*. What are some problems in implementing the marketing concept in a manufacturing firm?

2. What factors do you think could account for the innovative Henry Ford's becoming the arch-conservative? Do these have implications for other entrepreneurs and innovative firms?

3. How can marketing adjustment to a changing environment be more prompt?

4. Why are foreign markets slow to accept the marketing concept? Does this suggest that it is not transferable to different environments?

5. Besides the four examples of marketing innovators, many other success stories could have been given. Some of these exhibited later problems which caused their demise or slowed their progress; others continued to expand, almost without hesitation. Can you develop some prescriptions to assure innovators their continued responsiveness and growth?

6. How do you account for the fact that often large firms, despite research and development departments, marketing research, long-range planning staffs, and the like, seldom are innovators—innovation seems usually to come from a brash newcomer or from some firm outside the industry?

7. Do you think the marketing concept is equally appropriate for all firms? Can you think of some where it would not be useful?

8. Why is a marketing research department often one of the components of the marketing concept?

Project

Gather as much material as you can about three firms (local or otherwise) that will help you judge how much each has adopted the marketing concept. Do you know of any firms which appear to practice responsive marketing? What data led to your conclusions?

Exercise in Creativity

Consider the shops and stores near your campus. What other kinds do you think might have potential, and why?

Now get together with a group of your classmates and brainstorm regarding additional merchandise and service possibilities near the campus. Record the number of ideas you initially generated, and then the number generated by brainstorming.

What conclusions can you draw from this exercise regarding creativity?

Role-playing Case

You have just been promoted to district sales manager for a major appliance manufacturer. Before leaving for your new assignment, Mr. Beggs, the president, tells you:

"Jed, sales are in the doldrums in the Southwest District. Our salesmen just are not pushing hard enough. It's up to you to get them producing again. We'll be watching you."

"I'll do my best, Mr. Beggs," you assure him.

Upon arriving at your district headquarters, you query both your salesmen and some of their customers—large retailers and wholesalers— about the situation.

The salesmen repeatedly tell you how much more difficult it is to get orders from the old accounts than it used to be.

Several buyers for large retail firms were most critical about your firm's service: "You folks just don't stand behind your products."

Based on this and other feedback, you reluctantly reach the conclusion that your company is not practicing the marketing concept.

Draw up a list of recommendations to submit to Mr. Beggs for improving the customer orientation of the company. What objections would you anticipate from Mr. Beggs?

CHAPTER 3

MARKETING

INSTITUTIONS

AND THE

SMALL FIRM

Marketing institutions are the establishments and agencies between the manufacturer and the final consumer or user. In this chapter we examine these retailing, wholesaling, and service institutions, and how some of them are changing. The role of small business—most small firms are marketing rather than manufacturing firms—is considered along with the problems and opportunities it presents would-be entrepreneurs. Franchising, an alternative for entrepreneurs coping with large competitors, is also described and evaluated. Finally, we examine minority entrepreneurs, their problems and accomplishments. Terms you will encounter include:

channel of distribution	service establishments
marketing functions	wholesaling
patronage factors	trade associations
wheel of retailing theory	franchising
scrambled merchandising	labor intensive

THE INSTITUTIONS OF MARKETING

The sequence of institutions involved in a particular flow of goods and services is called a *marketing channel* or a *channel of distribution*. Typical channels for the various categories of goods and services are shown in Figure 3-1.

Users of industrial goods include manufacturers who buy raw materials, supplies, and partially processed goods for further refinement and manufacture, institutional purchasers such as hospitals and schools, and governmental buyers ranging from the huge De-

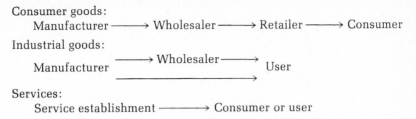

Figure 3-1. Channel of distribution.

partment of Defense to smaller state and local agencies. Industrial goods may be bought either directly from manufacturers or from wholesalers, but no retail firm is involved.

Service establishments provide such things as repairs, recreation, and lodging—they are not primarily involved in the sale of merchandise. Another category of services facilitates and supports other business firms. These include marketing research firms, advertising agencies, transportation and storage facilities, and credit and collection agencies. Services are provided without the need for manufacturers or middlemen.

The primary institutions of marketing, then, are the many types of retailers, service establishments, and wholesalers. Manufacturers, of course, are involved in marketing activities, such as product planning, advertising, and market research, but their facilities are used mainly for manufacturing, so we do not consider them marketing institutions. In chapter 11 we will discuss in detail the channel of distribution and distribution strategies.

Functions of Marketing

Marketing institutions exist to provide certain services or functions. The service provided is called a *utility*. In economic terms, a utility is the ability of a product or service to satisfy human wants. There are four basic utilities: form, possession, place, and time. Manufacturing creates form utility, as raw materials are converted into finished products such as automobiles, clothing, and stereo sets. Possession utility comes at the time of sale, when the customer takes ownership. Place utility means that the product is available where the consumer wants it; time utility is achieved by making goods available *when* the customer needs them. This may be illustrated as follows:

Marketing Functions	Utilities Provided by Marketing
Buying and selling	Possession
Transportation	Place
Storage	Time

Marketing Functions
    Facilitating functions:
       standardization
       market financing
       risk bearing
       market information

Marketing institutions bring buyers and sellers together in the *exchange process,* that is, the exchange of goods and services usually for money. Marketing institutions also are involved with physical handling—bringing goods to places convenient to customers and storing until needed, thus providing both place and time utilities. The facilitating functions make possible the other functions. Standardization involves sorting out and regrouping products to provide assortments and standards that meet customers' needs. Market financing includes extending credit to customers and investing in inventories. The owner of goods assumes the risks of price changes, fire, floods, and other catastrophes, bad-debt losses, and having to sell at a loss. Gathering market information is essential to meet the needs and desires of customers, and it can enable a marketer to be more responsive.

All of these functions must be performed by someone, whether by the manufacturer, a retailer, wholesaler, or all three. Marketing institutions flourish where no other firm can do the job as efficiently and economically. One manufacturer may open its own retail stores —and some have done so, notably Singer (sewing machines), Firestone, and Goodyear—thus eliminating both wholesalers and outside retailers. Another manufacturer may bypass the wholesaler and open regional warehouses, expanding the sales staff to deal directly with retailers. A large retailer may take on some wholesale functions, such as expanded storage and risk bearing, and deal directly with manufacturers. But the marketing functions, and the costs involved in providing them, while they may be shifted to some other member of the channel, cannot be eliminated.

THE RETAILING STRUCTURE

A retail establishment is engaged in making sales primarily to the ultimate consumer. Retailing is one of the more visible aspects of marketing, and we are familiar with most types of retail firms.

The number is huge, with about 1.7 million retail stores in the United States having total annual sales of about $400 billion. Over 11 million persons are employed in some facet of retailing, and this represents almost 14 percent of our labor force.[1]

The major function of retailers is (or should be) to make the

[1] U. S. Department of Commerce, Bureau of the Census, *Statistical Abstract of the United States 1971*, pp. 210 and 725.

consumer's buying job as easy and convenient as possible. To this end, goods are accumulated in assortments considered pleasing to customers and at convenient locations, financing and other services may be supplied, and the contact between marketing and the final consumer takes place.

**MARKETING
IN
ACTION**

A Different Kind of Retailer—the Truck Stop

Thirty years ago, Oran Jarrell started his own business, a two-pump gas station. Today he still has just one station, but he's a millionaire. His station—now Jarrell's Truck Plaza just north of Richmond, Virginia— has yearly sales of $10 million. (There are about 2,700 full-service truck-stops in the U. S. having combined sales of over $5 billion a year. The average truckstop does $2 million a year.)

On a busy day, over 4,000 trucks pull into his 15-acre lot. They often have to wait in line to get to one of the 16 diesel pumps. The truck stop has two restaurants, a parts and repair department, a 40-unit motel, a game room, and a variety store carrying everything from citizens-band radios to country hams.

What is the key to Jarrell's success? "The food is good . . . but standard roadside fare. But drivers get extras such as free towels for showers, two television lounges, a separate restaurant that has bigger, softer chairs and charges them slightly lower prices than the public pays."

Like other successful businesses, however, Jarrell relates to his cus-tomers. He knows many of them by name; he spends much of his time visiting with customers; he'll even help a trucker out if he's short of funds or caught speeding. The latest addition to the truckstop is a repair shop for the citizens-band radios that most truckers carry to keep each other posted about nearby policemen and speed traps.

SOURCE: "Roadside Riches," *Forbes,* November 15, 1974, pp. 96–98.

For thought and discussion:

Jarrell's is a combination retail and service establishment, aimed at a narrow part or segment of the market, the intercity truck driver.
Would a similar enterprise likely be successful which catered to the
 traveling salesman? the family on a trip? why or why not?

Retailing is *labor intensive.* By this we mean that it takes more retail employees to produce the same amount of sales dollars that a manufacturer, for example, might produce with a smaller work force. This accounts for the large number of persons employed in retailing and, since many of these are relatively unskilled and young, retailing requires a larger proportion of executives and managers than in most other businesses.

Classification of Retailers

There are many different kinds of retailers. We may classify them by (1) ownership and (2) categories of merchandise handled. Non-store retailers form a distinct group and will be discussed separately. We will describe these briefly in Table 3-1, and then look at changes in retailing more closely.

Table 3-1.
Classification of Retailers

By Ownership	
Independent retailers	These may be single-store operations run by an individual or partners, or there may be several outlets or branches. While most independents are small, large firms can also be independent in the sense that they are not part of a larger group of stores such as a chain.
Corporate chains	A chain is a string of stores characterized by single ownership, with all units having a similar motif and merchandising and operating policies. Management policies are more or less centralized at a headquarters. Sears and J. C. Penney are well-known examples.
Leased departments	These are specialized departments operated within a store by someone other than the management of the store. Many leased departments are operated by chain organizations who pay a flat rental fee or a percentage of sales to the host store. Beauty salons, shoe-repair shops, and auto accessory departments are frequently leased in department and discount stores.
Franchised operations	A franchise is a contractual arrangement in which the independent franchisee operates a business according to a prescribed format, and benefits from such an affiliation. Examples are McDonald's and Holiday Inn.
Military post exchanges (PXs) and commissary stores	Stores provided by the military for their personnel and dependents and which furnish certain goods and services at much lower prices than elsewhere.

Table 3-1. (Continued)

By Merchandise Handled

Department stores	Stores—generally large—carrying many categories or departments of goods, including furniture and appliances, wearing apparel, and household items. Examples are Macy's, Marshall Field, and Sears.
Discount stores	Departmentalized stores carrying a wide variety of goods but providing fewer services, more austere surroundings, and lower prices than traditional department stores. Examples are K Mart and Zayre.
Discount catalog showrooms	Concentrating on traditionally high markup items such as jewelry, sporting goods, photographic equipment, and small appliances, these discount stores display their merchandise through catalogs and samples in a showroom. Best Products Company is the largest.
Supermarkets	Supermarkets are large departmentalized food stores that feature self-service shopping. Examples are A & P and Safeway.
Convenience food stores	Typically small, these offer a thin assortment of the most wanted grocery and certain nonfood items, at somewhat higher prices than standard supermarkets; and they are open long hours. The largest chain of these stores is 7-Eleven.
Variety stores	These were originally "5 and 10 cent stores," although they have traded up much beyond this. However, they still concentrate on lower-price categories of goods. Examples are Kresge and Woolworth.
Specialty stores	Specialty stores comprise a wide variety of shops and stores which carry a limited line of merchandise. Examples are women's apparel, furniture, and shoe stores.

Table 3-2 shows the major types of nonstore retailers.

Table 3-2.

Nonstore Methods of Retailing

Vending machines	Vending machines are major factors in certain merchandise lines: cigarettes, candy bars, and soft drinks. Their great advantage is their convenience, but they are relatively high-cost operations and their prices are usually higher than those of conventional retailers.
Catalog (mail order)	While this type of retailing dates back to the beginning of mass selling, the end of the 1800s, it is still popular today because of the convenience it affords of leisurely ordering at home, and often from a wider variety than available in stores. For example, the Sears semi-annual catalog has over 150,000 items.
Door-to-door selling	The antecedent of this is the Yankee peddler. However, it is still popular today and affords the convenience of in-home shopping. Avon, the Fuller Brush man, the Good Humor ice-cream truck, and Tupperware parties are examples.
Street peddling	Today many big cities are filled with peddlers selling everything from leather goods to hot dogs.

One type of nonstore retailer is the street vendor, here represented by a New York hot dog vendor. *Courtesy New York Convention and Visitors Bureau.*

Changes in Retailing

Significant and sweeping changes in the structure of retail institutions have been occurring since before the turn of the century. In chapter 2 we examined some of the innovators responsible for certain of these changes. In this section let us take a broader perspective and consider theoretical explanations for major changes in retailing, how society benefits, and possible opportunities for further changes which may better satisfy consumer needs and wants.

Retail innovations of importance and their periods of establishment have been: the early forms of the traditional department stores from 1870 to 1890; general merchandise mail-order selling from 1890 to 1910; variety, general merchandise, and food chain stores from 1900 to 1930; the food supermarkets after 1930; and the discount department stores beginning around 1955. Each of these new retail forms had a major impact on the existing retail structure; each offered the consumer something which had been lacking in the original structure.[2]

One of the newer innovations in retailing is the catalogue store chain. In a catalogue store, customers see only sample merchandise, which they then order from a warehouse attached to the store. Shoplifting and overhead costs are thus reduced, allowing the store to offer lower prices. *Photo by Helena Frost.*

[2] Fred C. Allvine, "The Supermarket Challenged!" *Business Horizons*, October 1968, pp. 61–72; David L. Appel, "Market Segmentation—A Response of Retail

A retail firm attracts customers because of its particular way of doing business, its merchandise, or its location. The major incentives for shopping—we call these *patronage factors*—are the following:

Price
Convenience
Quality of goods—freshness, craftsmanship, fashion
Variety of assortment
Services offered—delivery, credit, return-goods privilege, courteous and knowledgeable salespeople, reputation

When these patronage factors are not sufficiently satisfied by existing retailers, the door is open for an innovator who can satisfy them. The department store, mail-order firm, chain store, supermarket, and discount store, when first introduced, all offered consumers lower prices, but other patronage factors were also involved.

Department stores offered a wider assortment of goods, grouped into departments for greater ease of shopping, and an array of services and efficiency that existing retailers could not match. Mail-order firms, with their early appeals to the rural market, provided such consumers an expanded array of goods, far more than local stores offered. Chains brought standardization of merchandise and very rapid dissemination of styles across the country. Supermarkets provided all kinds of food products in a single store; probably more important, they introduced the convenience and novelty of self-service. Discount stores, although making their major appeal to price, have also catered to the desire for convenience, with longer shopping hours, including Sundays in some locations, free parking, and self-service shopping.

Two other types of retailers have prospered recently by appealing to convenience. *Convenience food stores* typically are small and offer a thin assortment of the most wanted grocery and certain nonfood items, at somewhat higher prices than standard supermarkets. Shopping is quick—no waiting at checkout counters—and parking is at the door. The hours are long—one major chain is called 7-Eleven, which also denotes the hours open—and since the outlets are inexpensive to build and operate, they are much more thickly located than the larger supermarkets. *Vending machines* also appeal to convenience, being located in office buildings, bus, railroad, and air terminals, apartment buildings, stores, college dormitories, and a myriad of other locations. Prices are usually higher than for such goods (cigarettes, candy, milk) purchased elsewhere.

Innovation," *Journal of Marketing*, April 1970, pp. 64–67; Steven R. Flaster, "A Consumer Approach to the Specialty Store," *Journal of Retailing*, Spring 1969, pp. 21–31.

The boutique, a form of specialty shop, became popular in the late 1960s as an alternative to the bigness and impersonality of many stores. Small, intimate, and stocked with unique goods, they made shopping easy and fun.

MARKETING
IN
ACTION

Marketing Innovation—7-Eleven Stores:
Shortly after World War II, Jodie Thompson had an idea, but not much money. He saw the trend toward ever bigger supermarkets, and he decided to buck it. He opened small roadside stores whose aim was shopping convenience rather than variety of merchandise. He named them 7-Eleven Stores since they were open from 7 a.m. to 11 p.m., seven days a week. He charged premium prices and customers didn't seem to mind because of the fast and convenient shopping and the next-to-door parking.

And the firm grew. Today it has more than 5,000 convenience grocery stores, with sales of over $1.4 billion in 1973. Now his sons, John and Jere, run the business.

SOURCE: "Come 7-11," *Forbes*, September 15, 1974, pp. 103–04.

For thought and discussion:
In some metropolitan areas, supermarkets are staying open to midnight or even 24 hours a day. What effect would you see this having on convenience food stores such as 7-Eleven?

How much extra do you think customers are willing to pay for convenience?

What factors might this depend on?

Theories of Retail Institutional Change

Several theories have been proposed to explain (and perhaps predict) the major changes in retail institutions. The best known is the "wheel of retailing."

Wheel of Retailing Theory. According to this theory, new types of retailers enter the market as low-status, low-markup, low-price operations. As they become successful, they move into more elaborate buildings, offer more services, and generate higher operating costs and higher prices as a result. Eventually they become vulnerable to new low-status, low-markup, low-price retailers, and the cycle begins again. Figure 3-2 illustrates how in the late 1950s department stores had moved up on the price and service scale, leaving room for discount stores to enter the marketplace with few services and much lower prices.

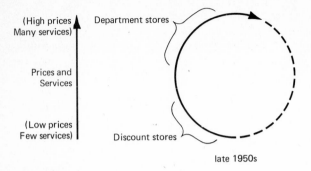

(High prices Many services)

Department stores

Prices and Services

(Low prices Few services)

Discount stores

late 1950s

Figure 3-2. Wheel of retailing theory

This theory offers an explanation for the development of department stores, mail-order houses, the chains, supermarkets, and discount stores—the major retail innovations. It does not provide an explanation for the entry of the convenience food stores and vending machines, since these entered the retail competitive market on a higher cost and markup basis than existing retailers.

The wheel of retailing theory offers a narrow view of retailing change. It implies that price is paramount, that failure to meet this buying motive, even though better assortment, quality, or service may be offered, still leads to vulnerability. It disregards competition on any basis other than price, but we have seen that at least two competitive forms have entered on a convenience appeal while offering substantially higher prices.

The General-Specific-General Theory.[3] Another general theory concerning institutional change relates to a buying motive other than price, that of assortment. According to the general-specific-general theory, the American retail system has experienced:

1. An era in which institutions offering an extremely wide variety of merchandise dominated the retail system
2. An era during which the retail system was characterized generally by a high degree of specialization
3. An era during which there was once again little specialization by merchandise lines

In the first era, the old-time general store stocked everything from dry goods to groceries to drug items. The specialty store developed as a greater variety of consumer goods became available—more than the general store could possibly stock—and as population became more dense so that sufficient sales volume could be gener-

---

[3] Ronald E. Gist, *Retailing* (New York: Wiley, 1968), pp. 97–98.

ated. The return to the "general" retail institution has come as the department store, supermarket, and more recently, the discount general-merchandise store have evolved, offering a wide variety of goods under one roof. This theory does describe historical change, but its usefulness for prediction is not clear.

We briefly described the merchandise diversification of *scrambled merchandising* in the last chapter. This refers to the prevalent practice of adding nontraditional lines to the regular assortment, items likely to enjoy strong consumer preferences and to be purchased frequently. For example, drugstores are stocking cameras, jewelry, lawn furniture, and even auto accessories. Variety stores (the former "dime stores") are handling many nontraditional and higher-priced items; supermarkets do a sizable volume on nonfood products such as housewares, hosiery, health and beauty aids. These are all beginning to take on some of the characteristics of the general store: a wide variety of merchandise lines, but limited assortment within any single line.

The sameness of many stores today, offering similar merchandise ("best sellers" only) in similar impersonal surroundings (emphasis on self-service) with similar price categories and promotions, suggests emerging opportunities for something different—perhaps for stores offering the widest possible assortment in limited product lines, providing expert personal service, with minimum price appeals and an image of distinctiveness. We are already seeing such a trend as boutiques become increasingly popular.

Other Retail Trends

You are probably familiar with the growth of the suburbs and their shopping facilities. The struggle of downtown areas to maintain a share of the market is critical in many cities: despite urban malls and slowly increasing parking facilities, downtown stores increasingly have to depend on people working in the downtown area and lower-income residents for their business.

Some developers are building ever-bigger shopping complexes:

> Billed as the world's largest enclosed, multi-level shopping center, Woodfield opened twenty-five miles northwest of Chicago. It cost $90 million to construct, has two million square feet of space, 215 shops and services, and three major department stores, including the largest stores Sears and Penney have ever built and the largest suburban store that Marshall Field has ever put up.
>
> Taubman, developer of Woodfield, says: "We are not competing against other centers or suburban business districts. We are competing against downtown Chicago. So we must come as close as we can to the strength and depth of

selection you find in Chicago's core area. And if that kind of philosophy means building gigantic centers, then that's what we'll build."[4]

The quick reaction of retailers to population growth in the suburbs, however, was partially nullified by their shortsighted merchandising approach once they arrived.

MARKETING
MISTAKE

Encouraging Discount-Store Inroads

After World War II there was a strong population movement to the suburbs, and retailers for the most part followed with branch stores. However, the established retailers—the downtown department and specialty stores—in their moves to the suburbs often brought the "top of their line," their best merchandise, their higher-priced items and departments. The bargain basements and budget shops which offered lower prices remained downtown. But the families of the suburbs, with their burgeoning needs and limited budgets, found the branches of downtown stores not nearly as attractive as the newly developing discount stores. Eventually the branch operations were forced to adapt to the competition of the discounters, but entry had been won.

For thought and discussion:

Why do you think the bargain basements were not moved with branch stores?

If they had been, would this have prevented discount stores from being successful?

Why or why not?

Retailers are getting bigger, as we can see from Table 3-3. Note particularly that, while total retail sales have more than doubled in this 20-year period, the total number of retailers has actually decreased. Although these figures are influenced by the rise in the price level during the period, this by no means accounts for the entire increase. These statistics suggest that retailing is becoming more concentrated, that is, more business is being done by large firms, and Table 3-4 confirms this.

While multiunit firms or chains are particularly dominant in the department store (reflecting branch stores) and variety store fields,

[4] "Shopping Centers Grow into Shopping Cities," *Business Week*, September 4, 1971, pp. 34–38. Some counter influences to giantism are described in: "Environmental Clashes Held Up Construction of Shopping Centers," *Wall Street Journal*, September 25, 1973, pp. 1 and 19; and "To Reduce Land Costs, More Developers Are Building High-Rise Shopping Centers," *Wall Street Journal*, May 13, 1974, p. 28.

Table 3-3.
Total Retail Trade in United States, 1948–1972

	1948	1958	1963	1967	1972
Total sales (000,000)	$ 130,521	$ 200,202	$ 244,202	$ 310,214	$ 459,040
Number of stores (000)	1,770	1,795	1,708	1,763	1,913
Average sales per store	$ 73,800	$ 111,700	$ 141,200	$ 175,958	$ 239,000

Source: *U.S. Census of Business:* Retail Trade (for respective years), United States Summary.

Table 3-4.
Percentage of Sales Made by Multiunit Firms, 1963 and 1967

Kind of Business	Percentage of Total Retail Sales					
	Four or More Stores		Eleven or More Stores		Over 100 Stores	
	1963	1967	1963	1967	1963	1967
Total retail sales	30.1	39.8	25.5	29.4	15.8	18.6
Variety stores	80.9	81.4	78.3	79.2	72.2	71.9
Department stores	85.6	90.6	70.5	78.8	33.0	45.5
Shoe stores	50.8	47.7	44.3	44.0	34.0	35.0
Food stores	48.9	53.0	44.2	48.5	32.1	33.8
Drug stores	26.1	33.0	22.5	29.0	11.0	15.0

Source: *1963 Census of Business,* Retail Trade, *Single and Multiunits; 1967 Census of Business,* Retail Trade, Single and Multiunits.

it is interesting that multiunit food stores account for a relatively smaller proportion of total food sales, despite the fact that the largest grocery chains—A & P, Safeway, Kroger, Acme Markets, National Tea, Food Fair, Winn-Dixie, Jewel, and Grand Union—are among the 20 largest retailers. This results from the very large number of small "Mom and Pop" grocery stores.

THE SERVICE SECTOR

Table 3-5 shows the trend in sales and number of establishments of certain consumer-service businesses. The increase in sales volume is noteworthy, and reflects the greater role that services are playing in our total purchasing habits as we become more affluent and have more leisure time.

Consumer-service establishments and retail firms have similarities, even though the first offer an intangible "product" such as entertainment, lodging, repairs, or personal services such as laundry and

Table 3-5.

Number and Sales Volume of Selected Consumer-Service Establishments, 1958, 1967, and 1972

Kind of Business	Number of Establishments			Sales Volume (millions)		
	1958	1967	1972	1958	1967	1972
Hotels, motels, etc.	85,580	87,006	79,685	$ 3,888	$ 7,039	$10,638
Personal services (laundry, dry cleaning, beauty shops, barber shops, photographic, shoe repair, funeral, alterations, etc.)	411,507	498,935	503,378	7,394	11,750	14,050
Automobile repair and other automotive services	125,240	139,243	168,959	3,853	7,028	12,081
Miscellaneous repair services (electrical, watch, jewelry, furniture, etc.)	144,759	138,014	148,925	2,262	3,826	5,855
Motion picture theaters	16,353	16,752	12,699	1,172	3,476	1,833
Amusement, recreation services, except motion pictures (dance halls, theatrical presentations, bowling, billiards, commercial sports, etc.)	74,696	96,029	124,729	2,661	4,827	8,702

Source: *U.S. Census of Business—Selected Services,* 1958, 1967, 1972.

haircutting, while retailers sell tangible products (often with some element of service such as alterations, gift wrapping, and delivery). But both types of firms must be concerned with marketing because customers have needs and problems to be met with either products or services. Typically, to be successful both retailers and service firms must have customers as satisfied as those who return week after week to Oran Jarrell's service center for truck drivers.

Certain services, especially repair services, have been subject to considerable criticism, some of it justified. The mysteries of repairing dwellings, cars, and appliances make abuse very possible, abuse in the form of both careless work and unneeded repairs. Service establishments are often small; many have never heard of the marketing concept or a consumer orientation. Consequently the service sector provides some of the best opportunities for the firm that can offer better and more empathetic work than competitors.

Business services are another major part of the service sector, consisting of some 200,000 firms having sales of over $22 billion.[5] These services include advertising agencies, consulting firms, credit bureaus, computer services, stenographic services, research firms, employment agencies, telephone answering services, and even armored car operations.

[5] U. S. Census of Business 1967.

Marketing a Service: Midas Mufflers

Gordon Sherman, 29, started his venture in automobile mufflers in 1956. Two years later, he had over 235 franchised dealers in 41 states and Canada, with sales over $20 million. The secret?

He brought unique service into the auto repair business. Attendants were trained in courtesy, there were clean waiting rooms, some shops even had playpens for the children of the mothers waiting for the work to be done. He featured speed of repair: the average time required to install a muffler was 15 minutes (on parting, each child was given a cardboard "Midas" crown). Although prices were competitive, price was not emphasized as much as durability, with each muffler guaranteed for as long as the car belonged to its owner. Sherman relied heavily on radio and magazine ads aimed at housewives. He even painted his mufflers a golden hue to make their appearance more attractive to his customers.

In 1972, the Midas-International Corporation, with sales of around $70 million, merged into Illinois Central Industries.

SOURCE: Adapted from "The Midas Touch," *Fortune,* July 1958, p. 229, and *Moody's Industrials.*

For thought and discussion:

Can you think of other auto repair services that could benefit from the Midas approach?

Is it appropriate for auto dealer service departments?

Why or why not?

THE WHOLESALE STRUCTURE

The U. S. Bureau of the Census defines wholesaling as being

concerned with the activities of those persons or establishments which sell to retailers and other merchants, and/or to industrial, institutional, and commercial users, but who do not sell in significant amounts to ultimate consumers.[6]

Although wholesalers can provide many services for their retailer and manufacturer clients, from negotiating the sale and purchase of goods to financing and furnishing market information and management counseling, major contributions are in the areas of transportation and storage. By bringing in carload shipments (at

[6] *Standard Industrial Classification Manual* (Washington, D. C.: Government Printing Office, 1957), p. 147.

lower freight rates), wholesalers can then break these into the smaller shipments their local retailers require, thereby providing them with lower transportation costs and faster delivery than if they ordered directly from manufacturers. From the manufacturers' point of view, wholesalers save them money by assuming some warehousing and inventory functions; and retailers can carry less inventory as they buy smaller quantities more often and minimize lost sales due to lack of stock.

Wholesalers fall into two major categories: full service and limited service. Table 3-6 briefly describes the various kinds of wholesalers or middlemen.

Table 3-6.
Classification of Wholesalers

Full Service	
Merchant wholesalers	These take title to the goods they handle. They may provide full service, or more limited service if the customer wishes.
Rack jobbers	These also take title to the goods they handle, but they provide a different service. They became important as supermarkets added nonfood items such as notions and housewares, although they have expanded their activities to other retailers having some self-service. They usually furnish racks or displays and physically maintain the goods, refilling shelves, pricing, fixing displays, and keeping inventory records—retailers then only have to furnish the space.
Limited Service	
Drop shippers (desk jobbers)	Drop shippers seldom take physical possession of the goods. They obtain orders and the producer ships directly to these customers; however the drop shipper does take title of such goods until they are delivered to the customer. Drop shippers are used mostly for bulky goods, such as coal, lumber, and heavy machinery where transportation costs are a factor.
Agents and brokers	Agents and brokers do not take title to the merchandise they handle; they negotiate the purchase or sale of goods, but they perform fewer services than do merchant wholesalers.

Table 3-6. (Continued)

Limited Service	
Selling agents	These essentially have control over the marketing efforts of manufacturers and may actually be used in place of their marketing departments.
Manufacturers' agents	These agents are restricted to a particular territory and perform functions for manufacturers similar to that of a salesman or branch office.
Commission merchants	These are agents who do not serve continuously, but are engaged temporarily to dispose of specific lots of merchandise.
Brokers	Brokers serve only on a temporary basis, being agent middlemen whose prime responsibility is to bring buyers and sellers together; any negotiations started by the broker have to be confirmed by the principals before they become binding.
Auction companies	These are used to dispose of specific lots of goods on a temporary arrangement, and provide the physical facilities.
Specialized types:	
Petroleum bulk plants and terminals	Storage and handling facilities are provided oil companies.
Assemblers of farm products	Agricultural products for many small producers are sorted and accumulated in order to ship them to market in economical quantities.
Factors	Factors specialize in financing, by buying clients' accounts receivable, thereby providing them working capital. They are most common in the textile industry.

Adaptability of Wholesalers

In the 1800s, the wholesaler was dominant in American marketing; at that time the environment consisted of many small producers and small retailers, often poorly financed. As these firms grew, and especially as the chains developed, the wholesaler became threatened by both producers and retailers attempting to bypass him and deal directly with each other, thus eliminating the wholesaler's commission.

The viability of wholesalers today indicates both their adaptability and the importance of their unique functions. Some general-merchandise wholesalers have not survived, but many were able to stay in business by shifting to a specialty wholesale operation, with private brands and franchised lines. In the grocery and hardware fields, for example, wholesalers sponsor voluntary chains (these will be described later in this chapter), have their own brands, and perform management services that bind them closer to their customers. Other wholesalers have improved their operations and developed flexible policies to meet the requirements of their customers. And there are still many small retailers who need the merchandising, financial, and counseling services of the wholesalers.

MARKETING
IN
ACTION

Streamlining Food-Service Distribution

While still a student at New York University, Steven Sanford thought he saw in the food-service industry one that was ripe for consolidation. He noted that restaurants, hotels, hospitals, and other institutions that serve food had to buy their supplies from a number of middlemen: meat from one distributor, fish and seafood from another, produce from still another. He sensed the need for an all-in-one service that would provide a complete line of foods.

He started with only an idea and $1,000 in assets. It took him six months to gain financial backing, and then he founded International Foodservice Systems. He bought three meat, grocery, and restaurant-equipment companies in Puerto Rico and the Virgin Islands, turned these into an integrated food supplier, and it prospered. Soon he was acquiring other companies in the U. S., Hawaii, and the Bahamas, and turned them into integrated food suppliers. By the time he was 28, he was chairman of the board of a $120-million-a-year and growing company. At that time he was the youngest chief executive of any company listed on the American Stock Exchange.

SOURCE: "Millionaires—Doughnuts to Dollars," *Time*, August 9, 1971.

Table 3-7 shows how total wholesale trade and number of establishments has continued to rise over the last 30 years; it also compares wholesale and retail sales over this period. Wholesalers, it seems, are thriving, despite the growing size of retailers and producers.[7]

[7] For perhaps the most current discussion of the viability of wholesalers, see Richard S. Lopata, "Faster Pace in Wholesaling," *Harvard Business Review*, July–August 1969, pp. 130–43.

Table 3-7.
Trend of Wholesale Trade in the United States, 1939–1972

	1939	1948	1958	1963	1967	1972
Number of wholesaling establishments	190,000	216,000	287,000	308,000	311,464	369,791
Wholesale trade, billions	53.8	180.6	285.7	358.4	459.5	695.2
Retail sales, billions	42.0	130.5	200.2	244.2	310.2	459.0

Source: *U.S. Census of Business,* Wholesale Trade and Retail Trade, for respective years, U.S. Summary.

Costs of Wholesaling

Expenses and profits of wholesalers vary greatly from one type of firm to another. Table 3-8 shows the operating expenses expressed as a percentage of net sales of the various major types of wholesalers for 1963 and 1967. Net profits would need to be added to these figures to determine the total cost of doing business with wholesalers, but net profits as a percentage of sales are very modest for wholesalers, usually ranging around 1 to 1½ percent of net sales.

The difference in operating expenses results from the wide range of services provided. The merchant wholesalers, for example, offer many services; brokers on the other hand do not even handle goods but only bring buyers and sellers together. One cannot judge that one type of middleman is more efficient than another without considering the services provided.

For wholesalers to maintain a viable position in the channel of distribution, costs must be commensurate with services provided, and the wholesaler must beware of inefficiencies which might en-

Table 3-8.
Operating Expenses of Wholesalers, 1963 and 1967

Type of Operation	Expenses (percentage of net sales)	
	1963	1967
Merchant wholesalers	13.5	13.8
Manufacturers' sales branches (with stocks)	10.6	11.3
Manufacturers' sales offices (without stocks)	4.2	4.1
Agents and brokers	3.6	4.0
Brokers	2.8	3.2
Selling agents	3.9	4.2
Manufacturers' agents	6.0	6.4
Assemblers of farm products	9.0	8.6

Source: *U.S. Census of Business,* 1963 and 1967, Wholesale Trade, U.S. Summary.

courage someone else to take over some of the activities. A comparison of expense figures for 1963 and 1967 shows a general constancy of expense ratios even though this was a period of rising costs, suggesting that efficiency was being maintained.

**MARKETING
IN
ACTION**

Growing Role of Food Brokers
A food broker performs in his local market the sales function and related services for an average of 25 manufacturers (or principals). The food brokerage firm is strictly a selling agent, and does not take title or possession of goods; prices, terms, and other conditions of sales are set by the manufacturer.

In addition to selling principals' products to wholesale merchants, chain stores, supermarket groups, and industrial users, the food broker pushes special deals and promotions developed by the principals. Market information is provided them on competitors' activities, special promotions, and the like.

The biggest advantage to using brokerage distribution is that the manufacturer knows his selling cost in advance: the food broker is paid a percentage—2 to 5 percent—of sales produced. Often a manufacturer cannot operate his own sales force this economically. And since food brokers are in close touch with local buyers and the market situation—they are local firms themselves—their efforts are often more effective than a company sales force.

The trend is to greater use of food brokers: in the five-year period from 1965 to 1969, 41 percent more items were distributed through brokers, and 10.8 percent more manufacturers went to this type of distribution.

SOURCES: Small Business Administration, "How Food Brokers Help Small Manufacturers," Washington, D. C.; and "Food Brokers: A Comprehensive Study of Their Growing Role in Marketing," *Grocery Manufacturer*, December 1969, pp. 2–19.

For thought and discussion:
Can you think of any limitations in using food brokers?

ROLE OF SMALL BUSINESS

The great majority of retail and service firms are small businesses. Their successes and failures affect our society and also affect marketing efficiency and consumer satisfaction. Some would argue that small business is overprotected and inefficient; others that small business is the mainspring of our economy. The answer probably lies somewhere between.

Public Concern

In this country there has been a traditional concern for the viability of small business even as big business has continued to grow and dominate certain industries. Most businesses were small before the Civil War, but this rapidly changed as economic power became concentrated. Eventually the need to protect against the growth of corporate monopolies led in 1890 to the first of the antitrust laws, the Sherman Act, and laws and regulations replaced the laissez-faire, unregulated competition.

The Great Depression of the 1930s brought all businesses to a low point, but smaller, marginal operations were especially vulnerable. Chain stores, which had mushroomed in the 1920s, became the bogeyman of independent retailers. Antichain legislation was passed in many states and took the form of resale-price-maintenance laws, unfair-sales-practices acts, and chain-store tax laws. (These and other laws and regulations relevant to marketing are discussed in detail in chapter 5.)

Public sympathy for small business resulted not only in restrictive legislation; some positive measures were developed to enhance opportunities and aid small business operations. The most notable at the federal level is the Small Business Administration which was established as a separate agency in 1953. This agency provides three types of aid to small firms: (1) helps them gain access to adequate credit on reasonable terms, (2) assists with their management problems, and (3) provides financial assistance when businesses have been damaged by disasters such as hurricanes and floods. Recently, the SBA has focused its efforts on the problems of black entrepreneurs and small businesses in the ghetto.

Competitive Position of Small Business

Before considering the viability of small business, we need to define it. Precise and uniform definitions are lacking, but the Small Business Administration generally considers that retailers having less than $1 million annual sales are small businesses, although there are some exceptions. The Department of Commerce has defined a small business as one having annual sales under $50,000. Manufacturers may be considered small if they have fewer than 500 employees.

The easy entry into retailing and such services as barbershops, restaurants, and repair firms contrasts with the substantial investment usually required for plant, equipment, and material in manufacturing. It is not surprising to find that underfinanced, poorly qualified people open retail and service stores, and often fail. Statistics compiled by Dun & Bradstreet indicate that often over half of business failures are of retailers, particularly those in the smallest sales-volume classes and in the first two or three years of operation.[8]

[8] Published regularly in the monthly issues of *Dun's Review*.

These failures are economically wasteful and represent inefficient use of human and other resources; the individual psychological effects can only be imagined.

The decreasing importance of small retailers in our economy can be seen from Table 3-9, which shows the percentage of small retailers (defined as those under $100,000 in annual sales) relative to total retail stores and total sales. The downward trend of these small retailers, both in proportion of stores and proportion of total sales, is unmistakable (although the figures represent the situation as worse than it really is, since with inflation a store of $100,000 in sales in 1967 would have been considerably smaller than a store having such a sales volume in 1939).

Competitive disadvantages of small firms. Because of their size, small firms—especially retailers—cannot ordinarily enjoy the lower costs that come from large-scale purchasing. They are vulnerable financially, too; credit is more difficult to obtain, interest rates are higher than those enjoyed by large firms (because of greater lending risk), and opportunities may be limited to take advantage of cash discounts, special purchases, and expansion. Specialized executive resources—for marketing research, computer utilization, detailed recordkeeping, and other assets of professional management—are often unavailable due to the limited resources of the small businessman, who may even lack general managerial ability. Mass advertising is also priced out of reach for the small firm, which must rely on less effective circulars, display signs, or inconspicuous newspaper advertisements.

Competitive advantages of small firms. Small firms do have some inherent advantages. They can be more flexible than their larger competitors who are restricted by policies often set at a distant headquarters. Small firms can better cater to particular customers. They can stock special merchandise, design services to fit the particular desires of their clientele, and develop a unique store personality, a well-defined character. The opportunity for close personal contact can be a welcome change to customers dissatisfied with the impersonality of larger firms. A small firm may have lower operat-

Table 3-9.
Retail Establishments Under $100,000 Annual Sales with Share of Total Stores and Sales, 1929–1967

	1929	1939	1948	1954	1963	1967
Percent of total retail stores	94.8	96.9	85.2	80.1	71.0	67.8
Percent of total retail sales	54.3	57.7	33.7	26.7	17.3	13.2

Source: *U.S. Census of Business,* Retail Trade, for years indicated.

ing expenses because of lower salaries (often family members contribute time), a less expensive location, and more reliance on unskilled part-time help. Small retailers in particular were often open longer and more convenient hours for customers than larger firms; however, this advantage is being minimized as convenience food stores and discount firms now remain open evenings and often on Sundays.

MARKETING
IN
ACTION

Small Business Opportunity—Developing a Unique Personality
Today we are seeing a revival of old abandoned monuments to America's past: firehouses, waterworks, banks, abandoned churches, railway stations —many are being reantiquated into thriving "atmosphere" restaurants.
For example:
> The Last National Bank Restaurant in Hartford, Connecticut occupies a building that once housed the Hartford National Bank & Trust Co. Diners eat behind 30-ton vault doors—one room is lined with safe-deposit boxes. Ancient glass-covered safe doors serve as tables, wine lists arrive in zippered moneybags, and placemats are blown-up replicas of $1,000 bills. Checks are paid to a cashier appropriately ensconced behind a teller's window. A six-ton armored car drives through town as an advertisement, and to make a reservation one has only to dial the telephone letters, A HOLDUP.

Successful? You bet. Opportunities for thriving small businesses based on unique "gimmicks" abound. Nostalgia is "in" now, and it may represent one of the best themes for emerging small businesses today.

SOURCE: "A Steak in the Past," *Time,* September 9, 1974, p. 55.

For thought and discussion:
Can you think of any "nostalgia" opportunities in your community?

Competitive Responses of Small Firms

Certain newer developments are strengthening many small businesses and giving them some of the advantages of their bigger competitors. Group cooperation of independents under the auspices of trade associations, assistance programs of wholesalers and manufacturers, and (most significant) franchising are increasing in importance.

The trade association. A trade association is a group of firms with common business interests; they share problems, operating and market information, and sometimes attempt to influence public opinion and legislation in their favor. While some trade associations consist of major firms banded together for strong lobbying influence, others are composed mostly of smaller firms—often the more progressive small firms—who belong because of the management aid provided. Sometimes members have the opportunity for group purchasing of store supplies and display material. An example of such a trade association is the Menswear Retailers of America, composed of some 3,300 member firms, mostly small. In addition to other services they conduct seminars for their members to help them do a better job of managing. Examples of seminar topics are:

Protecting your inventory investment through effective budgeting and control
Breakthrough in data processing for menswear stores
Key signs for recognizing financial problems
Modern application for credit management

Assistance programs of wholesalers. Many wholesalers have found it advantageous to cement relations with smaller retailers because the large retailers tend to explore the feasibility of bypassing the wholesaler. Small firms offer a measure of security. Therefore, progressive wholesalers are providing various kinds of advice and operational assistance. Their salesmen are sometimes not even called salesmen, but counselors. Programs in merchandising, store arrangement and display, modernization, accounting, and sales training are areas where wholesalers are helping their small accounts. And both parties can benefit.

Franchising. The most significant strengthening of the competitive position of small retail and service firms has resulted from the growth of franchising since World War II. Franchising is a contractual arrangement in which the franchiser (a supplier who may be a wholesaler or a manufacturer) extends to independent franchisees (retail or service firms) the right to conduct a certain kind of business according to a developed format. All the franchised outlets are identifiable as members of the group, with a common trade name. There are two main types of franchising systems: (1) a voluntary association of retailers and/or wholesalers, commonly known as a *voluntary chain,* and (2) a network of retail or service outlets initiated and controlled by a manufacturer.

Wholesaler-sponsored chains are composed of independent firms who contract to buy all or most of their merchandise from a particular wholesaler who will furnish various services, such as advertising aids, accounting and stock-control records, store layout plans, and other managerial help, including field supervisors. Because of the combined buying power, prices can be competitive with those of the corporate chains; some items may be marketed under the private brand of the association, such as IGA (Independent Grocers Alliance), and Super Value. Other examples of wholesaler-sponsored chains are Ace Hardware, Ben Franklin Stores (variety stores), Western Auto, and some Rexall and Walgreen drug stores.

Small groceries, such as this one in upstate New York, find advantages in belonging to a voluntary association, in this case IGA. *Photo by Helena Frost.*

Some chains are sponsored by a group of independent retailers who jointly operate a wholesale warehouse. These are known as retailer-cooperative chains, of which Associated Grocers and the Certified Grocers are the largest in the food field.

Manufacturer-sponsored systems[9] are numerous. They are not new, having long been used by the automobile industry and oil companies to franchise dealers, but the idea has spread to restaurant chains (Colonel Sanders), coin-operated laundries, child-care centers, swimming pools, hearing aids, auto rentals, and numerous other businesses—from Holiday Inns to Kelly Girl part-time help.

Franchising offers substantial advantages to both franchisee and franchiser. The franchisee benefits from proven managerial and promotional techniques—there is less risk of business failure—and from group buying power. Sometimes the franchisee has an exclusive outlet for a product or service in a particular area. The franchiser, on

[9] We will also consider as manufacturer-sponsored those franchise systems in which the central idea, format, system of operation, and/or recipes (for food-franchise operations) are furnished by the franchiser, even though these are not tangible products.

the other hand, can rapidly expand his number of outlets, since the franchisee is putting up some or most of the money; more conscientious people usually can be obtained, since they are entrepreneurs rather than hired store managers; and there is more opportunity for control of the product and distribution than when dealing with big retailers.

Generally the competitive viability of small business has improved with franchising. However, some types of franchise operations are becoming saturated, particularly fast-food restaurants and motels. We may question how many hamburgers, buckets of chicken, hot dogs, and donuts an average family can consume;[10] some firms have fallen by the wayside, even some associated with prominent people, such as Joe Namath's "Broadway Joe's."

In order to escape the saturated suburbs, fast-food franchisers are turning to downtown locations for their new units. Although rental rates per square foot are higher than suburban rates, sales volume may be three times as high.[11]

Conclusions on opportunities in small business ownership. There have always been opportunities for self-employed people, often much greater than those that come to employees. Great success is possible and does happen every day. But risks are high and security uncertain; this often limits entry to the highly confident, and the desperate. And the self-employed person may work harder than he or she ever would have as an employee.

**MARKETING
IN
ACTION**

Drawbacks of Small Business Ownership—the 7-Eleven Franchisees

Some 42 percent of the 7-Eleven stores are franchise operations. With the long hours these convenience food stores are open, this results in very long working hours for the operators: 80-hour weeks are normal: seven-day weeks may be worked for months without a break. Under such conditions marriage and home life can break down.

But a 7-Eleven franchisee can get into the business with only $5,000. And the company builds the store and provides strong accounting controls and supervisory help. With an average gross profit of $200,000 a year, a franchisee can earn for himself $60,000 a year. As one 7-Eleven franchisee puts it: "I'm breaking my back, but it's worth it."

SOURCE: "Come 7-Eleven," *Forbes*, September 15, 1974, pp. 103–04.

---

[10] "Speculative Bellyache?" *Barron's*, August 25, 1969, p. 3; "Many Franchise Firms Fall on Hard Times After a 75-Year Boom," *Wall Street Journal*, May 29, 1970, p. 1ff.

[11] "Fast-Food Franchisers Invade the City," *Business Week*, April 27, 1974, pp. 92–93.

Perhaps the most prevalent cause of business failure is the notion that it is not difficult to run a business, that no special talents or training are needed. In this day of increasing professionalism in management, the less competent will seldom survive. At the same time, the advances made by franchising and the opportunities presented for more sponsored and supervised entrepreneurship increase the opportunities in small business today. There is always room in our competitive environment for the innovator, the man or woman with the fresh idea and the confidence and competence to pursue it.

The Minority Entrepreneur

Minority entrepreneurs have particular problems in operating businesses. We will concentrate on black businesspeople, but many of the same observations apply to other groups such as Puerto Ricans, Mexican-Americans, and Indians.

Although blacks comprise 12 percent of the U. S. population, they own barely 1 percent of the private business firms. While one of every forty white Americans is a proprietor, only one black person in 1,000 is, and these are mostly "mom and pop" operations: one quarter of the black firms are barbershops or beauty salons. A 1968 survey found that only 20 of 13,762 commercial banks were black-owned or controlled; only 0.02 percent of the insurance industry; only 8 of 6,000 radio stations; and only 7 of 17,500 auto dealerships.[12] A Small Business Administration study of 138 franchising companies having some 27,155 outlets showed that only 354 of the outlets were owned or leased by members of minority groups.[13]

Even in very small businesses—restaurants, bars, grocery stores, and cleaning establishments—there are few minority entrepreneurs. Most small businesses in the black ghetto are white-owned.

There are reasons for the lack of black success in self-employment: inferior education, fear of failure, despair or apathy due to ghetto life, a lack of capital, and a lack of business experience and training. Perhaps an even greater deterrent, however, is that there is no heritage of business management and ownership. Yet there are strong incentives for encouraging more black ownership:

> The conviction that Negroes should have a "piece of the action" in U. S. business, and that broad-based ownership of business by blacks is essential to help defuse racial enmity. If the Negro is to escape from poverty and discrimination . . . the U. S. must develop a Negro managerial class to lead, hire, and inspire.[14]

[12] Fred C. Allvine, "Black Business Development," *Journal of Marketing*, April 1970, p. 1.
[13] As reported in "Franchising Near Maturity," *Washington Post*, June 28, 1971, p. D11.
[14] "The Birth Pangs of Black Capitalism," *Time*, October 18, 1968, pp. 90–99.

Aid for the black entrepreneur. Money is a big problem for any small business; obtaining it can be even more difficult for the black businessman. Typically, he has inadequate financial and managerial knowledge to make acceptable credit applications and to combat the wariness of white financial managers. The Small Business Administration's Economic Opportunity Loan Plan has made or guaranteed millions of dollars of loans for black businesspeople. Unfortunately, such efforts to make instant entrepreneurs of untrained people often proved ill-advised as default rates soared.

Counseling for black entrepreneurs is just as necessary as financing. The SBA has been conducting management workshops and seminars; it sponsors the Service Corps of Retired Executives (SCORE), which helps out when a business needs intensive study.

Students in many universities give time and service to minority businesses seeking assistance. Both students and firms gain from this in experience, in rapport, and in actual accomplishment.[15] Some large white firms, among them, Warner & Swasey, Xerox, and Safeway, have made efforts to help black businesses. And some successes have occurred where white-owned businesses in the ghetto have been sold to blacks. For example, five automobile agencies in Chicago ghettos were transferred to black ownership, and sales increased appreciably as the black community enthusiastically supported the change.[16]

Example of a successful Negro venture. Although few Negro firms are large—the biggest ones are life insurance companies and banks —there are some notable successes. Henry G. Parks, Jr., was featured on the cover of *Business Week,* May 18, 1968, and the aggressive marketing strategy and growth of his company and the product, Parks' Sausages, were graphically described. Parks first built his company on understanding the buying habits of Negroes: they are insecure shoppers and rely heavily on brand names as an assurance of quality. He developed a strong initial demand for his brand in the ghetto by distributing free samples. With a quality product and a heavy advertising budget—7 percent of sales—now 75 percent of his customers are white. Initially, he said, "I couldn't get financing from banks because I was black." Today the company has blue ribbon bank connections and the executive vice president was the first black to become a Baltimore bank director.[17]

Cautions regarding black capitalism. Black capitalism or entrepreneurship is often cited as the means to correct ghetto conditions. It should increase racial pride; it should provide jobs for ghetto dwell-

---

[15] Richard N. Farmer, "The Pros of Black Capitalism," *Business Horizons,* Indiana University Graduate School of Business, Winter 1970, p. 37.

[16] Allvine, *Black Business Development,* p. 4.

[17] "A Negro Integrates His Markets," *Business Week,* May 18, 1968, pp. 90–95.

ers. But black capitalism is by no means the final answer to ghetto problems.

Parks' Sausages is a successful business and has undoubtedly increased racial pride in Baltimore and the surrounding area. However, the employees are not all blacks and the firm has not significantly improved the over-all employment situation. The success of Parks is largely attributable to the acceptance of the products by suburban consumers rather than ghetto dwellers. Other moderately successful black-owned enterprises can be cited which also owe their success to acceptance by nonghetto dwellers: Soul Brothers Liquors and Joe Louis Milk Company in Chicago, for example.[18]

Can black capitalism improve the ghetto retail situation? The answer may be more negative than positive. It does not solve basic business structure problems. Small black-owned retail and service establishments are just as vulnerable financially as other very small businesses; only the owners' color is different. Because a store is black-owned rather than white-owned is no guarantee of honest, equitable, and desirable practices. And the ghetto is not an easy place to conduct a business. For example:

> A black-owned shopping center—the Medical & Shopping Center—opened on Chicago's heavily black South Side. It is a $2.2 million center which stands at one end of a twelve-block string of high-rise public-housing apartments that are plagued by assault, theft, and vandalism. Some 5,000 youngsters headed for three local schools pour out each morning with the shopping center in their direct path. Shrubbery and grass were quickly destroyed. Every window has been broken at least once, leading to a major investment in steel-mesh protective screening. Cars have been driven into the Walgreen drugstore display windows at night to get merchandise. Holes have been punched in roofs in attempted break-ins. A radio-television store, burglarized three times in a few months, no longer stocks floor models, and customers must buy sets sight unseen from catalogues.[19]

In short, the problems of any small business are intensified for the black entrepreneur. Nevertheless, black businesses are increasing, and a growing and influential managerial class has positive long-term benefits.

[18] "Will an Ethnic Pitch Sell the Black Market?" *Business Week*, April 12, 1969, p. 88.
[19] "Black Leaders' Plans to Build Ghetto Stores Often End in Defeat," *Wall Street Journal*, May 1, 1972, pp. 1, 14.

1. What changes would you expect in the institutional structure of marketing in the foreseeable future?

2. Would you expect the "wheel of retailing" theory to be as valid in the future as it has been in the past? Why or why not?

3. The mortality rate among retail stores is the highest of all types of business institutions (with the exception of some service establishments). Why is this?

4. What is a specialty store? How does it differ from a department store? How is it able to compete with a department store?

5. Retailing is several times more expensive than wholesaling—that is, retail markups often average 40 percent or more, while as Table 3-8 indicates, operating expenses even of merchant wholesalers are not much over 10 percent. How do you account for retailing being more expensive than wholesaling? Does this mean that retailing is less efficient than wholesaling?

6. How do you account for the lack of black entrepreneurship, even in the ghetto? What prescriptions would you offer for the development of more black managers and owners?

7. Develop a list of pros and cons of going into business for yourself as compared to doing so through a franchising arrangement? On balance, which seems more desirable from your viewpoint?

8. Why is there the substantial variation in operating expenses among the various types of wholesalers, as shown in Table 3-8?

Project

Investigate for comparison purposes two franchise operations of the same general type of merchandise or service. For example, you might select a McDonald's and a Burger King; or a Holiday Inn and a Howard Johnson or Ramada Inn.

You should compare what it takes to start (money, experience, other); potential profits and risks; general operational restrictions. Evaluate the strengths and weaknesses of the two you choose.

Exercise in Creativity

You have just opened a children's store in a suburban shopping center. How many creative ideas can you develop which would make your business unique and attractive to customers?

Role-playing Case

In a particular community you are planning to open a dress store. You appraise your competition as coming from a prestige department store, two discount stores, Sears, and two chain dress shops (of the Lerner type). The community is average in income, etc. What particular ways of appealing to customers (patronage factors) do you think might present the best opportunity for a new store in this market?

CHAPTER 4

ETHICS,

SOCIAL RESPONSIBILITY,

AND MARKETING

RESPONSIVENESS

Marketing takes place in a social environment where people, as represented by firms, products, and advertisements, interact with other people in a seller-buyer relationship. In such a setting, questions and controversies arise as to what indeed is ethical behavior, and what, if anything, a firm owes to society. In this chapter we first explore this murky ethical dimension and some aspects of the just as controversial topic of social responsibility, and then consider certain positive efforts that marketers might undertake to improve their public image and furnish greater satisfaction. Key terms are:

ethics	social responsiveness
caveat emptor	customer service
Better Business Bureaus	warranties
industry codes	role playing
social responsibility	consumer ombudsman

WHAT IS ETHICAL MARKETING BEHAVIOR?

Ethics is concerned with standards for decision making and right conduct. Unfortunately there is little agreement as to just what constitutes ethical behavior; at the extremes, of course, there is not much dispute—the outright fraud and deceit which characterize the "dark side of the marketplace,"[1] such as representing used goods as new, would be considered unethical by most observers, just as a "no questions asked" refund policy would be regarded as ethical. But

[1] Warren Magnuson and Jean Carper, The Dark Side of the Marketplace, 2d ed. (Englewood Cliffs, N.J.: Prentice-Hall, 1972).

there are other practices that shade into a "gray area," not clearly unethical and not illegal, and yet maybe not entirely ethical either:

1. Using "high pressure" tactics in persuading people to buy
2. Emphasizing sex in advertising appeals
3. Employing appeals to strengthen the motives of materialism and "keeping up with the Joneses"
4. Trying to make people dissatisfied with what they have[2]
5. Using handicapped or poor people to sell products through emotional appeals.

Disagreement as to what is ethical also arises in regard to the amount and veracity of information which should be supplied the consumer making buying decisions. This is particularly an issue when the inexperienced, poorly educated, and disadvantaged consumers of the ghettos are involved. The increasing pressure being applied for direct legislation for tire standards, unit prices, the design life of durable goods, truth in lending, and the like attests to a growing conviction in consumer and governmental circles that anything less than full disclosure is not ethical—and may soon not be legal either. Yet most marketers see nothing unethical in extolling (perhaps with the "exaggeration of enthusiasm") the virtues of their products, while maintaining complete silence on any known inadequacies: "This is simply part of selling."

The relationship between ethical conduct and the law sometimes is confusing. For example, can certain actions be ethical but against the law? Fair-trade laws, which prohibit a retailer from offering a certain brand and product below a designated price (we will discuss fair-trade laws in more detail in chapter 14), are a case in point. If a firm engages in illegal price cutting, is this unethical? Or is the violation of "blue laws" (laws prohibiting doing business on Sundays) unethical? Many people see these acts as ethical, even though against the law.

At the other extreme, to rationalize that "if it's legal, it's ethical" is hardly a satisfactory rule. Many practices are within the law, such as firing an employee just before retirement benefits become vested, or charging a naïve customer more than a fair price; yet some people at least would see these as unethical practices.

INCENTIVES FOR QUESTIONABLE PRACTICES

Questionable conduct, aimed at deception and avarice, may be seen as the consequence of

1. Overemphasis on measurement of performance (individual and firm)

[2] Howard R. Bowen, *Social Responsibilities of the Businessman* (New York: Harper & Row, 1953), pp. 214–15.

2. Intensity of competition
3. Expedience and/or indifference
4. Tradition

In most firms, performance is measured by sales and profits. Job promotion and increased remuneration depend on achieving greater sales and profits. This is true not only for individual employees and executives but for departments and divisions—indeed for the entire firm. The value that stockholders and investors, creditors, and suppliers place on a firm is to a large extent dependent on growth as evidenced by increasing sales and profits. The better the rate of growth, the more monies are available for further expansion and growth by investors and by creditors at attractive rates; suppliers are more eager to do business, and often customers as well; top-quality personnel and executives are also more easily attracted. However, this emphasis on performance may lead to unethical practices. In a situation of intense competition, a few firms in an industry may generate a "follow-the-leader" situation: their quasi-deceptive practices and ballyhoo may be adopted by other firms "in order to compete."

Infatuation with tradition still characterizes some marketing. The adage of caveat emptor—let the buyer beware—has described business dealings quite completely until the last few decades when a more forthright policy began to be practiced by some enlightened marketers.

We generally think we have come a long way from the outright falsehoods of such nineteenth-century medicine ads as this:

> Dr. Owen's Body Battery! For Man and Woman. Contains
> 10 degrees of strength. Current can be increased, decreased,
> reversed, or detached at will, and applied to any part of the
> body or limbs by whole family. *Cures General, Nervous and
> Chronic Diseases.* It is light, simple and superior to all others.
> Guaranteed for one year . . .[3]

But sometimes we wonder how far we have indeed come:

---

[3] S. Watson Dunn, *Advertising, Its Role in Modern Marketing,* 2d ed. (New York: Holt, Rinehart and Winston, 1969), p. 28.

**MARKETING
IN
ACTION**

Comeback of the Elixir, Hadacol—Ethical?
In the late 1940s and early 1950s Hadacol was successfully peddled amid claims of curative powers and hints at aphrodisiac properties. In practically no time, thanks to an initial $300,000 advertising campaign which went

into a touring extravaganza billed as "The Greatest Medicine Show on Earth," Hadacol became something like a religion in the Bible Belt, and thousands of testimonial letters poured in, such as that of one woman who wrote:

> My husband has had a stomach ailment for 20 years. But now after drinking six bottles of Hadacol, he'll put his stomach up against anyone's.

The cures claimed in the letters covered almost the entire spectrum of diseases known to medical science: cancer, tuberculosis, heart trouble, diabetes, paralysis, epileptic fits, delirium tremens, neuralgia, migraine, blood diseases, stomach ulcers, rheumatism, arthritis, high or low blood pressure, asthma, swelling of the waist, hands, and legs, cataracts, sinus trouble, and weakness and rundown condition following colds.

The originator sold out to Eastern investors for a small fortune in 1951, and Hadacol went downhill, changing hands at least eight times. Now, Robert Brock, former truck driver and management consultant, is gambling $750,000 that Hadacol can make a comeback. He believes that all he need do is trigger memories of the alcohol-laced (22 proof) potion and consumers will rush to pay $2.39 for eight ounces of the stuff. The advertising approach is simplicity itself: "Hadacol is Back!" Research indicates that 87% of a random sample of people in the South still recognize the name Hadacol, with the typical recollection that it was a "tonic that made you feel good."

Since Hadacol costs only 52 cents a bottle to make and sells for about the same price per ounce as Scotch, it can be highly profitable. Customers who follow directions on the bottle will be spending about $5 a week at the Hadacol counter.

SOURCE: "Hadacol's Comeback May Ease Nostalgia—If Not Neuralgia," *Wall Street Journal*, July 23, 1974, pp. 1 and 15.

For thought and discussion:
How do you feel about the ethics of promoting Hadacol?
Do you see any merits in such a product?

VOLUNTARY POLICING AND CODES OF ETHICS

Self-Regulatory Agencies

In order to curb abusive practices, industry groups have developed codes of conduct for their members. *Better Business Bureaus* are the best-known instruments of self-regulation, and there are some 120 bureaus in major U. S. cities and some foreign countries. Complaints to these bureaus may come from customers or from businesses; the charge will be investigated and if a malpractice does exist, persuasion and the threat of publicity often results in corrective action.

Individual advertising agencies and the American Association of Advertising Agencies (AAAA) exercise some control over advertising. For example, the AAAA can refuse membership to agencies not considered ethically qualified. It and the Association of National Advertisers review questionable ads and exercise group pressure on advertisers and agencies judged guilty of objectionable advertising.

Some media screen the advertising they will accept. The *New York Times* for more than fifty years has had a strict set of standards. *Good Housekeeping* evaluates samples and "other pertinent data" of the products and services advertised in the magazine and gives a "Consumers' Guaranty" that the claims are truthful and the products not defective. *Ms.* magazine does not accept advertising it considers insulting to women.

Self-regulation, via industry codes, is employed more heavily in television and radio than in the print media, largely because they are government-licensed media. Two types of self-regulating machinery are used: (1) internal network control or clearance departments, and (2) the Television Code of the National Association of Broadcasters. Most commercials are screened at the network or station level by a special department.

The Television Code was instituted in 1952 and has had many revisions. It bans certain types of advertising and products. For example, advertising liquor is prohibited, while firearms and fireworks are acceptable only subject to federal and local laws. The Code also limits the amount of time devoted to commercials.

Several publications directed to the advertising industry have pushed for better practices. *Advertising Age* has strongly criticized its readers for the poor taste of some advertising. *Printers' Ink* sponsored the Printers' Ink Model Statute as early as 1911. This statute (and its revisions in 1945) was designed to make advertising more truthful, deceptive statements being punishable as a misdemeanor. While all but three states have adopted the Printers' Ink Statute, its severity as a criminal statute mitigates its enforcement.

Effectiveness of Self-Regulation

In general, industry codes and attempts at self-regulation have not been notably successful. When competing firms agree to abide by certain business standards, there is danger of violating antitrust laws, so that such agreements are entered with trepidation if at all. Too often codes are vague and general instead of being specific and concrete. For example, the standards adopted by the National Association of Purchasing Agents call for the purchasing agent "to avoid sharp practice"—but we disagree as to what constitutes "sharp practice."

By far the biggest handicap to effective self-regulation is the lack of enforcing power: the force behind such codes is only a social sanction and some individuals and firms simply ignore it. Furthermore, some firms refuse to join industry associations or sign industry codes and, of course, feel no sense of being bound by any prescribed standards.

THE SOCIAL RESPONSIBILITY OF MARKETERS

Probably the most controversial topic in business and marketing is that of "social responsibility." The question is one of priorities: where does a firm's primary obligation lie—to its stockholders, to its customers, to the public, to society? Thus the following are issues:

> Should a railroad downgrade commuter and passenger service to the point of obsolete equipment and horrendous operations, because it makes money only on its freight operations?
> Should a utility refuse to place transmission lines underground when they can be placed overhead for one-tenth the cost?
> If a utility has an adequate supply of skilled labor, should it nevertheless spend money to train members of underprivileged groups to raise their levels of opportunity? If it does so, should ratepayers or taxpayers bear the cost of the training program?
> Should a company discontinue the use of nonreturnable containers, even though customers prefer the convenience of these to the returnable ones and competition continues to use them, in order to better the environment?
> Should a retail chain open outlets in ghetto areas, even though past experience has found that such outlets invariably lose money?[4]

Table 4-1 shows the range of opinion of 300 business leaders concerning the question of how much, if at all, businessmen should be willing to compromise their profit-making responsibility in pursuit of social ends. Only 17 percent felt that business should sacrifice profits, although this is almost twice as many as thought there should be a complete disavowal of the needs of society.

Other surveys suggest that public pressure may be mounting for business to take a more active social role. A poll by Opinion Research Corporation found that 65 percent of stockholders felt that business should play an active role in the war on poverty.[5] A survey by Gallup Poll showed that 86 percent of Americans are concerned about environmental deterioration and that many blame industry.[6]

[4] "The War That Business Must Win," *Business Week*, November 1, 1969, p. 64.
[5] Reported in "The War Business Must Win," p. 65.
[6] Ibid.

Table 4-1.
Attitudes of Business Leaders Concerning Profit-Maximization
Priorities Relative to Social Needs

Percent of 300 Total Respondents	Attitude Categories
10	"Sole business of business is profits."
20	"Business should concentrate on profits, but pay more in taxes and human resources to solve social problems."
8	"Business should develop know-how in solving social problems, and make its skill available to the government at a profit."
42	"Business first must make an 'adequate' profit, then must assume public responsibilities that may not be profitable."
17	"Business should assume public responsibilities even at the cost of reduced profits."
3	Not responding

Source: Arthur M. Louis, "What Business Thinks," *Fortune,* September 1969, p. 94.

A poll of MBA students found 60 percent disagreeing with the statement that "businessmen should consider stockholders' interests first, and only after that consideration may they be interested in society's problems."[7] It may be that the new generation of executives, being less willing to settle for aims of merely increasing market share, will see responsibilities in what to today's executives would be economically irresponsible.[8]

Business may no longer be able to disavow social responsibility:

> To the extent that businessmen—or any other group—have
> social power, the lessons of history suggest that social
> responsibility of an equal amount arises therefrom. Stated
> in the form of a general relationship, social responsibilities of
> businessmen arise from the amount of social power they have.[9]

[7] *Stanford Graduate School of Business Bulletin,* Spring 1968, pp. 14–17.

[8] As reported in "Business and Society," *Business Week,* December 6, 1969, p. 144.

[9] Keith Davis, "Understanding the Social Responsibility Puzzle," *Business Horizons,* Winter 1967, p. 48. See also Michael Mazis and Robert Green, "Implementing Social Responsibility," *MSU Business Topics,* Winter 1971, pp. 68–76; Roy L. Ash, "Realities vs. Rhetoric: The Dilemma of Social Cost," *The Conference Board Record,* July 1971, pp. 38–40.

Arguments against Social Responsibility of Business

Philosophical objections to the desirability of business's assuming a greater social role have been raised. If we are to view the issue in perspective, we should examine these arguments. Objections to business's involvement in social matters are generally of two types: the position that businessmen have no legitimate authority outside of business and the fear that such involvement will lead to a business dictatorship.

The first argument raises a provocative point. Businessmen are not elected by the people and consequently they are not responsible to them. Furthermore, business leaders are not representative of the people and can hardly be judges of what is in their best interest. Their performance in the past of subordinating everything else to their special interests does not augur well for future expectancies.

It can also be argued that the resources of business, if turned to noneconomic pursuits, could lead to a monolithic society controlled by business—a business dictatorship.[10] This then would replace our present pluralistic society (where power is diffused among a large number of groups). Despite the imperfections of a pluralistic system —and at its extreme it would be a fragmented, chaotic society—it still is the most responsive and most democratic system yet devised. The alternative is hardly acceptable.

Conclusions on Social Responsibility of Marketers

Critics of greater social responsibility in business tend to go to extremes. The probability of a business dictatorship resulting from the attention of business to social problems is no greater than the probability of our pluralistic society's dissolving into anarchy and unreconcilable fragmentation. Joseph McGuire suggests that the critics "... apparently would like business not to try to adapt to a changing world":

> This [societal] context forces businessmen to behave in a responsible fashion. That the society has been altered does not mean that profits are any less important than before. Now, however, businessmen must consider new variables and pursue profits within a new societal framework.[11]

Social responsibility, in short, may become a necessity, rather than an option, for business. If urban and minority problems cannot

---

[10] Theodore Levitt, "The Dangers of Social Responsibility," *Harvard Business Review,* September–October 1968, p. 44. Another negative view is that of Milton Friedman, "Social-Minded Businessmen," *America,* October 3, 1970, p. 226.

[11] Joseph W. McGuire, *Business and Society* (New York: McGraw-Hill, 1963), p. 150.

be solved, then tension and unrest will increase risk and curb purchasing power. An improved social and physical environment with its attendant effect on the quality of life, has positive economic consequences for all of us, marketer and consumer.

SOCIAL RESPONSIVENESS

There is a subtle difference between *social responsibility* and *social responsiveness*. As generally used, social responsibility suggests that a firm recognize a responsibility to more than its stockholders, perhaps a responsibility to its employees, its customers, its suppliers, the community in which it does business and, projected to its furthest, a responsibility to society at large. Since the needs and demands of these groups differ and are not always compatible, some priorities of corporate responsibility must be established. A complete acceptance of social responsibility would be a willingness to sacrifice profits for other priorities, especially those of a social and environmental nature.

Social responsiveness, as we will use the term, suggests a more active response to the environment. It is oriented to action that attempts to correct or improve certain conditions. This could mean a commitment to social needs at the expense of profit, but it can also indicate a willingness to forego short-run profit in favor of long-range profitability. A willingness to abandon the status quo and welcome innovation is also part of social responsiveness. It implies not shying away from running efficient passenger trains or opening supermarkets in the ghetto; rather, it would be concerned with finding innovative approaches to bring such "do-good" endeavors to profitability.

These rather intangible aspects of social responsiveness are not alien to marketing thinking. As we have seen, the marketing concept stresses a consumer orientation—that the desires of consumers should guide the activities of a firm. Unfortunately, marketing has a history of selfish interest. The environmentalist Rene Dubos points out, however, that "in doing the right things," sometimes businesses discover new opportunities. He cites the example of the pasteurization of milk. It was common medical knowledge that disease came from contaminated milk, and merely heating milk eliminated this problem. The dairy industry, however, complained of the expense, and its powerful lobby for years prevented milk from being pasteurized. Eventually an aroused public opinion resulted in a law. Within a few years, the pasteurization process became very effective, and the dairy industry found that, far from increasing the cost of milk, it decreased the cost by lengthening the shelf life.[12]

[12] Rene Dubos, as interviewed by *Forbes*, September 15, 1970, pp. 64–66.

Marketers do not need to be trapped by traditional practices, and there are many ways in which they can increase their responsiveness:

1. Greater attention to public image
2. Greater sensitivity to society's changing value systems
3. Concrete efforts directed to customer service

These efforts are designed to improve the marketing process itself, better satisfy consumers, and not the least, improve the public image of marketing.

Attention to Public Image

Marketers have in the past often misinterpreted or been indifferent to the effects of their actions on their public image and that of marketing in general. Some "responsible" business leaders were in strong opposition to the truth-in-packaging and truth-in-lending hearings:

> The truth-in-packaging bill became the target of a ludicrously all-out war with the might of a number of America's most powerful industries deployed against . . . a bill which merely sought to establish a degree of uniformity in weights and measures.[13]

The widespread publicity given such opposition spotlighted what many people considered to be the selfish interest and disregard for consumers of a large segment of business. In similar fashion, the powerful lobby of the drug industry fought greater regulation of drugs, until the thalidomide tragedy brought a shocked public reaction. Opposition of the food industry to a New York City regulation for mandatory unit pricing also received wide publicity. A decade ago, two marketing experts noted the incongruity: marketers had developed persuasion and communication to a fine art, and yet, justifiably or not, few other aspects of society were perceived in as poor a light.[14]

Marketers are now making an active effort to counter the attitude that there is a widening gap between business and consumer interests. The image of marketing will benefit if opposition to consumer legislation were toned down, and if marketers are more willing to concede that there are certain imperfections in our marketing system.

Some firms are tackling the image problem by more systematic efforts to tell their side to students, educators, labor union members, and others. As an example:

[13] Sidney Margolius, *The Innocent Consumer vs. the Exploiters* (New York: Trident Press, 1967), p. 35.

[14] D. Beryl Manischewitz and John A. Stuart, "Marketing under Attack," *Journal of Marketing*, July 1962, pp. 1–6.

E. Mandell de Windt, chairman of Eaton Corporation, was appalled at the antibusiness attitude he encountered in a speech to a group of business students at a midwestern college. As a result he assigned high priority in the company to telling the business story to the public. Some 105 Eaton executives have received training in public relations and communications. Almost every day someone from Eaton is talking to labor unions, trade groups, schools and civic organizations. One of the biggest misconceptions these executives are encountering is that people think corporation profits are far higher than they really are.[15]

Sensitivity to Changes in Social Values

Marketing research, in most cases, has not provided or been pro-grammed to provide, usable information on changing social values; neither has it been able to identify potential consumer issues before they arise. In an era of rapid change of social attitudes and mores, this is important, and businesses need to be more sensitive.

The use of a representative sample of a firm's customers to ob-tain opinions as to contemplated marketing actions has been pro-posed. This would serve to guide management in searching for responsible marketing practices. The appointment of a representa-tive "Customer Review Board," which would consider and react to certain proposed marketing decisions, also would facilitate closer communication and rapport with the other side of the market. These devices would probably be most effective when they generated nega-tive reactions to contemplated decisions from the representative group of customers.[16]

As organizations become larger, it becomes more important to maintain static-free and easily accessible lines of communication with customers. Such communication is one of the more powerful arguments for a "consumer ombudsman" or "vice-president—consumerism."

A Commitment to Customer Service

An improvement in customer service is one of the most tangible im-provements a firm can make to demonstrate its responsiveness, and increase customer satisfaction. To many customers, it seems that marketers' preoccupation with making the initial sale leaves no room for after-sale helpfulness or concern. Many consumer complaints in the past have centered on vague and misleading warranties and in-

[15] "Worried about Image, Business Makes Effort to Sell Itself to Public," *Wall Street Journal,"* June 12, 1973, pp. 1 and 17.
[16] James M. Patterson, "What Are the Social and Ethical Responsibilities of Marketing Executives?" *Journal of Marketing,* July 1966, p. 15.

adequate warranty service. Now, however, all products made after July 4, 1975 are covered by a new federal law that for the first time specifies what a warranty must contain and how it is to be worded.[17]

Marketers may fail in other aspects of customer service as well, resulting in lost customers and sales. There is little literature on the subject of customer service. In view of its importance, the balance of this chapter will be devoted to various aspects of customer service.

CUSTOMER SERVICE

Defining Customer Service

Viewed in the broadest sense, customer service includes all offerings of value to a firm's customers beyond the product itself.[18] Repair and warranty service usually receives the most attention (and complaints), but customer services include such diverse things as return-goods privileges granted by retail stores, conveniences such as delivery, telephone ordering, customer parking, courteous salespeople, dealer displays, and even training aids for dealers' salespeople.

Many services fall into the area of promotional activities. For example, trading stamps, games, and contests could be considered customer services; however, they are used as a form of direct promotion and are more conveniently discussed under such a topic. Dealer aids, such as point-of-purchase displays, are a service rendered by manufacturers to their dealers, but these also may be more relevantly discussed under promotion. On the other hand, efforts by manufacturers to train dealer and distributor salespeople may be considered both a service to the middlemen customers of a manufacturer, as well as to final consumers. While the distinction with promotional efforts is somewhat hazy, we will consider activities as customer services when they only indirectly affect sales generation.

Importance of Customer Service

The importance of customer service has been disregarded by some marketers. This may reflect the defeatist attitude that qualified service personnel cannot be obtained in sufficient quantity and that salespeople and other personnel in contact with customers cannot

---

[17] "Marketing's Credibility Gap," *Sales Management*, June 15, 1968, p. 25; and George Fisk, "Guidelines for Warranty Service after Sale," *Journal of Marketing*, January 1970, p. 63 and "The Guesswork on Warranties," *Business Week*, July 14, 1975, pp. 51–52.

[18] Alfred R. Oxenfeldt, *Executive Action in Marketing* (Belmont, Calif.: Wadsworth, 1966), p. 599.

be motivated to provide good service. But a wise marketer reduces possible friction points as much as possible.

A customer-service program can increase profits in these ways:[19]

1. Attracting new customers
2. Increasing sales to present customers
3. Permitting higher product prices
4. Reducing vulnerability to price competition
5. Providing miscellaneous indirect benefits

The effect of a firm's reputation on attracting potential customers and preventing the loss of existing customers is obvious. Less obvious is the protection from price competition that a good reputation for service can provide. While some customers are more swayed by a "better" price, many place a higher value on a firm's reputation for quality and dependable service. Some services are easily imitated: extended warranties, free delivery, return-goods privilege, telephone ordering, and the like. Others are less easily imitated, and their effective performance slowly builds reputations. The Whirlpool Appliance Corporation has built a solid reputation for quality products by conscientious warranty performance. And then there is Zippo:

> The manufacturer of Zippo cigarette lighters offers perpetual repair free of charge—no one has ever paid to have a Zippo lighter repaired. Not many manufacturers, of course, can offer such service and diligently support it. In Zippo's case, the item is extremely durable and any costs of servicing are not high.

Indirect benefits can come from a customer-service program. A firm's good reputation can make customers more receptive and more tolerant. A company's public image can affect its employee recruitment and the morale and turnover of its personnel. Even dealings with legislatures and government regulatory bodies may be smoothed.[20]

Service Versus Price

Sometimes services are furnished for an extra charge. Many retailers charge for delivery. Marketers of complex products such as color TVs and air conditioners charge for separate service contracts having the characteristics of insurance policies. Other customer services may be provided without extra charge although the costs may result in a higher selling price. Some trade-off must be made between providing greater service and still maintaining reasonable cost, but often it has been in the direction of lower prices *and* reduced service.

[19] Oxenfeldt, p. 604.
[20] Ibid., pp. 605–06.

Especially in regard to warranty and after-sales service, this may be misguided.

Of course, too many costly services can be offered, so that a firm or an entire industry is vulnerable to competition. This situation occurred several decades ago as many retailers allowed costs to rise to a level that encouraged competitive entry by discounters offering lower prices without the frills.

Types of Customer Service

Services can be classified by the type of value they provide for customers, as shown in Figure 4-1. We will discuss each of these in more detail.

Risk Reduction. Services that reduce a customer's risk of getting the wrong product, or one which is defective, are (1) adjustment and return-goods privileges, and (2) warranties or guarantees. Many retailers offer adjustments and refunds, even though the product may not be at fault. The customer is thus permitted to examine the purchase at home without risk or a rigid commitment.

Warranties or *guarantees* have caused the greatest problems. These are obligations assumed by a seller, designed to give the buyer greater assurance when making a purchase. Warranties may be explicit or implied. Implied (nonwritten) warranties have been delineated by the Uniform Sales Act, which is in force in over 30 states, and have been interpreted in numerous court cases. Usually a buyer has some protection without a written warranty, even though he has examined the goods before purchase, if latent defects are later discovered.

Most manufacturers issue written warranties. Sometimes these are legal disclaimers of responsibility, attempting to limit the responsibility to only the expressed provisions.[21] Warranties have often been stated in ambiguous language, they have been unnecessarily complex, and such terms as "unconditionally guaranteed," and

[21] *Report of the Task Force on Appliance Warranties and Service,* Special Assistant to the President on Consumer Affairs, January 8, 1969, pp. 39–47.

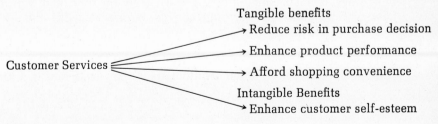

Figure 4-1. Customer services.

"lifetime guarantee," often concealed disclaimers and qualifications that made the warranty effectively worthless. Then there is another type of meaningless "warranty":

> A Dispoz-a-Lamp sold for 66¢. While it was an unfamiliar product, it had a "guarantee." Closer inspection of this guarantee, usually made after the product was bought and failed to work properly, revealed that all the customer had to do was send it back to the factory together with $1 "to cover postage and handling charges."[22]

Recognizing that good warranties provide the assurance in purchasing that leads to better satisfied customers, Maytag eliminated "all exceptions" and stipulated that its warranty would be carried out even if the customer moved out of the selling dealer's area. Now with the new 1975 federal warranty law more firms will be coerced to do likewise. While the law does not require manufacturers to issue warranties, it does specify that if a manufacturer wants to promise a "full" warranty, repair must be made "within a reasonable time and without charge" for any defects, and replacement of merchandise or a full refund given if the product still does not work. If the manufacturer does not want to meet this tough standard, then the warranty must be "conspicuously" promoted as a "limited" warranty. Thus the federal government has stepped in to prescribe stiff standards where many firms were not responsive enough to consumer demands.[23]

Performance Enhancement. Services that improve product performance included the tailoring, alteration, or adjustment needed to fit the product to the particular customer's requirements. Also included are special training or instructions that help the consumer to use the product properly. Such instruction may prevent costly warranty repair work. Home demonstrations by public utility representatives are examples of such consumer training.

Effective and fairly priced repair and maintenance service is a major factor in performance satisfaction. But this along with warranty imperfections has been a major source of consumer complaints. The growing problems consumers have had with obtaining adequate service for everything from cars to hair dryers led *Time* to a feature article titled "America the Inefficient." *Time* suggested that America has become a land governed by the so-called Murphy's Law which chides: If anything can go wrong, it will—and at the worst possible time.[24]

Some firms are upgrading their product-servicing departments and even turning them into assets through technical training centers and special courses for their technicians. Other firms find it difficult

---

[22] Bill Gold, "The District Line," *Washington Post,* March 20, 1972, p. D10.

[23] "The Guesswork on Warranties," p. 51.

[24] "America the Inefficient," *Time,* March 23, 1970, p. 72.

to attract skilled and experienced workers, either in manufacturing or in servicing. Manufacturers, on their part, are seeking to simplify their products and make them more easily repaired. Designing products that would consist of plug-in modules is another possible solution, since relatively inexpensive replacement units would make repair unnecessary.

Statistical quality control, which accepts a predictable number of defective units, may have to be replaced by a complete quality control that accepts "zero defects," for some items in which serious servicing problems cannot otherwise be eased. Multiple inspections of critical parts are rejected by most firms as too costly. But compared to the costs of customer brand switching and costly callback programs, improved quality control might sometimes offset the increased costs.[25]

Convenience Services. Retailers offer a variety of services that contribute to customer convenience, such as delivery, telephone ordering, free parking, gift wrapping, credit, catalogs, etc. Manufacturers often furnish services to their dealers, such as displays, training for dealer salesmen, and sometimes even business-help consultation.

The main problem for a firm offering convenience services is deciding how far to go; how much additional expense is warranted and likely to produce sufficient increased business to justify it? For example, dealer display aids provide a service if used, but often they do not meet dealers' needs, and are wasted.

Intangible Customer Services. In addition to the tangible services, another type of service warrants attention—the so-called overtones, which enhance customer needs for self-esteem and self-respect.[26] These are the supposedly simple services, such as courtesy and respect, prompt attention, and consideration. These take place (or do not) at the point of contact between a firm and its customers, and as such are vital ingredients in establishing a positive or negative public image.

Most executive time is spent in supervising facets of the operation other than customer relations. There are reasons for this. Operational crises and problems claim managerial attention: a production bottleneck cannot be ignored; a decision on advertising scheduling cannot be delayed; a labor dispute must be settled; a rise in costs and consequent fall in profits must receive immediate attention. And the customer who is antagonized, who is ill-treated, whose special requirements are disregarded, who quietly fades away never to return—all this is missed in the pressure of "more important" matters.

Moreover, the complaints that reach the ear of responsible executives are only a small proportion of the total, which frequently induces them to believe that dissatisfaction involves only a small

[25] Fisk, p. 65.
[26] Oxenfeldt, pp. 628–41.

percentage of customers with mostly unjustified complaints. In a report to the Federal Trade Commission in 1969, General Motors "pooh-poohed" 129 warranty complaints the FTC had received on 1966 model cars, saying they amounted to "only .0015 percent of the 8,604,712 new cars sold" by the industry in that model year.[27]

Even the promptness and the quality of response to customer mail can result in positive or negative "overtones." A firm is well advised to devote some attention to this aspect of the firm-customer interaction: special training may be needed, special policies established, and some type of periodic follow-up used, to assure that the company's image does not deteriorate. The telephone is another point of contact that has overtones, yet is seldom checked for its positive or negative contribution.

**MARKETING
IN
ACTION**

Overtones Program at Bell Telephone

Bell Telephone Companies were early pioneers of planned overtones—that is, the intangibles that can make customers like doing business with a particular company. Servicemen are imbued with the need to leave customers' premises neat, and courtesy is stressed. Telephone operators are trained in the importance of overtones, and the "Voice with a Smile" has long been an important objective. Service representatives in the business offices are trained and rated according to various overtones components. They learn the technicalities of handling many different kinds of customer contacts through role playing, and they are judged on the quality of their speech, their understanding, explanations, and interested and helpful manner. Various overtones controls, including periodic retraining, are used to ensure continuous high quality.

SOURCE: Alfred R. Oxenfeldt, *Executive Action in Marketing* (Belmont, Cal.: Wadsworth, 1966), p. 639.

For thought and discussion:

Do you think good overtones can make up for a poor product? for higher prices than competitors?

How important would you see good overtones to be for a land developer? a physician? a police department?

Handling of customer complaints and adjustments is a sore spot for many firms, and many consumers. The distaste for handling irrational and unreasonable ones sometimes inclines the organization to view all complaints in this light. In many large organizations the

[27] Ronald G. Shafer, "Buckpassing Blues," *Wall Street Journal,* November 3, 1969, p. 2.

customer with a legitimate complaint (and most complaints are legitimate) has difficulty reaching someone in authority to gain satisfaction.

Two serious flaws in customer relations are (1) the "promise them anything" philosophy, which merely postpones the day of reckoning and compounds the dissatisfaction, and (2) the "passing the buck" routine between manufacturer and dealers as to who is responsible for the defective product or servicing.

MARKETING
TOOL

Role Playing

Role playing is a teaching device used widely in training salespeople. As we noted in the overtones program at Bell Telephone, it can also be used to improve customer-service contacts. Essentially, role playing consists of placing the trainee in a realistic situation and a confrontation with a simulated customer.

> For example, a trainee may be asked to sell to a particular customer, such as the purchasing agent of a real company. The "buyer" then needs to project himself into the particular role of purchasing agent in order to make the situation as realistic as possible.

The trainee learns by actually doing, can practice various techniques and approaches, and can adjust to unforeseen developments or objections that often arise in selling and customer relations. Furthermore, such things as voice, poise, mannerisms, and the like, which are important factors in dealing with people, can be worked on.

For salespeople, role playing is one of the most effective training devices. It is one thing to read about the various methods of approaching prospects, overcoming objections, and closing the sale, but the actual doing is considerably different. It takes practice to perfect techniques.

Role playing is best combined with critical observation and constructive correction; otherwise some errors may not be obvious to the person involved and would not be corrected. To leave the training—whether selling prospects, or servicing customers—to the actual on-the-job situation may have costly consequences. Sales may be lost and customers unsatisfactorily treated before performance is improved.

For thought and discussion:

A role-playing situation may be done before the entire group. What advantages and disadvantages do you see for this?

Can you think of some other uses for role playing?

Far-sighted firms are finding that well-handled complaints not only improve customers attitudes toward a company and its products, resulting in some promotional value, but they also can provide

useful feedback desirable for product improvement and better satisfying heretofore unrecognized needs. Complaint data then can supplement marketing research data.[28]

A successful overtones program requires a commitment by top
management. It must be a frequent topic of meeting and training
sessions; it must be given major priority or else other matters will
intrude and monopolize attention. Without constant pressure and
without suitable controls to provide feedback, an organization tends
to become indifferent to public relations. This is true for all manner
of organizations, from government agencies, to hospitals, schools,
police departments, and business firms large and small.

Organizing for Customer Service

Customer-service responsibility may be centralized or it may be diffused throughout the organization; ordinarily, a centralized function
permits greater attention and coordination.

If the customer-service department is to be effective it must
have authority for actions that may cross department lines; it must
be able to authorize prompt attention by engineering, finance, production, and other areas where this is warranted. This suggests that such
a department must have the full backing of major executives; otherwise it will soon have little real authority other than to placate and
temporize. Such a department, if permitted to be operationally effective, can be a vital cog in a firm's quest toward social responsiveness.

Vice-president of Consumerism? Perhaps the ultimate in organizational structuring toward a commitment to customer service is to
establish a position of vice-president for consumerism, with authority to "spell out the duties and responsibilities to the buying public
. . . along with precise objectives and methods of measuring performance in accomplishing these objectives.[29]

Such a commitment does recognize the importance of consumer
issues, but the role of such a vice-president has flaws. Presumably
this executive would be on a level with the other vice-presidents,
including the marketing vice-president. As a staff officer, he or she
would advise, persuade, or coerce the marketing department, depending on the support received from top management. And herein
lies the vulnerability: the vice-president for consumerism might become either a meaningless figurehead, or else a powerful influence.
If the former, his purpose in the organization would hardly be
achieved, although it might make good public relations; if the latter,

[28] C. L. Kendall and Frederick A. Russ, "Warranty and Complaint Policies: An
Opportunity for Marketing Management," *Journal of Marketing*, April 1975, pp.
36–43; and *The Nielsen Researcher*, No. 1, 1974, pp. 12–13.
[29] E. B. Weiss, "Marketers Fiddle While Consumers Burn," *Harvard Business
Review*, July–August 1968, pp. 51–52.

the position of the marketing vice-president might well become untenable.

A Consumer Ombudsman. Another approach to providing a better organization for customer service is the consumer ombudsman. This idea originated in Sweden in 1809 with two ombudsmen provided to protect the citizen in civil and military affairs.[30] The consumer ombudsman would protect—or be the spokesman for—the consumer in business affairs with the company.

Such an ombudsman is not placed into the organizational hierarchy at a level to interfere with normal functioning and authority of major executives. However, as a focus for consumer feedback and complaints, and as a person with enough authority to cross department lines and cut red tape where necessary and—theoretically at least—to bring to the attention of top management the consumers' point of view regarding relevant policies and decisions, the ombudsman can represent a significant improvement in customer relations.

QUESTIONS AND PROBLEMS

1. Marketing has always been the focal point for criticism from those who are concerned with unethical business practices. To what extent can unethical practices be controlled by (a) government action, (b) business itself?

2. Why have sellers or marketers historically been viewed in a bad light? Has this perception been justified?

3. Is a marketing manager's social responsibility incompatible with responsibility to stockholders? Can you reconcile the two?

4. Discuss the relationship between illegal acts and unethical acts. Are the two the same? If not, how and when might they differ? Give examples.

5. Do you think a firm should establish a vice-president for consumerism? Does your answer vary according to type and size of company?

6. Should a retail chain open outlets in ghetto areas, even though past experience has been that such outlets invariably lose money? Does your answer to this vary according to size of company?

7. Should a company discontinue the use of nonreturnable containers, even though most customers prefer the convenience of these to the returnable ones, and competition continues to use them? Discuss.

8. Is it ethical to persuade someone to do something which might not be in his long-term best interest—such as to spend money on cigarettes, or liquor, or to buy a more expensive appliance or car than he really can afford?

[30] Hans B. Thorelli, "Consumer Information Policy in Sweden—What Can Be Learned?" *Journal of Marketing,* January 1971, p. 51.

Project

Check on the status of fair-trade laws and of blue laws in your own and nearby communities. Are they still on the books? For what products? Are they enforced? If so, what are the penalties for violators? Are they being violated?

Exercise in Creativity

A medium-sized appliance manufacturer is having serious problems with the after-sales performance of his products, resulting in numerous customer complaints and bad feeling. It is felt that, short term, there is little that can be done to improve quality control because of the absence of sufficient highly trainable and well-motivated factory workers. Until such workers can be obtained and trained in sufficient numbers, it appears that better customer service is the best short-term or at least partial solution to this problem.

Think of as many ideas as you can for improving customer service. From these ideas develop a service strategy for this company.

Role-playing Case

A delegation has just entered your grocery store.

"We are protesting against nonunion lettuce raised in California," their spokesman whom you recognize as a local minister informs you. "As you know, the Chicanos are being victimized by the producers. We insist that you stop selling lettuce, or we will be forced to picket your store."

How would you respond to this demand? What do you think would be the consequences of your decision?

CHAPTER 5

GOVERNMENTAL

INFLUENCE:

LAWS

AND REGULATIONS

Any overview of marketing—or business in general, for that matter
—must take into account the legal environment: the influence and
constraints of government. Federal, state, and local taxes and assessments are one of the more painful aspects of this influence. Numerous laws and regulations, local and federal, regulate competition,
furnish protection to consumers and businesses alike, and make for
some degree of equitable and honest dealing. Government agencies
provide statistical and other services, including loans for large and
small businesses. Government is the nation's biggest customer, consuming hundreds of billions of dollars of goods at all levels. And government, as the largest employer, provides the payroll that is essential to the health of many communities and firms. In this chapter our
concern is with the issues and constraints imposed on marketing by
laws and regulations, and also with the potential for coercive influence. Important terms are:

laissez faire	price discrimination
Sherman Act	acquisition
Clayton Act	Federal Trade Commission
Robinson-Patman Act	consumer protection
price fixing	government coercive influences

HISTORICAL BACKGROUND OF MARKETING REGULATIONS

Government regulation of business activity is fairly recent in the
United States. One provision of the Constitution, however, had
a major impact on marketing: it banned all tariffs on interstate com-

merce, so that the goods of all states could move freely and without assessments.

The first substantial law affecting business was the Sherman Antitrust Act of 1890, although the use of the mails to defraud had been unlawful since 1872. The economic philosophy of laissez faire, given expression by the British economist Adam Smith, held sway to the end of the nineteenth century. Smith wrote in 1776: "Every man, as long as he does not violate the law of justice, is left perfectly free to pursue his own interest in his own way."[1] Laissez faire assumed that what is good for the individual entrepreneur is likely also to be good for society at large.

But laissez faire proved inadequate as industrialization, following the stimulus of the Civil War, brought large-scale production and a concentration of economic power. This led to an unequal competitive warfare where larger firms used cutthroat tactics to drive out smaller rivals. The "robber barons" and the growth of monopolies belong to this period. If a competitive order was to be retained, government had to enforce it with laws and regulations.

We will examine three major types of legislation affecting marketing:

Federal laws affecting competition
Federal laws aimed at consumer protection
State and local laws affecting marketing

FEDERAL LAWS AFFECTING COMPETITION

Between 1890 and 1950 a series of federal laws were passed with the intent of protecting competition.

Table 5-1 outlines the legislation and the purposes and major clauses of each enactment.

Sherman Act

The Sherman Act of 1890 was intended to protect business competition in the wake of the many mergers and combinations taking place after the Civil War. It established statutory public policy against restraint of trade and monopoly in interstate and foreign commerce. Section 1 condemns "every contract . . . or conspiracy, in restraint of trade," while Section 2 expresses opposition to monopolizing or attempts to monopolize. As with many federal laws, ambiguous wording and varying court interpretations have led to confusion regarding what is legal and what is not. In 1911 the U. S. Supreme Court established the "rule of reason," by which not every contract or agreement among businesses was illegal, but only those that "re-

[1] *Wealth of Nations,* 1776.

Table 5-1.
Outline of Federal Legislation Affecting Competition

Date	Law	Purpose	Major Clauses
1890	Sherman Act	Forbade monopolistic and noncompetitive practices.	Outlawed monopolies; outlawed restraint of competition.
1914	Federal Trade Commission Act	Provided watchdog agency.	Developed machinery for policing; dealt with unfair methods of competition.
1914	Clayton Act	Same function as Sherman Act, but spelled out more specifically.	Prohibited certain practices where "effect" . . . may be to substantially lessen competition or tend to create a monopoly.
1936	Robinson-Patman Act	Amended the Clayton Act, to help small businesses by better regulating price discrimination.	Concerned with defining unfair price discrimination, and inequitable quantity discounts, brokerage payments, and promotional payments.
1937	Miller-Tydings Act	Amended Sherman Act in the interest of "fair trade."	Exempted interstate fairtrade (price fixing) agreements from antitrust prosecution.
1938	Wheeler-Lea Act	Amended FTC Act to clarify phrase "unfair methods of competition."	Outlawed "unfair or deceptive acts or practices in commerce."
1950	Celler-Kefauver Antimerger Act	Amended Clayton Act, to remedy loopholes regarding corporate growth through merger and acquisition.	Broadened power to prevent intercorporate acquisitions where acquisition may have substantially adverse effect on competition.

strain trade."[2] As a result, each case had to be judged individually against the rule of reason, and it became clear that more definitive legislation was needed.

The most celebrated recent violation of the Sherman Act was the electrical conspiracy of 1960. Here, for the first time in the history of the act, prison sentences were imposed on corporate officials for conspiring to fix prices.

The Antitrust Division of the Justice Department has recently been looking into price fixing in the service industries, such as fee

[2] Standard Oil of N.J. v. U. S., 221 U. S. 1 (1911).

fixing by architects, engineers, lawyers, physicians and dentists, and real estate brokers. For example, minimum fee schedules of the Oregon State Bar Association have been attacked.[3]

MARKETING
MISTAKE

The Electrical Conspiracy of 1960—Price Fixing

In 1960, 29 electrical-equipment manufacturers and 53 of their executives were indicted for price fixing. This represented practically the entire electrical-equipment industry and included some of our largest and most well known firms, such as General Electric, Westinghouse, and Allis-Chalmers. The price fixing was involved in sealed bids (one firm would submit the lowest bid on each contract; the other firms by agreement would bid higher) so that the contracts were rotated among the participants on a fixed percentage basis.

Rather than contesting the indictment, most of the firms pleaded *nolo contendere* (no contest) to almost all the Justice Department's charges. Fines totaling about $2 million were imposed on the companies and on 45 of the individuals. And for the first time in the history of the Sherman Act, jail sentences were imposed: seven corporate officials received thirty-day sentences, while 23 others were placed on probation. In addition the companies faced more than 1,800 suits brought by their customers for triple damages.

SOURCE: For a detailed account of this conspiracy and of the background and factors leading to price fixing, see Richard Austin Smith, "The Incredible Electrical Conspiracy" *Fortune,* April and May 1961.

For thought and discussion:

None of the executives indicted was a top executive; they were from middle management ranks. How do you account for top management not being aware of such a widespread conspiracy?

Can you suggest some factors that might have led to such a conspiracy?

Federal Trade Commission Act

The deficiencies of the Sherman Act, especially under the "rule of reason," led to the establishment in 1914 of an administrative agency —the Federal Trade Commission (FTC)—with power to investigate and issue "cease and desist" orders. This act, therefore, provided both the method and the machinery for enforcement. More latitude for prosecution was supplied by declaring "unfair methods of competition" to be illegal. Subsequent legislation and amendments have broadened the duties of the commission considerably. The FTC now

[3] "Bigness is Okay; Badness is Not," *Forbes,* October 1, 1974, pp. 23–24.

has jurisdiction not only in antitrust cases, but in many other matters that concern marketers more directly, such as those involving deceptive practices.

The *Wheeler-Lea Amendment* in 1938 gave the FTC jurisdiction over practices which injure the public but may not involve a competitor; it also prohibited false advertising of food, drugs, and cosmetics.

The *Lanham Trade-Mark Act* of 1946 authorized the FTC to institute proceedings for cancellation of the registration of trademarks where obtained by fraud or used to deceive or violate the antitrust laws.

Further legislation gave the FTC additional duties in the area of consumer protection, and we will discuss some of these later in this chapter.

Clayton Act

The Clayton Act was also passed in 1914, and attempted further to strengthen the Sherman Act. Various actions were prohibited "where the effect will be to substantially lessen competition, or tend to create a monopoly." The use of this language, while it still required interpretation in the courts, meant that the government no longer had to prove an actual monopoly or conspiracy, only that competition was substantially affected. The law was made more specific in regard to price discrimination (charging different customers different prices for the same goods), *tying contracts* (where the purchaser agreed not to use goods provided by competitors of the seller), interlocking directorates in directly competing companies, and intercorporate stockholdings (one firm acquiring stock or assets of another company)—all these were illegal if, thereby, competition was substantially lessened. The Clayton Act is enforced by the FTC. The regulated utilities, labor, agricultural and marketing cooperatives, insurance, and foreign trade are exempted from its restrictions.

**MARKETING
IN
ACTION**

Coops—Freedom from Income Tax and Most Antitrust Laws
There are basically two types of coops. One is a supply coop, a means for farmers to pool their buying power. The other is a marketing cooperative, which gets the crops to market without benefit of middlemen; among the latter are such familiar names as Ocean Spray (cranberries), Sunkist (citrus fruits), and Welch (grape juice). The sales of marketing cooperatives in 1973 amounted to $36 billion, and includes 75 percent of the nation's dairy products, 35 percent of the grain, 30 percent of fruit, vegetables and cotton, and 15 percent of all livestock.

Ocean Spray is an example of a marketing coop. It sets its own market price for cranberries, but is committed to purchase the full production of its 800 member-growers. At the end of the year it distributes some of the profits to its members; the rest it retains to build its own capital. While this income is taxable to the grower, Ocean Spray is tax-exempt. In 1973 Ocean Spray bought 14 percent more cranberries than it was able to sell; the balance it freezes and thereby holds off the market. Were private businesses to do this they might well go to jail, since two aspects of the Sherman and Clayton antitrust laws would be in violation—artificially limited supplies, and price fixing.

SOURCE: "Speaking of Bigness," *Forbes,* October 15, 1974, pp. 57–60.

For thought and discussion:
What rationale do you see for agricultural coops being exempt from
    antitrust laws?
Do you think this is fair to other businesses?
Do you think society is benefitted by this situation? Why or why not?

Robinson-Patman Act

Price discrimination continued to be a problem, however; it was difficult to prove in court that it reduced competition. The rise of the big chains in the 1920s and the difficulties suffered by small retailers during the Depression led in 1936 to the Robinson-Patman Act. Before the act, the large firms and especially the chains were often able to buy lower, not always because of only real economies in doing business, but because of their vastly superior bargaining power over smaller competitors.

The act reads in part:

It shall be unlawful . . . to discriminate in price between
different purchasers of commodities of like grade and quality
. . . where the effect . . . may be to substantially lessen
competition or tend to create a monopoly, or to injure, destroy,
or prevent competition . . .

The inclusion of the phrase "to injure, destroy, or prevent competition" meant that the FTC no longer had to prove that competition was *substantially* lessened, but only that it was *injured*. This was soon interpreted to mean "injury to competitors," and greatly increased the ease of prosecution.

Defenses against Price-Discrimination Charges. Not all price discrimination is illegal. We should clarify that the Robinson-Patman Act has nothing to do with the prices a retailer charges—retailers may discriminate if they wish; it is concerned only with the prices of a manufacturer or wholesaler to dealers. A firm charged with price discrimination has two available defenses: a cost defense, and a good-faith defense.

If a seller can prove that specific cost savings result in the "manufacture, sale or delivery resulting from differing methods or quantities," price differences—such as quantity discounts—may be permitted. But the *cost defense* has been quite difficult to use since most firms do not have such cost data available. Other firms do not want to bare their confidential cost figures, and there is always the risk that the method of computing costs may not be acceptable to the FTC and the courts.

In the *good-faith defense,* a seller attempts to prove that a price was lowered in good faith to meet competition. Until lately, this has been a permissible defense if it occurred as a defensive rather than an aggressive action, but a more recent Supreme Court decision makes this more murky. A small firm, the Utah Pie Company, entered an established market with discount prices. This led to price cutting, including sales below cost by the larger national companies. The defense of the national manufacturers that they were meeting competition was disallowed since it involved "persistent sales below cost."[4]

The Robinson-Patman Act also outlaws brokerage payments to buyers unless they actually perform the function of a broker. The major chains had been claiming such discounts due to their large purchasing volume, but were consequently denied this. The act also requires that advertising allowances or any special services be provided on "proportionately equal terms" to all buyers. That is, firms may not provide demonstrators, advertising allowances, or display material to some customers and not to others. Proof of injury to competition is not even necessary for prosecution of such cases.

The Borden Case. This landmark case in 1966 tested the prohibition of price discrimination among buyers of a product of "like grade and quality." Borden had been marketing part of its milk under the Borden label; the other part, which was physically and chemically identical with the Borden-labeled milk, was packaged under a customer's brand. Borden charged a higher price for its own brand than it charged customers for their private-branded milk.

The Supreme Court refused to consider that brand name imparted any dissimilarity of quality: a well-known brand alone does not make a product different from one having an unknown label. Only physical identity was considered relevant in determining likeness of quality of products. Consequently, the fact that there were price differences in products of "like grade and quality" was prima

---

[4] "Court Raps Price Cuts," *Business Week,* April 29, 1967, p. 50; and "Utah Pie Co. v. Continental Baking Co. et al.," *Journal of Marketing,* October 1967, p. 74.

facie evidence of price discriminations in violation of the Robinson-Patman Act.[5]

This case could potentially have extensive effects on firms that sell goods under several brand names—tangible physical differences might even have to be built into the different brands—but the FTC has not vigorously pursued this tack.[6] The threat remains, however.

Miller-Tydings Act

The Depression stimulated other concerns with price competition and its effects on small firms. Beginning in 1931, state laws were enacted permitting manufacturers to set retail prices by requiring retailers to sign contracts agreeing to maintain the prices. Since this did not bind the nonsigners, California passed a law in 1933 that bound all the retailers in the state if one retailer signed such a contract. Fair-trade laws were eventually passed in 45 states, but their legality was questionable because in effect they sanctioned price fixing. The Miller-Tydings Act of 1937 exempted these contracts from federal antitrust legislation.

The Miller-Tydings Act did not specifically mention the *nonsigner's clause.* Consequently, in 1952 the *McGuire Act* clarified the legality of the nonsigner's clause. We will discuss fair trade in more detail in chapter 14.

Celler-Kefauver Antimerger Act

A major avenue of business expansion, one that is faster than internal growth, is growth by acquisition or merger. This prompted the Celler-Kefauver amendment to the Clayton Act in 1950.

Forms of Acquisition. A firm may expand horizontally, vertically, or by unrelated, conglomerate-type acquisitions. *Horizontal mergers* involve acquiring firms at the same level of activity. If a meat processor merges with another meat processor, this is an expansion of horizontal operations. A firm may expand to two or more successive stages of production or distribution. An example of this is a retailer integrating backward into wholesaling and manufacturing. Firestone Tire and Rubber Company has achieved almost a complete *vertical integration*—owning rubber plantations, manufacturing tires, and selling them through its own Firestone retail outlets. In the *conglomerate merger* there is no relationship in the nature of the business between the acquiring and acquired firms.

[5] Federal Trade Commission v. Borden Co., 383 U. S. 637 (1966).

[6] Ray O. Werner "Marketing and the United States Supreme Court 1965–1968," *Journal of Marketing,* January 1969, pp. 16–17; Morris L. Mayer, Joseph B. Mason, and E. A. Orbeck, "The Borden Case—A Legal Basis for Private Brand Price Discrimination," *MSU Business Topics,* Winter 1970, pp. 56–63; and "Price Differentials on Brands Upheld," *Business Week,* July 29, 1967.

The Clayton Act was directed primarily against horizontal mergers that lessened competition "substantially." Vertical integration was not regulated under the Clayton Act.

The Celler-Kefauver Antimerger Act widened the restriction and led to increasingly vigorous control of both horizontal and vertical integration of large companies. But a merger across industry lines— a conglomerate merger—seemed to have antitrust immunity since it neither lessened competition by removing a competitor (as does the horizontal merger), nor did it create a captive market in place of a free one (as the vertical merger).

Consequently, 70 percent of the mergers by the late 1960s were of the conglomerate type.[7] However, the inherent dangers of exuberant acquisitions of nonrelated firms were illustrated when a tight money situation and a falling stock market brought some conglomerates, such as LTV and Litton Industries, into financial jeopardy. Acquiring firms was somehow easier than trying to manage the resulting unwieldy package. Meantime, government agencies began to have second thoughts about the legality of conglomerate mergers.

Procter & Gamble's Divestiture of Clorox. Procter & Gamble, the nation's largest producer of soap and detergent products, in 1957 acquired Clorox, the maker of a dominant brand of household liquid bleach. Since Clorox was not a direct competitor, this was not considered a horizontal acquisition and therefore was thought to be safe from government scrutiny as a conglomerate merger. However, the great marketing and advertising power of P & G was judged a threat to the competitive balance in the laundry-bleach industry and a deterrent to entry of new firms. Procter & Gamble was forced to sell Clorox.

This case is of major significance because a powerful firm replacing another firm in a related (but not identical) industry now may well come under attack. The FTC has also forced Procter & Gamble to sell part of the assets of the Folger Coffee Company, which it had acquired, and has forbidden this division to share in joint promotions with other P & G products, or benefit from media discounts.

FEDERAL LAWS AIMED AT CONSUMER PROTECTION

The second major type of federal legislation has been in the field of consumer protection.

Table 5-2 outlines some of the major federal legislation aimed at consumer protection and elimination of deceptive practices.

[7] Commerce Clearing House, *Trade Regulation Reporter*, par. 50.147, pp. 56 and 181.

More consumer-protection bills are pending in Congress and may be passed in the next few years. Most notable are bills to create a federal consumer-protection agency or ombudsman, to tighten up warranty protection, and to establish national no-fault auto insurance.

Table 5-2.
Notable Federal Consumer-Protection Legislation

Date	Law	Purpose and Major Provisions
1872	Mail Fraud Act	Outlawed the use of the mails to defraud.
1906	Pure Food and Drug Act	Outlawed adulterated and misbranded foods and drugs sold in interstate commerce.
1906	Meat Inspection Act	Provided for federal inspection of slaughtering, packing, and canning plants that shipped meat across state lines.
1938	Federal Food, Drug, and Cosmetic Act of 1938	Modernized Pure Food and Drug Act of 1906; strengthened earlier definitions of adulteration and misbranding, required preclearance of new drugs to show they would be safe for use, extended law to include cosmetics and therapeutic devices, and authorized federal inspection of factories producing items subject to the law.
1939	Wool Product Labeling Act	Required full disclosure of percentages of new wool, reprocessed wool, and other fibers.
1951	Fur Products Labeling Act	Made compulsory the labeling of fur content.
1953	Flammable Fabrics Act	Provided sanctions against wearing apparel so highly flammable as to be dangerous when worn by individuals.
1966	Fair Packaging and Labeling Act (truth in packaging)	Provided for more informative labeling of most products found in the supermarket.
1968	Credit Protection Act (truth in lending)	Required disclosures of credit and annual rates of finance charges.
1968	Interstate Land Sales Full Disclosure Act	Provided safeguards against unscrupulous practices in interstate land sales.
1970	Public Health Smoking Act	Banned cigarette advertising on radio and television after January 2, 1971.

Table 5-2. (Continued)

Date	Law	Purpose and Major Provisions
1970	Amendment to Federal Deposit Insurance Act	Prohibited issuance of unsolicited credit cards, limited a consumer's liability to $50, regulated credit bureaus, and provided consumers with access to their credit files.
1970	Clean Air Act Amendments	Provided for establishment of air-quality standards.
1972	Consumer Product Safety Act	Created commission with power to prescribe mandatory safety standards for virtually all consumer products except those for which specific safety legislation already existed.

ADMINISTRATIVE LAW—THE REGULATORS

More than 100 federal agencies exercise some measure of regulation over private business. Some have been around a long time, such as the Interstate Commerce Commission established in 1887 to protect farmers from exorbitant charges by monopolistic railroads (now it protects railroads from truck competition). The Federal Trade Commission (FTC), established in 1914 and strengthened in 1938 by the Wheeler-Lea Amendment, has become more aggressive in recent years as consumerism and public pressure demanded action.

The FTC is particularly concerned with false or deceptive practices and unfair methods of competition which may hurt both the public and other business firms.

MARKETING MISTAKES

Practices Which Led to Federal Trade Commission (FTC) Consumer-Protection Action

Aamco. In 1970 the Federal Trade Commission issued a complaint against Aamco, a franchiser of automatic transmission rebuilding and repair shops. The case illustrates the vulnerability of consumers in the automobile-service field, and the need for stringent protection measures. The complaint alleges that Aamco's advertisements were full of misrepresentations, such as a $23 removal and inspection service for transmissions, free towing service, "easy credit terms," and "lifetime" guarantees.

Aamco was also charged with requiring its franchises to advise customers—after road-testing and checking the car—that the problem was inside the transmission, which consequently had to be dismantled, and was then proclaimed to be "badly worn, damaged, and contaminated." With the old transmission torn down and disassembled, the customer was then faced with additional undisclosed charges to reassemble the transmission to its former condition, in the event he resisted the "pressures" to buy a new or rebuilt transmission.[a]

Interstate Publishers Service. This complaint charged that Interstate sold magazines it was not authorized to sell, failed to deliver magazines to subscribers within a reasonable time, and falsely promised good earnings to prospective magazine salesmen. Furthermore, the firm's door-to-door salespeople used personal sympathy pleas and misinformed potential buyers that they worked for a charitable organization, according to the complaint.[b]

Bristol-Myers and Dry Ban spray antiperspirant. The FTC challenged commercials which indicated that Dry Ban, when sprayed on the body or on a surface, went on dry and left no discernible or visible residue after application. Evidence, according to the judge, indicated to the contrary: Dry Ban is wet and watery when applied to the body, remains wet for several minutes, and upon drying leaves a substantial and visible residue.

The judge as a result issued a broad and sweeping order, requiring Bristol-Myers and its advertising agency to cease and desist from using deceptive product feature or product superiority demonstrations for "any product" in their line.[c]

The FTC has challenged these advertised "claims" and demanded that they be substantiated:

"Macleans rates low on abrasion . . . in the lowest third of toothpastes."

"Ultra-Brite freshens breath like a mouthwash . . . It's got real mouthwash ingredients built in."

"Pertussin 8 Hour Cough Formula effectively quiets coughs due to cold or flu for up to 8 hours."

"Dristan Tablets effectvely relieve the body aches which may accompany a cold or the flu."[d]

"Firestone's 'The Safe Tire' stops 25 percent quicker."[e]

Claims that products such as Bayer Aspirin, Cope, Midol, Vanquish, Bufferin, Anacin, and Excedrin relieve nervous tension and similar symptoms.[f]

SOURCES: [a]"Legal Developments in Marketing," *Journal of Marketing,* January 1971, p. 82. [b]"Legal Developments . . ." July 1972, p. 81. [c]"Legal Developments . . ." July 1974, p. 84. [d]"Legal Developments . . ." July 1972 p. 79. [e]"Legal Developments . . ." January 1974, p. 77. [f]"Legal Developments . . ." October 1973, p. 90.

For thought and discussion:
What defense can you give for the above-mentioned practices?
Do you see any dangers in continued FTC actions of this kind?

The Food and Drug Administration (FDA) has also had a notable effect on recent marketing practices as they affect the general public. It is particularly concerned with public health and safety and is empowered to prohibit and regulate "adulterated" and "misbranded" foods, drugs, cosmetics, and medical devices. It has conducted laboratory tests on more than 100,000 such items, banning some from distribution as a result. Two other agencies especially concerned with protecting the general public are the Consumer Product Safety Commission established in 1972 to investigate and identify products responsible for various injuries, and the National Highway Traffic Safety Administration for automotive research and regulation.

Other agencies regulate the production and distribution of energy, the operation of the transportation system, communications, and banking and securities.

> The extent that business must deal with federal agencies is illustrated in the case of General Electric Company which a few years ago faced eleven agencies having direct regulatory impact on how it conducted its affairs. These ranged from the Federal Communications Commission to the Atomic Energy Commission and the Defense Department.[8]

Later in this chapter we will see how budget limitations, cumbersome procedures, a sometimes nonobjective viewpoint, and division of responsibility have reduced the effectiveness of some agencies.

STATE AND LOCAL LAWS AFFECTING MARKETING

Many state and local laws affect marketing. Most are restrictive in some way and reflect entrenched special interest groups in state and local communities who want to keep out or restrict competitors, in contrast to federal laws protecting competition. Frequently the large corporation or "outside-owned" chain or discounter is the object of the restrictions. Table 5-3 shows the major types of such legislation.

Many of the laws aimed at restricting competition date from the 1930s when small merchants' fear of big firms and especially the chains was at its peak. The influence of such laws is waning today in many states. Consumer-protection legislation, however, is increasing.

[8] "The Regulators Can't Go On This Way," Business Week, February 28, 1970, p. 60.

Table 5-3.
Restrictive State and Local Laws and Regulations

Type	Stipulations
Zoning	Restricts types of stores in a given area.
Licenses	Certain types of stores, such as liquor stores, and certain occupations, such as accounting, law, and medicine, require licenses. Certain standards are thereby enforced, but competition is also limited.
Blue laws	Restrictions on store hours and on Sunday selling.
Green River ordinances	Activities of salespeople representing firms located outside the city are banned.
Chain-store taxes	Chain stores are taxed, usually graduated according to the number of stores operated in the particular state.
Unfair trade practices acts	Retailers are prohibited from using **loss leaders** and offering goods at or near cost
Fair-trade laws	Retailers are prohibited from selling certain branded goods below a designated "fair trade" price.
Consumer-protection laws	Various state and local laws aimed at protecting consumers from deceptive practices.

On May 1, 1975 fair trade regulations were lifted in New York State; this store window stresses that fact in promotion. *Photo by Helena Frost.*

Philosophical Issues in Public Policy

The basic principle behind the Sherman Act and subsequent anti-trust legislation is that business firms should be able to operate free of restraints by other firms. There is no agreement, however, as to just what kind of competition the antitrust laws should preserve. Few would advocate the regulated competition of cartels along European lines, free to fix prices and divide up the market. However, the other extreme—that of protecting business from competition—may not be quite desirable either.

In efforts to protect small business, our laws and their judicial interpretations may have gone too far, at the cost of restricting the legitimate advantage of more efficient firms, whether they be large or not:

> A firm can be forced out of business because of downright inefficiency, because it is too small to achieve economies of scale, because it is not keeping up with technology, or because it is the victim of the market power inherent in the size of a larger firm. If competition is to be maintained by law, then the law should protect firms only from the last-mentioned factor.[9]

Yet the fair trade laws and unfair practices acts do tend to reduce the advantage of efficiency. The Robinson-Patman Act and its limiting of quantity discounts denies economies of scale, while prohibiting brokerage allowances to any except independent brokers, even though the buyer performed his own brokerage service, inhibits efforts toward introducing more efficiency.

There is disagreement, and concern, over the concentration of market power—the growth of "bigness." The courts have sometimes viewed bigness as evil per se: the Clorox case, with Proctor & Gamble forced to divest primarily because of the threat of its market power, is an example, Another view, however, criticizes the harassment of the big firms. Industries fragmented with many small firms, such as homebuilding, are not models of efficiency. Furthermore, large nationally based firms appear to be more cognizant of social responsibilities, and are leading the way in hiring and training the hardcore unemployed and in working to clean up pollution.

The questions of how much and what kind of consumer protection is needed have not been resolved. Few would publicly advocate a "hands off" policy; however, some stress educational programs to help consumers protect themselves.

[9] Marshall C. Howard, *Legal Aspects of Marketing* (New York: McGraw-Hill, 1964), pp. 150–51.

Statutory Uncertainty

Existing antitrust legislation does not always make clear what is legal and what is illegal. While some offenses, such as price fixing, are illegal per se, others are not, and any illegality is subject to varying judgments. Much of this legislation is phrased in general terms, with key words requiring interpretation. Such words and phrases as "unreasonable," "monopolizing," "substantially," and "tend to create" can be variously interpreted by reasonable people.

Courts differ in their interpretations and decisions; the Federal Trade Commission and the Department of Justice staffs themselves are not always in agreement. Cases which have been brought before the Supreme Court have often been decided by close votes. Furthermore, the long process of litigation and appeal can extend the uncertainty of legality for years: in the Clorox case, ten years elapsed (1957 to 1967) from the first FTC complaint challenging the acquisition to the Supreme Court decision.

Operational Effectiveness

Benjamin Rosenthal, congressman from New York, has been one of the most vocal spokesmen in consumers' behalf. He notes that:

> The worth of any law is found, ultimately, not by measuring how it has been designed, but by measuring how it is being executed. The mere enactment of consumer laws, without effective consideration of how these laws are to be administered, and by whom, is deceptive.[10]

In this section we will examine the problem of operational effectiveness of existing regulatory devices within the legal framework. Some of the problems and obstacles that affect marketers and consumers are:

Budget deficiencies
Orientation of regulatory agencies
Cumbersome regulatory procedures
Fragmentation of responsibility
Lack of congressional follow-up

Budget Deficiencies. Congress has often been more willing to pass laws and create regulatory bodies than to provide adequate resources for them to perform their assigned tasks: ". . . with 1,150 people and a $13-million budget, you can't watch over 4,900,000 companies, the generators of a $695 billion economy."[11] Although meager budgets have affected antitrust and price discrimination efforts, they have

---

[10] Benjamin S. Rosenthal, "Producer versus Consumer: The Unequal Battle," *Economics and Business Bulletin,* Winter 1970, p. 38.

[11] Paul Rand Dixon, quoted in *Advertising Age,* March 29, 1965, p. 26.

had more nullity in the area of consumer protection. This is true particularly at the state and local levels. For example, Pennsylvania's Bureau of Consumer Protection, budgeted at $400,000 a year, had only 28 men to cover the entire state with a total population of 11.8 million.[12] And in Los Angeles County, there was one "fraud catcher" for every 166,000 people, but one dog catcher for every 1,400 dogs.[13]

Some consumer crusaders have called this "fake reform," and cautioned against being fooled by "new toothless laws with no funding and enforcement."[14] The temptation undoubtedly exists for some legislators, faced with the sometimes incompatible demands of their constituents and of powerful lobbyists for special business interests, to vote for additional consumer laws while denying them more than token enforcement funds.

Orientation of Regulatory Agencies. A very real criticism of many of the federal agencies involved in consumer protection is that their orientation is pro-industry, that they lack a consumer interest, that they are vassals of the very industries they are charged to regulate. While outright corruption has not been charged, the influence is often pernicious, and reflects the system of regulatory agency appointments. The industry usually influences the selection of appointees to top spots, establishes rapport quickly through invitations to speak at industry conventions and meetings, and probably most important, offers the lure of a good job at the end of an appointive term.[15]

The provisions of the watered-down final version of the truth-in-packaging law, for example, reflect the nonconsumer orientation of important regulatory agencies. In its original form, the law would have eliminated confusing description of package sizes, regulated use of promotional devices, and set standards for slack fill in containers. When enacted, the law specified that the above requirements would be set *at the discretion* of the administering agencies: Department of Commerce, Food and Drug Administration, and Federal Trade Commission. As a result of the discretionary provision, the law was substantially weakened. The responsible agencies have not only exempted many products from the law but also long delayed implementation of the mandatory as well as discretionary provisions of the act.[16]

A further example of the inability of federal agencies to serve the regulated industry and the consumer equally is reflected in the descriptive terminology permitted by the Consumer and Marketing Service of the Department of Agriculture for producers to use in

[12] "New York Leads the Consumer Crusade," *Business Week,* January 31, 1970, p. 52.

[13] Ibid., p. 52.

[14] Ibid., p. 53.

[15] "The Regulators," pp. 64–65.

[16] Sylvia Porter, "Packaging Truth Best No-Law Law," *Evening Star,* Washington, D.C., November 1969, p. D8.

describing various commercial foods: the designations of "U.S. Grade A" and "No. 1" are often used to describe the medium grades: whereas, "U.S. Grade AA" and "U.S. Extra Fancy" are in fact the top grades. For apples, the grade "U.S. No. 1" is lower than "U.S. Fancy" and "U.S. Extra Fancy."[17]

Cumbersome Regulatory Procedures. Bureaucracy lends itself to red tape, complex flow of paper work, and endless delays. One example of the typical action-orientation of our bureaucratic agencies concerns the submission of a report to the president and Congress by the Department of Health, Education, and Welfare, as required by the Flammable Fabrics Act of 1967. The report, due December 31, 1968, was considered important because its contents were to guide the Department of Commerce in upgrading flammability standards to reduce burn injuries and deaths. In July 1968, the draft report was first submitted; on July 14, 1969 it was finally hand carried from the assistant secretary for health and scientific affairs to the secretary's office, after passing through thirteen different submissions and reviews.[18]

The cumbersome machinery of the FTC can be tied up for years before a contesting firm need comply with commission orders. Therefore abuses may continue long after FTC complaints. The deceptive advertising of Geritol, for example, continued for over eleven years after the FTC opened the case. Part of the blame for such impotence must go to Congress, which had refused to grant the FTC such weapons as a preliminary injunction, or the right to impose penalties for initial violations.

Fragmentation of Responsibility. The fragmentation of program responsibilities among numerous and uncoordinated federal agencies is a serious deterrent to effective regulation, not only in regard to consumer protection, but in other areas as well. Congressman Rosenthal has pointed out that:

> Responsibility for enforcing the Truth-in-Lending Act is vested in nine separate agencies.
> Administration of the Fair Packaging and Labeling Act is divided among three agencies—the Federal Trade Commission, the Food and Drug Administration, and the Department of Commerce.
> Five federal agencies are responsible for consumer protection of the poor.

[17] Executive Office of the President, *Consumer Issues '66: A Report to the President from the Consumer Advisory Council* (Washington, D.C.: General Services Administration, 1966), p. 21.

[18] U.S. Congress, House, Committee on Government Operations, *Collection and Utilization of Accident and Injury Data, Hearings,* before a subcommittee of the Committee of Government Operations, House of Representatives, 91st Cong., 1st Sess., 1969, p. 57.

Programs to control air and water pollution are found in half a dozen agencies.

The Flammable Fabrics Act of 1967 is shared by the Department of Commerce, the FTC, and the FDA.[19]

This fragmentation, with each agency taking separate action, or more often, leaving any action to someone else, is a powerful argument for combining all consumer-protection responsibilities under a central agency, such as a new consumer department.

The effects of uncoordinated regulation can also be seen in the area of transportation. The Interstate Commerce Commission (ICC) regulates railroads, long-distance buses, moving vans, common carrier truckers, some barge lines, and oil shipment by pipeline. The Civil Aeronautics Board (CAB) has all the commercial airlines. The Bureau of Public Roads is responsible for the highway system, while the Army Corps of Engineers administers rivers and harbors, and builds canals and dredges rivers for barge traffic. The result has been that each agency operates as if nothing else existed, with routes, rates, and subsidies being approved for its regulated industry without regard to the effect on competing modes of transportation. Consequently we have seen railroads faltering at a time when they offer the best alternative to highway congestion, energy problems, and pollution.

Lack of Congressional Follow-up. Under the Reorganization Act of 1946, congressional committees are responsible for following the legislation under their jurisdiction to evaluate its implementation and effects upon the public. Congress itself, therefore, is responsible for some of the flaws that have been described.

Part of this failure to monitor the regulatory agencies reflects attention paid to special interest groups by committee and subcommittee chairmen. As one example, the chairman of the House Appropriations Agriculture Subcommittee was responsible for overseeing the Department of Agriculture's regulation of pesticides. Despite substantiated charges of Agriculture's laxity in such regulation, he remained a staunch supporter of the pesticide industry and did not take action to see that the Department carried out its responsibilities in the area.[20]

Influence of Government as a Coercive Force

In recent years the federal government, and most especially the office of the president, has exerted certain coercive pressures upon occasion. While Republican presidents have been more reluctant to exercise such authority, the potential and the historical effectiveness

[19] Rosenthal, "Producer versus Consumer," p. 39.
[20] U. S. Congress, Senate, *Congressional Record,* November 14, 1969, p. S14365.

of such pressures can hardly be ignored by large firms pursuing actions which affect the economy.

Under Kennedy and Johnson. The most dramatic recent confrontation of the might of the federal government against the behemoths of industry occurred in spring 1962, with John F. Kennedy and United States Steel the principal participants. The nation was facing increasing inflationary dangers at that time and the Steelworkers Union, largely through the personal efforts and influence of President Kennedy, had accepted a small noninflationary wage settlement, one in line with the increase in productivity. Shortly after this settlement, the steel industry, led by United States Steel—in a monumental example of poor timing—announced a substantial boost in steel prices. This action stirred a furious reaction from the administration which now saw a new wave of consumer price rises. Kennedy denounced the action the next day at a news conference:

> tiny handful of steel executives whose pursuit of private power and profit exceeds their sense of public responsibility . . . show utter contempt for the interests of 185 million Americans.[21]

In addition to the use of widespread condemnatory publicity emanating from the office of the president, government pressure and the threat of pressure was immediately exercised. Intimations were made to look into the pricing practices of the steel industry, to seek evidence that steel's "follow the leader" pricing practices were indeed a violation of antitrust laws. Economic pressures were exerted as the Defense Department threatened the price increasers with loss of business and alerted its contractors to buy only from companies that held the line on prices. In the face of the severity of the government reaction and the refusal of several smaller steel companies to follow the rest of the industry, U. S. Steel and its followers rescinded their price hike.[22]

The use of "guidelines" for price decisions by big companies in basic industries was characteristic of the Johnson years. Washington welcomed businessmen who wished to discuss government reaction to contemplated price changes, and in general used private persuasion to slow inflationary price changes.

Under Nixon and Ford. During much of the Nixon administration, business was given a free hand in price setting. Finally, with rampant inflation and shortages of some strategic supplies, wage and price controls were temporarily enacted. With their removal, inflation continued unabated, only lessening somewhat with the severe recession of the Ford administration. But the potential for coercion by the federal government, short of direct controls, remains.

[21] Reported in "The Storm over Steel," *Business Week,* April 14, 1962, p. 32.
[22] "No Room for Ill Will," *Business Week,* April 21, 1962, pp. 25–30.

It is unlikely that laissez faire will return to this country. The trend is toward ever more regulation and restriction—more government involvement. Where will it end? When does it become too much? Here marketers and social activists differ. More responsive marketing, however, may help reduce social pressures for ever more restriction and control of business.

QUESTIONS AND PROBLEMS

1. What accounts for the common practice of Congress's passing laws and creating regulatory and enforcing agencies for compliance, but not appropriating sufficient funds for these agencies to perform effectively? What consequences do you see this having (a) for the individual firm, (b) for society?

2. Do you think the federal government should establish a Consumer Protection Agency? What pros and cons do you see for this?

3. Differentiate between the Unfair Practices Acts and Fair Trade Laws.

4. The Robinson-Patman Act was enacted to prevent the price advantage that large retailers were gaining over their smaller competitors. Describe the principal provisions of the act, its defenses, and the implications it has had on marketing efficiency.

5. Many of the problems marketers have with the government are due to the hazy and unclear wording of many of the laws: for example, the Sherman Act, the Clayton Act, and the Robinson-Patman Act. Do you think it would be desirable to have more clearly worded legislation so that there would consequently be less dependence on judicial interpretation?

6. Do you approve of the role of the federal government—and especially the office and influence of the president—as a coercive force in the marketplace? Why or why not?

7. What are Green River ordinances? In what ways are these characteristic of many other local laws and ordinances? What are the implications?

8. What are the implications of the Borden case?

Project

Through research, determine how many consumer bills are being considered by Congress, and how these may be classified (that is, how many deal with automobiles, credit, safety, warranties, etc.).

Exercise in Creativity

You are an FTC agent assigned to a medium-size metropolitan area. You have one full-time agent under you, plus secretarial help. You are charged to investigate for the purpose of issuing complaints as many cases of unfair selling practices as possible. With the limited manpower available, draw up guidelines for the most effective accomplishment of your responsibility.

Role-playing Case

You are a salesman for a mattress manufacturer. One of your bigger customers is the Golden Rule discount chain. Mr. Ketchum is the mattress buyer for Golden Rule and he has always been aggressive to the extreme in trying to get price breaks. Today after writing up a sizable order, he says, "Mel, my merchandising v.p. has issued orders to us that we must get some advertising money from our suppliers. Now with this big order I must have from you a 2 percent advertising allowance."

"I'm not authorized to give any discounts or allowances, Mr. Ketchum. We don't do it with any other customers."

"I don't care about any other customers. I tell you we must have the 2 percent—that, or no order," he states, looking menacingly at you.

"I'll call my sales manager."

"Do that. I'll keep the order on my desk until you come back."

Your sales manager, Josiah Goodfellow, doesn't raise as much objection as you had anticipated. "Mel, they're too big an account to lose. Let's give them the 2 percent."

"How about our other customers?" you query.

"Don't let them know we're doing this, and everything will be fine."

What potential problems do you see with this course of action? What would you advise Josiah Goodfellow?

PART II

UNDERSTANDING AND ANALYZING THE MARKET

CHAPTER 6

UNDERSTANDING

BUYING

BEHAVIOR

The consumer, whether householder or industrial purchaser, should be the focus of marketing efforts. If the consumer is not wooed toward a particular brand and product or is not reasonably satisfied with the purchase, a firm stands to lose business to competitors who do a better job. In an effort to understand consumers better and influence them favorably, marketers are conducting a huge amount of research into customer decision making. However, so far the study of consumer behavior has shown primarily how really complex this subset of human behavior is.

The traditional view of the consumer, originating in economic theory, was the *economic man* doctrine; it asserted that:

> The consumer acts completely rationally in the marketplace,
> with perfect information of competitive offerings and prices,
> and as a result is able to maximize satisfactions or utilities.

Of course, this hardly fits the real-world situation in which we are influenced by persuasion, by family and friends, and by our own motivations or personalities, and where we have far less than perfect knowledge about the products and services we buy. Furthermore, orthodox economic doctrine assumes that economic behavior can be studied in a timeless vacuum, untouched by changing values or habits. Therefore, while economics laid the groundwork for the study of buyer behavior, the behavioral sciences such as psychology and sociology provide better models for understanding people and their reasons for buying certain products and brands and patronizing particular stores.

In this chapter we will examine the more significant influences on consumer behavior, as well as their practical applications. The following model will serve as a unifying theme for this very complex subject.

121

	Prepurchase Influences	Point-of-Purchase Influences	Postpurchases Influences
External:	Ethnic (cultural)	Impulse buying	Dissonance
	Social		Brand loyalty
	Demographic		
	Marketing		
Internal:	Learning		
	Motivation		
	Perception		

Prepurchase influences will receive the most attention, but all the factors interact and affect buyers in various ways and with different degrees of intensity, depending on the particular situation and individual. In addition to the terminology of the model, you will encounter the following in this chapter:

reference group   SR bond
innovator   generalization
group pressures   discrimination
opinion leader   subliminal perception

PREPURCHASE INFLUENCES

Ethnic and Cultural Factors

The study of culture—a society's design for living—has become increasingly important to marketers as American firms have expanded overseas. For example, French housewives have long considered shopping a daily social outing, and many are reluctant to sacrifice it for the greater convenience of supermarkets and "one-stop shopping." Colors have different connotations in different cultures. For example, white denotes mourning in some parts of the Far East, blue the same in Iran, and green is the nationalist color of Egypt: none of these colors should be used commercially in such countries. In the Arab world, schedules are of far less importance than in American society.[1]

The importance of cultures and ethnic groupings is not confined to international marketing. Blacks have received the most attention, but other ethnic groups within the United States, frequently overlooked, are the Hispanic-American, the French Canadian, the Indian, the Polish, the Creole, and others.

[1] Edward T. Hall, "The Silent Language in Overseas Business," *Harvard Business Review*, May–June 1960, pp. 87–96; Charles Winick, "Anthropology's Contribution to Marketing," *Journal of Marketing*, July 1961, pp. 53–60; "How to Talk Business with Arabs," *Forbes*, September 15, 1974, pp. 106–10.

A common mistake is to regard ethnic groups as homogeneous and to treat all members alike. For example, the black market exhibits most of the same demographic characteristics as the white market, although the proportions are somewhat different. Perhaps even more significant, the black market is dividing psychologically or attitudinally. Not long ago this market was considered to have two groups: those striving upward for the material standards of the whites, and those who had abandoned the attempt. Now a whole new sector has evolved: black people interested in the products and symbols of their own race and their African heritage.

**MARKETING
IN
ACTION**

Tapping the Spanish-speaking Market:
The Spanish-speaking market seldom receives marketing attention. In size, however, it rivals the black group, being some 11 million strong in the United States, 6 percent of the total population. Furthermore, it is highly concentrated in New York City, Miami, the Mexican border area, and California. Its rate of growth is greater than that of the white English-speaking majority. And it is relatively homogeneous, being basically a low-income segment but better off (higher income) than the black ghetto market. It can be very attractive for those firms having products adaptable to the needs of this group. Its concentration and the use of the Spanish language make for effective promotional efforts via Spanish-speaking radio stations, newspapers, magazines, and even UHF-TV stations and Spanish-language movie houses.

Procter & Gamble and Colgate-Palmolive, in particular, have successfully catered to this market by advertising on Spanish radio and TV, and by hiring Spanish-speaking salesmen to contact the small Spanish grocery stores (bodegas) and drug stores (farmacias); there are 5,000 bodegas and 750 farmacias in New York City alone. Some food companies likewise have made conscious efforts to tap this segment, but the soft-drink companies—the Spanish-speaking people are great consumers of all kinds of beverages—have exerted strong efforts to gain market share. Sometimes it is necessary to change the packaging. Welch Foods was having little success with its grape juice until it created a label in Spanish—"Welchito."

SOURCE: Adapted from "Habla Usted Espanol?" *Marketing Insights,* January 12, 1970, pp. 12–16.

For thought and discussion:
Analyze the similarities and differences between the black and
    Puerto Rican ethnic groups.
How do these differences affect marketing efforts?

Social Factors

The Family. A family goes through a number of stages during its life cycle, as children are born, reared, and eventually leave home. Clearly each stage calls for different products and different life-styles.

The role of family members in the buying process also has marketing significance. Typically in our society the wife acts as the household purchasing agent, for products ranging from food items, to household furnishings, to men's clothing. Children may play a surprisingly important role for certain food products, toys, pets, even for vacations and other recreation. For younger children the influence may be a type of *passive dictation*—a refusal to eat or use a particular product. The husband may influence the purchase of such expensive items as an automobile or major appliances, although even here the impact of the other members of the family may be considerable.[2]

Marketers often direct their advertising to particular family members, and this technique has been questioned, particularly with respect to children. Heavy advertising of cereals directed to children has been attacked as exploiting an audience naïve and easily swayed.

Reference Groups. Reference groups are those individuals and groups with whom an individual identifies. A group becomes a standard, a point of reference for forming or evaluating one's own norms, personal values, status, and behavior.[3] People may actually belong to their reference groups; these are called membership groups. But a reference group may also be one that the consumer does not belong to and perhaps never will, such as an athletic team, or "the astronauts," or the "jet set."[4] There is substantial evidence that these "cultural heroes" may have considerable influence on purchase behavior.[5]

Testimonial advertising is effective because of this influence of admired people and groups. The duffer can identify with Arnold Palmer by buying his golf clubs and balls; similarly, the figure of the "Marlboro Man" conjures up images of independence and outdoor ruggedness which many people find attractive. However, some

[2] For more specifics on important changes that have occurred in the purchasing roles of husbands and wives during the last two decades, see Isabella C. M. Cunningham and Robert T. Green, "Purchasing Roles in the U. S. Family, 1955 and 1973," *Journal of Marketing,* October 1974, pp. 61–64.

[3] James E. Stafford, "Reference Theory as a Conceptual Framework for Consumer Decisions," in Robert L. Ring, ed., *Marketing and the New Science of Planning* (Chicago: American Marketing Association, 1968), pp. 280–84.

[4] See, for example, M. D. Beckman, "Are Your Messages Getting Through?" *Journal of Marketing,* July 1967, pp. 34–38; James E. Stafford, "Group Influences on Consumer Brand Preferences," *Journal of Marketing Research,* February 1966, pp. 68–75.

[5] A. Benton Cocanougher and Grady D. Bruce, "Socially Distant Reference Groups and Consumer Aspirations," *Journal of Marketing Research,* August 1971, pp. 379–81.

potential customers may be repelled by controversial people such as Joe Namath.

Reference groups may also be negative; an individual wants actively to avoid them and their connotations: these are known as *dissociative reference groups*. Sometimes, especially in second-generation families in this country, parents with "Old World" customs and ideas may act as a dissociative reference to the children.

One researcher has studied the influence of reference groups in product and brand purchases. He points out that in order for reference-group influence to be present in a brand or product-buying decision, the product must be *conspicuous*. There are several aspects to this conspicuousness. First, the item must be conspicuous in the sense that it can be seen and identified by others—in other words, it must be visible. Second, it must be conspicuous in the sense of standing out and being noticed—if everyone owns the product, then even though visible it is not conspicuous.[6]

How can the idea of reference groups be applied to marketing? A marketer faces two problems in using the concept:

1. Determining whether purchases of his product are governed to any great extent by reference groups
2. Determining which types of reference groups are most influential[7]

A person usually has more than one reference group, some being membership groups, some "distant others," so the identification of relevant group influence is no simple matter. Yet the effectiveness of capitalizing on reference group influence—in this case, racing drivers—is well illustrated in the success of the STP Corporation during the 1960s.

---

[6] Francis S. Bourne, *Group Influence in Marketing and Public Relations* (Ann Arbor, Mich.: Foundation for Research on Human Behavior, 1956), pp. 1–2, 7–11.

[7] James H. Myers and William H. Reynolds, *Consumer Behavior and Marketing Management* (Boston: Houghton Mifflin, 1967), p. 181.

**MARKETING
IN
ACTION**

Promoting to Reference-Group Influence: STP

The major product of the company is STP Motor Oil Additive—the largest-selling such additive in the United States (the term "STP" stands for "Scientifically Treated Petroleum"). The oil additive promises to reduce oil consumption, free sticking valves, make engines run more smoothly, and prevent many repairs. It is rather interesting, however, that petroleum engineers, the experts in such matters, describe these additives as "mouse milk."

Sales of the STP Corporation were $9 million in 1963 when Andy Granatelli, a well-known figure in auto racing, took over as president. He felt that if speed could sell cars and tires, it could sell additives; STP was associated with professional race drivers. Extra cash was offered racers who pasted STP decals prominently on their cars, and STP and Granatelli became conspicuous at race tracks and particularly at the Indianapolis "500."

By 1968 sales had risen to $44 million and profits to $6 million. And for every dollar of sales, the company was spending 45 cents on promotion; this was 18 cents more than it spent on the can and contents.

The claims of STP are based on an insecure foundation as far as product merits are concerned. No scientific data supports the contention that additives do any good. Automobile manufacturers do not recommend them. While additive manufacturers imply that the use of a $1.50 can of additive with every oil change can forestall the expense of a valve and ring job, most motorists either scrap or sell their cars before such major repairs would be needed. That the product itself, offered at a premium price many times higher than the cost of production, is of dubious benefit is disregarded in the glamor associated with professional racing. (In recent years, widespread adverse publicity has cut somewhat into the popularity of STP.)

SOURCES: "Wheeler Who Deals in STP," Business Week, May 31, 1969 pp. 56–57; and "Big Profits in Little Cans," Time, August 8, 1969, pp. 70–71.

For thought and discussion:
For what products do you think professional football players would be an effective reference group?
Why?

Social Factors in New Product and Style Adoption. The first persons to adopt new products or styles in a community, the innovators, or opinion leaders, or tastemakers, are crucial in the initial efforts to market a new product. If marketers can identify such consumption leaders through research, they can then:

1. Direct marketing efforts to these leaders
2. Be particularly careful to maintain goodwill and enthusiasm among the leaders
3. Predict the kinds of products and services that eventually would be widely accepted

Several interesting theories have been developed for identifying these leaders.

One approach sees them as *tastemakers.* The Opinion Research Corporation theorized: "The central thread of our modern society is mobility. The leadership elite is that group of people who possess this quality in greater degree than do other people."[8] The dimensions of mobility were: level of education, travel, job promotion, social contacts, advance in income, intellectual development, kinship mobility, and geographic movement.

The development of objective criteria enabled Opinion Research Corporation to identify and locate people on a scale of mobility. It sampled 105 households in Ridgewood, New Jersey, and found that mobility was not synonymous with high income: high mobiles were found at every income level. Seventy-five high-growth products and services were studied, and the theory received substantial support. The high mobiles tended to lead in the early adoption of about 85 percent of these new consumer products and services, in some cases being ahead of medium and lower mobiles by five to ten years. This included such things as stereo equipment, modern paintings and reproductions of masterpieces, foreign movies, electric blankets, auto rentals, wild rice, Irish whiskey, and travel credit cards.[9]

Promising as this theory is in generating hypotheses, it needs further refinement perhaps even through sampling on a national basis.[10]

Another researcher focused on *innovation*. He conducted an empirical study of characteristics of innovating and noninnovating families for the Touch-Tone (push-button) telephone in the small middle-class Chicago suburb of Deerfield, Illinois. While he studied somewhat different characteristics than the tastemaker research, the results for the most part were supportive, as the following indicates:[11]

Factors	Innovator Characteristics Compared with Noninnovative Neighbors
Venturesome	More so: more willing to take new product risks
Socially integrated	More so; more popular and more socially integrated within their neighborhoods
Cosmopolitan	Less oriented outside their local community

[8] *America's Tastemakers*, vols. 1 and 2, Princeton, N.J.: Opinion Research Corporation, April and June, 1959.

[9] Ibid.

[10] This view is essentially expressed by Steven J. Shaw, "Behavioral Science Offers Fresh Insights on New Product Acceptance," *Journal of Marketing*, January 1965, p. 11. Also see Laurence P. Feldman and Gary M. Armstrong, "Identifying Buyers of a Major Automotive Innovation," *Journal of Marketing*, January 1975, pp. 47–53.

[11] Thomas S. Robertson, "Consumer Innovators: The Key to New Product Success," *California Management Review*, Winter 1967.

Factors	Innovator Characteristics Compared with Noninnovative Neighbors
Social mobility	More aspiring and actual climbing up the social class ladder
Financial	More financially privileged; more discretionary income and perceive themselves to be richer

While less cosmopolitanism does not support the tastemaker theory, consumer information sources are so diffuse today that one need not look beyond the local community for most new products, although cosmopolitanism may be a factor for products that are of specialized interest and have no mass appeal.[12] Another study, this time of mobile executives—those who have contacts in professional groups outside their organizations and who have moved relatively frequently—found that they also tend to be more innovative in their organizations.[13]

Considerable research has been done to identify early adopters of new fashions—especially millinery and ready-to-wear—and what route the trend of adoption tends to follow. Two theories have been suggested: "Trickle down" and "trickle across." It had long been thought that the upper socioeconomic classes adopted fashions first, as symbols of exclusiveness. The lower classes, each and in turn, according to the trickle-down theory, emulated the upper-class leaders and at a certain level of adoption, the fashion became "vulgarized" and then discarded by the upper class in favor of a new set of fashions.[14]

Today the evidence supports the conclusion that fashions do not trickle down from the upper class, but rather that the transmission of personal influence "trickles across," or flows primarily horizontally within a socioeconomic grouping,[15] instead of vertically through the various groupings.

Still another area of research looks at the pressure of conformity. Once a fashion—whether in clothing or some other aspect of life style—becomes established in a particular social setting, the pressures exerted on individuals to conform often are difficult to resist. A classic series of experiments were conducted by Solomon Asch, a social psychologist, to test the effects of group pressure

[12] Ibid.

[13] R. K. Merton, "The Environment of the Innovating Organization: Some Conjectures and Proposals," in Gary A. Steiner, ed., The Creative Organization (Chicago: University of Chicago Press, 1965).

[14] Dwight E. Robinson, "The Economics of Fashion Demand," Quarterly Journal of Economics, 75:3, 1961, p. 376.

[15] Charles W. King, "Fashion Adoption: A Rebuttal to the 'Trickle Down' Theory," in Stephen A. Greyser, ed., Toward Scientific Marketing (Chicago: American Marketing Association, 1964), p. 111.

upon the distortions of judgments. He asked groups of students to judge the length of a given line as compared with three unequal lines. In his experiments, all except one of the group had met previously with Asch and been instructed to respond with wrong answers. The naïve subject was therefore placed in the position of being a minority of one in the midst of a unanimous majority which was repeatedly contradicting the evidence of his senses. And what do you suppose were the results? Many individuals in this situation went along with group opinion, either mistrusting their own perceptions, or facing an overmastering need not to appear different from others.[16]

Venkatesan made similar discoveries about decisions in buying situations. Again, male college students were used in an experiment, with the subjects required to evaluate and choose the best suit among three identical ones. The subjects were told that there were quality differences and that the study was intended to find out whether consumers would be able to pick the best one. Group pressure was again utilized; three members of each group were preinstructed, while the fourth member was faced with a unanimous majority opinion. Venkatesan confirmed the finding that the individuals tended to conform to the group norm, and concluded that consumers accept information provided by their peer groups on the quality of a product or a style, etc., which is hard to evaluate objectively.[17]

Opinion Leaders and Two-step Flow of Communications. Related to the influence of reference groups and innovators is that of opinion leaders. Opinion leaders appear to affect their associates in a variety of matters, from public affairs to fashions to ordinary products and brands. Sometimes these opinion leaders may be the same as the tastemakers or innovators. However, the concept is somewhat broader: the opinion leader may not necessarily be an innovator. Word-of-mouth communication is crucial here.

The effectiveness of such influence in buying household appliances has been found to be particularly significant:

> More than half the buyers turned for advice to acquaintances . . . a third of the buyers bought a brand or model that they had seen in someone's home . . . Information seeking through shopping around in stores appeared to be of lesser importance than information seeking from relatives, friends, and neighbors.[18]

---

[16] Solomon E. Asch, "Effects of Group Pressure upon the Modification and Distortion of Judgments," in Harold E. Kassarjian and Thomas S. Robertson, eds., *Perspectives in Consumer Behavior* (Glenview, Ill.: Scott, Foresman, 1968), p. 299.

[17] M. Venkatesan, "Experimental Study of Consumer Behavior Conformity and Independence," *Journal of Marketing Research,* November 1966, pp. 384–87.

[18] Robertson, "Consumer Innovator."

Related to this very real power of personal influences is the hypothesis that ideas flow from impersonal sources (the mass media) to opinion leaders, who in turn influence the nonleaders by means of word of mouth: this is known as a *two-step flow of communication*. Diagrammatically, this is illustrated in Figure 6-1, comparing the one-step with the two-step flow.

The rationale for this is that opinion leaders are more exposed to the mass media than nonleaders and are more influenced by impersonal communications. While all the ramifications of the theory are not clear at the present time, there has been enough support to make it viable. Recent evidence suggests that this communication process is a genuine interaction, with the nonleaders also sharing information with the opinion leaders.[19]

How may marketers identify opinion leaders or influentials? In general, it has been found that they are of the same social status as their advisees, they are gregarious, and they generally have a greater degree of innovativeness; their age may vary by product class. For example, older family women have been more typically found to be leaders for homemaking information, while younger, sometimes single, women may be for fashions.

The cost of identifying and using innovators and opinion leaders to influence their followers may be greater than the cost of advertising to everyone. But not always; in industrial selling, for example, a certain firm may have the reputation of being a leader in the industry, and certain professionals such as doctors and dentists influence their peers in the use of new drugs and other products.

Persons in public view or in prestigious positions are often thought to be opinion leaders. Some years ago Chrysler Corporation offered the use of an Imperial automobile for a trial period to doctors and lawyers. But while such persons are likely to be influential for products within their own fields, such as physicians for drugs and dentists for electric toothbrushes, it is doubtful that they exercise much influence in automobile purchase decisions.

[19] Johan Arndt, "A Test of the Two-Step Flow in Diffusion of a New Product," *Journalism Quarterly,* Autumn 1968, pp. 457–65.

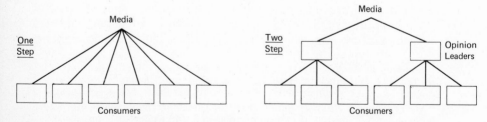

Figure 6-1. Models of Communication Flow

Table 6-1.
Warner Social Class System: Total U.S. Society and That of Chicago

Class	Definition	Percentage of Total Population of United States	Chicago
Upper-upper	Aristocracy	0.5	} 0.9
Lower-upper	New rich	1.5	
Upper-middle	Professional and managerial	10.0	7.2
Lower-middle	White-collar workers	33.0	28.4
Upper-lower	Blue-collar workers	40.0	44.0
Lower-lower	Unskilled laborers	15.0	19.5

Sources: W. Lloyd Warner with Marcia Meeker and Kenneth Eells, *Social Class in America* (New York: Harper & Row, 1960); Pierre Martineau, "Social Classes and Spending Behavior," *Journal of Marketing,* October 1958, pp. 121–30.

Some marketers compare subscription mailing lists of appropriate magazines to identify those persons who subscribe to several and who therefore might be opinion leaders or innovators (since they have more exposure to mass media than nonleaders).[20] It has also been found that buyers of new products are usually more influential than other people and these often can be identified from purchase records.[21] Once such influentials are identified, they can be deluged with information, samples, and free use of products to gain the favorable response to a product and brand which is necessary if they are to be a positive influence.[22]

Social Class Influence. Social classes—their characteristics, attitudes, and behavior—are crucial to defining a market and planning market strategy.

The criteria used to differentiate social strata vary. In many countries kinship and family ancestry are important differentiating criteria. These are less important to our society, where occupation, income level, and education more is crucial. A widely used delineation of social class hierarchy is that of the sociologist W. Lloyd Warner which is based on occupation, source of income, residential area, and type of dwelling.[23] Table 6-1 divides American society into

[20] Myers and Reynolds, p. 308.

[21] Thomas S. Robertson, *Innovation and the Consumer* (New York: Holt, Rinehart, and Winston, 1971).

[22] For further references to opinion leadership, see John O. Summers, "The Identity of Women's Clothing Fashion Opinion Leaders," *Journal of Marketing Research,* May 1970, pp. 178–86; Thomas R. Robertson and John G. Myers, "Personality Correlates of Opinion Leadership and Innovative Buying Behavior," *Journal of Marketing Research,* May 1969, pp. 164–68. For a note of caution, see David A. Schwartz, "One Drawback to Courting the Restless, Innovative Consumer: She May Not Even Exist," *Sales Management,* April 2, 1973, p. 32.

[23] Harold H. Kassarjian and Thomas S. Robertson, *Perspectives in Consumer Behavior* (Glenview, Ill.: Scott, Foresman, 1968), p. 373.

six classes on a Warnerian scale, and the social class hierarchy of Chicago into five classes.

However, there is merit in using an index constructed solely of two factors, education and occupation. This measurement of social class presumes that occupation reflects the skill and power of individuals in society, while education reflects not only knowledge but cultural tastes. Therefore, social class can be measured without considering income.[24] And there is an advantage in excluding income because it is not an accurate index of family consumption standards: the young professional or executive and the skilled blue-collar worker may have the same income, but "their buying behavior, their tastes, their spending-saving aspirations can be poles apart."[25]

Significant class differences have been found in shopping behavior: the brands preferred, the stores shopped, products bought, spending and saving patterns, even psychological perspectives and viewpoints. Especially important is the type of store preferred by the different classes. Glamorous "high-status" stores may be shunned by lower-social-class consumers who assume they would feel uncomfortable there. Even different supermarkets within the same income area have been found to attract different types of customers: in a Chicago study, A&P was stronger with the mass market, while Jewel appealed more to the middle classes.[26]

Differences in values, in interpersonal attitudes, in patterns of daily life, in media and advertising viewing, as well as shopping, have been found. For example, lower-status people value education less than do middle-class people; self-fulfillment is more valued and achieved in the higher social groups, while lower-class women in particular may see life as dull and unrewarding. Attitudes toward the role of children, the definition of a "real man," the way vacations are spent, even the use of sanitary protection and deodorants have been found to have marked social class dichotomies. The distribution and use of time also shows marked social class differences, with lower-class women more prone to agree that "a woman's job is never done."[27]

[24] H. Lee Mathews and John W. Slocum, Jr., "Social Class and Commercial Bank Credit Card Usage," *Journal of Marketing,* January 1969, p. 72.

[25] Pierre Martineau, "Social Classes and Spending Behavior," *Journal of Marketing,* October 1958, pp. 125–26.

[26] Ibid. See also H. Robert Dodge and Harry N. Summer, "Choosing between Retail Stores," *Journal of Retailing,* Fall 1969, pp. 11–21; and V. Kanti Prasad, "Socioeconomic Product Risk and Patronage Preferences of Retail Shoppers," *Journal of Marketing,* July 1975, pp. 42–47.

[27] Sidney J. Levy, "Social Class and Consumer Behavior," in Joseph W. Newman, ed., *On Knowing the Consumer* (New York: Wiley, 1966), pp. 146–60. See also Joseph N. Fry and Frederick H. Siller, "A Comparison of Household Decision Making in Two Social Classes," *Journal of Marketing Research,* August 1970, pp. 333–37; and Chester R. Wasson, "Is It Time To Quit Thinking of Income Classes?" *Journal of Marketing,* April 1969, pp. 54–56.

Practical Applications of Social Class Concepts. The practical applications of social class delineation are often readily apparent. For example, the working-class male, more than his middle-class counterpart, offers the prime target for manufacturers of guns and other hunting and fishing equipment. The working class also is more inclined to put money inside the house in the deluxe models of appliances and overstuffed and ornate furnishings, than typically do the middle and upper classes. Brand loyalty and reliance on national brands characterize the lower classes as they attempt to make sure they are getting a good buy."[28]

Sources of information and entertainment, not surprisingly, also have been found to vary among social classes. TV programs appeal to different audiences; for some products total audience ratings may not be the best indicator of effective exposure. For example, "Star Trek," a science fiction action series, consistently had low Nielsen ratings but had high popularity with the upper-middle professional and managerial class. Marked differences are found in readership of newspapers and of magazines such as *Fortune, Vogue, The New Yorker, True Story,* and *Redbook.*[29]

Despite practical marketing implications found in this social class structuring, some cautions are in order. There is an aura of naïve simplicity attached to assigning people to specific classes. It assumes that the people in each group are homogeneous, not only in demographic characteristics such as income and occupation, but also in attitudes and behavior. Little recognition may be given to individual differences, and no attention is paid to geographical or environmental influences.

It is more realistic to regard social classes not as discrete groups, but rather as having merging boundaries—in other words, as a continuum from lowest to highest. From this perspective, some people will be nearing another social class and will have some characteristics and life styles reflected in the adjacent class, while others will be more deeply enmeshed in typical patterns of their class.

Demographic Factors

By demographics we mean such statistical factors as age, family size, sex, income, occupation, education, home ownership, even religion. Some of these are, of course, embodied in the social class in-

[28] M. Ross, "Uptown and Downtown," *American Sociological Review,* vol. 30, 1965, pp. 255–59.

[29] For more discussion on this, see William H. Peters, "Relative Occupational Class Income: A Significant Variable in the Marketing of Automobiles," *Journal of Marketing,* April 1970, pp. 74–78; S. U. Rich and S. C. Jain, "Social Class and Life Cycle as Predictors of Shopping Behavior," *Journal of Marketing Research,* February 1968, pp. 41–49; and John W. Slocum and H. Lee Mathews, "Social Class and Income as Indicators of Consumer Credit Behavior," *Journal of Marketing,* April 1970, pp. 69–74.

fluences which we have just discussed. Obviously some of these demographic characteristics will play a major part in purchasing behavior: for example, the home owner will have needs entirely different from an apartment dweller regarding lawn care products, patio furniture, and home improvement equipment and supplies. Income will certainly be a factor in the purchase of some items, as also will education. We will not discuss demographics to any extent here. They are the more obvious of the factors affecting consumer behavior. Indeed, most marketers give them the preponderance of attention, failing to recognize that other behavioral factors also influence buying.

Marketing Factors

Here are included all the presale marketing efforts to which a consumer is exposed, such as advertising, window displays, the package, a salesperson. Again as with demographic factors, we will not discuss these influences in this chapter; it is enough to recognize that along with a variety of social, cultural, and demographic forces, the efforts of marketers should influence, in a major or a minor way, the final buying decision.

Influence of Internal Factors: The Learning Process

Learning refers to those changes in behavior that occur owing to experience or practice. It can be differentiated from motivation—a force or impelling agent.

Buying a product represents a learning process that has brought the consumer to the decision that this product suits his or her wants the best. This decision may subsequently be changed as the result of new learning, or the pattern may be continued to the point where the buying response becomes practically automatic or habitual.

Learning Concepts. Building *associations* is a simple form of learning, and the behaviorist school of psychology theorizes that all forms of human behavior can be reduced ultimately to associations between stimuli and responses—"S-R bonds." Most advertising is directed toward building favorable associations for corporate or brand images. The association of the rugged outdoor individualist with Marlboro cigarettes has been effectively put across by the Philip Morris Company.

The classical experiments of Pavlov involved establishing associations by conditioning. In this famous research with dogs, a bell was rung every time food was given to a dog. Eventually the dog salivates upon hearing the bell, even though no food is given.

We as consumers are also susceptible to conditioning. We associate the highest quality with the highest price, even when this may not be true. We associate the best value—sometimes mistakenly—

with the largest size container. We have certain associations or images of the people who drink tea, or eat hot cereal, or drive Volkswagens, or drink a certain brand of beer.

The learning process is facilitated and habits developed when some form of reward or *reinforcement* is present. Thus, if the consumer tries a new product and it solves the particular problem for which it was bought, a pleasant association is established which may lead to repeat purchases and then to a habituated response in which the brand and product decision becomes nearly automatic. A firm whose competitor has a high proportion of loyal, habitual purchasers is seriously disadvantaged in winning some of these customers, because there is little cognitive activity involved to "work on."

Two other learning principles have marketing relevance: generalization and discrimination.

Generalization refers to a person's tendency to make the same response to similar (but not identical) stimuli. For example, a poor company image may be generalized to all its products and activities; one defective or poorly performing product may contaminate consumer perceptions of all products of that brand. On the positive side, favorable experience may also be generalized to other products of the company or brand; this is one of the arguments for "family" brands, such as Heinz and Green Giant, where all the products can benefit from strong positive associations.

Discrimination is the individual's ability to respond selectively to similar cues or stimuli. Firms with relatively similar products, such as cigarettes, detergents, and gasoline, have often heavily advertised trying to induce consumers to see differences in brands and make discriminatory responses.[30]

Practical Applications of Learning Concepts. The more practical aspects of the learning process for marketers concern the retention of learning and the relationship of learning and brand loyalty.

Many decades of experimental studies, both with animals and humans, have produced a considerable body of knowledge about various factors affecting the learning process. Some of these are particularly relevant to marketers—especially advertisers—who face the difficult task of making their product, brand, or promotional message more memorable to the consumer. The more relevant conclusions are:

1. Unpleasant things may not be as conducive to learning as those more pleasant or rewarding; but neutral or bland stimuli are the most ineffective.
2. Things learned and understood are better retained than things learned by rote.

[30] Thomas S. Robertson, "Consumer Behavior: Psychological Dimensions," in Frederick D. Sturdivant et al., eds., *Managerial Analysis in Marketing* (Glenview, Ill.: Scott, Foresman, 1970), pp. 174–75.

3. Learning occurs better when distributed over several periods than when concentrated into a single period.
4. The rate of forgetting tends to be very rapid immediately after learning, but then reaches a more stable level.
5. Material presented first (primacy) or last (recency) is better retained than that presented in the middle.
6. Learning is aided by active practice rather than passive reception.
7. The more completely material is initially learned, the greater is retention.[31]

We know that repetition is related to learning, that is, the more a message is repeated the more likely it will be remembered. However, there is a point of diminishing returns at which further repetition will not increase memorability; this point apparently varies according to the type of product, its strength in the market, and the advertising format.[32]

Another problem that advertisers must contend with in regard to memorability of their ads is that the cute song or skit may be remembered, but not the brand name. For example, how many of you can recall certain commercials, but not the sponsor? To develop brand memorability is a major challenge for advertisers.

Motivation

Motivation is the condition—arising from wishes, desires, needs, drives—that directs or channels behavior toward some goal. Psychologists disagree about the basic nature and relative importance of these various driving forces, but certain types can be distinguished.

Some Classifications of Motives. Broadly considered, there are two types of motives: physiological or biogenic, and psychological or psychogenic. Such needs as hunger, thirst, warmth, and sex are physiological. Psychological needs are harder to define and have no universal agreement; and the number listed may range from 3 to 100. One concise classification of psychological needs or motives is:

1. Affectional needs—the need to form and maintain warm, harmonious, and emotionally satisfying relations with others
2. Ego-bolstering needs—the need to enhance or promote the personality; to gain prestige and recognition; to satisfy the ego through domination of others

[31] These principles are based on Leo Bogart, *Strategy in Advertising* (New York: Harcourt, Brace & World, 1967); and Stewart Henderson Britt, "How Advertising Can Use Psychology's Rules of Learning," *Printers' Ink,* September 23, 1955, pp. 74–80.
[32] M. Ray and A. Sawyer, "Repetition in Media Models: A Laboratory Technique," *Journal of Marketing Research,* vol. 8, 1971, pp. 20–29.

3. Ego-defensive needs—the need to protect the personality; to avoid physical and psychological harm; to avoid ridicule and "loss of face"; to prevent loss of prestige; to avoid or to obtain relief from anxiety.[33]

The psychologist A. H. Maslow has proposed a widely publicized hierarchy of needs, ranging from the lowest—those of thirst, hunger, etc.—and ending with the need for self-actualization or self-realization:

1. Physiological needs: food and water
2. Safety needs: security and protection
3. Love needs: affection and belonging (family and friends)
4. Esteem needs: self-respect, prestige, success, and achievement
5. Self-actualization need: desire for self-fulfillment[34]

This conceptualization suggests that various drives take precedence over the others, but that certain ones are basic and must be satisfied before higher-level drives take over. It is probably evident that most of us are operating at the third and fourth levels, striving to satisfy these love and esteem needs. These models lend an interesting and credible perspective to our understanding of basic human motivational forces and their expression, but their practical relevance in the marketplace is less clear.[35]

Fifty years ago Melvin Copeland presented a classification of motives more useful to management. He thought that motives could be rational (aroused by appeals to reason), and emotional (impulse promptings).[36] And marketers have been intrigued with these ever since. Numerous "emotional" motives have been listed that, presumably, if appealed to effectively would induce people to buy products they otherwise might not if appeals were made strictly to reason, that is, citing quality, service, performance, dependability, economy in operation, and the like. Some of these emotional appeals are social approval, pride of personal appearance, romance, welfare of loved ones, and status.

However, it is difficult to judge the potency of these simplistic classifications since the average person may make a purchase for a number of reasons and to satisfy a number of needs, some quite definable and some not, while individual differences in buying motives

[33] James A. Bayton, "Motivation Cognition, Learning—Basic Factors in Consumer Behavior," *Journal of Marketing*, January 1958, pp. 283–84.

[34] A. H. Maslow, *Motivation and Personality* (New York: Harper & Row, 1954).

[35] B. Curtis Hamm and Edward W. Cundiff, "Self-actualization and Product Perception," *Journal of Marketing Research*, November 1969, pp. 470–72; John McFall, "Priority Patterns and Consumer Behavior," *Journal of Marketing*, October 1969, pp. 50–55.

[36] Melvin T. Copeland, *Principles of Merchandising* (New York: Shaw, 1924), pp. 155–67.

Table 6-2.
Distribution of Consumer Types by
Shopping Orientation

Type of Consumer	Number	Percent
Economic	41	33
Personalizing	35	28
Ethical	22	18
Apathetic	21	17
Indeterminate	5	4
Total	124	100

Source: Stone, "City Shoppers and Urban Identification."

for a given item may vary considerably. Furthermore, people may express motives in different ways and may be motivated to purchase different types of products.

Classifications of Buyer Behavior. Some researchers, rather than trying to single out the complexities of individual buying motives, have attempted to classify consumers by their dominant buying orientations. For example, consumers may be classified as:

> *Economic*—primarily interested in shopping for values, and extremely sensitive to price, quality, and assortment of merchandise.
> *Personalizing*—shopped where she was known, and had strong personal attachment with store personnel, and the store itself
> *Ethical*—willing to sacrifice lower prices and better assortment of goods in larger stores or chains, in order to help the smaller stores
> *Apathetic*—shopped because she had to, wanted to finish as quickly as possible, and bought primarily on the basis of convenience[37]

The distribution of these classifications is shown in Table 6-2.

Several later studies have supported these findings.[38] A further indication that the proportion of consumers who are "economic"

[37] G. P. Stone, "City Shoppers and Urban Identification: Observations on the Social Psychology of City Life," *American Journal of Sociology*, July 1954, pp. 36–45.
[38] See William R. Darden and Fred D. Reynolds, "Shopping Orientations and Product Usage Rates," *Journal of Marketing Research*, November 1971, pp. 505–08; and P. Ronald Stephenson and Ronald P. Willett, "Analysis of Consumers' Retail Patronage Strategies," in Philip R. McDonald, ed., *Marketing Involvement in Society and the Economy* (Chicago: American Marketing Association, 1969), pp. 316–22.

(that is, who are primarily interested in shopping for values) has held rather steady may be found in those shoppers reportedly using unit pricing (where retailers post prices by the ounce, pound, or other standard measure in addition to the regular prices per package, thereby making it easier to compare values). In a survey of customers in middle-class areas of Washington, D. C., 37 percent reported themselves as using this information,[39] a surprisingly close figure to the 33 percent classed as "economic" shoppers by Stone.

Practical Applications of Motivational Concepts. Motivation itself has not received much attention in recent marketing research. To an extent, this reflects the inability to pursue further this complex area in any productive way.[40] The excesses of motivation research, which we will discuss in the next chapter, may also have discouraged further research.

However, there may be something significant for marketers in the consumer-classification studies and the support for them furnished by the unit-pricing surveys. That at least one third of our consumers apparently are not unduly moved by emotion or impulse, but are more cognitive and rational, is probably reflected in the consumerism of today and suggests that conventional advertising and marketing practices need to be reassessed.

Selective Perception

Perception occurs when stimuli are detected by the senses. This detection, which is referred to as sensation, must be interpreted and classified meaningfully, and apparently a comparison process is involved. Several influences seem to be operative in this comparison process: (1) characteristics of the stimulus itself and its relationship to its background, such as the size, the contrast with its surroundings, the distance, the color, etc., and (2) personal factors such as motives, personality traits, attitudes, the whole system of personal values and needs, many of which are derived from the social context.

We are bombarded by so many stimuli that the nervous system must ignore much that reaches it, and perception becomes highly selective. We are exposed to over 1,500 advertising messages alone every day[41]—it is not surprising that many do not register on our consciousness or memory.

A number of experiments and demonstrations have established that most people are especially sensitive to drive-reducing stimuli, such as food for the hungry man, and respond quicker to stimuli that

[39] Reported in "A 'Success,' Unit Price is Unused," *Washington Post*, September 10, 1971, p. A10.

[40] Harold H. Kassarjian, "Personality and Consumer Behavior," *Journal of Marketing Research*, November 1971, pp. 409–18.

[41] John S. Wright and Daniel S. Warner, *Advertising*, 2d ed. (New York: McGraw-Hill, 1966), p. 3.

are consistent with their basic values, while the perception of various aspects of the environment can be influenced and distorted in a number of ways (as, for example, the Asch study on group pressure indicated). People suffering from headaches notice advertisements for headache remedies; people with small children notice advertisements catering to their needs; people are more interested in advertisements extolling the brands they own than those of competing brands. This selective perception offers an advantage to advertisers in reaching those people who offer the most potential for the product. But problems are also created by selective perception.

Fewer readers are attracted by advertisements attacking an established brand since satisfied customers are not as likely to allow competing product information to pass through their selective perceptual filters. This suggests that brand loyalty, when well established, is difficult to crack. It is far better for a marketer to seek those consumers not wedded to a particular brand.

Selective perception acts to impede or short circuit incoming information or sensations in three ways: (1) selective exposure to the message, (2) distortion of its content, and (3) selective retention. We will look briefly at these three aspects of selective perception at work.

Evidence is quite convincing that people tend to shun messages that are inconsistent with their attitudes. Political talks have found their greatest audience among the believers—members of the same political party.[42] Studies have been made of readership of articles alleging a relationship between smoking and cancer. One such study found that 67 percent of nonsmokers claimed high readership, while only 44 percent of smokers did so.[43]   •

Even when a message gets through to the individual, its meaning can be distorted and perceived and interpreted in a manner consistent with the predispositions toward that topic. A number of studies of political messages have confirmed this,[44] and it has been found that different people interpret the same information in varying ways after exposure to public information campaigns.[45] An interesting study of the selective perception inherent in brand names found the same samples of beer to be rated quite differently in a taste test, depending upon whether or not the brand names were identified.[46]

[42] W. Schramm and R. F. Carter, "Effectiveness of a Political Telethon," *Public Opinion Quarterly,* vol. 23, 1959, pp. 121–26.

[43] C. F. Cannell and J. C. MacDonald, "The Impact of Health News on Attitudes and Behavior," *Journalism Quarterly,* vol. 33, 1956, pp. 315–23.

[44] B. R. Berelson, P. F. Lazarsfeld, and W. N. McPhee, *Voting* (Chicago: University of Chicago Press, 1954); A. L. Edwards, "Political Frames of Reference as a Factor Influencing Recognition," *Journal of Abnormal and Social Psychology,* vol. 36, 1941, pp. 34–50, are two examples.

[45] G. Hyman and P. B. Sheatsley, "Some Reasons Why Information Campaigns Fail," *Public Opinion Quarterly,* vol. 11, 1947, pp. 412–23.

[46] "Does the Label 'Change the Taste?," *Printers' Ink,* January 12, 1962, pp. 55–57.

Therefore, it is evident that the brand name can substantially affect perception of product qualities, including taste.

Practical Applications of Selective Perception. Research on the presence and influence of selective perception—much of it coming from psychologists and other social scientists—indicates the difficulty of swaying or convincing people against their will or their inclinations. The relevance of this to marketing should be obvious, but some advertisers persist in equating advertising expenditures and sales generation. It is easier to swim with the current than against it; to try to change people's attitudes and preferences is extremely difficult. It is more effective to make appeals and products compatible with consumers' tastes. The tendency of people to screen out messages contrary to their positions, whether regarding politics or brand loyalty, makes the establishment of new brands difficult. Despite substantial infusions of advertising dollars, a considerable portion may be wasted by not being perceived, while selective retention may lead to easy forgetting of some of that which does get through.

Subliminal Perception. In the middle 1950s an advertising phenomenon occurred that appeared to have great significance and social implications, and caused wild controversy. Over a period of weeks, these messages were flashed on a motion picture theater screen for 1/3000 of a second, a speed below the sensory threshold: "Eat Popcorn," and "Drink Coca Cola." During this period, popcorn sales increased 57 percent and Coca Cola sales 18 percent.[47]

An individual who was truly influenced by such subliminal stimuli might be powerless to resist appeals flashed on TV and movie screens; subliminal messages could be used not only for marketing, but for thought control, à la George Orwell's "Big Brother" influence of 1984. It was little wonder that Congress was alerted and critics immediately attacked the ethics of subliminal influence.

However, subsequent research failed to support the initial experiment. Although studies indicate that perception without awareness apparently can take place,[48] the original implications that appeals to consumers at below-threshold levels would circumvent their powers of selective perception appears to be unsupported: perceptual defense is still maintained. Two researchers state this unequivocally, "There is nothing to suggest that action can be produced against the subject's will or more effectively than through normal, recognized messages."[49]

[47] Brooks, "The Little Ad That Isn't There," *Consumer Reports,* January 1958, pp. 5–11.
[48] J. V. McConnell, R. L. Cutler, and E. B. McNeil, "Subliminal Stimulation: An Overview," *American Psychologist,* vol. 11, 1958, p. 230; and J. K. Adams, "Laboratory Studies of Behavior Without Awareness," *Psychological Bulletin,* vol. 54, 1957, pp. 383–405.
[49] B. Berelson and G. A. Steiner, *Human Behavior: An Inventory of Scientific Findings* (New York: Harcourt, Brace & World, 1964), p. 95.

The behavioral concepts and factors we have described so far in this chapter might be thought of as behind-the-scenes influences on the buying decision. Now let us look at some of the more direct influences.

Deliberation versus Impulse Buying

Decisions to buy may be made months in advance or at the moment of purchase. The amount of deliberation involved varies among people and for different products. Some persons are more deliberate than others: they are more cautious, more inclined to compare and evaluate; others simply have a hard time making up their minds. The amount of deliberation can vary according to the circumstances. For example, a particularly persuasive salesperson, a striking display, or a reduced price may close a sale that otherwise would have involved more time and probably more shopping.

Expensive products or those perceived as being very important usually involve more deliberation and more comparison shopping. Planning a family vacation, buying a house, a car, even an appliance, are examples. However, consumer planning periods typically are short. One half the purchases of durable household goods appear to be planned no more than two months in advance.[50] With food purchases, less than half are planned, suggesting that the buying decision for many products is delayed to the last minute and is influenced by what is seen as the customer strolls through the store.[51]

Because of this lack of planning and the consequent prevalence of impulse buying, point-of-purchase displays become important, especially in supermarkets and other self-service stores where no salesperson is around to influence the sale. We will discuss point-of-purchase sales efforts in more detail in a later chapter, but it is worth noting here the critical importance of spacing and display in the supermarket.

Because so much buying is unplanned, consumers have often been regarded as casual or impulsive, easily swayed by emotional appeals, and consequently neither rational nor objective. But this is not always a valid assumption. Much of what is called "impulse buying" actually may be called deferred purchasing. A consumer has a background of product experience, and when suitable merchandise is seen under attractive circumstances the decision is made to purchase.[52] For example, you may be interested in buying a new jacket;

[50] Joseph W. Newman, ed., *On Knowing the Consumer* (New York: Wiley, 1966), pp. 9–10.

[51] James D. Shaffer, "The Influence of 'Impulse Buying' or 'In-the-Store' Decisions on Consumers' Food Purchases," *Journal of Farm Economics*, May 1960, pp. 317–24.

[52] Newman, p. 9.

it is not an urgent need, and for several weeks you have given jacket displays and advertisements a little more attention than normally. One day, however, you encounter a particular display and an attractive price. You buy on "impulse."

Some "impulse" buying may actually be planned in advance. Candy, however, is a traditional impulse item, as these dispensers at check out points suggest. *Photo by Helena Frost.*

**MARKETING
IN
ACTION**

Effect on Sales of Spacing and Display in the Supermarket
With impulse buying so important, a number of studies dealing with the sales impact of changing displays and shelf position have been made for supermarkets. Some examples of the effectiveness of display are as follows:

	Percent change in unit sales
Maintaining a fully stocked shelf rather than a normally stocked shelf which would have some low-stocked and even out-of-stock conditions	+20
Displaying individual items with related goods rather than presented by themselves elsewhere in the store	+418
Using "as advertised" signs	+124
Using "cents-off" signs	+23
Moving an item:	
from waist level to eye level	+63
from waist level to floor level	−40
from floor level to waist level	+34
from floor level to eye level	+78

SOURCES: "How In Store Merchandising Can Boost Sales," *Progressive Grocer,* October 1971, pp. 94–97; "How the Basics of Special Display Affect Sales and Profits," Progressive Grocer, January 1971, pp. 34–45; "How To Make Displays More Sales Productive," *Progressive Grocer,* February 1971, pp. 34–45.

For thought and discussion:

Why do you suppose the "as advertised" signs had much greater impact than "cents-off" signs?

What would be some criteria for selecting products and brands to place at the choice eye-level spacing in a supermarket?

POSTPURCHASE INFLUENCES

Most buying is repetitive, that is, the same brand or the same types of goods are needed periodically: the tube of toothpaste, the box of detergent, the six-pack of beer. Other items, such as automobiles, still are purchased often enough so that repeat business is a factor. And repeat business for a particular brand is usually determined by customers' satisfaction with the original purchase: this provides feedback for subsequent purchasing decisions. Hence the postpurchase factors are important to both the marketer and the purchaser. In this section we will consider the implications of postpurchase doubt or dissonance, and the vital subject of brand loyalty.

Cognitive Dissonance

The Theory of Cognitive Dissonance. Cognitive dissonance is a concept, first introduced by Leon Festinger, that describes certain psychological consequences relevant to consumer behavior, in which "dissonance" occurs if, after a decision, a person is faced with doubt as to whether he made the right choice.[53] This being a uncomfortable psychological state, the individual is thus motivated to reduce dissonance, either by changing his own position, by downgrading the validity of incoming information, or by seeking material such as advertisements which will support the decision.

This theory has been substantiated by a number of studies which indicate that initial impressions may be changed so as to reduce any major discrepancies.[54] Other studies have shown that purchasers of major items such as cars read more advertisements of the make they own than of other makes.[55]

It must be noted that the theory, despite its popularity in marketing literature, has by no means been fully explored, and serious methodological weaknesses have been encountered in much experimentation concerning it.[56] New owners may not be reading advertisements about their make or brand to reduce dissonance. "It is more probable that the owner will be 'set' to notice advertisements more than he otherwise would be, simply because an important new product has entered his life."[57]

Even though the full significance and the relative influence of cognitive dissonance have not been explored or confirmed, the idea warrants serious attention from marketers. Dissonance is present as a result of buying decisions, and this has been fairly well established when:

1. The decision is important to the individual in terms of its psychological significance to him, financial outlays, etc.
2. The alternatives not chosen have desirable features[58]

Practical Applications of Cognitive Dissonance Theory. Most marketing interest in this theory relates to the postpurchase situation and brand loyalty. Repeat sales are important with most products and, as was noted in the section on selective perception, once brand loyalty is established, it is difficult to circumvent by competitors: messages

---

[53] Leon Festinger, *A Theory of Cognitive Dissonance* (New York: Harper & Row, 1957).

[54] Leon Festinger, "Cognitive Dissonance," *Scientific American,* October 1962, p. 93ff.

[55] D. Erlich, I. Guttman, and P. Schonbach, "Postdecision Exposure to Relevant Information," *Journal of Abnormal and Social Psychology,* vol. 54, 1957, pp. 98–102.

[56] James E. Engel, David T. Kollat, and Roger D. Blackwell, *Consumer Behavior,* 2d ed. (New York: Holt, Rinehart, and Winston, 1973), pp. 541–42.

[57] Ibid., p. 541.

[58] Leon Festinger, *Theory of Cognitive Dissonance;* and J. W. Brehm and A. R. Cohen, "Re-evaluation of Choice Alternatives as a Function of Their Number and Qualitative Similarity," *Journal of Abnormal and Social Psychology,* vol. 58, 1959, pp. 373–78.

inconsistent or contradictory to previously established attitudes and beliefs tend to be screened out, distorted, or forgotten.

However, if consumer expectations are not fulfilled by product performance, dissonance may well be generated; buyer dissatisfaction and erosion of brand loyalty would then be the probable result. Many advertisements and promotional messages invite disillusion because of the "puffing," or "little" exaggerations of product claims. Therefore, the theory of cognitive dissonance, incomplete and evolving though it is, has implications that all marketers should heed: advertising and selling should not promise more than the product can offer.

Furthermore, retailers and manufacturers should be alert to ways to help their customers reduce dissonance short of brand-switching behavior. Literature could well be distributed assuring the purchaser that his choice was a wise one; after-sales follow-ups might be made to clarify any problems in product use, allay any complaints, and give further assurance of the wisdom of choice; advertisers might even design some ads for recent purchasers as well as potential buyers (word-of-mouth advertising by satisfied buyers is a potent persuasive method). For example, Volkswagen of America puts out a magazine called *Small World,* sent to recent VW buyers. It contains contributions by enthusiastic owners, hints for getting the most out of your car, and general assurance to VW buyers that they have done the right thing.

One study suggests that, since the purchaser is sensitive to information about his new purchase, he may also be sensitive to information about related products by the same manufacturer.[59] While this hypothesis has not been confirmed, it is logical in view of what we know of cognitive dissonance and selectivity of exposure and recognition. It directs attention to what might be a significant additional source of business. All too often a customer is forgotten and ignored once the sale has been completed.

More research is needed concerning cognitive dissonance. We need to discover whether some products are more affected than others; for example, the importance of the decision to the individual may be related to the degree of dissonance. Methods of reducing dissonance may vary from product to product, and this needs further exploration. And we need to develop better measures of this phenomenon.[60] Yet, the implications of cognitive dissonance theory to practical marketing are intriguing.[61]

[59] Leonard A. LoSciuto and Robert Perloff, "Influence of Product Preference on Dissonance Reduction," *Journal of Marketing Research,* August 1967, pp. 286–90.

[60] Engel, Kollat, and Blackwell, pp. 541–43.

[61] For further discussion on dissonance, see S. Oshikawa, "Can Cognitive Dissonance Theory Explain Consumer Behavior?" *Journal of Marketing,* October 1969, pp. 44–49; Joel B. Cohen and Marvin E. Goldberg, "The Dissonance Model in Post-Decision Product Evaluation," *Journal of Marketing Research,* August 1970, pp. 315–21; and Del I. Hawkins, "Reported Cognitive Dissonance and Anxiety: Some Additional Findings," *Journal of Marketing,* July 1972, pp. 63–66.

Brand Loyalty

Most measurements of brand loyalty specify that a certain percentage of a household's purchases must go to one brand over a period of time. However, this says nothing about the strength of the feeling or loyalty to the brand and how easily the consumer might be induced to switch. The amount of brand loyalty varies by product. We know that for certain food products from 35 to 60 percent of the buyers are repeat or loyal customers. On the other hand, for appliances or hard goods there appears to be less loyalty to brands.[62]

We know that learning is important in establishing and maintaining brand loyalty, with reinforcement or reward leading to habitual behavior. Even when there is no discernible difference between brands, some consumers will become brand loyal.[63]

Considerable research has been directed at determining the characteristics of those consumers most loyal. But most of the findings to date are inconclusive and/or contradictory. It does appear that brand-loyal people cannot be distinguished from other consumers on the basis of demographic or psychological factors; further, it appears that there is no generalized loyalty by individuals across all product lines. This situation reduces the practical implications of brand loyalty. However, a certain proportion of loyal customers show a reluctance to change brands because of inertia; for these customers, pointing out significant product benefits or price reductions of a competing brand may induce them to change.[64]

INTERMEDIATE AND INDUSTRIAL BUYERS

Most behavioral concepts are applied almost exclusively to final consumers in the marketplace. Another group of purchasers generally is neglected as a topic of behavioral theories: intermediate and industrial buyers. These either purchase goods for resale to others (as do wholesalers and retailers), or else they buy goods involved in their own production and operational processes. In sheer numbers such buyers are only about 11 million, compared with some 200 million final consumers (less those too young or otherwise incapable of buying). However, these professional buyers purchase more goods than final consumers, because the same product will often be sold several times and in various forms en route to the final user.

There are differences in resources and sophistication between the small farmer or beauty shop operator and the purchasing agent of a large manufacturer, but for our discussion we will consider

[62] Newman, pp. 16–17.

[63] Jagdish N. Sheth, "How Adults Learn Brand Preference," *Journal of Advertising Research*, September 1968, pp. 25–36; W. T. Tucker, "The Development of Brand Loyalty," *Journal of Marketing Research*, August 1964, pp. 32–35.

[64] Engel, Kollat, and Blackwell, pp. 557, and 574.

these as having similar motivations and, within reason, similar behavior in the purchasing situation. We will focus the following discussion primarily on industrial customers since these are generally
representative of all professional buyers.

Comparison of Industrial Buyers and Final Consumers

The industrial buyer or purchasing agent is often thought of as the
completely rational consumer, the opposite of the household customer. Without doubt, one is a professional, a specialist, while the
other is an amateur. The extremes of buying behavior can be represented by the following continuums:

Objective Rational	Subjective Emotional
Knowledgeable Purchases well planned	Confused Impulsive and/or careless
Careful evaluation of competitive offerings	Inability or un- willingness to evaluate com- petitive offerings
Coldly analytical	Easily swayed

Figure 6-2. Continuums of Buying Behavior

General impressions would place the industrial buyer at the
extreme left of the continuums, while the household consumer would
generally be thought to exhibit behavior described at the right end.
How valid are these assumptions? Certainly not all consumers deserve to be placed at the extreme right, characterized by the easily
swayed, the confused, the emotional. Placement toward the middle
of the continuums would be more valid. And industrial buyers? Are
they as objective, as coldly analytical, as careful as commonly
thought?

Probably not. While purchasing agents and their buying motives
and behavior differ significantly in certain respects from consumers,
there are similarities. And many of the behavioral concepts we have
examined in this chapter are relevant for both kinds of buyers.

Purchasing agents generally must be considered specialists;
they are often highly trained and may belong to a professional association such as the National Association of Purchasing Agents. Purchases are made with knowledge of product characteristics and
supplier dependability, while performance and price may be care-

fully weighed. Where technical know-how is needed—as in purchasing certain installations and equipment—elaborate tests may be used to compare competing products, and other company experts brought into the evaluation.

However, less than completely rational motivations may still affect professional buyers, especially where competing products are fairly equal. These buyers are concerned with their position in the company and their chances for promotion. They may be susceptible to appeals to their ego, to their progressiveness, to their desire for security. Aspirations and reference groups may be factors much as they are with consumers. And there is the human tendency, other things being equal, for the buyer to give the order to the salesman he likes best.[65]

The industrial purchase may be subject to *multiple* or *diffused buying influences.* For major purchases a number of different executives and/or technical experts may be involved in the buying decision, even though the purchasing agent may actually sign the order. Several studies of industrial firms have found that the number of persons who influenced buying averaged from three to more than eight.[66] This may lengthen the negotiation period and also make more complicated the task of determining and reaching those most influential in the decision. Status and relative power positions may introduce less than fully rational elements to this purchase situation. The factor of multiple influence is not unique to industrial buyers; consumers also are influenced by various members of the family, by friends and associates in some buying situations, especially those involving major outlays such as automobiles.

A more unique characteristic of the industrial situation in some instances is the rather controversial practice of *reciprocity.* This essentially means, "If you buy from me, I'll buy from you." While this has long been common in the oil, steel, and chemical industries, it apparently has spread to many others.[67] Of course, for reciprocity to be operative, a firm's customers must supply products which it

---

[65] For further development of the characteristics of professional buyers, see Walter Gross, "Rational and Nonrational Appeals in Selling to Businessmen," *Georgia Business,* February 1970, pp. 1–3; Frederick E. Webster, Jr., "Modeling the Industrial Buying Process," *Journal of Marketing Research,* November 1965, pp. 370–76; Delbert J. Duncan, "Some Basic Determinants of Behavior in Industrial Purchasing," *Pacific Purchaser,* May, June, July, August 1965; and Jagdish N. Sheth, "A Model of Industrial Buyer Behavior," *Journal of Marketing,* October 1973, pp. 50–56; Leon G. Schiffman and Vincent Gaccione, "Opinion Leaders in Institutional Markets," *Journal of Marketing,* April 1974, pp. 49–53.

[66] Reported in Ralph S. Alexander, James S. Cross, and Richard M. Hill, *Industrial Marketing,* 3d ed. (Homewood, Ill.: Irwin, 1967), p. 87; Robert E. Weigand, "Why Studying the Purchasing Agent Is Not Enough," *Journal of Marketing,* January 1968, pp. 41–45; "Who Really Makes the Purchasing Decisions?" *Industrial Marketing,* September 1966, pp. 76–81.

[67] "Reciprocity: Dangerous Selling Tool Winning New Users!" *Sales Management,* May 20, 1960, p. 40; Reed Moyer, "Reciprocity: Retrospect and Prospect," *Journal of Marketing,* October 1970, pp. 47–54.

can use; sales are traded though probably not in equal proportions. The prevalence of reciprocity may subordinate the search for the lowest prices consistent with quality and dependability; yet, this practice may be forced on purchasing departments by the sales department. Where prices and quality are competitive, a reciprocal arrangement is difficult to overcome by an outside supplier. However, the federal government is beginning to view reciprocity with a jaundiced eye, as smacking of restricting competition.

Therefore, while there are some fundamental differences between industrial buyers and ultimate consumers, in many instances these result from the nature of the buying situation: that is, the technical requirements to be met, the limited number of products capable of meeting the requirements, the size and importance of the orders, and the necessary spcialization of these buyers. The motivations, the development of favorable or unfavorable perceptions and attitudes —all these influence behavior (within the constraints of budgets and formalized specifications and procedures), despite the perceived rationality of the industrial marketplace.

CONCLUSIONS ON BUYER BEHAVIOR

We have described some of the better-known concepts and theories relevant to buyer behavior that have either real or potential applications to practical marketing. Certain practical implications were presented, but you may well wonder how all these diverse concepts can be sorted out and integrated so as to be helpful to the marketing manager. And that is the problem. Human behavior itself is complex, still unfathomable. So naturally buying decision making is also complex and only dimly understood.

Trying to understand buying behavior is an intriguing challenge, however. Marketers stand to gain in two ways from continued and accelerated research: (1) better understanding and predicting of actions and attitudes of buyers in the marketplace, and (2) developing better tools and techniques for marketing and consumer research.

QUESTIONS AND PROBLEMS

1. How accurate is income as an index to family consumption patterns? Explain.
2. What is cognitive dissonance? How would you apply this concept in a practical marketing situation?
3. "Emotional motives account for a good part of final consumer purchasing. For industrial purchasing, this emotionality is virtually nil." Evaluate this statement and its marketing significance.

4. What makes a product susceptible to reference-group influence, and what are the implications?
5. Impulse buying is generally assumed to be nonrational buying. Evaluate this assumption.
6. Cite some specific ways in which an advertiser could use learning theory in developing more effective advertising.
7. If there were not actual or threatened restrictive legislation, do you think subliminal advertising would be widely used today? Why or why not?
8. How do you account for the fact that many people have very real brand preferences even when product offerings are about the same?

Project

Observe the articles and advertisements appearing in several trade journals directed to industrial buyers. In general, how would you assess them with regard to buying appeals, objective presentations, and professionalism? What conclusions can you draw from this regarding differences in buying behavior of purchasing agents and household buyers?

Exercise in Creativity

What marketing efforts and appeals would you use in attempting to encourage women to smoke little cigars? Develop as many ideas as possible, and then single out those you think would be most practical.

Role-playing Case

You have recently been promoted to assistant purchasing agent for the machine tools division of your firm. In the process of filling a requisition for metal stampings, your boss, the chief purchasing agent, tells you:
"Tony we always buy metal stampings from Xenia Mills. So there's no need for you to look at other suppliers."
"All right, Mr. Jensen," you reply. Then as an afterthought you ask, "Are their prices always better than the other firms?"
"Not necessarily. But we have a reciprocal arrangement—they buy all their machine tools from us."

After you have been in purchasing for a while you have reason to suspect that Xenia may not be the best supplier. Evaluate the pros and cons of reciprocity. What information would you want to have before approaching your superiors to try to have the reciprocity arrangement overturned?

CHAPTER 7

MARKETING RESEARCH: MANAGERIAL ASPECTS

Marketing research may be defined as:

> systematic collection and analysis of data for problem solving and decision making in the field of marketing.

In this chapter we examine the role of marketing research in the firm, its historical development, and its major uses in planning marketing strategy. Limitations of marketing research are also considered. Finally we turn our attention to a newly developed role for research as a major component in a total information system. In chapter 8 we will look at how data for marketing research is gathered and analyzed. Terms encountered in this chapter include:

sales forecasting	Survey of Industrial Purchasing Power
Delphi method	
market analysis	test market
sales quotas	problem formulation
market potentials	payoff for research
Survey of Buying Power	information system

ROLE OF MARKETING RESEARCH IN THE FIRM

Marketing research by definition is systematic; this suggests that hunches and intuition do not qualify, and neither does an impromptu and cursory accumulation of scattered bits of data. Marketing research is a staff activity for management, that is, it provides information to aid decision making. In its ultimate role, marketing research becomes part of the intelligence system of a firm, used to conduct investigations for specific problems or decisions. This differs from routine flow of information, such as weekly sales data and salesmen's reports, which do not go through the marketing research department when other specialized channels for processing this data have been established.

Although the amount spent on marketing research is small compared to the billions spent on technological research and development, firms are becoming aware of the need for better information in making marketing decisions. As firms become larger and develop widespread markets and long, complex distribution channels, managements often lose touch with their customers. Personal contact no longer provides adequate feedback. Launching a new product involves risk, and any efforts that might reduce this risk should be welcomed. Furthermore, the wide acceptance of the marketing concept, with its stress on customer orientation as a key to marketing success, requires some research to determine consumer wants.

Difference between Data and Information

An important distinction exists between data and information. Computers are capable of spewing out vast quantities of data—an executive can well be inundated. Information, on the other hand, can be defined as knowledge derived through the analysis of data.[1] This might include such important measurements or judgments as market potential, market share, consumers' attitudes toward the company and its products. Therefore, while data usually is needed to supply information, in its raw and unanalyzed form, it can be useless and confusing.

Characteristics of Good Information

For information to be useful in making marketing decisions, it needs certain characteristics. If some of these are missing, the research will suffer. Good information is

1. Timely—available when decisions need to be made.
2. Current—based on up-to-date data.
3. Accurate.
4. Sufficient—allows a decision to be made with minimum uncertainty.
5. Necessary—does not cloud the issue with too much information.
6. Reliable—the same data processed by someone else or at a different time would yield substantially the same information.
7. Economical.

[1] James H. Myers and Richard R. Mead, *The Management of Marketing Research* (Scranton, Pa.: International Textbook, 1969), p. 5.

8. Understandable—jargon is minimized, definitions are consistent and understood by all parties.
9. Acceptable—unacceptable information will not be used. This does not mean that information is slanted. It means that the best method of presentation must be sought and adopted.
10. Usable—without further modification.
11. Information—not data.[2]

While most of these criteria of good research output are self-explanatory, those of "Sufficient" and "Necessary" deserve further explanation. Sometimes more information can be developed than is really needed for a particular decision: this makes for wasted research time and expense. A continuum can be used to depict this:[3]

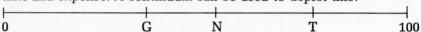

If all possible information bearing on a problem is placed on a continuum running from 0 to 100, the information needed to make a rational decision may be at point N. However, the decision maker may be a gambler who is willing to make a decision with less information at point G; on the other hand, he may be timid, and require information at point T or even beyond to total information. The marketing-information system should be responsive to the needs of the decision makers.

HISTORICAL DEVELOPMENT OF MARKETING RESEARCH

When firms were small, owners were able to deal directly with customers and observe at first hand their wants and preferences. As businesses became larger, indirect methods were needed. As an organized business activity, marketing research began in the early 1900s.[4] Modern marketing research is generally thought to have started with the establishment of a Commercial Research Division in the Curtis Publishing Company in 1911. In the next few years, similar departments were established in the U. S. Rubber Company and Swift and Company. The first book on commercial research was published in 1919.[5] But until the late 1920s, most research simply

[2] This classification is taken from Myers and Mead, pp. 5–6.

[3] Ibid., pp. 9–10.

[4] For a more detailed discussion of the historical development of marketing research, see: Lawrence C. Lockley, "Notes on the History of Marketing Research," *Journal of Marketing*, April 1950, pp. 733–36; and Albert B. Blankenship, *Consumer and Opinion Research* (New York: Harper & Row, 1943), p. 4 ff.

[5] C. S. Duncan, *Commercial Research: An Outline of Working Principles* (New York: Macmillan, 1919).

consisted of analyzing government statistics. More sophisticated methods of research, and particularly of opinion and attitude research, began in 1926 by Crossley, in 1933 by Roper, and in 1935 by Gallup. Sampling techniques became particularly important.

MARKETING MISTAKES

The *Literary Digest* Fiasco

The *Literary Digest* election poll fiasco in 1936 developed the reputations of Roper and Gallup. The *Literary Digest,* a weekly magazine, had been conducting an extensive mail poll of its readers before national elections for many years. For over a quarter century it had never failed to reflect the distribution of actual votes in its preelection polls. In 1936 it conducted probably the largest sampling ever undertaken, before or since: more than 10 million ballots were mailed to its readers and to names drawn from auto registrations and telephone directories. Some 2,350,000 people responded to the poll. Of the ballots returned, 55 percent favored Landon and 41 percent were for Roosevelt. On this basis, the *Digest* confidently predicted a Landon landslide. Actual results? Roosevelt polled 60 percent of the vote cast and his was the landslide.

That same year Gallup used a sample of only a few thousand interviews with voters, yet accurately predicted Roosevelt's election and that the *Literary Digest* would be in error.

For thought and discussion:

What do you think accounts for the grievous error of the massive *Literary Digest* poll?

Pollsters also erred in predicting the winner of the 1948 Dewey-Truman election. What do you think accounted for the error in this election?

Is such an error likely to occur again?

The relationship between political forecasting and marketing—particularly new-product forecasting—is close. The great accuracy of carefully chosen samples, and the corresponding dangers in relying merely on size of the sample in opinion research, stimulated more sophisticated research techniques.

Not until World War II did marketing research become a significant element in business. But then the trend of expenditures rose sharply, reaching over $500 million dollars today. This amount is small compared to that spent on advertising (over $25 billion), or on technological research and development (almost $20 billion). But the upward trend illustrates the growing recognition of the need for research.

Most research applications in marketing fall into these areas:

1. Sales forecasting
2. Market analysis
3. Product research, and especially new-product feasibility research
4. Advertising research
5. Test marketing

These are not necessarily discrete groups: for example, test marketing and market analysis will be involved in new-product feasibility studies. Now let us examine each of these in more detail.

Sales Forecasting

Forecasts of sales for the period ahead, usually a year, are basic to business planning. Many important decisions are based on the planned sales figure: production scheduling, raw material purchases, advertising expenditures, sales force outlays, even capital investments for machinery and equipment. Accuracy then becomes very important and a serious deviation from estimates could cause heavy inventory accumulation, unexpected expenses, and probably idle equipment; on the other hand, too conservative an estimate would probably preclude the firm from meeting its potential since enough goods could probably not be produced, nor enough salesmen be available.

The use of the computer to analyze data has made forecasting techniques much more sophisticated, but prediction remains inexact. In general, inaccuracy seems to increase as forecasting goes from the national economy, to industry sales, to company sales, and finally to territory and product sales. Some industries are more stable than others and generally permit better forecasting; the utilities characteristically have enjoyed this position. However, serious forecasting problems can even beset utilities.

In 1969, the American Telephone and Telegraph Company experienced a service crisis in New York City. The number of delayed dial tones and circuit-busy signals grew to more than 4,000 serious complaints in the first eight months, more than three times as many as in all of 1968. Pay phones were broken or vandalized and remained unfixed; telephone installation took two to three months' lead time. The strategic importance of New York City as a communication center made the service breakdown all the more serious.

Although many factors led to this situation, faulty forecasting and analysis of changing conditions were not the least. In 1967, for example, the New York Telephone Company expected the gross national product growth curve to flatten out in 1968. Accordingly, it cut its construction budget. Meanwhile a trading boom developed on the stock market which increased telephone traffic unexpectedly. Unpredicted changes in calling patterns developed in both residential and business areas—for example, welfare clients in New York City were allowed to have a telephone paid for by the city, and a huge increase in calling between hitherto little trafficked areas occurred. And the reliance of AT&T on historical trend-line planning proved inadequate.[6] More recently, service has improved.

An easy way to forecast sales is to have a number of executives make independent forecasts of sales for the next period: this is the *jury of executive opinion*. The various estimates may be averaged, or the executives asked to agree on a single figure acceptable to all. While a number of different, specialized viewpoints can be presented —such as those of the finance, marketing, and production people— executives tend to be influenced in similar directions and to be overly optimistic or pessimistic in unison. Averaging a number of views, or forecasting by compromise, often leaves much to be desired.

A more sophisticated and often rather effective variation of the "expert opinion" or "prophecy" approach to forecasting is the *Delphi method* developed by a senior mathematician at the Rand Corporation. While this was primarily applied to technological forecasting, it is relevant to business, especially under conditions of relative uncertainty, or where major innovations or improvements are forthcoming that will affect the firm or the industry. In the Delphi technique, experts in the area of investigation are questioned as to their views, then the results of the survey are distributed to the experts again, and they are successively questioned, thereby allowing changes in opinion and prophecies based on feedback from the other experts—a process of successive feedback and reevaluation of expectations. If the questions and experts are well chosen (and if circumstances favor the honest opinion of a range of knowledgeable people, which suggests that under severe competitive circumstances this may not be practical), then the ability of Delphi to make rather valid predictions is probable.[7]

Salesmen's estimates may be used. With this method, each salesman estimates his own next year's sales, and these estimates are cumulated to arrive at a company forecast. The rationale for this approach is that salesmen are familiar with customer reactions and

---

[6] See *Business Week*, December 27, 1969, p. 40 ff. for a detailed discussion of AT&T's woes in New York City.

[7] For more discussion of the role and usefulness of the Delphi method, see James Bright, "Can We Forecast Technology?" *Industrial Research*, March 5, 1968, p. 2 ff.; and Daniel D. Roman, "Technological Forecasting in the Decision Process," *Academy of Management Journal*, June 1970, pp. 127–38; for the use of this method in determining the market potential for fish protein enriched products in Latin America, see David Meredith Ambrose, "A Study of Marketing Fish Protein, Concentrate Enriched Products to Preschool Children in Latin America." Unpublished DBA dissertation, George Washington University, 1970.

are more aware of the local market, what competitors are doing, and of any changes looming on the horizon. But salesmen tend to alternate between pessimism and optimism, depending on whether their forecasts are used as sales quotas or as some subsequent measure of their performance. They are seldom familiar with changing economic conditions or proposed changes in company strategy.

Instead of executives or salesmen, surveys and panels of consumers or channel members, such as retailers and wholesalers, may be employed. While such information may be helpful, overreliance often is dangerous. Surveys of consumers dealing with buying intentions have usually yielded little accuracy.[8]

Statistical methods are increasingly being employed. These can range from very simple trend projections to sophisticated multiple-correlation analyses and mathematical models. Computers have made the latter possible and intriguing, especially to large firms.

Trend projections or extrapolations assume that sales will change to the same degree in the future as they did in the past. Figure 7-1 illustrates this, with the dotted line indicating projected sales. If conditions remain stable, this will probably yield a reasonably satisfactory forecast. Moving averages and other mathematical techniques can be employed to lend more sophistication to such projections. One can always question, however, the assumption that conditions—the economy, competition, customers—will continue to remain stable. The AT&T service breakdown in New York City shows the danger inherent in complacently projecting on the basis of historical trend data when other environmental factors may be poised for change.

[8] James Tobin, "On the Predictive Value of Consumer Intentions and Attitudes," *Review of Economics and Statistics,* February 1959, pp. 1–11; Jean Namias, "Intentions to Purchase Compared with Actual Purchases of Household Durables," *Journal of Marketing,* July 1959, pp. 26–30.

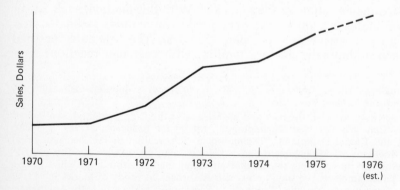

Figure 7-1. Sales Projection

Correlation analysis is used in sales forecasting to measure the relationship between a company's sales and other economic data. If a lead-lag relationship can be found between some economic series and the company's sales, then this technique becomes most worthwhile. Frequently, leading indicators can be found which work most of the time although, alas, they are not infallible either. Many companies have found that personal income may lead sales of their products by several months: a jump in personal income may presage a jump in company sales a few months hence, and vice versa. So the search goes on for mathematical models and multiple correlations that will match with company sales as closely as possible.[9]

Econometric models (econometrics is the branch of economics that specializes in quantitative measurement and mathematical model building) have been heralded as leading to a breakthrough in forecasting the course of the economy. In 1968, two econometricians were awarded the first Nobel Prize in economic science.[10] But econometric models have a crucial weakness: they are projections based on past experience; unexpected changes are not taken into account, nor is the consumer sufficiently predictable.

Several consumer research polls or indexes are of special interest to firms and economists interested in durable goods sales (sales of autos, appliances, and the like). The Survey Research Center at the University of Michigan periodically conducts a nationwide probability sample of about 1,500 households, to measure consumer willingness to buy. Other indexes have been developed to attempt to measure consumer confidence, and expected new car and other appliance purchases.[11]

Intention-to-buy surveys of industrial buyers, as to plant, equipment, and materials, are conducted by the Department of Commerce and by *Business Week* publication. These stated intentions have usually been accurate within plus or minus 10 percent.

Most of what we have discussed about forecasting has concerned the short term, one year and under, which is about the longest span of most definitive company sales forecasts. Longer-range projections are frequently used to make company capital investment decisions for expansion. These long-term forecasts can often be reasonably accurate, especially when the company's products can be related to

[9] For more detail about forecasting techniques, see Robert Ferber and P. J. Verdoorn, *Research Methods in Economics and Business* (New York: Macmillan, 1962); E. C. Bratt, *Business Forecasting* (New York: McGraw-Hill, 1958); *Forecasting Sales,* Studies in Business Policy No. 106 (New York: National Industrial Conference Board, 1964).

[10] "Forecasters Turn to Group Guesswork," *Business Week,* March 14, 1970, pp. 130–34; and "They Call It 'Instant Research,'" *Business Week,* January 25, 1969.

[11] See *Business Week,* November 8, 1969, p. 108 ff.; see also "University of Michigan Diligently Measures Mood of Consumers," *Wall Street Journal,* December 12, 1974, pp. 1 and 10.

certain economic or demographic data for which fairly reliable projections are available. For example, the prediction of population composition can be made with great accuracy, and this can be used for long-term forecasting by firms marketing to the youth market, the family market, and the elderly.[12]

Market Analysis

Market analysis seeks to determine the entire potential of a company's product lines—it might be called a measure of "company opportunity"—and this is broken down into the sales potentials for individual geographic markets. For example, a market analysis might indicate that Denver, Colorado, has four times the sales potential of Cheyenne, Wyoming, for a firm's products. Assuming that the analysis is reasonably valid, it would be useful in

1. *Defining sales territories.* The salesman should have enough sales potential in his territory so that he can use his time to advantage, and yet not so much potential that he cannot handle it all and sales are lost.
2. *Allocating sales efforts.* Decisions on how much local advertising and sales promotion to direct to areas are usually based on relative market potential. In the example given above, Denver supposedly would receive four times the local advertising dollars as Cheyenne. Of course, competition, availability of suitable local media, and ability to follow up the promotional efforts are other considerations.
3. *Setting sales quotas.* These should generally be set after the market potentials have been established and after the sales effort allocations. Relative differences in competition in various sales territories, of course, must be considered. When used in conjunction with the market potentials, the sales quota becomes more equitable and more easily defended, as well as being a good measure of the efficiency of salesmen. For example, the following illustrates how total sales production of salesmen may not give the best measure of their performance.

| | Salesman | | | |
	A	B	C	D
Sales last year	$ 210,000	$ 300,000	$ 225,000	$ 400,000
Territorial potential	2,000,000	3,500,000	1,400,000	4,000,000
Percent of potential	10.5	8.6	16.1	10.0

[12] For a complete classification of forecasting techniques and when to use any particular one, see John C. Chambers, Satinder K. Mullick, and Donald D. Smith, "How To Choose the Right Forecasting Technique," *Harvard Business Review,* July–August 1971, pp. 45–74.

Obviously salesman C is doing the best job in cultivating his territory; the man with the highest total sales is not as effective in his territory. A sales manager might well wonder whether a shift of territories might not yield more total sales for his district.

The methods used for deriving market potentials generally differ for consumer goods and for industrial goods. The number of industrial buyers is typically much smaller; for example, in 1973 the consumer market consisted of over 210 million persons living in almost 70 million households. In vivid contrast, there were fewer than 200,000 manufacturing corporations, and of these, the top 5 percent —those with sales of over $5 million—accounted for 85 percent of the total business done by manufacturing concerns.[13] We will examine the differences in calculating market potentials for consumer and for industrial goods next.

Deriving Market Potentials for Consumer Goods. Market potential may be developed from a single factor or index, such as total industry sales relevant to the product under consideration or perhaps to a related product. For example, registration data on Plymouth cars in each sales territory could be used as a single factor index to estimate potential for Plymouth parts.

Complex multiple factor indexes have also been developed and have the advantage of taking into account many influences on the sales of a given product. By tailoring a multiple factor index to a firm's particular products and experience, a better measure of market potential may be gained. However, some general multiple factor indexes which give measures of market potential for consumer goods in general are widely used, especially by smaller firms.

One of the best-known sources of market-potential information for consumer goods in general is that provided by *Sales Management* magazine. It publishes annually, usually in a June issue, a "Survey of Buying Power" with data and estimates on population, income, and certain categories of retail sales for city, county, and metropolitan areas in the United States and Canada, expressing these as a percentage of the total. This information is particularly useful for certain retailers and consumer-goods manufacturers, and since it is updated each year it provides needed statistics between censuses. Figure 7-2 shows some sample items from the Survey of Buying Power for two contiguous counties of metropolitan Washington, D. C.

Deriving Market Potentials for Industrial Goods. Since industrial customers are relatively few and typically concentrated in only a few parts of the country, statistics based on total population, income, and

[13] "Survey of Industrial Purchasing Power," *Sales Management,* April 22, 1974, pp. 13–14.

DISTRICT OF COLUMBIA

D.C. — POPULATION— 12/31/73

County	Total (thou-sands)	% of U.S.	% White	Median Age of Pop.	0-5 Yrs.	6-11 Yrs.	12-17 Yrs.	18-24 Yrs.	25-34 Yrs.	35-49 Yrs.	50-64 Yrs.	65 & Over	House-holds (thou-sands)	Under 25 Yrs	25-34 Yrs	35-44 Yrs	45-54 Yrs	55-64 Yrs	65 & Over
							% of Population by Age Groups									% of Household Heads by Age Groups			
WASHINGTON	3,070.4	1.4558	74.6	28.2	9.7	11.2	11.9	11.9	16.8	18.3	13.8	6.4	1,010.0	10.3	27.2	19.7	19.0	13.3	10.5
District of Columbia, D.C.	742.6	.3521	26.8	30.2	9.3	9.6	9.9	12.1	17.3	17.3	14.6	9.9	273.0	10.8	24.7	16.4	16.6	15.5	16.0
Charles, Md.	55.1	.0261	70.8	23.2	12.2	14.7	14.8	11.4	14.1	16.6	10.9	5.3	14.8	5.4	29.1	20.9	18.9	13.5	12.2
Montgomery, Md.	576.6	.2734	94.1	29.0	8.4	11.0	12.9	12.2	13.7	19.1	15.9	6.8	183.0	6.2	23.4	21.3	22.9	15.1	11.1
Prince Georges, Md.	707.2	.3353	84.6	26.4	10.8	12.5	12.1	12.0	16.8	18.1	11.5	4.4	219.6	12.8	32.0	20.3	17.3	10.5	7.1
Alexandria, Va.	108.9	.0516	84.6	30.1	10.6	9.4	8.2	10.4	22.4	17.3	14.5	7.2	44.3	17.4	30.3	14.0	16.0	12.6	9.7
Arlington, Va.	168.3	.0798	92.2	32.7	8.0	7.7	7.6	10.6	20.9	17.8	18.4	9.0	71.0	13.0	25.1	14.2	18.5	16.8	12.4
Fairfax, Va.	506.3	.2401	95.4	26.8	9.0	11.8	14.2	12.3	14.9	20.5	13.9	3.4	148.9	7.8	26.9	25.7	24.0	10.8	4.8
Fairfax city, Va.	21.7	.0103	97.7	25.7	9.4	12.2	14.2	13.0	14.4	20.0	13.2	3.6	6.4	10.9	26.6	25.0	23.4	9.4	4.7
Falls Church, Va.	10.4	.0049	98.1	31.4	9.6	9.9	10.0	11.3	14.4	16.4	19.4	9.0	3.9	10.3	20.5	12.8	20.5	20.5	15.4
Loudoun, Va.	42.5	.0202	87.1	26.6	11.0	13.2	13.2	10.3	14.4	18.2	12.0	7.7	12.8	5.5	28.1	21.1	15.6	14.1	15.6
Prince William, Va.	130.8	.0620	87.0	22.6	13.6	15.1	14.4	10.6	18.1	18.7	6.9	2.6	32.3	10.8	39.7	25.7	12.7	6.5	4.4
TOTAL ABOVE AREAS	3,070.4	1.4558	74.6	28.2	9.7	11.2	11.9	11.9	16.8	18.3	13.8	6.4	1,010.0	10.3	27.2	19.7	19.0	13.3	10.5
STATE TOTALS	742.6	.3521	26.8	30.2	9.3	9.6	9.9	12.1	17.3	17.3	14.6	9.9	273.0	10.8	24.7	16.4	16.6	15.5	16.0

D.C. (Cont.) — EFFECTIVE BUYING INCOME— 1973

County	EBI ($000)	% of U.S.	Per Capita EBI	Median Hsld. EBI	Avg. Hsld. EBI	$0-$2,999 Hslds.	$3,000-$4,999 Hslds.	$5,000-$7,999 Hslds.	$8,000-$9,999 Hslds.	$10,000-$14,999 Hslds.	$15,000-$24,999 Hslds.	$25,000 & Over Hslds.	Buying Power Index	EPP (Economy Priced Products)	MPP (Moderate Priced Products)	PPP (Premium Priced Products)
								% of Hslds by EBI Groups							Graduated Buying Power Indexes	
WASHINGTON	17,278,071	1.9616	5,627	12,341	17,107	5.8	5.5	14.6	12.6	24.5	24.0	13.0	1.7613	1.2470	1.5490	2.1060
District of Columbia, D.C.	4,300,939	.4883	5,792	11,373	15,754	8.8	7.2	16.0	12.0	21.8	21.4	12.8	.4345	.3343	.3681	.5626
Charles, Md.	200,198	.0227	3,633	10,001	13,527	10.9	9.0	17.1	13.0	23.1	18.1	8.8	.0250	.0229	.0234	.0177
Montgomery, Md.	3,578,805	.4063	6,207	13,257	19,556	4.2	4.1	12.7	12.3	25.7	25.5	15.5	.3518	.2020	.2900	.4648
Prince Georges, Md.	3,350,800	.3805	4,738	10,901	15,259	4.5	5.5	18.7	16.5	26.8	20.8	7.2	.3710	.3088	.3873	.3590
Alexandria, Va.	665,678	.0756	6,113	11,521	15,027	6.3	6.7	16.1	13.2	25.0	22.4	10.3	.0715	.0550	.0692	.0799
Arlington, Va.	1,232,904	.1400	7,326	13,211	17,365	5.5	4.8	12.7	10.9	25.1	26.8	14.2	.1145	.0707	.0984	.1439
Fairfax, Va.	2,997,378	.3403	5,920	14,942	20,130	3.0	3.1	9.0	9.3	25.9	31.3	18.4	.2802	.1623	.2186	.3600
Fairfax city, Va.	128,140	.0145	5,905	15,024	20,022	2.7	1.7	7.6	10.1	27.8	32.9	17.2	.0200	.0132	.0178	.0201
Falls Church, Va.	70,014	.0079	6,732	13,733	17,952	4.3	3.5	10.1	10.8	28.5	28.5	14.3	.0096	.0068	.0090	.0117
Loudoun, Va.	179,966	.0204	4,234	9,024	14,060	14.2	11.4	18.5	11.5	16.9	15.1	12.4	.0199	.0212	.0163	.0191
Prince William, Va.	573,249	.0651	4,383	12,614	17,748	5.4	6.0	15.3	11.9	21.9	23.3	16.2	.0633	.0498	.0509	.0672
TOTAL ABOVE AREAS	17,278,071	1.9616	5,627	12,341	17,107	2.7	1.7	7.6	10.1	27.8	32.9	17.2	1.7613	1.2470	1.5490	2.1060
STATE TOTALS	4,300,939	.4883	5,792	11,373	15,754	8.8	7.2	16.0	12.0	21.8	21.4	12.8	.4345	.3343	.3681	.5626

D.C. — RETAIL SALES BY STORE GROUP— 1973

County	Total Retail Sales ($000)	% of U.S.	Food Total ($000)	Food Super-markets ($000)	Eating & Drinking Places Total ($000)	General Merchandise Total ($000)	General Merchandise Dept. Stores ($000)	Apparel Total ($000)	Furn-House-Appl Total ($000)	Furn-Home Furnishings ($000)	Auto-motive Total ($000)	Gas Station Total ($000)	Lumber-Bldg-Hdwre Total ($000)	Drug Total ($000)
WASHINGTON	8,383,280	1.6309	1,828,020	1,660,218	731,196	1,299,316	1,092,595	494,322	391,953	265,536	1,547,959	637,341	267,804	412,860
District of Columbia, D.C.	2,055,562	.3999	351,656	301,009	312,578	283,813	254,915	175,027	110,630	69,337	196,150	121,800	37,800	120,039
Charles, Md.	144,061	.0280	32,904	26,186	26,617	3,779		1,215	1,049	670	29,101	21,336	11,309	6,195
Montgomery, Md.	1,609,897	.3132	334,124	301,383	86,006	302,620	258,615	99,058	95,078	65,204	338,340	110,865	56,859	57,157
Prince Georges, Md.	1,947,604	.3789	480,276	435,932	136,250	308,081	244,143	102,682	60,733	39,824	416,953	160,198	51,263	92,298
Alexandria, Va.	399,923	.0778	62,968	59,820	19,249	104,392	96,820	26,313	13,611	9,120	105,406	21,513	8,455	15,016
Arlington, Va.	488,556	.0950	77,076	73,222	51,246	74,342	63,855	18,747	25,106	19,214	150,053	29,166	11,224	22,340
Fairfax, Va.	1,062,976	.2068	315,606	299,826	73,168	199,461	164,081	51,690	54,259	40,136	94,795	103,307	50,582	63,011
Fairfax city, Va.	182,633	.0355	38,670	36,737	6,698	1,899		2,955	10,057	7,036	85,065	14,327	4,840	8,738
Falls Church, Va.	80,465	.0157	16,999	16,149	1,762	893		2,623	5,669	3,968	39,501	4,623	3,356	2,614
Loudoun, Va.	96,541	.0188	28,517	26,631	3,955	2,077		2,597	2,425	1,697	17,075	11,303	12,785	6,208

Figure 7-2. Representative Page of Survey of Buying Power

Source: © 1974, Sales Management Survey of Buying Power, July 8, 1974. Further reproduction is forbidden.

MARKETING TOOL

Survey of Buying Power

To gain a feel for the usefulness of this tool, place yourself in several different marketing situations:

Example 1—Determining Territorial Sales Quotas (based on market potential). In order to judge performance in various territories, it is desirable to have sales quotas based on territorial sales potential; otherwise sales efforts cannot be evaluated equitably.

Assume that you are the marketing analyst for a cereal manufacturer. You have been asked to calculate sales quotas for the District of Columbia and the Maryland counties of Montgomery and Prince Georges that comprise part of metropolitan Washington, D. C. Planned sales for the entire U. S. are $20 million.

Since this is a relatively low-priced cereal sold to the general population, but with heavier sales to children, you find these statistics from Figure 7-2 relevant for your purposes:

	Age groups		Population
	0–5 yrs.	6–11 yrs.	% of U.S.A.
District of Columbia	9.3%	9.6%	.3521
Montgomery	8.4	11.0	.2734
Prince Georges	10.8	12.5	.3353

On the basis of relative populations, you assign these quotas:

District of Columbia	$20,000,000 × .3521 = $70,420
Montgomery	20,000,000 × .2734 = 54,680
Prince Georges	20,000,000 × .3353 = 67,000

However, in examining the age distributions you decide to reduce the District of Columbia quota by $6,000 (since it has the smallest percentage of children under 12 years old), and the Montgomery County quota by $4,000, and add these amounts to the quota of Prince Georges County (which has more young children relative to total population). Thus you arrive at these adjusted quotas:

District of Columbia	$64,420
Montgomery	50,680
Prince Georges	77,000

Example 2—Allocating Sales Efforts. Assume that you are a marketing manager for a firm distributing a rather high-priced line of cosmetics. You want to determine how much local advertising and displays efforts to put into various markets, including the same three territories as in the preceding example. You have a $2 million national budget for local newspaper and other local advertising.

From Figure 7-2 you pull these statistics:

	Effective buying income (% of U. S.)	Population % of U. S.	Buying Power Index
District of Columbia	.4883	.3521	.4345
Montgomery	.4063	.2734	.3518
Prince Georges	.3805	.3353	.3710

You are somewhat uncertain as to which statistics are most relevant for your decision. The type of product suggests that income is important; but population is also. You note that Montgomery County, with the smallest population, has almost as much total buying income as the District of Columbia and more than Prince Georges County. But then, Montgomery County is one of the wealthiest counties in the entire nation.

The Buying Power Index interests you. This is a general index constructed from three weighted factors: disposable income (weighted by 5), retail sales (weighted by 3), and population (weighted by 2). You decide to use this in allocating your marketing efforts, and assign these territorial budgets:

District of Columbia	$2,000,000 × .4345 = $8,690
Montgomery	2,000,000 × .3518 = 7,036
Prince Georges	2,000,000 × .3710 = 7,420

For thought and discussion:

What other data from Figure 7-2 do you think warrants consideration in these two allocations?

What statistics from the Survey of Buying Power would you recommend using in determining territorial potentials for (a) hunting equipment, (b) industrial tools, (c) house paint.

retail sales generally are useless in assessing potential. However, when potential buyers in each market or territory can be identified and their product needs estimated and cumulated, then market potential can be rather directly calculated.

The *Standard Industrial Classification System (S.I.C.)* identifies manufacturers by product and type of operation. Twenty major industrial groups are classified by two-digit numbers, and then further divided into three- and four-digit groups. For example, all apparel manufacturers are identified under number 23; they are further given a more detailed classification, with #2394 denoting apparel manufacturers dealing with canvas products primarily.

The industrial marketer has most often used the Census Bureau's annual *County Business Patterns,* which provides industrial employment data on a county basis. However, this is far from an ideal guide since, depending on the industry and technology level, employment does not relate very well to plant output level. For example, some types of production require more labor input than other, more automated ones: the apparel industries typically are low in labor productivity while the petroleum industry, which is highly automated, ranks high in output per employee.

Sales Management's recently instituted "Survey of Industrial Purchasing Power" is designed to provide more precise information than available before. On a per county basis, it provides:

1. Dollar value of the output of all plants in the county having 20 or more employees
2. Total value of shipments accounted for by large plants, those with 100 or more employees in the county
3. Dollar value of shipments for all four-digit S.I.C. industries totaling at least 1,000 employees in the county[14]

Figure 7-3 shows a representative page from the Survey of Industrial Purchasing Power.

New Product Research and Test Marketing

Thousands of new products are introduced every year into the American market. Heavy costs are involved in trying to carve out a place in the market, and there is substantial danger of new products failing: estimates range as high as 90 percent for new products that fail and are taken off the market. And some of these failures had been heavily promoted, as were the following:

> Campbell's Red Kettle Soups
> Best Foods Knorr Soups
> Colgate's Cue Toothpaste
> General Foods' Post Cereals with Freeze-Dried Fruit
> Hunt's Flavored Ketchups
> Scott Paper's Babyscott Diapers
> Brown-Forman's Frost 8/80 "Dry White" Whiskey

A number of techniques are common in new product research, but the large proportion of new product failures casts some doubt on their effectiveness. Too often there is pressure to push the product out into the market without adequate research, "before competition gets the jump." Complicating the research efforts is the limited usefulness of such conventional questions as, "What features do you want in this product?" and "Would you buy this product?" Such questions apparently do not measure feelings and motives that affect preferences, especially in the marketplace environment where the consumer is bombarded by myriad products and claims. Clinical interviewing techniques—an aspect of motivation research—are sometimes worthwhile, and various scaling devices can be used to obtain an approximate rank of product attributes.

Test marketing is a rather common phenomenon with many con-

---

[14] "Survey of Industrial Purchasing Power," *Sales Management*, April 22, 1974, pp. 13–17.

STATE County SIC	Industry	Number of Plants Total Plants	Number of Plants Large Plants	Total Shipments $Mil.	% Of U.S.	% In Large Plants
INDIANA (cont.)						
Lawrence	All mfg	25	9	312.9	.0496	92
3361	Aluminum castings	1	1	51.3		100
3717	Motor vehicles & parts	2	1	203.6		99
Madison	All mfg	55	19	736.8	.1168	94
3423	Edge tools	2	1	25.8		96
3642	Lighting fixture	2	1	140.8		99
3694	Engine electrical equip	2	1	339.3		99
Marion	All mfg	517	153	3,895.9	.6178	88
1911	Guns, howitzers, mortar	1	1	60.0		100
2011	Meat Packing plants	3	3	177.7		100
2051	Bread & related prod	7	5	39.7		95
2711	Newspapers	3	1	29.7		95
2834	Pharmac preparations	2	2	486.0		100
3321	Gray iron foundries	5	3	47.9		94
3519	Internal comb engines	2	2	57.9		100
3531	Construction mach	3	3	52.0		100
3544	Special dies & tools	31	4	42.6		32
3566	Power trans equip	3	3	77.5		100
3585	Refrigeration machinery	6	4	164.2		97
3651	Radios & TV receiv sets	3	3	524.3		100
3661	Teleph & teleg equip	1	1	254.1		100
3694	Engine electrical equip	3	2	92.9		99
3713	Truck & bus bodies	3	1	115.7		97
3717	Motor vehicles & parts	14	11	344.8		96
3729	Aircraft equip n.e.c.	6	3	35.7		90
Marshall	All mfg	33	9	149.0	.0236	79
Martin	All mfg	3	2	12.6	.0020	84
Miami	All mfg	32	7	71.5	.0113	51
Monroe	All mfg	21	11	213.2	.0338	95
3632	Household refrigerators	2	2	116.2		100
3662	Radio & TV comm eqp	2	2	16.6		100
Montgomery	All mfg	19	10	95.5	.0151	89
2732	Book printing	1	1	44.0		100
Morgan	All mfg	17	2	27.7	.0044	40
Newton	All mfg	3	3	14.8	.0023	100
Noble	All mfg	35	11	119.0	.0189	72
Ohio	All mfg	2		3.3	.0005	
Orange	All mfg	8	3	22.9	.0036	78
Owen	All mfg	5	1	7.6	.0012	46
Parke	All mfg	3	1	4.9	.0008	69
Perry	All mfg	13	7	68.9	.0109	75
2511	Wood furn not upholst	3	3	24.0		100
3671	TV rec electron tubes	1	1	14.5		100
Porter	All mfg	20	7	420.7	.0667	95
3312	Blast furn & steel mill	2	2	363.0		100

Figure 7-3. Representative Page of Survey of Industrial Purchasing Power

Source: *Sales Management,* April 22, 1974.

MARKETING
TOOL

Survey of Industrial Purchasing Power

To understand the usefulness of this tool, place yourself in this marketing situation:

You are the general sales manager of a small firm manufacturing a specialized machine adapter, and distributing this in Indiana, Michigan, and Ohio. Your customers are in three industries: S.I.C.s #3522 farm machinery; #3531 construction machinery; and #3537 industrial trucks and tractors. You need to determine the relative market potential for these states in order to allocate your sales efforts most effectively and assign sales quotas to your salesmen as equitably as possible.

To determine the relative market potentials, you turn to the Survey of Industrial Purchasing Power and find the value of shipments data for the three S.I.C. industries in the three states to be as follows:

	(000,000)	
Indiana	**Michigan**	**Ohio**
#3522 #3531 #3537	#3522 #3531 #3537	#3522 #3531 #3537
$177.5 $107.8 —	— $34.1 $111.7	$127.7 $313.2 $131.7

Totals: Indiana $ 285.3 (million)
Michigan 145.8 "
Ohio 572.6 "

Grand total $1,003.7 (million)

Then the market potential of each state is:

Indiana $\frac{285.3}{1,003.7}$ = about 29 percent

Michigan $\frac{145.8}{1,003.7}$ = about 14 percent

Ohio $\frac{572.6}{1,003.7}$ = about 57 percent

SOURCE "Survey of Industrial Purchasing Power," *Sales Management*, April 22, 1974, pp. 18–20; 50–57; 68–70; 90–95.

For thought and discussion:

How would you use the Survey to guide your expansion into other states?

In the above example, if you have 15 salesmen, how would you allocate them?

If your sales plan is $25 million, how would you assign quotas by state?

sumer packaged goods. It provides a "firing line" test of actual sales results, and it can give some indication of probable sales potential extrapolated to the entire United States. A market test involves introducing the product (or the changed advertising, or price, or whatever is being tested) into one or more test areas—these should be as comparable and representative as possible. The test is conducted over time, and the firm must have some basis for measuring the movement of merchandise.

This may take the form of a store-audit in which movement is carefully observed in a sample of outlets in the test market. If several products are being tested, or a before-and-after study is being made to test, for example, a package change, it is necessary to set up control markets so that the effect of the change can be ascertained. Test marketing can be costly and time consuming. Extensive planning is usually necessary, the test has to be run long enough to furnish realistic results, and provision has to be made for collecting the data.

What can be tested? While we frequently think of marketing tests in conjunction with new product research, they are also used for determining the optimum price, the most effective advertising appeal, media, promotion or premium, and a number of other uses.

With so many new products coming on the market, many of the favored test cities—such as Albany, N. Y., Columbus, Ohio, Peoria, Ill., and South Bend, Ind.—are becoming saturated. This detracts from the results as consumers become aware of the testing and develop indifference. Companies have become adept in "jamming" a competitor's tests with special promotions of their own products, and this leads to difficulty in appraising results. Other firms, faced with the decision to test market or not, fear that the longer a product remains in test, the easier it is for competitors to duplicate it.

The expense of test marketing—which can run to over $1 million for a single product—might be tolerable if test market results guaranteed success. But they often do not: most of the product failures mentioned above had been test marketed. Another example of a successful test-market failure was the "cooking stick" developed by Anderson, Clayton & Co. This was a new margarine designed solely for the frying pan rather than the table. It was better for cooking than other margarines because it did not create a black residue at high temperatures. And it had a successful test market. But the "cooking stick" bombed out, and was completely off the market within a year.[15]

To save the time and expense, firms are increasing their use of small panels of consumers who judge products in each stage of development, from conception to completion. Usually this involves consumer-use tests, with a sample of consumers actually using the product. In these tests, however, panel members sometimes become "experts" and give opinions not representative of consumers at large. There is also uncertainty among respondents as to just what

[15] "New Products: The Push Is On Marketing," Business Week, March 4, 1972, p. 74.

products they prefer. But on balance, and judging from increasing business use, consumer panel and use tests offer considerable promise.

**MARKETING
RESEARCH
IN
ACTION**

Customer Panel for New Product Research—Consumer Goods
In the Cleveland Convention Center, 1,400 people who had bought a new compact car within the last two years met to evaluate future compact cars for the Ford Motor Co. On display for evaluation were five full-size car models, three exteriors, and the mockup interiors. Each was made of clay. Survey participants were given a questionnaire and were asked what they liked or disliked about certain features. The five clay model cars were brought from Ford headquarters in Dearborn in a special air-conditioned van, under the tightest security possible. The invitations for the participants were nontransferable. Each couple who took part was paid $15.

SOURCE: "1,400 Here Secretly Evaluate Ford Cars," *Cleveland Plain Dealer,* August 5, 1974, p. 6-B.

Customer Panel for New Product Research—Industrial Goods
In a "focus" group interview, invited guests sit around after lunch or cocktails and talk about what they would like to see in products and other subjects. One such was a group of engineers who were discussing process-control equipment at Beckman Instruments, Inc. A year later, the manufacturer of precision instruments introduced the fruits of that research: a major new line of process-control equipment that it claims is one of the first to be designed by customers themselves.

For the focus interview, the company recruited 46 engineers, offering them cocktails and $40 "for expenses," and "the chance to talk with other people in the field." The sessions were set up for after work, and they were asked for three hours of time. The first 30 to 45 minutes were spent filling out a detailed questionnaire on the process-control field; the rest of the time went to questions, answers, and open discussion. The sponsoring firm was kept anonymous to insure an objectivity which might not have been possible otherwise.

SOURCE: "Beckman Gets Customers to Design Its Product," *Business Week,* August 17, 1974, pp. 52–54.

Advertising Research

Expenditures for advertising have risen to over $25 billion a year. In light of such huge outlays, it is no wonder that advertising research receives great attention. Boyd and Westfall estimate that through the years more money has been spent on advertising research than on research in any other area of marketing.[16] Yet the answer to these questions still is elusive: "What should be said about the product?" "What media should be selected?" "What sales generation has directly resulted?" "How much longer term or carry-over effect has this campaign had?" "How can we predict the success of this advertisement or campaign?"

Advertising research generally falls into several types: *appeals research, copy tests,* and *media selection and scheduling.* Research into the effectiveness of individual ads as well as entire advertising campaigns, while relevant to the present discussion, will be treated more fully in chapter 12—see particularly Table 12-3. Motivation research is frequently used in selecting appeals since it can furnish information as to consumer images of the product, or the images that certain segments of the market might have. Copy testing falls into two major kinds: "before" and "after." "Before" tests are used before the advertisement or commercial is actually released, so that improvements in copy, illustration, or headline can be made. For example, prior to launching a TV commercial, agencies screen it before test audiences; sometimes sophisticated devices are used to get reactions. Word association, sentence completion, psychological tests such as the Minnesota Multiphasic Personality Inventory, and extensive indirect questioning, are some of the methods. Other tests may use elaborate equipment. The "galvanic skin-response test" measures the perspiration level—supposedly related to degree of interest—through electrodes clamped to hands. Eye cameras may be used to record the dilations of the viewer's pupils while watching a test commercial. If the pupils widen, this indicates greater interest.

Recall and *recognition* tests are most commonly used to test an advertisement or commercial *after* it has been run. The objective is to guide the development and use of the more effective ads in subsequent campaigns. After-tests are based on the respondent's memory, and give a measure of the relative memorability of the various ads or commercials being tested. The assumption is that the greater impact the ad has in memorability, the more effective it will be in generating sales. But this assumption may sometimes be suspect, since there need be no definitive correlation between remembering an ad and buying that product.

Both the size and the characteristics of the audience are important in selecting media. Readership studies are available concerning the printed media, while radio and television programs are rated by various methods including the "audimeter," used in developing the Nielsen ratings that spell the life and death of TV programs. The *audimeter* is an electronic recorder attached to a radio or TV set that

---

[16] Harper W. Boyd, Jr. and Ralph Westfall, *Marketing Research,* 3d ed. (Homewood, Ill.: Irwin, 1972), p. 653.

records when the set is operating and what programs are on. A carefully chosen sample of homes is used, and this sometimes leads skeptics to question the validity of small numbers. But there is a more substantial limitation: that a set is "on" does not indicate that anyone is watching or listening. And this limitation is especially serious with radio recording.

LIMITATIONS OF RESEARCH

Research can be expensive and time-consuming. Many problems occur often in many variations. Any single decision may not be sufficiently great to warrant the time and expense necessary to research adequately the alternatives.

Some problems do not lend themselves to valid research conclusions with the tools and techniques available today. There may be too many variables involved. They may be intangible and incapable of precise measurement. This is often the case where an optimum allocation is sought for merchandising and promotional efforts. When is the optimum reached? How can it be obtained? How is it to be measured? The answers to these "simple" questions defy us.

Some analyses rest on the shaky foundation of subjectivity. Consumer preference statements often are not translatable into actual sales. Information on consumer segments has to be interpreted subjectively, as to specific products and services to offer. It still requires imagination to turn consumer information into sales.

Full reliance upon marketing research does not guarantee a right decision. Much research consists of collecting data of past and present. While this is helpful in predicting the future, such predictions are not certain. As Boyd and Westfall suggest, research can only decrease the area of uncertainty.[17] Entenberg points out that, regardless of techniques used, there is no substitute for either executive leadership or perceptive judgment.[18] Intuitive judgment may even be important in certain situations: when all facts cannot be gathered, when conceptual and logical arguments are fuzzy, or when immediate action is required without waiting for long, rational analysis.[19]

Therefore research is no panacea. Generally the most that can be expected from it is that the "batting average" of decisions may be improved. It seldom points out the optimum decision. However, "satisficing" decisions[20] (in which executives are content to select

[17] *Marketing Research,* p. 25.

[18] Robert K. Entenberg, *Effective Retail and Market Distribution* (Cleveland: World, 1966), p. 48.

[19] William H. Newman and Charles E. Summer, Jr., *The Process of Management* (Englewood Cliffs, N.J.: Prentice-Hall, 1961), p. 222.

[20] Herbert A. Simon, *Administrative Behavior* (New York: Macmillan, 1957).

from among satisfactory alternatives) may well be ample for most problems and lead to reasonable solutions within the bounds of practicality.

Adverse management attitudes toward research may stem from poor experience with research in the past, and lead to such criticisms as these:

1. Research conclusions are incorrect and lead to bad decisions, if relied upon.
2. Research findings are imprecise or do not really measure the key factors involved in the management problem.

Such criticisms relate to the quality of the research. Poor-quality research may be the result of ill-defined objectives and of studies carelessly planned or inadequately timed. Poor communication between line and staff may be at fault, so that there is a misinterpretation of the findings or of the probabilities involved. The caliber of personnel used for research varies considerably. Undoubtedly this can affect research quality. An upgrading of status is necessary in many firms; yet this upgrading may only come when the research department has delivered meaningful and important results.

PLANNING, ANALYZING, AND PRESENTING RESEARCH

Marketing research projects ordinarily involve the following steps:

1. Problem definition and planning of the study
2. Selection and utilization of various data-gathering methods
3. Processing, analyzing, and presentation of the research findings

We discuss the second step in the next chapter. The first and third will be treated here since they are particularly relevant to the role and status of research in the firm. The effectiveness with which these are performed has a vital effect on the management acceptance of the entire research function.

Problem Definition and Planning

Problem formulation is the crucial first step in a research endeavor. Too many times there is pressure from management to gather data, usually through the field work of a survey, while planning and exploratory preliminary work is viewed with impatience Yet unless the problem is well defined and the planning carefully done, the answers obtained may not be relevant and they may not be worth the effort and expense. An example of a study in which the problem was ill defined and the value of the study—what management might do with the results—undesignated, was an extensive survey of suburban consumers. The survey, conducted with the assistance of an outside research firm, cost upward of $100,000. It had these "earthshaking" conclusions: People are younger in the suburbs and are more inclined to leisure living than nonsuburbanites. As a result of this unproductive research effort, the firm became disillusioned and abandoned further consumer research.

A major purpose of this problem formulation stage is to give a sense of direction to research efforts. This task requires creativity and imagination, as well as a firm understanding of the problem itself. The groundwork needs to be laid for the internal and external investigations that lie ahead. The special nature of a given problem must be determined; seldom does the same design fit different problems. Finally, problem formulation helps provide economy of operation and prevention of wasted effort or the accumulation of superfluous data; in addition, it may reveal that the necessary data is already available, either in published reports or company records, and thus obviate the need for an extensive survey.[21]

At this stage the estimated payoff of the study should be considered: are the results likely to be obtained going to be worth the cost and effort of the study? The ill-fated study mentioned above disregarded any considerations of payoff at the planning stage, and as a result the findings were not commensurate with the cost.

Generally speaking, where the risk of a decision is substantial, the value of research in reducing this risk can be substantial. However, risk itself is a function of two factors: the importance of the decision, and the chances of making an incorrect decision. And costs of doing the research must be considered. If the costs are high relative to the risk-reducing value, then the payoff may be insufficient, or negative, and the satisfaction with the findings—the acceptance—is reduced accordingly.

Therefore, *payoff,* as a criterion for the planning of research, can be considered as composed of three elements:

1. Cost of doing the research
2. Importance of the decision
3. Risk of the decision

This can be diagrammed as in Figure 7-4.

The cost of the research should be less than the perceived risk of the decision.[22] This has, or should have, a profound effect on the

---

[21] For an expanded discussion, see Robert Ferber, Donald F. Blankertz, and Sidney Hollander, Jr., *Marketing Research* (New York: Ronald, 1964), pp. 151–52.

[22] The use of this criterion for determining the need for, and the value of, research follows the thinking of Alexander. Although he did not use the word *payoff,* he proposed these three criteria, which are essentially the same as our interpretation of payoff:

1. The difficulty of getting the needed information
2. The stakes involved in the decision
3. The chances of making a mistake in the decision

(Ralph S. Alexander, "The Marketing Manager's Dilemma," *Journal of Marketing,* April 1965, p. 19.)

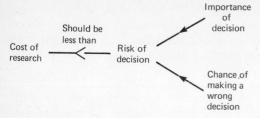

Figure 7-4. Payoff Factors

type of activities the research department should undertake. Ancillary to the criterion of payoff (which has a quantitative connotation) is the factor or constraint of time. As noted before, certain decisions that could benefit from research must be made without it, because of the need for immediate action.

**MARKETING
RESEARCH
TOOL**

Determining Guidelines for Research Expenditures
Although subjective judgments often must be used to ascertain payoff for any research project, usually these are far better than proceeding with research without payoff constraints. Consider the following:
What expenditure for research would you recommend in this instance?

Estimated risk of making an incorrect decision:
 without research   50 percent
 with $50,000 study   30 percent
 with $100,000 study   15 percent
Estimated investment at stake: $500,000

Solution:

Estimated cost of risk:
 without research—   50 percent of $500,000   = $250,000
 with $50,000 study—   (30 percent of $500,000) + $50,000   = $200,000
 with $100,000 study—(15 percent of $500,000) + $100,000 = $175,000

Therefore, with these probability estimates, the firm would be advised to make the $100,000 study, since this would minimize the risk/cost relationship.

For thought and discussion:
If the estimated investment at stake were $200,000, what should the decision be for research, assuming the same estimated risks?

Analysis and Presentation

The presentation of research findings and conclusions to management sometimes suffers from one of two weaknesses. The analysis may be vaguely stated, a hedging conclusion may be proffered, and management may be left with the reaction that nothing much was accomplished from the time and money spent. The other extreme is also common. The analysis and interpretations may be so esoterically presented as to be incomprehensible to the average executive not versed in research methodology and terminology. Either extreme impedes action and acceptance. In general, we may assess researchers as follows:

1. Researchers are strongest in methodology or techniques.
2. They are less strong in pinpointing problems and then translating them into appropriate methodology.
3. They are even less strong in the full interpretation of the data gathered.
4. They are least strong in presenting results in simple, persuasive, business language.[23]

If research is to become a more viable and integral part of the marketing operation of most firms—and this needs to be reflected in more than just dollars spent and research departments established—then perhaps a first step is the development of a closer communication and rapport between the marketing or operations researcher, and the middle and upper management levels.

MARKETING RESEARCH EXPANDED TO INFORMATION SYSTEMS

A marketing information system is an expanded version of market research. The focus is on broad, centralized, and current processing of information to help management in decision making. In the quest for such data, however, firms run the risk of being deluged with too much unassimilated material, as computers and duplicating machines spew out hundreds of billion of pages of statistics.[24] Therefore, in addition to providing wide-ranging data, a marketing information system must provide screening and order. The computer, of course, can play an important part.

What is the role of marketing research in an expanded market-

---

[23] Ferber et al., p. 428. For a recent empirical study of the researcher's role in presenting findings to management, see Robert J. Small and Larry J. Rosenberg, "The Marketing Researcher as a Decision Maker: Myth or Reality?" *Journal of Marketing,* January 1975, pp. 2–7.

[24] E. B. Weiss, "The Communications Revolution and How It Will Affect All Business and All Marketing," a special issue reprinted from *Advertising Age* (Chicago: Advertising Publications, 1966), p. 22.

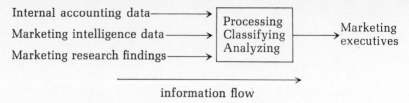

Figure 7-5. Marketing Research and Information Systems

ing information system? This can be seen in Figure 7-5 in which marketing research material is only one of three categories of information developed.

Information Systems

Internal information about sales, inventory levels, customers, etc., is often not current enough or detailed enough for fast reaction, perhaps to changing competitive conditions. The computer is a major help here in delivering timely reports. The danger is that too much undigested data will be provided.

Marketing intelligence gathering can be systematized so that changes in the market are quickly filtered to those executives needing to know. Salespeople, who are often first to hear of rumors and changes, can be encouraged to listen carefully and pass on such information. Other information can simply be obtained from such public sources as trade journals, business-oriented periodicals, dealers, trade shows, and the like. The problem is systematizing the data gathering, classifying it, and assuring that relevant material reaches the attention of people concerned.

Marketing research in such a general information system then refers to planning, conducting, and analyzing those special studies needed—perhaps of the market potential for a new product, or a study of advertising effectiveness, in short, the nonroutine type of information.[25]

Marketing research, in the absence of an information system, in general neither provides the continuous flow of market information, nor uses as many sources of both internal and external data, nor is it able to analyze and disseminate as much total information as an information system is designed to do.[26]

[25] For a detailed discussion of marketing information systems, see Richard H. Brien and James E. Stafford, "Marketing Information Systems: A New Dimension for Maketing Research," *Journal of Marketing*, July 1968, pp. 19–23; Conrad Berenson, "Marketing Information Systems," *Journal of Marketing*, October 1969, pp. 16–23; and William R. King and David I. Cleland, "Environmental Information Systems for Strategic Marketing Planning," *Journal of Marketing*, October 1974, pp. 35–40.

[26] Lee Adler, "Systems Approach to Marketing," *Harvard Business Review*, May–June 1967, pp. 105–18.

QUESTIONS AND PROBLEMS

1. How would you evaluate the effectiveness of a marketing research department?
2. Why is so much marketing research subject to the criticism that it furnishes the right answers to the wrong questions? How can this be avoided?
3. What steps would you take in doing a marketing research study?
4. Should the marketing research director's role be to make recommendations on the basis of information gathered or to present only the facts and leave interpretation to others? Discuss.
5. Explain how the concept of a marketing information system is different from the marketing research function as traditionally performed.
6. Why is there relatively little use of marketing research by wholesalers?
7. What can be done to improve the status of marketing research in the typical firm?
8. How could marketing research departments have furnished better data and analysis to management on the seriousness of an emerging consumerism in the marketplace? Where were they deficient? Do you think such deficiencies have been corrected today?

Project

Top management of a large multiline firm is seriously considering buying a small company which manufactures a wide range of sporting goods equipment. This would be a new line for the firm. Develop a marketing research proposal that would cover the important questions raised about such an acquisition candidate.

Exercise in Creativity

Using the Delphi technique with your classmates, develop a forecast or prophecy of the effect of an energy shortage—electricity, natural gas, and petroleum—on boating, shopping patterns, and transportation in the next ten years.

Role-playing Case

You are the director of a six-person corporate research department for a major department store corporation. Six months earlier, top management had authorized a $150,000 study by an outside research consulting firm on the impact of a gasoline shortage on suburban shopping patterns. The 84-page report essentially stated that a gasoline shortage induces suburban customers to "shop less frequently, but purchase more at a time."

The executive vice president, Mr. Curtis, has just called you into his office. He nods for you to sit down. "Ms. Levine, we are planning next year's budgets as you know. Now I regret to say that we have to cut back rather drastically in some areas—one such area is your department. We've decided to reduce your staff from 6 to 2 people, besides yourself, of course."

"But . . . ?"

Mr. Curtis holds up his hand to interrupt your protests. He leans back and gazes out the window. "You see, we just don't see that much value in research. That study on the gasoline shortage—oh, I know your people didn't do it—but it, well, soured us on much research . . . $150,000 to tell us something we could have figured out over coffee, or a martini."

What rebuttal would you give Mr. Curtis?

How would you defend the need for research?

What assurances could you give that costs of future research would be geared to the value of the research?

CHAPTER 8

MARKETING RESEARCH: TOOLS AND TECHNICAL ASPECTS

In the last chapter we examined the role and function of marketing research in the firm—its usefulness, but also its limitations. In this chapter we consider the more technical aspects of research, such as how data should be gathered and analyzed so that it becomes useful *information* and not just a meaningless mass of numbers. Sometimes this may require going out into the "field" to gather primary data specific to the study; at other times, ample material may be available from company records and other sources.

Generally the marketing manager cannot be skilled and technically proficient in all the techniques to be described in this chapter. Staff people or outside consultants will provide the expertise. However, the marketing executive does need to be able to communicate with the technicians. More than this, he or she needs enough background in marketing research and operations research techniques to be able to interpret results intelligently. Finally, the marketing head needs to be sufficiently knowledgeable to realize that although research findings may be presented in sophisticated fashion, if the sampling was not well designed, the questions unbiased, and secondary data well investigated, then conclusions arising from such findings may need to be viewed more skeptically.

Terms to be encountered in this chapter include:

sampling	**nonprobability sample**
probability sample	**survey**

population
primary data
secondary data
motivation research

semantic differential
experimentation
consumer jury or clinic
operations research

MARKETING RESEARCH AND SCIENTIFIC RESEARCH

Marketing research cannot approach the mathematical precision of research in physics, chemistry, or other physical sciences, because much of it deals with the complex and unexpected actions of human beings. Prediction is particularly difficult: asking a person what he will do in the future—"Will you buy the product when it is available?"—is a most unhappy indicator: what people say and what they do are often completely different.

The ultimate of scientific research involves experimental procedures, in which the researcher controls all the variables except that one being studied. And in marketing this is generally impossible. Does this mean then that marketing research cannot be scientific? No. It rather means that the results, and the finality of their interpretation, must be seen as relative rather than absolute.

Experiments in animal and plant biology share some of the complexities of marketing problems and provide a certain rationale for our use and our expectations of marketing research.[1] The agricultural experimenter cannot control (anymore than the marketer can) all the factors that affect his situation, since it is impossible to have every seed planted in soil of exactly the same composition, and with the same conditions of sun, wind, rain, and insect population. Nevertheless, much productive experimental research has been conducted. The key is in the results sought: not the establishment of absolute values, but a comparison of alternatives or of relative values, such as which seed variety is the most resistant to rust infestation, which drug is the most effective in relieving certain ailments, which price, or distributor is better used:

> When we are concerned with comparisons of relative effectiveness, experimental requirements are greatly simplified. All we must do is evaluate the performance of several alternatives in such a way that nothing in the procedure itself will favor one or more of the alternatives over the others.[2]

[1] For a fuller treatment of the uses and limitations of agricultural experimentation vis-à-vis marketing research, see Seymour Banks, *Experimentation in Marketing* (New York: McGraw-Hill, 1965), pp. 1–5.

[2] Ibid., p. 2.

Theory of Sampling

Sampling is basic to all research, both in the physical and social sciences:

> Sampling allows us to draw conclusions about a larger group on the basis of experience with a part of it.

We do this every day; for example, we may select a magazine on the basis of looking at a few pages; we decide on the basis of one meal whether or not to return to a restaurant; we may choose to take the class of a certain professor as the result of discussing him with one or a few of our acquaintances.

Collecting data by sampling rather than going to the whole population *saves time* and *money*. When carefully done, sampling can be far more accurate than collecting vast amounts of data. The classic example of the effectiveness of careful sampling came during the 1936 presidential election; the 10-million ballot preelection poll by the *Literary Digest* (described in the last chapter) failed, while Gallup, using a carefully chosen sample of only a few thousand interviews, accurately predicted Roosevelt's election.

Sample Designs

There are many sample designs, from simple to complex. Two general classes of methods are: probability and nonprobability.

In a *probability sample* every item or person in the particular universe being studied has a known chance, or probability, of being included in the sample. Sample items are chosen independently of the person making the study. Chance governs the selection of these items, so errors should occur only on a random basis, and such random error (differences between the sample and the total population) can be measured using probability theory and statistical tests. Table 8-1 describes the major types of probability sampling methods.

Table 8-1.
Types of Probability Sampling Methods

Type	Description	Examples
1. Simple random	Every item or person in the population has an equal chance of being selected and included in the sample.	In the simplest example, one of two items is selected by flipping a coin. In a more complex example, such as selecting lottery winners, names or numbers are pulled from a hat or a barrel.

Table 8-1. (Continued)

Type	Description	Examples
2. Stratified	The total population to be sampled is divided into subgroups or strata, and each stratum is treated as a separate random sample. This is done to decrease sampling error caused by a skewed population. It assures that each category is sampled according to its importance in the population.	If a sample is to be drawn from retail firms in a community, the various firms can be grouped into size categories, and a desired number selected from each group or stratum.
3. Cluster	The total population to be sampled is divided into subgroups or clusters, and only some of the clusters are chosen at random to be sampled. This is commonly done where it is difficult to secure a precise list of the population, but geographical areas are readily definable and can be sampled. While this type of sample is not as efficient as the other probability samples, it is often less costly and more practical in the marketing research situation. Cluster samples are further divided into *area* and *systematic* samples.	*Area sample:* An area to be sampled can be divided into parts of the city (or census tracts), with only certain ones selected at random to have every nth house surveyed. *Systematic sample:* After a random start, every nth name in the telephone directory or the charge account list is sampled.

Probability samples are relatively costly and require considerable expertise to plan and conduct properly. For these reasons, *nonprobability samples* are often used in marketing. A nonprobability sample is at least partially subjective, because the researcher, rather than chance, determines which items to interview or observe. Every item in the universe does not have a known chance of being included in the sample, since the selection is made on the basis of convenience, or judgment, or according to some quota. Statistical tests based on probability theory consequently cannot be used to measure sampling error. Table 8-2 describes the major kinds of researcher-controlled, nonprobability samples.

The precision necessary in political polling (where an error of a few percentage points could mean a prediction for the wrong candidate) usually requires the careful use of probability samples. Marketing research often does not need the same precision. The quota design if carefully done can be quite representative. Judgment and convenience samples are more useful for exploratory work; they may be indispensable in emergency situations where a decision has to be made quickly and some "feel" of the situation is needed.

Table 8-2.
Types of Nonprobability Sampling Methods

Type	Description	Examples
1. Con-venience	Items are chosen for the sample purely on the basis of convenience to the researcher: they may be readily accessible, more articulate, or otherwise easy to measure.	Most man-in-the-street interviews are convenience samples.
2. Judgment	The researcher uses his judgment to select those items (persons) who might be regarded as "representative" in some sense.	In the sports world, judgment samples are used to choose those football coaches and sports writers who make football ratings. Knowledgeable executives (or professors) may be surveyed to give their "expert" opinions regarding impending business conditions.
3. Quota	This is similar to stratified random sampling in that the population is subdivided; however, respondents (those to be interviewed) are selected arbitrarily by the researcher up to the number designated for each stratum (the quota). This is rather widely used in marketing research, since it is assumed to be more representative of the population than the other nonprobability samples, while not costing as much as probability designs.	An interviewer may be required to select respondents according to the percentage of age distribution in the population, so that perhaps 10 percent should be senior citizens, etc.

We have been using the term *population* throughout the discussion of sampling. What do we mean by population? In sampling terminology, population refers to the source of items (or subjects) from which the sample is drawn and expected to represent.

As you can imagine, the size and distribution of the population —that is, whether concentrated geographically or widespread—can affect the type and size of sample to be used. The characteristics of the population also may affect the way in which data is gathered for the study. You can see from the following examples of research populations that size and composition can vary widely:

Designated Population of Study	Approximate Size
Total work force in the U. S.	80,000,000
Subscribers to a particular magazine	1,600,000
Home owners of a particular city	475,000
Number of industrial buyers of electronic instruments in U. S.	20,000
Number of Junior Chamber of Commerce members in a given community	350
Grocery wholesalers in a specific city	16

SOURCES, METHODS, AND APPROACHES

There are two major sources of material for any research study: primary and secondary data. See Table 8-3 for a concise classification

Table 8-3.
Classification of Data for Research Studies

Secondary	Information that someone else has compiled and usually for other purposes than the present study.
Internal	Available within the company or organization from records and previous research reports.
External	Available from external sources.
	1. Census and registration data
	2. Other publicly circulated material in books, periodicals, monographs, reports, etc.
	3. Data collected for sale on a commercial basis, such as by Nielsen
	4. Miscellaneous
Primary	Data collected by the researcher for the purpose at hand.
Observation	Direct recognizing and noting of facts or occurrences.
Survey	Asking questions of people who are thought to have the desired information. May be conducted by
	1. Personal interview
	2. Telephone
	3. Mail
Experimentation	Manipulation and control of variables under conditions which permit some determination of the effects of various inputs. This may be done through
	1. Test markets—certain representative cities, areas, or stores are used for the experiment.
	2. Laboratory methods—data (usually interview information) are gathered outside the marketplace, perhaps in a central meeting place such as an auditorium or a room with special facilities.

of data sources. *Primary data* are those gathered specifically for the study at hand. *Secondary data* are those already available that have been collected for other purposes and usually by someone else.

A common mistake is to rush out to collect primary data when the information may already be cheaply and readily available in secondary form. However, secondary data may not be current—for example, U. S. Census of Population data (gathered only every ten years) may well be out of date for many purposes, such as developing quotas for salesmen. Furthermore, the reliability of the source may sometimes be suspect, as might be the case where a trade association publication seeks to influence government legislation.

Sources of secondary data are many and varied. For some studies, real detective work may uncover material that might make gathering of primary data unnecessary. Internal company records, governmental agencies, trade and business associations, universities, private firms, advertising media—all are potential sources of relevant secondary data.

However, secondary data may not be relevant to the problem at hand, inasmuch as it was usually developed for some other purpose. Or, as we noted before, it may be dated or its credibility and accuracy may be suspect. Then the need for primary data becomes evident.

Methods of Gathering Primary Data

Primary data may be gathered by observation, survey, and experimentation. The choice of method usually depends on the nature of the information sought, the size of the sample required, and the time, money, and personnel available.

Observation. Data may be collected by observing some action of the respondent. Suburban stores have used this technique to determine where the majority of their customers live: license numbers of cars in the parking lot are recorded, and addresses then traced through license bureaus. Observation has been used to trace the path of shoppers through supermarkets and the time spent at various displays. The Nielsen Audimeter acts as a mechanical observer in recording what TV or radio station is tuned in.

A major disadvantage of the observation method is its limited application. Behavior can be observed, but can preferences be inferred from it? For example, because a person is observed buying hamburger, we cannot assume that he prefers this to steak; because a man is observed going to the opera with his wife, dare we conclude that he necessarily is an operaphile? Another major disadvantage of the observation method is its impracticality for many problems: the use of a product in the home can seldom be observed; in other situations, the observer may spend much time waiting to observe a consumer performing the act.

Survey. The survey method is most widely used for collecting primary data, despite the often considerable expense and time required. Surveys may be conducted by personal interview, by telephone, and by mail. There are inherent advantages and limitations in each of these methods. The primary advantage of the survey is that preferences, opinions, and buying intentions may be measured. However, underlying motives may not be revealed by direct questioning, and motivation research techniques (which are a form of survey) may need to be used.

Personal interviews often are the most practical of the three survey methods, although they tend to be relatively costly, require more planning and supervision, and may introduce bias in the interviewing process. Control sometimes can be a problem with a large survey and a resulting large number of interviewers: Are they following instructions carefully? Are they faking any interviews? If a large national sample is required, interviewing may become impractical, but it is possible to obtain more information by personal interview than by phone or mail, and the problem of nonrespondents—which plagues mail surveys—can be virtually eliminated.

A *telephone survey* can usually be conducted more rapidly and at less cost than either personal interviews or mail surveys, and wide geographical areas can be covered without the time and cost requirements of personal interviews. However, conversations must be short if people are to cooperate, and certain socioeconomic groups are not covered: the lower social groups who probably do not have phones, and the upper who may have unlisted numbers. Telephone surveys are commonly used to ask people whether they are watching television and whether they can name the program and sponsor.

A *mail survey* costs less than personal interviewing and is particularly well adapted to large national surveys. Since the questionnaires are sent out and returned by mail, there is no problem with interviewer supervision and bias. However, compiling a mailing list may present difficulties, and the questionnaire usually must be quite short and simple to understand, if a good return rate is to be achieved. Considerable time needs to be allowed for the returns to come in; frequently it is necessary to send one or more requests and reminders to encourage a greater return.

A low return rate characterizes most mail surveys; the percentage of nonrespondents on a questionnaire mailed to the general public may be as high as 90 percent, and sometimes even higher. In the *Literary Digest* poll, the nonrespondents were a little less than 80 percent of the total sample, and undoubtedly contributed to the erroneous results. It is generally true that those not responding have different characteristics than those who do respond. For example, the lower-income groups are less likely to respond than the middle classes, and people who are more interested or have stronger feelings or preferences about the subject under study will respond more readily. Hence, it is seldom advisable to consider those replying as representative of the entire sample and to extrapolate this data to the population, unless some follow-up work—such as telephone or personal interviews with a sample of nonrespondents—is done to assure that any differences are not substantial.

**MARKETING
RESEARCH
IN
ACTION**

A "Goof"
A massive traffic jam during the morning rush hours developed on the outskirts of Washington, D.C., when the Virginia Department of Highways stopped thousands of motorists for a traffic survey. Hundreds of persons were made late for work. The survey was designed to show how traffic would be affected if the Interstate were extended. It began at 6 A.M. with 27 highway department interviewers and two state troopers stationed at the Interstate exit to the Beltway. Five questions were to be asked under the original plans for the survey; these would take about 30 seconds and the complete survey was to run for 12 hours.

But by 7:30 A.M. plans had gone awry as the traffic backed up 6 miles and numerous cars had pulled off the road with overheated engines or empty gas tanks, and state troopers were being cursed and jeered.

"We just goofed with this survey," said the state highway commissioner. "We didn't foresee the problems that could be caused by the crush of 50,000 cars."

SOURCE: "I-66 'Survey' Causes Huge Traffic Jam," *Washington Post*, May 17, 1972, p. B7.

For thought and discussion:
How would you plan such a survey to prevent similar problems?

Experimentation. An interest in more sophisticated analysis of marketing problems has encouraged the use of experimentation. Survey conditions may be manipulated in an effort to measure the influence or impact of certain controllable factors. For example, in a common experimental design, a group of consumers may be surveyed for product preferences *before* and *after* an advertising campaign in an attempt to determine its effectiveness; in order to isolate the effect of the advertising, another group of consumers, carefully chosen to be as similar as possible to the first or experimental group, would act as a control group and not be exposed to the advertising. By trying to hold all the factors except one—the experimental variable which in this instance is the advertising—as nearly constant as possible, a measurement can be made of the effect of that variable.

Experimental designs can be used for measuring the effects of alternative courses of action for a variety of marketing problems in all functional areas, from product policies, to promotion, pricing, and distribution decisions. Some representative questions that can be answered by experimentation are:[3]

> Can we increase profits by servicing small accounts by mail rather than from branch stores?
>
> Does the number of times that a salesman calls on a particular account in a given time period affect the size of the order obtained from that account?
>
> Is a given newspaper advertisement more effective in color than in black and white?
>
> Which of several promotional techniques is most effective in selling a certain product?

Test markets, described in chapter 7, are a common area for experimental methods. In spite of their limitations and problems, test markets can provide one of the best measures of new inputs into product or marketing efforts.

---

[3] Keith K. Cox and Ben M. Enis, *Experimentation for Marketing Decisions* (Scranton, Pa.: International Textbook, 1969), p. 4.

**MARKETING
IN
ACTION**

**Example of Marketing Experimentation—Ascertaining Effect
of Flavor Change by Test Marketing**

Two test markets in cities similar in size and population characteristics—were set up for this experiment. A flavor change for a new soup is to be tested. If the flavor change has a positive effect in sales, it will be instituted nationwide. The schema for the experiment is as follows:

	1st month's sales *before* flavor change	2nd month's sales *after* flavor change
Experimental city	X_1	X_2
	1st month's sales, *no* flavor change	2nd month's sales, *no* flavor change
Control city	Y_1	Y_2

Formula for effect of experimental input: $(X_2 - X_1) - (Y_2 - Y_1)$

Results were:
$$X_1 = 1500 \text{ units} \qquad X_2 = 2200 \text{ units}$$
$$Y_1 = 1350 \text{ units} \qquad Y_2 = 1550 \text{ units}$$

Therefore, the effect of the
flavor change is: $(2200 - 1500) - (1550 - 1350)$
$$= 700 - 200$$
$$= 500 \text{ unit increase in sales from the}$$
flavor change.

Consequently, the decision is made to make the flavor change.

For thought and discussion:
What contaminating factors, if any, can you see in such an experiment?

In order to control certain variables better, as well as to shed light on specific aspects of consumer behavior and reactions, laboratory methods are sometimes used. In the laboratory, the reactions of subjects can be observed when environmental conditions are changed. In this type of data collection, subjects—usually groups of people rather than separate individuals—are interviewed or examined in a central meeting place.

There are two broad types of laboratory methods. In a common form, information is obtained on consumer attitudes or reactions (to products, advertising, etc.) by direct questioning, perhaps followed by group discussion. This is commonly known as a *consumer jury* or *clinic*. A fairly recent development is the experimental *game*, which attempts to simulate in the "laboratory" some aspect of consumer behavior. This is isolated and subject response observed— e.g., the tendency of people to gamble, to shop around before making a decision, or their reaction to certain prices. Because the environment is artificial and differs from the real-life situation, questions can be raised as to the reliability of such studies.

It is beyond the scope of this book to present a detailed discussion of this very complex aspect of marketing research.[4] The intriguing potential of marketing experiments in understanding causal relationships should make them more widely used in the future and should add measurably to the efficiency of marketing. To date, however, their use has been limited, due primarily to the time and cost involved. The demands for fast research results—at the price of jeopardizing the effectiveness of the research—is one of the burdens that research directors frequently face.

[4] For more depth and a more technical discussion, see R. A. Fisher, *The Design of Experiments*, 2d ed. (New York: Hafner, 1960); and Seymour Banks, *Experimentation in Marketing* (New York: McGraw-Hill, 1965).

Attitudinal Research

Both in business and in various aspects of social and political research, a determination of attitudes is frequently desirable. How a person feels about a particular thing or person can affect product and brand sales, the success of a bond issue, or the election of a political candidate.

The eminent social psychologist L. L. Thurstone has described an attitude as the degree of positive or negative affect associated with some psychological object.[5] ("Affect" is the same as "feeling" in psychological literature. A psychological object can be a particular job, food, symbol or phrase, slogan, person, institution, product, company, brand, idea—almost anything, tangible or intangible.) Collectively, attitudes may be defined as "dispositions to react to objects on various occasions with signs of like or dislike."[6] The marketing significance of attitudes is that they represent latent behavior, which presumably translates into product and brand preference and sales.

How are these attitudes determined? A simple method would seem to be direct *questioning*—asking the person how he or she feels about a particular object. However, there are certain disadvantages to direct questioning. Some people may be reluctant to give public expression to their feelings. This is especially true with controversial issues where the true answer might be embarrassing and where status or prestige may be involved. True feelings or attitudes may also be distorted where the interviewee feels pressure to conform.

Empirical evidence of the biasing effect of perceived pressure of the interviewee was obtained by researcher Allen Edwards. Shortly after the Korean War, college students interviewed residents of Seattle about their attitudes toward a proposed state legislative bill to provide a cash bonus to war veterans. Half the interviewees were directly asked for their attitudes and the other half were given secret ballots. It was found that many more "don't know" responses were obtained by direct questioning; the proportion of unfavorable responses was much higher in the secret ballot. Some weeks later at the election, votes closely paralleled the results obtained from the secret ballot. Apparently most of the interviewers were veterans or of an age to be; respondents with unfavorable attitudes were reluctant to express these attitudes openly.[7]

Sometimes persons may not really be aware of their feelings. Clinical psychologists often find that people who express great dis-

---

[5] L. L. Thurstone, "Comment," *American Journal of Sociology*, No. 52, 1946, pp. 39–50.

[6] Gunnar Sandell, "Effects of Attitudinal and Situational Factors on Reported Choice Behavior," *Journal of Marketing Research*, November 1968, p. 405.

[7] Allen L. Edwards, *Techniques of Attitude Scale Construction* (New York: Appleton, 1957), pp. 3–4.

like for something may be reacting against unconscious impulses of the opposite nature. Also, many feelings may be mixed and confused —we are not really sure how we feel on balance, since both positive and negative feelings are associated with some psychological objects. More evaluation may well be needed before we can reply on the spur of the moment to an interviewer's question.

Therefore, while direct questioning would seem the most practical way to elicit attitudinal information, sometimes it may yield inaccurate results. Another method of obtaining such information is by *direct observation of behavior.* This also, at first glimmer, would seem an effective way of obtaining attitudinal feedback: a person's behavior, especially toward some object, one might think would reflect his feelings, at least to the perceptive observer. But as we noted earlier in this chapter, there is no necessary one-to-one relationship between overt behavior and internal attitude. A few examples will confirm this:

A man may dislike his job, but go to work every day.

A person may buy the local newspaper because it has good stock market news, even though he detests the editorial policy.

The thousands of commuters who ride the New Haven Railroad into Manhattan every day scarcely imply from their behavior that they are favorably disposed toward the railroad: indeed, most are thoroughly disgusted with dirty cars, unreliable service, and general inefficiency and lack of customer concern.

If attitude determination is to be most effective—and especially if it is to permit assessing attitudinal relationships among persons and objects—it is important to know the degree or intensity of positive or negative affect: for example, whether a sufficient number of people are barely favorable or strongly favorable toward a particular brand or company. Direct questioning and observation give only crude classifications, often little more than "favorable," "unfavorable," and "undecided."

In order to measure the degree of affect, rather sophisticated attitude scales have been developed. From replies to a series of questions or statements, a score can be computed that is taken to indicate a person's position on a scale of favorable or unfavorable attitudes toward the particular object. The major attitude scales are Thurstone's paired comparisons, equal-appearing intervals, and successive intervals, Likert's summated scale, the Guttman cumulative scale, the Shephenson Q-sort and the semantic differential.[8]

With the exception of the semantic differential, most of these are rather difficult to construct and administer and have been used

[8] See Edwards for a detailed discussion of all but the last two scales; for a less detailed but perhaps better perspective of attitude scaling, see Claire Selltiz, Marie Jahoda, Morton Deutsch, and Stuart W. Cook, *Research Methods in Social Relations,* rev. ed. (New York: Holt, 1962), Chap. 10.

more in social or personality research than in business research. The semantic differential, on the other hand, is well adapted to marketing research, especially for image studies, and deserves a more complete examination.

Charles Osgood and his associates developed the *semantic differential* to measure the meaning that a concept—perhaps a political issue, a person, a work of art, or in marketing, a brand, product, or company—might have for people in terms of various dimensions.[9] As originally developed, the instrument consisted of pairs of polar adjectives with a seven-interval scale separating the opposite members of each pair. For example:

good ___: ___: ___: ___: ___: ___: ___: bad

The various intervals from left to right would then represent degrees of feeling or belief ranging from extremely good to neither good nor bad, to extremely bad.

The instrument has been refined to obtain greater sensitivity through the use of descriptive phrases. Examples of such bipolar phrases for determining the image of a particular brand of beer are:[10]

Something special	___: ___: ___: ___: ___: ___: ___:	Just another drink
American flavor	___: ___: ___: ___: ___: ___: ___:	Foreign flavor
Really peps you up	___: ___: ___: ___: ___: ___: ___:	Somehow doesn't pep you up

The number of word pairs can vary from the classic list of 50 that were factor-analyzed by Osgood. Flexibility and appropriateness to a particular study may better be achieved by constructing tailor-made word and phrase lists. It is generally agreed that respondents should be encouraged to check their answers quickly, to give "top-of-mind" responses. Therefore, the use of the differential in mail questionnaires where respondents have more time to deliberate over judgments may not give the general image information desired.[11]

As with all attitude detection methods, there are cerain *limitations to attitude scales*. A "halo" effect may prevent the sensitive discrimination of various attributes that the instrument is attempting to measure: a respondent with a strongly positive or negative attitude will tend to project this feeling to all the attributes covered by

[9] Charles E. Osgood, George J. Suci, and Percy H. Tannenbaum, *The Measurement of Meaning* (Urbana, Ill.: University of Illinois Press, 1957).

[10] William A. Mindak, "Fitting the Semantic Differential to the Marketing Problem," *Journal of Marketing*, April 1961, pp. 28–33.

[11] Ibid.

the instrument, thereby biasing it. Small differences in attitudes are not likely to be distinguished. Furthermore, there is always some discrepancy between expressed attitudes and behavior, while the transitory nature of some attitudes raises reliability problems.

**MARKETING
TOOL**

Using the Semantic Differential
A major use of the semantic differential has been to compare images of particular products and brands against competing ones. The average of the checks of all respondents can be plotted to provide a "profile" for each brand, as shown below for three competing beers.

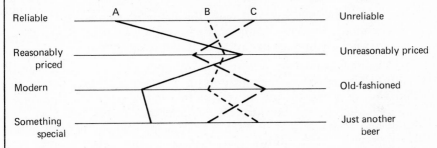

In this profile, Brand A shows the dominant image over its competing brands in three of the four categories; however, the negative reaction to its price should alert the company to reviewing pricing practices. Brand C shows a negative image especially as to the reliability of its product; the old-fashioned image may or may not be desirable, depending on the type of consumer being sought—at least it indicates that Brand C is perceived as being distinctive from the other two brands. Probably the weakest image of all is that of Brand B: the respondents viewed this as having no distinctive image, neither good nor bad. A serious image-building campaign is desperately needed if Brand B is to compete successfully; otherwise the price may have to be dropped to gain some advantage.

For thought and discussion:
How would you attempt to build up the image of Brand B?
What difficulties would you anticipate?

Attitude scales have been designed to measure the intensity of feeling, but another dimension—and potentially one of the most significant for marketing and advertising—has received little attention: modifiability.

If an attitude is intense, can it be abated, or redirected? Can incipient attitudes be accelerated and intensified? Can indifference be converted to pro-ness? Can an attitude toward established brand be weakened by a competitor?[12]

Despite the imperfections, however, attitude-scaling techniques such as the semantic differential offer the most fruitful means heretofore developed to obtain insight into the minds of consumers.

Motivation Research

Motivation research concentrates on emotional or "hidden" stimuli to consumer action. It is sometimes used to determine the "why" of behavior, for example, *why* consumers buy one brand or product instead of another. It may be designated as "qualitative research" since it is not concerned with developing quantitative data. It may be defined as:

> a set of tools, borrowed from the fields of psychology and sociology, to uncover and evaluate the motives or drives that are back of human behavior in the consumer market.[13]

The techniques of motivation research are many and varied. Depth interviews are frequently used. These are probing interviews that can be given to individuals or to small groups. In their more sophisticated form, they are best conducted by trained psychologists, and frequently take an hour or more. Projective techniques, such as word associations, sentence completion, story completion, pictorial techniques generally or the Thematic Apperception Test, are most frequently used.

Motivation research reached its height of popularity in the latter 1950s and early 1960s. The approach ran counter to the sampling techniques that had become popular in marketing and much social and political research, since large numbers of respondents were considered unnecessary and could not be handled in any practical fashion by motivation research. Often respondents were chosen without any regard for sampling requirements, and some analyses of results tended to assume too much cultural and social homogeneity.

Sometimes surprising interpretations resulted. That motivation researchers often disagreed was confounding, and cast doubts on some types and uses of motivation research. One of the better known examples of contradictory interpretations concerns research into the product image of California prunes. One motivation research organization, on the basis of its interpretation of 200 depth interviews, reported that the problem with prunes was, in effect, that they were

---

[12] Leslie A. Beldo, "Introduction to Attitude Research and Management Decisions," in James U. McNeal (ed.), *Dimensions of Consumer Behavior* (New York: Appleton, 1969), p. 368.

[13] From a talk, "Rationality and Irrationality in Motivational Research," by L. Edward Scriven, given to the Washington, D.C., chapter of the AMA, June 23, 1955. Reprinted in Robert Ferber and Hugh G. Wales, eds., *Motivation and Market Behavior* (Homewood, Ill.: Irwin, 1958), p. 65.

"a food with a purpose" (in part, laxative), and needed to be glamorized. Another motivation research organization, on the basis of word association tests, reported that the wise course would be to stress the laxative theme openly because this would release inhibitions that kept more people from eating prunes.[14]

Some conclusions of motivation researchers have been so fanciful as to trouble practical marketers. For example, motivation researchers have "found" that

> The origin of some "common colds" is the need for attention and the loss of security; bargain hunting is the need to outsmart others and to express aggression toward a substitute of the bad, refusing mother. . . . [15]

However, motivation research has revealed some interesting findings that probably could not have been gained in any other way. A classic study was Mason Haire's investigation into the attitudes of housewives toward instant coffee. Although the study is over twenty years old, it is one of the most quoted pieces of research in marketing; its design and the significance of the results are still worth examining.

It is well known that underlying attitudes sometimes distort the information a person supplies. This was suspected when a conventional survey was made concerning attitudes toward Nescafé, an instant coffee. The bulk of the complaints pertained to the flavor. Yet in blindfold tests, many of the same housewives could not distinguish between real coffee and instant coffee flavor, which suggested psychological resistance. An indirect approach (motivation research) was then used. Two shopping lists were prepared:

Shopping list No. 1	**Shopping list No. 2**
1½ lbs. of hamburger	1½ lbs. of hamburger
2 loaves Wonder bread	2 loaves Wonder bread
Bunch of carrots	Bunch of carrots
1 can Rumford's Baking Powder	1 can Rumford's Baking Powder
Nescafé instant coffee	1 lb Maxwell House Coffee (drip grind)
2 cans Del Monte peaches	2 cans Del Monte peaches
5 lbs. potatoes	5 lbs. potatoes

As can be seen, the shopping lists were identical in all respects, except that one specified Nescafé and the other Maxwell House Coffee; each was given to a different but comparable group. Both groups were asked to guess the social and personal characteristics

[14] Reported in Chester R. Wasson, *The Strategy of Marketing Research* (New York: Appleton, 1964), p. 72.

[15] These and other examples are presented in George Morsley Smith, *Motivation Research in Advertising and Marketing* (New York: McGraw-Hill, 1954), p. 21.

of the woman whose shopping list they saw. Here are the main characteristics of their descriptions.

1. 48 percent of the people described the woman who bought
   Nescafé as lazy; 4 percent described the Maxwell House
   buyer as lazy.
2. 48 percent described the woman who bought Nescafé as
   failing to plan household purchases and schedules well;
   12 percent so described the woman who bought Maxwell
   House.
3. 16 percent described the Nescafé woman as not a good wife;
   0 percent so described the Maxwell House woman.

Obviously the participants were imputing to the fictional housewife
their own anxieties and negative images about instant coffee. And
the company knew the nature of the resistance to its product and
could plan a campaign to change this negative image.[16]

A recent replication of the 1950 "shopping list" study found that
convenience foods in general as characterized by instant coffee no
longer arouse the former negative reactions: no significant differences were found between characteristics ascribed to Maxwell
House shoppers and Nescafé shoppers in this 1968 study.[17] Convenience goods—"boil in the bag" frozen foods, baking mixes, etc.—are
accepted today; instant coffee sales have likewise increased from
less than 20 percent of total coffee sales in 1955 to over 30 percent
in 1965.[18]

OPERATIONS RESEARCH AND MARKETING MODELS

Operations research, or management science, is the application of
scientific methodology and quantitative techniques to business and
other operating problems. Operations research (OR) was first used
for military bombing and supply problems during World War II. As
it spread, some thought it represented the answer to all business
problems, and most other problems as well.

Operations researchers frequently use models—usually mathematical models—in their analyses. Now a model essentially is a representation of some part of the real world. It can be as simple as a

[16] Mason Haire, "Projective Techniques in Marketing Research," *Journal of Marketing*, April 1950, pp. 649–56.

[17] Frederick E. Webster, Jr. and Frederick Von Pechmann, "A Replication of the
'Shopping List' Study," *Journal of Marketing*, April 1970, pp. 61–63. Another
study a few years later confirmed the change in negative attitudes toward instant
coffee: Johan Arndt, "Haire's Shopping List Revisited," *Journal of Advertising
Research*, October 1973, pp. 25–32.

[18] Ibid., p. 61.

$$Z_i = b_p \frac{P_i}{\Sigma P_i} + b_d \frac{D_i}{\Sigma D_i} + b_a \frac{A_i}{\Sigma A_i} + b_{pd} \frac{(PD)_i}{\Sigma (PD)_i} + b_{pa} \frac{(PA)_i}{\Sigma (PA)_i}$$

$$+ \; b_{da} \frac{(DA)_i}{\Sigma (DA)_i} + b_{pda} \frac{(PDA)_i}{\Sigma (PDA)_i}$$

where Z_i = fraction of potential brand shifters attracted as a result of merchandising

P_i = share of shifters attracted by brand i if price and product were the only merchandising variables; D_i and A_i are defined similarly for distribution and advertising respectively

$(PD)_i$ = the share of shifters attracted by i if the joint effect of price, product, and distribution were the only variables. The other interactions are similarly defined

b's = weighting factors, ranging from 0 to 1, for the importance of each single variable or variable interaction

Figure 8-1. Model of Brand Shifting
Source: John U. Farley and Alfred A. Kuehn, "Stochastic Models of Brand Switching," in George Schwartz, ed., *Science in Marketing* (New York: Wiley, 1965), p. 460.

company's organization chart depicting the formal authority relationships. But the model for some marketing processes can be exceedingly complex, and still express many of the variables and relationships imperfectly. Figure 8-1 is an example of such a complex model that is still too deficient to be practical.

Operations research, despite its appeal for systematizing and making use of concrete and quantitative analyses for problem solving, and despite its unassailable potential, has had relatively limited application to most marketing problems and decisions. But before we examine its limitations for certain marketing problems, let us see where it has been of value—for what types of decisions?

Operations research had its origins in engineering, and most efforts have been applied to production processes as well as to the mechanical aspects of such nonbusiness activities as military operations and traffic control. In marketing it has been well adopted for decisions involving the physical handling of merchandise. Some adaptations of OR are as follows.

Linear programming, indicating that the mathematical models used involve only linear equations (less complex than curvilinear), has been used to determine location of branch warehouses, the optimum number of salesmen to cover a territory, and the deployment of salespeople within a store.

Queuing theory—which applies the laws of probability to the normal processes of arrival and departure—can be used to optimize facilities as at a cafeteria line or an airline ticket counter or the number of checkouts in a supermarket. These types of situations have all elements of input under the control of management, and essentially the problem is one of allocation of effort among different possibilities.

When some elements are of an independent or autonomous nature—that is, not directly controllable by management—then a type of OR called *cybernetics* may be useful. This term is used to describe a control mechanism, translated into mathematical terms, which will provide feedback so that adjustment can be made in response to external conditions. (The familiar mechanical example of this is the household thermostat.) This technique has been applied to inventory problems that require that stock vary with response of information feedback from the market.

Search theory is used when the elements of the system are not identified: that is, the target needs to be found. Consumer behavior possibly could be studied by means of search theory, with emphasis on the information acquired by the shopper through repeated experience.

Game theory is an attempt to afford a more realistic interpretation of a complex environment to aid decision making. In contrast with the previous three OR applications, where elements in the systems are passive or to some extent controllable, game theory assumes an opponent, a competitor, who can act and react independently.

Simulation is used in some complex decision situations—such as allocation of marketing expenditures, or more specifically, media selection for advertising. Simulation uses a mathematical model representing some form of behavior to test cause and effect relationships. Computer simulation allows many variables to be analyzed simultaneously in an attempt to duplicate the very complex systems of interactions encountered in the real world of marketing decision making.

OR is at the present used mainly to solve relatively well defined problems such as inventory control and production scheduling. Definitive mathematical solutions have seldom proven effective given the complexities of real-world marketing situations, and many marketing problems are exceedingly complex, being composed of many dynamic interacting variables. The human element, not only consumers but distributors and competitors as well rules out the possibility of any absolute predictability.

With specific data necessary for developing solutions often unknown, it is common practice to express various probabilities in mathematical terms based on educated guesses by management: What is the likelihood that if we increase our advertising expenditures so much, our competitors will follow suit? is an example where probabilities can be assigned based on executive estimates. Unfortunately, even "educated guesses" are often in error.

Therefore, the challenges for the more effective use of the tools of OR remain. Potential applications and contributions are intriguing, and the computer with its ability to perform calculations in minutes which otherwise take man-days or weeks makes them possible, once the data and relationships can be realistically conceived.

COMPUTERS IN MARKETING

The computer can cut the time required for order-shipping-billing procedures; it can give managers daily reports of stocks and sales and can go beyond this to "inventory management" of staple goods; it can expedite sales analysis. Apart from the more strictly bookkeeping activities, it is a necessity for sophisticated mathematical models and similar OR formulations. In short, the computer has become essential to modern marketing.

Faster feedback and the great increase in the reports available to executives can make their jobs easier and their decisions better. However, the great quantity of data can also be a waste: a *Business Week* article noted with some wonderment that one department store furnished its executives each morning with an 81-page report that, for each of the company's nine stores, gave previous day's sales by store, by department, by dollar amounts, and a comparison with the previous year-to-date and the trend of sales, as well as a record of sales for selected items.[19] Useful? Perhaps. But how many busy executives have enough time to review such daily compilations? The 81-page daily report was eventually discarded in favor of more manageable data which was reported on "exceptions" only—that is, deviations of performance from plan or expectation.

Current Role of the Computer

In most businesses today, computers function as huge and very speedy bookkeepers. Provided that the "bookkeeper" can be kept virtually error-free, problems seldom arise. However, humans provide the input to these machines, and mistakes occur. The problem then is that mistakes are not always easily corrected: most of us know, either personally or from the reports of friends, of charge-account billing errors that seem nearly impossible to rectify. And most firms relying on computers to maintain inventory control find

[19] "The Computer's Newest Conquest: Marketing," *Business Week* Special Report, April 17, 1965.

that actual physical counts of goods on hand are required just as frequently as before, in order to correct errors and balance book and physical inventory figures.

The biggest contribution of the computer to date may be in what is known as *rote marketing,* or, fairly automatic decisions. Inventory systems have been particularly adaptable to this, with the computer assuming the responsibility of determining order points and issuing reorders. Some other semiroutine marketing decisions should be candidates for rote marketing via computers. Department stores can use computer programs to make ordering, pricing, and markdown decisions on some staple items and thus free buyers' time for less routine decisions; computers for manufacturers can be programmed to receive order inquiries, determine whether the orders can be filled, and schedule the delivery date or schedule production in the event of stockout.

However, these marketing applications of the computer are in the areas of order processing, billing, inventory management, and sales analysis; these are really routine and relatively simple tasks—they can be regarded as subfunctional in nature. In other words, the use of computers thus far does not always match the latest advances in technology.[20] Fuller computer utilizations give it an important role in corporate long-range strategic planning.[21] And in marketing research it can be vital for complex analyses of survey data, experimentation, and sophisticated sales forecasting.[22]

SOCIAL OBJECTIVES OF MARKETING RESEARCH

The ultimate objectives of the marketing research function may be described as follows:

1. To meet more effectively the desires of a consuming society
2. To improve marketing efficiency
3. To foster innovative thinking within the organization

In all of these areas challenges still remain for marketing research.

While consumer needs and desires have been ascertained and catered to by way of better products and services in many instances, sometimes there have been deficiencies. For example, many business firms did not anticipate the extent of consumer dissatisfaction that

---

[20] "The Dawn of the Age of Computers," *Marketing/Communications,* March 1970, pp. 47–53; Eugene J. Kelley, "From the Editor," *Journal of Marketing,* January 1971, p. 1.

[21] Kelley, "From the Editor," p. 1.

[22] For example, Jagdish N. Sheth, "Multivariate Analysis in Marketing," *Journal of Advertising Research,* February 1970, pp. 29–39; Paul E. Green, Frank J. Carmone, and Patrick J. Robinson, "Non-metric Scaling Methods," *Wharton Quarterly,* Winter-Spring 1968, pp. 159–73.

resulted in what is popularly known as consumerism. Marketing research that should have provided sensors of such dissatisfaction either failed or was ignored. *Responsive marketing* was lacking. There is need then for marketing research to provide a better feel of shifting social attitudes and desires.

While marketing research and market analyses have improved efficiency by enabling firms to cut costs and better meet customer needs, marketing operations could still be more efficient. New product failures continue to plague business and add to marketing costs. Furthermore, we know there is waste in advertising, but we have no direct way to measure the effectiveness of advertising despite 40 years of research efforts. Undoubtedly it is a tough research problem which may not be solvable. But tools and techniques for measuring advertising effectiveness have changed little in decades.

While marketing research has permitted firms to adapt better to a changing environment, its full potential to foster innovation has not always been realized. As we saw in chapter 2, major innovations have often come from smaller firms, while large firms with their marketing research departments have been the followers.

Some of you in your careers undoubtedly will be closely involved with marketing research. You may then be exposed to the intriguing challenges of developing better sensors, improving efficiency, and aiding long-range planning and innovation.

QUESTIONS AND PROBLEMS

1. A reproducible experiment is the ultimate test of scientific method. Why is it so difficult to run reproducible experiments in marketing? Does this mean that marketing research cannot be scientific?

2. Assume a particular research problem: for example, finding the type of person who buys the *Readers' Digest* at newstands. Can you describe the step-by-step process that might be used to solve this problem?

3. From the standpoint of methodology, what weaknesses, if any, do you see in the motivation research approach to the understanding of consumer behavior?

4. Evaluate the effectiveness of the following questions:
   "What beer do you usually drink?"
   "Do you have a General Motors car?"
   "How many machine tool salesmen have called on you in the last year?"
   "Do you expect to buy another house some day?"

5. What are the two major ways by which samples of human population may be selected? What is the essential difference between these two selection methods?

6. What are the limitations of operations research as applied to marketing problems?

7. Would you recommend the use of motivation research techniques in developing a new brand name? Why or why not?

8. What are the disadvantages of direct questioning to ascertain attitudes? Is observation a better method of attitude determination? Why or why not?

Project

Develop semantic differential scales for determining various dimensions of attitudes concerning the Ford Pinto, the AMC Pacer, and VW Rabbit.

Exercise in Creativity

As a marketing research consulting firm, you have been given $50,000 to do a study on the relative desirability of placing department stores in shopping centers or in free-standing sites (where no other stores are nearby). How would you design this research project?

Role-playing Case

In view of the rising operating costs of universities, an off-campus program often can play a major revenue-producing role, as well as meeting community needs. You have been asked by the president of your university to:

1. Develop a marketing research plan to determine the market potential for an off-campus university division
2. Develop a marketing research plan to aid in selecting an effective marketing strategy to increase off-campus enrollments

(We assume that any increase can be met without sacrificing quality.)

PART III

PROGRAMMING THE MARKETING STRATEGY

CHAPTER 9

PLANNING

MARKETING

EFFORTS

At this point we are ready to investigate the planning of marketing strategy. Chapter 9 will treat the over-all marketing approach; in following chapters we will look at each of the components of a marketing strategy in some detail. In addition, techniques for nonproduct marketing are examined. Important terms to be encountered are:

planning
profit maximization
market segmentation
product differentiation
remarketing

demarketing
marketing mix
corporate image
uncontrollable factors

NATURE OF PLANNING

Planning is deciding in the present what to do in the future. It involves not only anticipating the consequences of decisions, but also predicting events that may affect a business. Planning directs company efforts and resources toward common objectives. Without it, employees would be working at cross-purposes. One management text even warns that "without planning, an enterprise would soon disintegrate; its actions would be as random as leaves scampering before an autumn wind, and its employees as confused as ants in an upturned anthill."[1]

Firms vary widely in the extent and formality of planning. Some large ones have planning staffs and committees, and formal written documents; executives at all levels may be brought into the planning process, and performance may subsequently be evaluated by how well the planned objectives are met. Other firms limit planning to certain necessary budgets for financial or accounting purposes, and

[1] William H. Newman, Charles E. Summer, and E. Kirby Warren, *The Process of Management,* 2d ed. (Englewood Cliffs, N. J.: Prentice-Hall, 1967), p. 308.

managements give little heed to other than day-to-day problems and decisions. In this latter situation, many important decisions become "decisions by crisis," with little planning or anticipation. The ultimate in efficient and coordinated operation due to planning is the auto assembly line: every part and subassembly component converges from various overhead conveyor systems exactly at the right time to produce the car of the appointed color, styling, model, and optional features.

However, even careful planning does not guarantee a successful operation. Anticipating changes in consumer tastes, in technology, in the economy, in reactions of competitors, suppliers, channel members—these are not easy to predict. And even extensive planning cannot eliminate errors and miscalculations. For example, witness the ill-fated Edsel.

MARKETING
MISTAKE

The Edsel—Marketing Planning Gone Wrong
The Edsel was perhaps the most publicized new-product failure in business history. It was brought out in the late 1950s with a carefully designed and detailed plan, with great expenditures for marketing research, and massive injection of advertising. Yet it failed, and thereby cast a pall over the whole process of marketing planning and strenuous marketing efforts. Monday-morning quarterbacks did a lot of second-guessing, and after-the-fact judging, but it had been carefully researched.

Market research studies by our company on the Edsel have covered a period of almost 10 years. These studies concerned owner likes and dislikes, product identification and "imagery"—the pictures in people's minds of the kind of car they would like, the reason for the Edsel, and many market and sales studies.[a]

The decision to introduce the Edsel seemed wise then, with sales trends in the middle 1950s showing an increasing popularity of medium-priced cars. Ford cars were doing well in the lower-priced category, but there was a definite need for a model to compete with the Pontiac, Oldsmobile, and Buick group in the medium-price category to which low-price car buyers tended to move when they became more affluent. With the trend in consumer income definitely up and forecasts predicting continuation and acceleration of consumer disposable income, the decision seemed clear cut for Ford to go with the new Edsel and gain a share of the market.

Edsel styling began in 1954, and over 800 stylists agreed on the final concept after screening hundreds of sketches and ideas—eighteen models and four series were to be featured. Ford invested $250 million in the Edsel before a single car rolled off the production lines—". . . men in the company have matched the size of this risk with massive effort, in an attempt to reduce the margin of error in advance. We have studied and rehashed some 4,000 separate decisions, from the pros and cons of hubcap styling to the basic question—why build an Edsel at all?"[b] Edsel Division was established with its own personnel and executives. Also a separate dealer organization was set up and some 1,500 dealerships were established after screening from almost 5,000 inquiries for dealer franchises.

Extensive planning went into the public relations build-up of the car, into the determination of sales and marketing objectives, into the selection of an advertising agency and the development of detailed advertising plans. Dealers were not forgotten as special training and management aids were devised and emphasis directed toward their profitable operation.

The first Edsel came out in September 1957. Within a month, the lack of sales success became apparent, and finally in November 1959, little more than two years after its introduction, the Edsel was discontinued.

Some of the very decisions that in the planning stage had seemed wise and aggressive, in hindsight proved to be grievous errors. The expansion into a separate Edsel Division spread management too thin and greatly increased costs. The establishment of a separate dealership for the Edsel brought too many inexperienced, underfinanced dealers who did not do as well as the veteran Ford and Mercury dealers might have done. The wide array of models contributed to a multitude of "bugs" and before quality control could be established a damaging reputation was gained that was not to be shaken. The enormous publicity that preceded and accompanied the introduction of the Edsel may actually have raised consumer expectations so high that they could not possibly be satisfied. Despite the 800 stylists and designers who searched for ways to make the car different and distinctive, the front grill became a peculiarity and target for ridicule.

A new trend in consumer taste had begun by 1958, away from flashy big cars to economy cars and compacts. Despite extensive marketing research, this change had gone unnoticed by the Ford and Edsel planners who had done most of their consumer research seven years before and ignored the possibilities of dynamics in the marketplace. Of course, a recession in 1958 that made this a bad year for all cars did not help. And finally the Edsel name, confirmed by marketing research but really catering to management's preferences and not those of the public, proved colorless and unglamorous.

SOURCE:[a] Henry G. Baker, "Sales and Marketing Planning of the Edsel," *Marketing's Role in Scientific Management.* Proceedings of the 39th National Conference of the American Marketing Association, June 1957, p. 128.[b] Ibid., p. 131.

For thought and discussion:
Does this example refute the desirability of extensive planning?

How would you have planned marketing research for a better job of estimating consumer wants?

Marketing planning calls for establishing objectives or goals, formulating strategies, and developing specific programs to carry them out. The goal of a business firm may seem obvious at first: to make a profit. But this is an oversimplification; it is hardly specific enough to aid planning.

Firms usually have multiple goals, although in many firms—especially smaller ones—these may be implicit or ill defined. But there are important benefits in having goals and objectives explicitly stated and in the order of priority, since some may be conflicting. In addition, goals should be well communicated so that there can be consistency in decision making.

A detailed listing of business goals finds them surprisingly numerous. Following are typical ones:

Growth of the firm, of a division, a product line, a product
Short-term profit maximization
Profit maximization over the long run
Service to the country, society, the common good
Service to customers
Enlargement of size of market
Maintenance or increase in share of market
Establishment of an image for the firm, division, or product
Diversification of corporate activity
Achievement of industry leadership
Development of reputation and stature of management
Employee welfare and satisfactions
Securing a balance between government and domestic business
Securing a balance between domestic and foreign business
Making the firm a satisfying one for employees and managers
Maintaining employment at certain levels in particular plants
Minimizing risk of government antitrust enforcement activities[2]

Survival, minimizing risks, and maintaining the status quo are other company objectives seldom publicly stated.

Profit Maximization

Profit maximization is commonly accepted as the dominant business goal. This philosophy dates back to Adam Smith, who believed that the pursuit of maximum profits would automatically attract capital into useful areas and thereby lead to a high rate of growth and efficient allocation of resources. But the question can be raised in

---

[2] Eugene J. Kelley, "Ethics and Science in Marketing," in Eugene J. Kelley and William Lazer, eds. *Managerial Marketing*, 3d ed. (Homewood, Ill.: Irwin, 1967), p. 86.

today's society: Should business reevaluate its traditional emphasis on profit maximization?

Some firms do not really practice profit maximization. Automobile manufacturers at the end of World War II did not charge all they could have—all the market would bear—for the first cars produced in five years; on the contrary, their pricing structure during a period of unsatiated demand and limited supply was geared to moderate profits. Firms show increasing concern for investing in corporate-image advertising, for supporting community charities, for hiring and training—often at considerable expense—members of minority groups. Water and air pollution also are being attacked by some firms voluntarily. Perhaps "profit maximization" needs to be more clearly defined.

Short-run profit maximization would hardly be compatible with the above examples of corporate practice, but long-run profit maximization may be (and as we noted in an earlier chapter, this is compatible with responsive marketing). Today, government regulation and social issues have had an effect on profit maximization. For example, if business does not reduce pollution voluntarily, it will eventually be forced to do so. Similar reasoning can account for efforts to train minority group members: they may help alleviate social unrest. But how can the long-run profit maximization of such social services ever be determined? The concept of profit maximization is changing even in the eyes of the executives who presumably advocate and practice it.

Herbert Simon suggests that management today tries to "satisfice" rather than maximize profits.[3] That is, management pursues a goal of acceptable or satisfactory profits and turns away from the quest to maximize.

Viability of Growth (at Any Cost) and Status Quo Philosophies

Some firms see growth as the top-priority company goal. They eagerly seek acquisitions, whether or not compatible with existing operations and company talent. Eventually the realization may come that profits are adversely affected (or suboptimized). Greater market share and sales can be obtained by prodigious expenditures for advertising, but the costs involved may make for less efficiency and higher marketing costs. Sometimes too vigorous a pursuit of growth may jeopardize the survival of a company:

> The W. T. Grant Co. in the late 1960s and early 1970s
> embarked on an ambitious program to increase its number of
> stores and hence its sales. But it found that many were badly

[3] Herbert A. Simon, "Theories of Decision Making in Economics and Behavioral Science," *American Economic Review,* June 1959, pp. 253–83.

located, were staffed by unseasoned managers, and were resulting in an intolerable financial drain. In 1974, the $1.7 billion company lost $175 million, and 126 stores were closed in order to cut costs [and in 1975 it filed for bankruptcy].[4]

The opposite extreme to the "growth at any cost" philosophy is the attempt to maintain the status quo—in a rapidly changing world. This describes some family-owned businesses. And how tenable is this as a management philosophy? Although at first glance it might appear workable, such a business usually fails; it must go forward in order not to fall backward.

A firm that is obviously not growth-oriented loses its ability to attract able people. It will not be as attractive to customers and suppliers as a growing firm. Customers see the growth-oriented firm as viable and reliable and offering the most wanted products, as well as being eager to please. Suppliers tend to give favorable treatment to such a firm, since they hope to retain it as a customer when it reaches larger size. Many discount chains, during the period of rapid expansion of discounting, found manufacturers eager to do business with them instead of former customers, the conventional retailers, because of the opportunities inherent in their growth.

We may conclude that a firm's objectives might best be directed neither to the extreme of growth at any cost, nor to maintaining the status quo. Both are fraught with danger and threaten the viability of the firm.

MARKETING STRATEGIES: SEGMENTATION AND DIFFERENTIATION

Planning marketing strategy calls for determining the over-all design or program for achieving objectives; this can be for a company, a division, or perhaps for a product or product line. Two general marketing-strategy alternatives are available: *Market segmentation* pinpoints certain target markets and then tailors the product and marketing efforts to these groups or segments. *Product differentiation* stresses product differences even though the product may be similar to competitors', and it is geared to a broad sector of the market.

These two strategies require different allocations of promotional efforts, channel selection, and other inputs as we will examine in more detail.

Market Segmentation

For many products it is best not to consider the total market as homogeneous. Rather, it should be viewed as composed of many

---

[4] "How W. T. Grant Lost $175-Million Last Year," *Business Week,* February 24, 1975, pp. 74–76.

small homogeneous markets reflecting different wants, motivations, buying power, and other characteristics—the result is differing product preferences among important market segments. If the segments have been carefully chosen, and the product and marketing efforts well tailored to their requirements, then greater customer satisfaction will probably be obtained.

Segments can be large or small. The ghetto market, the teenage market, and the rural market are examples of huge segments that share certain features but also exhibit enough differences so that a finer segmenting or defining may be desirable, depending on the product. Sometimes a target segment may not be as large as expected, and a product specifically designed for it may fail. Rheingold discovered this when it introduced and heavily promoted no-carbohydrate Gablinger Beer, aimed at the diet-conscious beer market: the result was a $6 million loss.[5] More recently, however, other similar products have been introduced, such as Miller's Lite beer. Perhaps this market segment is growing, and Rheingold's problem was one of timing.

Segmentation Methods. The market can be divided in many ways. Geographic segmentation was first used, and a firm might market its goods first locally, then regionally, and eventually nationally. At this point, demographic segmentation might come into play, and targets would be defined as families with children, men, homeowners, etc. Recently, buyer behavior patterns—such as usage rate, brand loyalty, and price sensitivity—and various psychological and motivational variables have been added to the basic geographic and demographic bases of segmentation.

Following are segmentation possibilities:

Geographic
- region
- climate
- rural or urban
- city size
- density of population

Buying Behavior
- usage rate
- channel loyalty
- brand loyalty
- price sensitivity
- advertising sensitivity
- quality sensitivity
- service sensitivity
- buyer motive

Socioeconomic (demographic)
- age
- sex
- marital status
- family size
- education
- income
- occupation
- family life cycle
- religion
- race
- social class
- housing
- ethnic origin

[5] "Cold Drafts," *Barron's,* July 13, 1970, p, 18.

Psychological and Motivational (psychographic)

self-confidence	autonomy
leadership	gregariousness
compulsiveness	maturity
self-indulgence	ambitiousness
	adventuresomeness
	conservatism

Geographic and demographic characteristics are often readily measurable. Furthermore, many specialized media are available that enable a marketer to zero in on those consumers with the desired characteristics. For example, *Seventeen* magazine reaches teenage girls with little wasted coverage; the *MBA* magazine reaches the young executive market.

Psychological and motivational variables have not proved practical for segmentation since there is no easy way to identify individuals with these particular personality traits (after all, a marketer can hardly give many consumers a battery of psychological tests). Even if they could be identified, it is seldom practical to direct product and promotional efforts to the compulsive, or the self-indulgent consumer, for example, without unacceptable waste coverage.

Advances have been made, however, in the use of multivariate analysis to identify segments on the basis of certain psychological, attitudinal, and behavioral dimensions. This has popularly been termed *psychographic research,* and has often involved questionnaires designed to test a person's self-image. The assumption is that a person's self-concept is likely to be a major factor in buying behavior, and so promotional efforts, package design, and product features can be directed accordingly.[6]

Such aspects of buying behavior as usage rate, sensitivity to low prices, and brand and store loyalty are also difficult to use as bases for segmentation because it is so hard to identify the proper people through regular promotional media.

Designing the Segmentation Strategy. If a segmentation strategy is to be effective, three conditions should be present:

1. The segment to be appealed to must be *identifiable.*
2. It must be *sufficiently large* so as to be worth the marketing efforts directed to it.
3. It must be *reachable* with available promotional media

---

[6] For example, Robert P. Brody and Scott M. Cunningham, "Personality Variables and the Consumer Decision Process," *Journal of Marketing Research,* February 1968, pp. 50–57; and Jagdish N. Sheth and J. Scott Armstrong, "Factor Analysis of Marketing Data: A Critical Evaluation," in Philip R. McDonald, ed., *Marketing Involvement in Society and the Economy* (Chicago: American Marketing Association, 1969), pp. 137–44. Also related to this is Joseph T. Plummer, "The Concept and Application of Life Style Segmentation," *Journal of Marketing,* January 1974, pp. 33–37.

so that waste coverage (that is, people who do not represent potential customers) will be minimized.[7]

Once a firm has determined the characteristics of those consumers likely to be good target segments for its products, it becomes desirable to ascertain their geographical concentration. Zip codes developed to expedite mail handling provide an important tool both for identifying and for reaching certain consumer segments.

**MARKETING
TOOL**

Zip Codes: Aids in Segmenting

People with similar characteristics—of income, education, occupation, social class, family size—tend to cluster together. Because of this, zip codes developed by the U. S. Postal Service to speed up mail delivery can also be a valuable marketing tool. Some 35,000 geographic areas are designated by zip codes—in reality, these are small, relatively homogeneous sectors of consumers. Both the Internal Revenue Service and the Census Bureau provide statistics on income, race, education, occupation, and other population characteristics of each code area.

Consequently, a marketer wishing to reach consumers of certain social class or family patterns deemed favorable for his products can gain the attention of these target segments rather easily through product sampling and/or direct mail. Similarly, a retailer can base a store-location decision on zip code data and thereby tap those people most likely to be potential customers for the planned store.

In gearing marketing efforts to reach desired segments, the product, the promotional plan, and the methods of distribution all must be integrated toward the particular requirements of the target segments. Of the product itself, three factors are important: (1) the brand image, (2) the product form or characteristics, and (3) the quality and price. These factors overlap. For example, product characteristics relate to the quality and price, and the brand or product image should also be a reflection of this. However, promotional and distribution efforts more directly affect brand image, at least in the short run.

Some examples of successful use of market segmentation are the following:

Pepsi-Cola has long promoted its product so as to create an image of youth and vitality (an image appealing even to the oldster who wants to be "young at heart").

Virginia Slim cigarettes of the Philip Morris Company are "skinny" cigarettes aimed at women smokers.

[7] Philip Kotler uses slightly different terminology in *Marketing Management*, 2d ed. (Englewood Cliffs, N. J.: Prentice-Hall 1972), pp. 167–68.

Volkswagen concentrated on those consumers who wanted compactness, good engineering, and economy in transportation.

An untapped segment was recognized for a freezerless refrigerator, and for a time this became a best-selling major appliance directed to owners of home freezers.

The portable dishwasher met the particular needs of transient families for whom the custom installations in permanent dwellings were not practical.

Zenith Radio Corporation secured a strong position in the television receiver market by being the leading exemplar of product quality and good workmanship and meeting the needs of that consumer segment which gave the highest buying priority to purchasing reliability, even though this cost considerably more.

Rather like Zenith, the Maytag Company has appealed to a particular quality-conscious consumer segment.

**MARKETING
IN
ACTION**

Segmentation Strategy at Maytag

The Maytag Company is located in a small town, Newton, Iowa. Compared to its competitors it is a small company: sales in 1973 were just $227 million, compared to $1.7 billion for the kitchen and laundry appliance division of General Electric, and $1.3 billion for Whirlpool. But Maytag makes what many people—including *Consumer Reports*—consider to be the best equipment. It is also the most expensive: a typical Maytag automatic washer sells for $300, about $50 more than an equivalent General Electric.

Maytag has not directed its efforts to the new-home market and builders who demand price concessions. Instead, it has chosen as its major market the customer seeking a replacement for a cheaper machine that has given trouble. Such a customer often is willing to pay a premium for a trouble-free machine. And this Maytag has been able to achieve. The company makes no periodic model changes, a strategy which is unique in the appliance industry. Instead it seeks to simplify its products and make them more reliable. Profitability of this strategy? In 1973, return on equity was 31 percent, one of the best in all of industry.

SOURCE: "Just What the Doctor Ordered?" *Forbes*, September 15, 1974, pp. 32–33.

For thought and discussion:

Can you reconcile the conservative strategy of Maytag with the desirability of innovation which was discussed in chapter 2?

Married in 1932

Got Maytag in 1933

Both marriage and
Maytag still working

THE MAYTAG COMPANY, NEWTON, IOWA, SOLD IN CANADA AND THROUGHOUT THE WORLD

The Maytag in the picture at right is not the one that Mr. A. W. Bell of Vandergrift, Pa., bought for his wife back in 1933.

The Maytag Washer you see is his gift to Mrs. Bell simply because she wanted the most modern automatic available today.

Though her 27-year-old Maytag was still working, she felt it would be nice to have an automatic that has all the new features, plus the one that makes them work . . . Maytag dependability.

She expects both marriage and Maytag will continue working just as before. The remarkably long lives of so many of the 13,000,000 Maytags built since 1907 strongly suggest that Mrs. Bell has no reason to expect otherwise.

The best thing about it is that she gets all these new features right along with old-time Maytag dependability:

Automatic bleach dispenser that ends bleaching mistakes. **Lint-Filter Agitator** eliminates lint problems. **Safety lid** that stops action quickly when opened. **Automatic water level control** that saves water on partial loads. And a **zinc-coated steel cabinet** to protect against rust.

Maytag has built a reputation of quality and durability through ads such as this one. *Courtesy Maytag Company.*

The Maytag strategy is by no means new. For example, reproduced here is an ad that appeared in the March 17, 1961, issue of *Life,* one of the most memorable of all ads. Simple, nostalgic, yet it made the theme of dependability something to remember.

Some market segments are still relatively ignored and untapped, and they offer marketing opportunity (see the box on "Tapping the Rural Market").

We should note here that segmentation can be carried too far: a firm can offer too many colors, sizes, styles, and price ranges. Such diversification of product line leads to diseconomies. Production costs are increased because of short production runs. Selling costs are increased because sufficient selling and promotional efforts have to be allocated to a variety of offerings. Segmentation hypothetically could even be carried to the extreme of tailoring a special product to each individual customer. This harks back to the handicraft economy of olden days in which, for example, the shoemaker designed and made shoes to each person's specific order. But this is hardly compatible with a modern mass-production economy.

**MARKETING
IN
ACTION**

Segmentation Opportunity: Tapping the Rural Market

A broad market segment that has enough homogeneity to be a practical target for some products and firms is the rural market as characterized by rural small towns. A rural small town can be defined as a community under 25,000 population that is nonsuburban—that is, is not a bedroom community in or on the periphery of a metropolitan area.

A recent study found that these rural consumers were dissatisfied and had significant unfilled needs. This represents potential for those firms willing to design a strategy to satisfy this segment more effectively. Although these rural consumers perceived that they faced a price disadvantage when shopping in their small towns as compared with shopping in larger cities, this was not their major dissatisfaction. Most complaints focused on the belief that they had available only a poor variety of goods, and that new items were not being stocked by local merchants.

It had been expected that rural consumers, having comfortable cars and modern highways, would have shopping mobility and be able to take trips to large cities, but this was not borne out. Many were fearful of the congestion and complexity of large cities and of the unfamiliarity and impersonality of the stores.

Despite population movement to the cities, rural small towns still represent a substantial market. In many parts of the United States this segment is rapidly increasing in per capita income, while exposure to the mass media is increasing wants. Furthermore, competition is less keen in these markets than in the major centers of population.

SOURCE: Adapted from Robert F. Hartley, "The Perceived Importance of Price in Small-Town Shopping Behavior," *Southern Journal of Business*, April 1970, pp. 24–32.

For thought and discussion:
How do you think retail firms could better serve these people?

Product Differentiation or Market Aggregation

The alternative to segmentation is to treat each market as an aggregate and to design a product and a marketing program to appeal to the broadest number of buyers. This is a differentiation strategy, which may be likened to a shotgun approach, as contrasted to the rifle approach of segmentation. Figure 9-1 shows a model for a product differentiation strategy and, by way of contrast, Figure 9-2 shows a segmentation strategy model.

In a differentiation strategy, differences in the product relative to competitive products will be stressed; these differences may be minor, such as a new package, new flavor, or a new feature, perhaps "one silly millimeter longer." Promotion is often heavy since actual differences among competitive products need to be built up; these may even be psychological or image differences—perhaps a psychological difference of glamor, or of the type of person who uses the

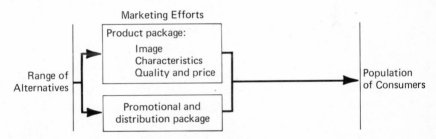

Figure 9-1. Model of Differentiation Strategy

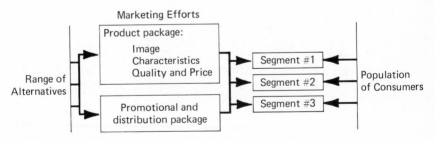

Figure 9-2. Model of Segmentation Strategy

product: for example, the "Marlboro Man," or the professional race-car driver. Products that appeal to mass audiences, such as cigarettes, soaps, foods, cosmetics, aspirins—the products you see advertised on TV—usually are subjected to this strategy of product differentiation. On the other hand, it may be too wasteful for the firm practicing segmentation to advertise in the mass media since so much of this advertising would be spent on audiences that are not likely prospects for the product.

Choice of Strategy

Segmentation is a practical approach for the smaller firm having limited resources. By concentrating its strength, it can gain a unique niche in the marketplace, one based on greater knowledge of certain aspects of the market. Expenses should be much less than would be incurred under product differentiation, because more selective advertising media can be used. For example, a firm wishing to tap the black market in a given city would find that certain radio stations, newspapers, and magazines cater directly to this market.

However, market segmentation is no guarantee of insulation from competition. A firm may first use segmentation as it seeks to penetrate a limited market. However, if the particular segment is large enough, competitors may also enter and a differentiation strategy then becomes necessary.

Products relatively homogeneous, such as gasoline, aluminum, and cigarettes, are difficult to tailor to specific segments, and differentiation is more natural. Products involving greater variety, such as automobiles, TVs, and sporting goods can be effectively marketed to segments.

A combination of segmentation and product differentiation is common, especially in large firms. Differentiated products are designed to appeal to large segments of the market, segments perhaps based on income or other demographic characteristics. Certainly where several competitors are aiming for the same segment some differentiation must be sought. The automobile industry is an example of this. Various models are geared to different target markets—the sports-car adherents, the family, the economy conscious, gadget buffs, the status conscious—yet, minor differences in trim, in accessories, in psychological image, are stressed because different makes appeal to the same segments.

The result has been a proliferation of products and claims, many based on minor, even contrived, differences; consumer choice is increased, but sometimes to the point of confusion. However, as the economy suffered from raw-material shortages, rising costs, and double-digit inflation, a reversal of product proliferation became necessary.

Refocusing Marketing Strategy in Time of Scarcity and Inflation

As costs rose rapidly and shortages of some goods and commodities became acute during the first half of the 1970s, companies began weeding out lower-profit items that appealed mainly to small customer segments. Product lines were pruned and consolidated to include only the higher-profit items. For example, paper manufacturers, upon finding that full-scale production still could not keep up with demand, simply shifted production to that of higher-priced and more profitable paper products. In the grocery store, Castle & Cooke, Inc., maker of Dole brand fruits and Bumble Bee seafoods, reduced the number of fruit cuts and can sizes from 27 to only 11— "product-line simplification," the company called it.[8]

New product development also was curtailed. Remarketing became important for some companies seeking to reduce the number of product offerings. Instead of devoting all their energies to developing new products, new uses were sought for old products. One example was given in chapter 2 of a new use for Arm & Hammer baking soda as an odor absorber. Another example of remarketing is the recent attempt by Johnson & Johnson to promote "baby" products (shampoo and oil) to adults in light of the falling birthrate in the U.S.

The term *demarketing* refers to efforts to discourage demand. When demand exceeds available supply, either temporarily or on a long-term basis, then there is a need to reduce this demand to more "comfortable" limits. Petroleum and natural gas firms and electric utilities have been major industry groups forced to practice demarketing. And how did they do this? By advertising tips for getting better performance and reducing waste, and by encouraging consumers to "Save a Watt"—in other words, to economize. There are dangers for a company in demarketing, however. Since the effectiveness of a demarketing campaign is seldom fully predictable, short-run demand may be reduced too much. More to be feared, irreparable harm may be done to long-term demand.[9]

---

[8] "Toward Higher Margins and Less Variety," *Business Week*, September 14, 1974, pp. 98–100.

[9] For more extensive treatment of demarketing, see Philip Kotler and Sidney J. Levy, "Demarketing, Yes, Demarketing," *Harvard Business Review*, November-December 1971, pp. 74–80; Philip Kotler, "The Major Tasks of Marketing Management," *Journal of Marketing*, October 1973, pp. 42–49; and Philip Kotler, "Marketing during Periods of Shortage," *Journal of Marketing*, July 1974, pp. 20–29. Messim Hanna, A. H. Kizilbash, and Albert Smart, "Marketing Strategy Under Conditions of Economic Scarcity," *Journal of Marketing*, January 1975, pp. 63–67. Also, David Cullwick, "Positioning Demarketing Strategy," *Journal of Marketing*, April 1975, pp. 51–57.

With target markets defined, those tactics most likely to tap them need to be selected. Many factors affect these decisions. Some are controllable by the decision maker (within the limits of certain constraints, such as reactions of competitors), while others, such as the state of the economy, are not controllable. We will examine both the controllable and uncontrollable factors and consider some of their interrelationships, their complexities, and the challenges they present in making marketing decisions.

The Marketing Mix

The *controllable factors* or the marketing decision variables are usually categorized as those pertaining to the "4 P's":

Product
Place
Price
Promotion

The combination or blend of these at any given time is called the marketing mix.[10] Later in this chapter we will consider a fifth "P," and suggest that it should also be considered part of the marketing mix.

Decisions must be made about the *products* to be offered, their features, quality level, branding and packaging, type of assortment, any service, warranties or guarantees.[11] Product decisions are not easy to make since there is considerable lead time required for product development, and meanwhile the preference of consumers may be changing. There is the constant threat of competitors' introducing new and improved products and innovations making present ones obsolete. Earlier in this chapter we described the demise of the Edsel, a product that had been planned to appeal to a growing sector of the car-buying market, but that finally was introduced to a market in which preference had greatly changed since the product was first conceived.

Place decisions concern channels of distribution and marketing institutions—the distribution structure—that will be used in getting the product to the final consumer. The efforts of a manufacturer to develop the best distribution structure for his purposes will reflect the decisions made regarding the product, price, and promotion.

---

[10] The term *marketing mix* was probably originated by Neil H. Borden, "The Concept of the Marketing Mix," *Journal of Advertising Research*, June 1964, pp. 2–7. E. Jerome McCarthy is generally credited with the mnemonic "4 P's."

[11] While we primarily are concerned with physical products, it is well to bear in mind that services are also a type of product, albeit intangible, and many of the same principles apply to them as apply to tangible products.

These decisions, along with the reputation of the producer, can make the product more or less attractive to prospective channel members.

Most marketers have some discretion in their *price* setting. There are constraints, of course. Production costs should act as a "floor" below which it would not be profitable to market the product. Competitive prices must be considered, even if there is some product differentiation. Governmental regulatory agencies and fear of governmental intervention may further hinder pricing freedom. Furthermore, the price selected must be compatible with the rest of the marketing mix. For example, if the product is to be distributed as a prestige item, the pricing must reflect this, as should also the distribution structure and the promotional efforts.

Promotion includes the allocation of advertising and sales promotional efforts as well as personal selling. Many alternatives are possible here and these decisions are some of the most complex the marketer faces. For example: How much should be spent for advertising? How should the money be allocated by products, by media, by time? What themes or appeals should be used? How many and what kinds of salespeople? Where should their efforts be concentrated?

The four P's are clearly interrelated. All affect, and are affected by, the other components of the marketing mix. Many alternatives are available for each, and they may be employed in endless combinations.

A few general guides can be offered for designing a marketing mix:

1. A mix should be specially tailored to a product or campaign, keeping in mind particular segments the firm most wishes to attract.
2. The various elements of the mix must be screened for compatibility. If the firm, for example, wants to appeal to those consumers interested in economy, its choice of channels, prices, promotional efforts, and of course the product itself must be geared to this objective.
3. Care must be taken to coordinate the components of the mix. To an extent, some are substitutes for one another. That is, more money could be spent on advertising, and the sales force could be reduced in quality or in numbers or both. If the price is made low enough and if distribution is through discount stores, then advertising and even sales personnel may be minimized (conversely, you could argue here that the presence of self-service may necessitate greater use of advertising to create consumer demand). This suggests then that the "mix" should be selected by one person or group, rather than having each element decided independently. It is a strong argument for placing all these functions under the control of a marketing manager or marketing vice president.

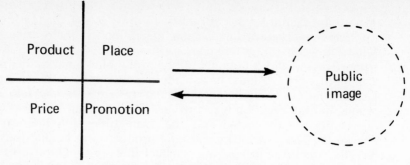

Figure 9-3. A Firm's Total Marketing Mix (the 5 P's)

The Fifth "P"

In today's climate, another element of a firm's marketing program, its *public image*, needs attention. We will call this the "fifth P" (along with Place, Product, Promotion, and Price) and treat it as one of the controllable factors of the marketing mix.

Public image refers to how a company is viewed by its customers, suppliers, stockholders, by the financial community, by its employees, by the communities in which it dwells, and by the various governments both local and federal. This is controllable in much the same way as products, prices, promotional methods, and channels of distribution.

Just as the other ingredients of the mix are interrelated, so the public image both is affected by and affects the other P's. Figure 9-3 illustrates this interaction.

For example, what people think of the quality of a firm's products and the fairness of its prices affects the public image, favorably or adversely. Advertising—whether involving honest, well-supported claims, or half-truths and omissions—also flavors the public image. Promptness and fairness in handling complains contributes to the image perceived by customers and their friends.

Let us now look at examples of major firms with image problems.

Image Change at Eastern Air Lines.[12] The public image of Eastern Air Lines had slipped badly; passengers rated it abysmally low in service, courtesy, and punctuality. A "WHEAL Club" had been formed: "We Hate Eastern Air Lines." After a management change, everything was redesigned, from inflight silverware to ticket counters.

[12] Adapted from "Companies Face an Identity Crisis," *Business Week*, February 20, 1971, pp. 52–53.

Drastic measures were undertaken to revamp service. In the process, the image was improved, aided by changed signs and trademark and other externals. In one year the company turned an operating loss of almost $6 million to a $30 million profit. Even in 1970 when the airline industry was in bad straits, Eastern fared better than most.

Public Image at Union Carbide.[13] Union Carbide gained the reputation of a polluter. One of its plants thirty miles from Charleston, W. Va., was labeled the "world's smokiest factory." Dense layers of smoke often blocked out the sun and poured out more health-endangering particles than the total emitted in all of New York City. Not surprisingly, this became the center of a controversy pitting the company against local citizens, environmentalists, and federal and state governments.

With the imposition of certain federal pollution-control deadlines, the company threatened to lay off 625 workers out of the total workforce of 1,500. Such "blackmail" was all the more drastic to West Virginians whose state had an unemployment rate in 1969 of almost twice the national average, a per capita income the fourth lowest in the nation, and a population decline in the decade of the 1960s the greatest of any state. The unconcern of Union Carbide and a general lack of cooperation with local citizens and government officials resulted in burgeoning public and governmental pressure. Even some of its stockholders petitioned the Securities and Exchange Commission to investigate "untrue statements" and omissions in company literature which underplayed its pollution problems.

Four years later, by 1974, the company's image had changed, to a "can-do approach" instead of "broken promises." Emission controls have reduced pollution by 97 percent. It cost Union Carbide nearly $35 million to do so, and increased production costs about 15 percent. But by tackling the job before many of its competitors, the company avoided even higher costs now facing other manufacturers. Union Carbide has finally erased its negative image in the eyes of the general public.

Many major firms—especially those that have widely diversified into nonrelated areas—have undertaken *corporate identity programs* to improve their images through new signs, business forms, packaging, plant and office designs, trucks, even the way receptionists answer the phone. Expensive consultants have been brought in to create the visible superficialities of such "new" images.

Indicative, however, that deep, unresolved problems will not be

---

[13] Adapted from "A Corporate Polluter Learns the Hard Way," *Business Week* February 6, 1971, pp. 52–56; and "Union Carbide's Big Cleanup Job," *Business Week*, November 9, 1974, p. 184.

Old and New Versions of the Eastern Air Lines and Con Edison logos.

overcome by superficial "face-lifting," Consolidated Edison of New York doctored its image with new logotypes, new corporate colors, new trucks; but neither its pollution, power shortages, or poor customer service has changed. And its public image remains as bleak as before. Face-lifting alone, without more fundamental changes, is seldom enough to change an image in a positive fashion.

Uncontrollable Factors

As we have seen, the elements of the marketing mix are controllable within certain limits by the marketing decision makers. Other factors are beyond control, at least in the short term. These are usually thought of as the environment of marketing, the outside forces that affect the decisions. The uncontrollable, environmental factors fall into the following categories:

1. Cultural and social factors
2. Governmental intervention
3. Economic forces
4. Ethical climates
5. Competitive factors
6. Technological developments
7. International influences

Cultural and *social* factors are those affecting attitudes, needs, preferences, and even discontent of consumers. Not only should the marketer attempt to interpret consumer sentiments in selecting target markets and developing a marketing mix, but a smart marketer watches for trends in over-all consumer attitudes toward business, society, and government.

Governmental intervention is becoming a more significant influence on marketing decisions today. Consumer-protection laws add additional constraints. Legislation, however, has long been a factor, and furthermore, the government as a monopsonistic buyer, as the major employer, as an exerter of various informal pressures, can seldom be disregarded.

Firms doing business overseas must consider the political environments of their foreign markets, since these can differ substantially from that in the United States. Some countries endeavor to attract foreign enterprises and foreign money. More common are restrictions and even expropriation of foreign firms. Of even more concern is the rapidity of political change in some overseas markets. A once-popular foreign-owned factory may become anathema as more nationalistic interests assume control of a country.

Economic forces of the environment are obvious influences. A recession can nullify the best-formulated plans. Chronic inflationary conditions bring rising costs, consumer dissatisfaction with high prices, and governmental response, actual or potential, affecting taxes, credit availability, interest rates, government purchasing, etc.

The *ethical* climate affecting marketing has received attention mostly in the last decade. As we have seen, disagreement is widespread as to what is ethical: for example, is it ethical to sell all kinds of goods on Sunday? There is often a subtle relationship between ethical and governmental factors. Conduct expectations are dynamic, and eventually are manifested in laws and regulations.

The *competitive* environment must be considered. Market-share analysis—the percentage of the total market for a product that a firm achieves relative to competition—plays a major role in company planning. Actions of competitors need to be countered. While competitive reactions are often unpredictable, sometimes certain patterns can be determined. If one firm greatly increases advertising expenditures, or significantly lowers its price, or introduces a greatly improved product, this usually invites reaction from other firms concerned with preventing their market share from eroding. Therefore, intraindustry competition (competition with other firms in the industry who market similar goods) is closely watched. Sometimes interindustry competition (competition with firms in other industries having goods which could be substituted, such as aluminum being interindustry competition for some steel products) is disregarded; this may have serious repercussions where the firms in one industry permit a sizable price hike, thereby encouraging a search for substitutes.

Technological developments bring product innovations and the obsolescence of old products. The impact of technology on marketing has sometimes been severe in shortening the life cycles of existing products. Yet new product failures continue to plague our marketing system: of products introduced into the market, the failure rate is as high as 80–90 percent. Advancing technology creates opportunities, even while it may upset the status quo.

Conditions in the rest of the world affect marketing, even if a company is not engaged in overseas operations. To an extent, these *foreign influences* cut across the other uncontrollable factors: economic and political actions in other countries may affect our tariffs, taxes, balance of payment situation and economic health; competition from foreign firms has in some industries seriously affected sales and profits of domestic firms due to lower cost and perhaps technologically superior foreign imports. The nations of the world are becoming more interdependent with the rapid communication and the desirability of free-flowing trade; disruptive actions anywhere in the world, such as turmoil in the Near East or seizure of a U.S. factory in Latin America, have repercussions on the stock market and reverberations in other economic sectors. And certainly a military involvement, such as Vietnam, has severe and long-lasting results.

The Search for Optimization

Many factors affect the success or failure of a typical marketing decision. As we have seen, some of these are controllable, such as the amount and type of advertising to use. Others are beyond control. Weather affects the sales of many products, from air conditioners to ski equipment. A blizzard a few days before Christmas can drastically affect retail sales and profits, since some of this lost business will never be regained. Technological breakthroughs may make obsolete existing products or ways of doing business. The competitive picture can be likened to a chess game, as opponents threaten, react, probe and parry, perhaps bluff and decoy, in efforts to gain competitive advantage.

So the uncontrollable environment presents complexities and unknowns, but even the controllable factors can be only imperfectly blended. Measures of advertising effectiveness are imprecise. Some advertising campaigns have had outstanding success while others, which appeared even more promising, have failed. It is almost impossible to isolate the effects of any single action on the sales figures. This may be illustrated by the following formula:

$$\text{Sales} = f \begin{array}{l} \text{(Price, Promotion, Product, Distribution Outlets,} \\ \text{Competitive Efforts, Unknowns)} \end{array}$$

The unknowns represent various environmental factors exerting indeterminate influence on sales.

Therefore, optimal marketing decisions are seldom attainable. But, far from being discouraging, this can offer a fascinating challenge to the man or woman with creative imagination, a willingness to take calculated risks and even to base some decisions on intuition, who at the same time knows when and where to get maximum guidance from available information and from the tools that can sharpen decision making.

And there are success stories, not all of them are from U.S. marketers. For example, Honda.

**MARKETING
IN
ACTION**

Achieving Market Penetration: The Honda Story

One of the most difficult tasks in marketing is for any unknown firm to penetrate a market long dominated by large and well-established firms. And when the newcomer is a foreign firm attempting to gain entry into this, the most sophisticated and advanced marketing environment in the world, the odds against success would seem even greater. This was the situation facing the Honda Company in the early 1960s. Successful penetration on a large scale usually is the result of careful market diagnosis and planning, a near optimum blend of the controllable factors—the marketing mix—and perhaps something else is needed: a favorable competitive environment in the sense that established competition reacts slowly and ignores untapped consumer needs.

In the late 1950s, the U.S. motorcycle industry was dominated by large high-powered machines. The major producer, Harley-Davidson, had completely captured the market for police and delivery motorcycles and was secure with the other major market segment, that of "hard core motorcyclists."

The Honda Motor Company started in 1948 as a small Japanese motorcycle manufacturer. At that time demand for cycles was increasing as many persons could not afford automobiles and the Honda served the need for transportation. While the postwar Japanese motorcycle industry was intensely competitive, Honda survived, having developed a superior product. As production increased and the domestic market was secured, Honda looked toward other potential markets. World reaction to Honda products—especially the smaller models—was favorable. Accordingly, a U.S. branch was established in California in 1959.

While at first Honda advertised through the trade magazine *Cycle,* it correctly assessed its market opportunity as existing among first-time riders who wanted a lightweight, inexpensive machine that would solve traffic problems. It soon began advertising directly to noncycling consumers through national magazines. With its lightweight cycles priced far below the "heavies," it emphasized the following in its promotional campaigns between 1959 and 1963:

1. Honda motorcycles are economical to own and operate.
2. They are easy to park.
3. Insurance rates are lower than on automobiles.

4. Hondas are fun to ride.[a]

An image problem impeded creating a new market among first-time riders: a mental picture of black leather jackets and "The Wild Ones." The ad campaign was shifted to winning social acceptance for the motor- cycle and its rider, and the new theme became, "You meet the nicest people on a Honda." A typical ad in *Life* magazine read:

> You meet the nicest people on a Honda. It's largely a question of personality. A Honda is easy going, dependable. Makes few demands. Prices start around $215. And it runs all day on a nickel's worth of gas. That's the kind of friend to have. Frugal. How about one in your family? World's biggest seller.[b]

National advertising was intensified to include radio and TV. Honda sales in 1964 broke company records, and in 1965 sales doubled. Motor- cycle registrations jumped from 500,000 in 1960 to nearly 1.9 million in 1966. A survey of Honda owners in 1964 showed that most had never ridden a motorcycle before they bought their Honda.[c] With the demand generated by massive consumer advertising, Honda dealerships expanded to every state, and service and spare parts were emphasized. Advertising had changed the image of the motorcycle and made it acceptable.

American manufacturers showed themselves complacent and oblivious to a changing environment. In a classic error of judgment, Harley-Davidson turned its attention to trying to penetrate the European market with its heavy motorcycles, even though Japanese imports were already beginning to make inroads in the United States.[d] So the door was opened wide for an aggressive foreign manufacturer to achieve market entry and dominance. One must admire the "audacity" of such a foreign manufacturer astute enough to realize that the consumer of a developing nation needing cheap transportation as well as the consumer of an affluent nation needing transportation that would solve mounting traffic problems could be customers for the same product.

SOURCE: [a] "Honda: Making Motorcycles an 'In' Product," *Printers' Ink,* July 23, 1965, p. 24. [b] Ibid. [c] "Mild Ones Roar Off with a Market," *Business Week,* Novem- ber 12, 1966, pp. 138–40. Also see "Japan's Competitive Cutting Edge, *Fortune,* September 1, 1968, p. 95. [d] "U.S. Motorcycles Makes Guns for Foreign Sales," *Business Week,* August 12, 1961, pp. 74–76.

For thought and discussion:
As a top Harley-Davidson executive, how would you have countered the Honda incursion into the U.S. motorcycle market?

NEW USES OF MARKETING STRATEGIES AND TECHNIQUES

Traditionally, we have thought of marketing as being limited to prod- ucts and to business firms. Today this conception of marketing is too narrow. A notable article contends that marketing is a pervasive societal activity that goes considerably beyond the selling of toothpaste, soap, and steel. Political contests remind us that candidates are marketed as well as soap; student recruitment by colleges reminds us that higher education is marketed; and fund raising reminds us that "causes" are marketed.[14]

Nonbusiness organizations, whether churches, schools, museums, police departments, charitable drives, labor unions, or whatever, cannot escape marketing. It is inherent in their operations, whether recognized by this name or not, and regardless of any conscious attention directed to it. Kotler and Levy suggest that the principles of "good" marketing in traditional product areas are transferable to the marketing of services, persons, and ideas.[15]

**MARKETING
IN
ACTION**

Nonproduct Advertising: Promoting Priesthood
In the Roman Catholic Archdiocese of New York, an advertising campaign was inaugurated with the twin objectives of elevating priests' public image, and soft-selling for priestly vocations. A $100,000 budget was allocated for ads appearing in selected New York metropolitan newspapers and regional editions of national magazines. One sample headline: "Father John O'Leary if He's Not in Church, He's Probably in Jail." (O'Leary is a chaplain at the Manhattan House of Detention.) Other ads show a black priest who runs a community center in Harlem, and a monsignor whose most important job, during a twelve-hour working day, "is to celebrate the Mass." For anyone interested in becoming a priest, the ads carry a special New York City telephone number which can also be dialed, "P-R-I-E-S-T-S" (774-3787).

SOURCE: "A Campaign to Retire Father O'Malley," *Time,* December 3, 1973, p. 74.

For thought and discussion:
How would you evaluate the effectiveness of this "priesthood promotion"?

Large city police departments frequently have a poor image among important segments of the population. The need to improve this image is hardly less important than for a manufacturer faced with a deteriorating brand image. A police department can develop a "marketing" campaign to win friends: promoting tours and open houses of police stations, crime laboratories, police lineups, cells,

---

[14] Philip Kotler and Sidney J. Levy, "Broadening the Concept of Marketing," *Journal of Marketing,* January 1969, pp. 10–15, p. 10.
[15] Ibid.

etc.; speaking at schools, sponsoring recreation projects such as a day at the ballpark for youngsters are examples of activities aimed at marketing a better image.

Public school systems, faced with taxpayers' revolts toward mounting costs of education and with the image-damage due to teachers' strikes, need conscious marketing efforts to obtain more public support and funds. One school system has used television programming to dramatize the work being done to combat the drop-out problem, to develop new teaching techniques, and to enrich the children.

MARKETING
IN
ACTION

Marketing in the Post Office

With the monolithic former Post Office Department now a government corporation called U.S. Postal Service, and attempting to operate on a breakeven basis, some creative marketing efforts are unfolding. Recognizing a potential for selling other items in its 32,000 post office lobbies, reproductions of oil paintings (in collaboration wth the National Gallery of Art) have been offered expermentally to determine the lobbies' rental potential.

The biggest potential probably lies in philately, or stamp collecting. These stamps go into collections, rather than onto mail, so that much of this is clear profit. The Postal Service is even using market surveys to determine the actual and potential number of stamp collectors in the United States. It is participating in international stamp shows and using a film to interest school children in stamp collecting, as a means to boost sales to the foreign and youth markets. Efforts are being made to make the stamps themselves more attractive, by better printing and designing (for example, James Wyeth, a noted artist, designed a Christmas stamp), and by emphasizing popular themes.

The Postal Service has begun extensive advertising—even including network TV—to boost stamp collecting. The accompanying ad is representative of its magazine advertising.

Critics of the U. S. Postal Service have pointed out that it still remains far less efficient than its major nongovernmental rival, United Parcel Service, which in 1973 handled 798 million packages, up from 514 million five years earlier. Yet the Postal Service has behaved like a monopolist, pressuring the Interstate Commerce Commission to turn down UPS's request to be allowed to serve 48 states. And the Postal Service has the absolute monopoly on the issuance of stamps and on delivery of letters.

SOURCE: "Break Up the Post Office," *Barron's,* November 23, 1974, p. 7.

Every few weeks, there's a little something new at your Post Office.

At least sixteen times this year, something special will happen at your Post Office. A special stamp.

One of them will celebrate Kentucky's First Settlement.

In 1774, Kentucky was no-man's-land. King George III forbade anyone to settle there. And the Indians not only fought and forced each other off the land, they forced everyone else off too. Including Daniel Boone. But a group led by James Harrod formed Kentucky's First Settlement in what is now called Harrodsburg.

This stamp gives you a small picture of the exciting story that lies behind every stamp. And there'll be more: like a Robert Frost stamp, a set of two Space stamps, and one on Expo '74.

At the Post Office we issue special commemoratives like these every few weeks. And they make a great American collection. But since each stamp is a limited edition, none will be available for very long.

So stop by your Post Office often. It's the place to discover the fun of stamp collecting.

Stamp Collecting. For the fun of it.

This ad encourages stamp collecting while at the same time aiming for a better public image for the postal service.
Courtesy U. S. Postal Service.

The Cleveland Orchestra, facing the common financial problems of most such cultural enterprises and recognizing that a handful of wealthy patrons that formerly supported art can no longer pay today's inflated bills, is reaching out to broader audiences. Attracting ethnic groups has been one such "marketing" approach that has jam-packed the orchestra hall; the Cleveland area has thousands of Americans who retain emotional links with their ancestors' homelands: Hungarian-Americans, Polish-Americans, Italian-Americans, Czech-Americans, and many others. Ethnic Nights were planned to "welcome" these groups and flourishes were deliberately designed to promote concert-going as a popular rather than upper-class diversion. For example, Czech Night featured a moderately priced dinner of Czech dishes, preceding the concert of works by Czech composers Dvorak, Smetana, and Janacek, under the direction of Czech conductor Karel Ancerl. Other promotional plans on the agenda to bring the orchestra to the people include jazz and pop concerts, student promotions, and a special campaign to woo the black community.[16]

Marketing and Politics

The marketing of political candidates represents the most extensive use of marketing techniques in nonbusiness areas. Two marketing tools are commonly employed: public opinion research or polling, and mass-media—particularly television—advertising. The use of these tools, and especially the latter, to win elections almost precludes the candidate without much money from effectively competing. With money, a candidate may bypass political party organization, can challenge entrenched incumbents, can in fact manufacture an instant public presence.

The costs of presidential political campaigns can reach hundreds of millions of dollars. A single candidate for a state gubernatorial or congressional nomination may spend from $500,000 to several million.

The most startling evidence of the effectiveness of image-building TV campaigning may have occurred in the Alaska election of 1968 when Mike Gravel, at that time relatively unknown, challenged incumbent Ernest Gruening in the Democratic primary:

> On a Saturday a week before the voting, a poll showed Gruening ahead 2 to 1. On Sunday, a heavily promoted film ran on television. On Monday, a new poll showed Gravel ahead 55 to 45. He then won by that margin.[17]

[16] The first two examples have been adapted from some described by Kotler and Levy, pp. 11–12; the last example featured in "Ethnic Nights Are a Box Office Hit," *Business Week*, October 23, 1971, p. 94.

[17] "Electronic Politics: The Image Game," *Time*, September 21, 1970, p. 43. Also see the best-selling book, Joe McGinniss, *The Selling of the President 1968* (New York: Trident Press, 1969).

At the hands of political image-building specialists, who carefully screen and edit perhaps hours of film into 30- and 60-second segments maximizing the candidate's assets, political advertising approximates product advertising, with the candidate substituted for the product. This political advertising, however, can have more potency than product advertising since there is seldom the surfeit of claims encountered in product advertising (after all, the number of competitors is limited to one or perhaps two), while promoting the person has a flexibility and human interest usually beyond the possibility of any product.

Implications of a Broadened Concept of Marketing

Wider Spectrum on Challenges. When we broaden our conception of the role and function of marketing beyond that of mere product management to the arena of service, persons, and ideas, a considerable expansion of the dimensions, the opportunities, and the challenges for marketing results. This could afford a new vitality both to the discipline and practice of marketing and to the persons attracted to it. And there may well be joint benefits accruing to both business and nonbusiness interests due to the interchange of information and insights.

Perhaps the most tangible challenge that an expanded concept of marketing offers is that of providing better service by nonbusiness organizations, such as hospitals, schools, governmental bodies, even labor unions. As Kotler and Levy point out, in the course of evolving, many such organizations grow self-serving, with a bureaucratic mentality dominating a service mentality, so that perfunctory and callous treatment is the rule.[18] Marketing, with its greater emphasis on satisfying consumer needs, can provide

> that function of the organization that can keep in constant touch with the organization's consumers, read their needs, develop "products" that meet these needs, and build a program of communications to express the organization's purposes.[19]

More recently, "social" marketing has received attention. This deals with how marketing concepts and techniques can be used in the solution of social problems, such as antipollution, safe driving, family planning, fund-raising campaigns, and the like.[20]

---

[18] Kotler and Levy, "Broadening the Concept . . . ," p. 15.

[19] Ibid.

[20] The July 1971 *Journal of Marketing* is replete with articles on an expanded role for marketing: "how the viewpoints, concepts, and techniques of marketing can be incorporated into the solution of social problems." For example, Philip Kotler and Gerald Zaltman, "Social Marketing: An Approach to Planned Social Change," pp. 3–12, consider applications to such social objectives as brotherhood, safe

Dangers. There are some potential dangers in an expanded, competent use of marketing techniques into other aspects of our social milieu. We can see some indication of this in the powerful utilization of mass-promotional techniques to "sell" political candidates. There is danger that the best-financed candidate, the one able to afford the massive promotional expenditures as well as the ablest image-builders, will win out over the better person. Indeed, there is the possibility that the bad—whether of ideas, organizations, or persons —may be effectively promoted to the disadvantage of society. As an example of the power of well-financed marketing techniques in furthering the cause of special interest groups, consider:

> In the 1974 elections in California, environmentalists lost a bitter fight to stop construction of a dam on the Stanislaus River in the Sierra Nevada mountains which would destroy some nine miles of spectacular white water, while providing enough power to supply a city of 200,000 people (of which there is no such city even remotely waiting to be built). Largely because of a well-financed campaign by farmers, land developers, and construction unions, the environmentalists lost and the dam will be built.[21]

However, lest we be carried away regarding the effectiveness of selling and influencing, it is good to remember that even the most sophisticated uses of product advertising have only limited effectiveness. We can seldom be influenced against our wills; we quickly become hardened to a proliferation of promotional efforts on the same theme or for the same product category and, in general, the powers attributed to selling, advertising, and marketing—by such critics as Vance Packard in *Hidden Persuaders*—are vastly overrated. We may already be reaching a point of diminishing returns with regard to promotional expenditures for political candidates as more and more turn to the mass media, and as the opportunity for originality diminishes and with it, the effectiveness. And money has not always proved effective against poorer contenders:

driving, and family planning; William A. Mindak and H. Malcolm Bybee, "Marketing's Application to Fund Raising," pp. 13–18, describe a case study of the successful application of marketing concepts to a March of Dimes fund-raising campaign; Gerald Zaltman and Ilan Vertinsky, "Hearth Service Marketing: A Suggested Model," pp. 19–27, furnish insights into the contribution that marketing activities can make to human welfare; John U. Farley and Harold J. Leavitt, "Marketing and Population Problems," pp. 28–33, discuss the possible role of marketing in changing attitudes and stimulating activities for population control.

For a discussion of the businessman's view of "social" marketing, as opposed to the academician's, see Andrew Takas, "Societal Marketing: A Businessman's Perspective," *Journal of Marketing*, October 1974, pp. 2–7. For another view of social marketing, see David J. Luck, "Social Marketing: Confusion Compounded," *Journal of Marketing*, October 1974, pp. 70–72.

[21] "Blackjack and Bras," *Time*, November 18, 1974, pp. 33–34.

In Florida during the 1970 elections, a challenger for a Senate seat poured $100,000 into commercials, while his opponent set out on a 1,000-mile hike through the state, which captured everyone's imagination, received free publicity, and won the Senate seat virtually free of charge.[22]

In the 1974 elections in New Jersey, voters by a two-to-one margin turned down attempts to legalize gambling casinos in the state. This, despite the spending by pro-casino forces more than 20 times that of the anti-casino groups.[23]

On the other hand, the idea of better serving and satisfying human needs in nonbusiness organizations is challenging.

QUESTIONS AND PROBLEMS

1. How can the marketing manager design a marketing mix that will produce the best results?
2. Distinguish between product differentiation and market segmentation. As a small manufacturer in an industry dominated by large firms, which approach would you probably find more practical? Why?
3. Why is the "status quo" philosophy not practical in today's environment?
4. Give some specific examples of how a firm's public image (the "fifth P") is both affected by and affects the other components of the marketing mix.
5. What is your evaluation of the present effectiveness of "marketing" political candidates? Give an on-balance appraisal. Also estimate the effectiveness of this use of marketing for the future.
6. What type of segmentation strategy would seem more effective for a professional athletic team?
7. What is the rationale for a profit objective of "satisficing" rather than maximizing?
8. How would you develop a segmentation approach based on the psychological trait of adventuresomeness?

Project

W. T. Grant Co. had a marketing strategy in recent years which led to disastrous consequences. Use the library to find out about the ill-fated situation of W. T. Grant, and (1) propose a different strategy that would not have settled Grant with its problems; (2) propose a strategy to resolve Grant's dilemma.

[22] "The Un-Magic of TV," *Time,* November 16, 1970.
[23] "Blackjack and Bras," p. 33.

Exercise in Creativity

Develop a plan or strategy for "marketing" a hospital. Assume that the hospital faces a chronic situation of overcapacity of rooms and that there is a need to achieve a better occupancy ratio. Furthermore, costs are fixed; there is no possibility of adjusting prices downward.

Role-playing Case

"Our public image is not very good," your boss confides to you one morning. "In a survey our marketing research department just finished, customers rated us below average in service—they also thought we were old-fashioned, not progressive."

"Our cars still get good ratings for dependability, don't they?" you respond.

"Yes, but that's not enough today. I want you to have on my desk by next Monday a proposal I can present to the board of directors on some concrete ways to improve this image."

Prepare a program to improve the image of a small automobile manufacturer. Also point out what difficulties you would expect in making such an image change.

CHAPTER 10

PRODUCT

DECISIONS

Placing a need-satisfying product into users' hands is a major goal of marketing efforts.

In this chapter we first consider the problem of product quality, a matter of concern to both consumers and marketers. Then various classifications of products, their life cycles, product mixes, and the implications of branding are discussed, as well as that constant target of critics, planned product obsolescence. We examine the important decisions involved in new-product development, and the risks involved. Product decisions are becoming more complex, not only because of product proliferation (which leads to shorter product life cycles), but also because public reaction looms more important. Terms encountered include:

industrial goods	product life cycle
convenience goods	fashion goods
specialty goods	planned product obsolescence
shopping goods	private brands
product mix	family brands

CONSUMER DEMANDS REGARDING PRODUCTS

A successful product must meet many challenges. An attractive price, convenient outlets, and substantial promotional efforts can usually induce consumers to try a product, but if it proves inferior, then repeat business will suffer and word-of-mouth publicity may hinder even initial purchasing. If product complaints are serious enough, government may intervene in the consumer's behalf.

Most complaints regarding products have centered on two areas: (1) defective products for which repair service is neglected or ill performed, and (2) product safety.

Defective Products and Sloppy Service

A freezer was delivered with a broken drain hose which resulted in water flooding the interior. It remained in that condition for six weeks. Subsequently the door fell off . . .

237

A housewife complained that her oven would not maintain the temperature at which the thermostat was set. She was informed that it was normal for oven temperatures to vary from 30 to 50 degrees, and that any calls to adjust the thermostat would be at her expense . . .[1]

Extreme examples? Perhaps. But these are two excerpts from a Federal Trade Commission's report on consumer problems.

As products become more complex, it seems almost inevitable that more defective items will reach the market. But a significant factor in the production of defectives is the loss of pride of workmanship which characterizes some of labor today. This unconcern with doing a good job afflicts the assembly-line worker and the carpenter building a house, as well as the auto and TV-set repairman. There has long been the word-of-mouth admonition to would-be car buyers to beware the "Monday" car, the car assembled on a Monday. Consumers Union, a nonprofit, private testing organization, distributed 20 deliberately broken TV sets and asked neighborhood repairmen to fix them: only 3 of the 20 were properly serviced.[2]

Yet many companies, including some of the biggest, refuse to admit there is any problem. The major automobile companies, in hearings before the Federal Trade Commission concerning warranty and service problems, cited a survey which indicated that 84 percent of car buyers were satisfied with their dealer's service. Only 14 percent rated the service "unsatisfactory" or "very unsatisfactory." Still, in numbers this would be over a million car owners, a not insignificant total.[3] Car makers continue to refuse to supply another car or a refund to a buyer who gets stuck with a "lemon."

Responsive marketing suggests a better awareness of customer needs and problems. Undoubtedly much consumer resentment of malfunctioning products and faulty service could be eased and goodwill maintained if firms would improve their customer-grievance procedures to provide more prompt and dependable service. The Whirlpool Corporation was one of the leaders in doing this:

A toll-free, 24-hour "cool line" was installed at Whirlpool headquarters, with customers calling with complaints or inquiries given immediate attention. Problems that must be referred to local service agents are followed up by the company to learn if the customer was satisfied. Calls have averaged 75 to 100 a day on the "cool line." As a further step to control service and complaints, Whirlpool took over direct management of its warranty repairs so that customers do not have to quibble with local dealers.[4]

[1] *Washington Post,* January 12, 1969, p. G.24.

[2] Reported in *Time,* December 12, 1969, p. 94.

[3] Reported in *Washington Post,* January 11, 1969, p. 2. Also see "What Makes the New Consumer Buy," *Business Week,* April 24, 1971, pp. 55–57.

[4] "Buckpassing Blues," *Wall Street Journal,* November 3, 1969, p. 2.

Product Safety

Product safety came to national attention with the publication of Ralph Nader's *Unsafe At Any Speed,* which condemned General Motors' Corvair and actually forced it off the market. He also aroused public attention to other dangers, ranging from unclean fish to the misuses of medical X-rays.

MARKETING MISTAKES

Too Lax About Product Safety?

Many potentially lethal toys have been found on the market: eleven Philadelphia children had to have tiny toy darts removed from their lungs after they accidentally inhaled them from a plastic blowgun; a child's electric stove was found to produce temperatures of 600 degrees; a baby's rattle was held together with spikelike wires.

A particular model of electric steam vaporizer, a device often left in a room with infants, was found to be easily tipped so that a child could drench himself with scalding water.

Unsafe glass doors for household use have caused an estimated 100,000 injuries a year, some of them fatal, the victims being mostly children who run into them.

Specific product injury statistics show: 30,000 injuries per year from faulty floor heaters, 140,000 from power lawnmowers, 30,000 from defective wall sockets and cords, 700,000 from children's toys, 200,000 from slides, and 500,000 from swings. While not all such injuries could be prevented, it is estimated that 20 percent could be with safe, well-designed products.

SOURCES: "Product Safety Gain Impetus," *Washington Post,* May 11, 1969, pp. 81–83; "New Consumer Product Safety Agency Aims To Cut Household Accidents," *Wall Street Journal,* July 11, 1973, p. 32; Walter Jensen, Jr., Edward M. Mazze, and Duke Nordlinger Stern, "The Consumer Product Safety Act: A Special Case in Consumerism," *Journal of Marketing,* October 1973, pp. 68–71.

For thought and discussion:

How would you counter the rationale of some marketers who are lax about product safety that they cannot be blamed for the consequences of "misuse" of their products?

Various aspects of product performance and safety now come under governmental purview. The Consumer Product Safety Act of 1972 created an independent Consumer Product Safety Commission with powers to prescribe mandatory safety standards. Furthermore, there is the growing influence in the courts of the small consumer against the large corporation, as well as the danger of a "bad press" and its effect on company and brand image. Recent court decisions have generally favored consumers in product-deficiency cases against manufacturers, with the number of successful suits and the size of awards increasing greatly.[5]

Responsive marketing again would seem to dictate that marketers be more concerned about the safety of their products, giving it number one priority, ahead of styling and other features. Self-defense against possible legal actions—a firm's self-interest—may bring safety features which add to the costs of many products; some, such as children's play stoves, might then become too high-priced and be driven off the market.

THE PRODUCT CONCEPT

A product is really more than its physical attributes or characteristics. How well and how safely it fulfills the purpose for which it is bought is the major concern, and this may involve intangible as well as tangible attributes. A marketer has many factors to blend in an attempt to make a product attractive in the marketplace. He may offer his cigarettes in a flip-top box; he may give a 50,000-mile warranty; he may have trading stamps or some kind of game or contest; or he may attempt to build a psychological image, such as "Be a legend in your own time, with British Sterling."

Classification of Products

Table 10-1 shows various ways that products may be classified. This affects marketing strategy. For example, industrial goods usually are bought by professional purchasing agents who differ in their buying motives and skills from the buyers of consumer goods. Consumer goods themselves differ in their shopping requirements, their distribution patterns, and their effective use of various advertising media.

Table 10-1.
Typology of Goods[a]

Industrial Goods	Goods destined to be sold primarily for use in producing other goods or rendering service.
Installations	Capital goods items, such as buildings and equipment, which are expended, depleted, or worn out during the years of use; they do not become part of the final product.

[5] David J. Rados, "Product Liability: Tougher Ground Rules," Harvard Business Review, July–August 1969, pp. 144–52; and Lynn J. Loudenback and John W. Goebel, "Marketing in the Age of Strict Liability," Journal of Marketing, January 1974, pp. 62–66.

Table 10-1. (Continued)

Accessory equipment   Capital items shorter-lived than installations, which still do not become part of the final product. Examples are typewriters, small lathes, and trucks.

Raw materials   Products which have been processed only as much as needed for safe, convenient, economical transport and handling; raw materials become part of the finished product.

Component parts   Items that are finished or near finished and require assembly or minor processing before going into the final product. Examples are small motors, batteries, wire, textiles, various forgings and castings.

Supplies   These do not become part of the physical product, but are consumed in the process of manufacture. Examples are maintenance materials such as sweeping compound and light bulbs, repair items such as nuts and bolts, operating supplies such as oils and greases, papers clips, and so on.

Consumer Goods   Goods destined for use by ultimate consumers or households, and in such form that they can be used without commercial processing.

Convenience goods   Goods that the customer usually purchases frequently, immediately, and with the minimum of effort in comparison and buying. Examples are tobacco products, soap, newspapers, small packaged confections, and many food products.

Shopping goods   Goods that the customer, in the process of selection and purchase, characteristically compares on such bases as suitability, quality, price, and style. Examples are furniture and appliances, and women's ready-to-wear and shoes.

Specialty goods   Items with unique characteristics and/or brand identification, for which a significant group of buyers is willing to make a special purchasing effort. Examples are stereo components, some sporting goods, men's suits, and photographic equipment.

Another Classification: Applies to Both Industrial and Consumer Goods

Durable Goods   Tangible goods that normally survive many uses. Examples are machinery, appliances, cars, and furniture.

Table 10-1. (Continued)

Nondurable Goods	Tangible goods that normally are consumed in one or a few uses. Examples are cleaning supplies, oil, food.
Services	Activities, benefits, or satisfactions offered for sale. Examples are management and consulting services, outside maintenance, recreational facilities, dental and medical aid.

[a] These descriptions are adapted from *Marketing Definitions: A Glossary of Marketing Terms* (Chicago: American Marketing Association, 1960), pp. 11, 14.

Convenience goods, such as cigarettes and many food products, require wide distribution and may use mass media advertising. Sometimes convenience goods are bought on impulse and are unplanned purchases.

Specialty goods, those consumer goods that have unique characteristics or strong brand identification, are more effectively marketed with a few carefully chosen outlets in each city. Durable goods tend to be bought infrequently and will generally be shopping- or specialty-type goods, require more personal selling, service, perhaps guarantees or warranties, and usually will command a higher margin. Nondurable goods and services are often purchased frequently, have a widespread distribution, may command a strong brand loyalty with a high percentage of sales being repeat business.

There are some limitations to the traditional convenience-shopping-specialty goods classification. It really represents more a classification of buying or patronage factors than of product factors: that is, what may be a convenience good for one consumer (for which he will be unwilling to exert much shopping effort), may well be a shopping or even, conceivably, a specialty good for another consumer with strong brand loyalty and inflexible requirements. (The advertising slogan, "I'd walk a mile for a Camel!" illustrates a manufacturer's tongue-in-cheek hope that his product—which for most people is the prime example of a convenience good—might somehow command a specialty-good status.) There is also more justification for depicting these categories on a continuum representing the degree of shopping effort normally expended in purchasing, than in discrete groupings.[6]

[6] For an empirical study supporting the convenience-shopping-specialty goods definitional system, based on customer shopping effort when attempting to purchase, see Arno K. Kleimenhagen, "Shopping, Specialty, or Convenience Goods," *Journal of Retailing*, Winter 1966–1967, pp. 32–39. For a proposal that the cognitive dissonance theory be used to provide some criteria for classifying consumer goods, see Stanley Kaish, "Cognitive Dissonance and the Classification of Consumer Goods," *Journal of Marketing*, October 1967, pp. 28–31. For the proposal that fashion goods be incorporated into the classification, see John E. Mertes, "Taste, Variety, and Change: Yesterday and Today," *Business Perspectives*, Fall 1968, pp. 4–11.

Product Mix

The product mix is the composite of products offered for sale by a firm. There are three aspects to planning or analyzing a product mix: (1) the width, (2) the depth, and (3) the consistency.

The width of the product mix refers to how many different product lines, or groups of closely related products, are offered by the company. Some firms—a decreasing number—market only one or a few types of products. For years, the Richard D. Irwin textbook company had a very narrow product mix, specializing in business and economics texts at the college level. Coca Cola also had a narrow product mix; until 1954 it offered only one product, Coca Cola, in a "sacred" 6½-oz bottle. It is easy to find examples of firms that have wide product mixes: General Electric produces transformers, jet engines, toasters, radios, light bulbs, electric blankets, and a host of other product lines. Minnesota Mining and Manufacturing Company (3M) has grown from a two-product company to one of over 27,000 products today.[7]

The depth of a product mix pertains to the average number of items offered within each category of products or product line. After 1954, Coca Cola deepened its product mix by offering king- and family-size bottles (10 and 12 oz.), and by introducing Sprite, Tab, and a range of Fanta flavors—grape, root beer, orange, ginger ale—in bottles and cans.[8]

Consistency of a product mix is the relationship of the various product lines as to production requirements, distribution channels, end use, etc. The Green Giant Company has practiced consistency of product mix, while adding new products such as frozen vegetables to its canned peas and corn. Coca Cola, in its route of expansion, has also kept to a fairly consistent product mix, with acquisitions of Minute Maid Corporation (Minute Maid and Snow Crop fruit concentrates, Hi-C fruit drinks, instant coffee and tea), and Duncan Foods (roasted coffee).

It has been fashionable in recent years for companies interested in rapid growth to diversify widely. Consistency with existing production and marketing knowhow and resources was disregarded in the quest for acquisition of other firms. For example, Litton Industries diversified from electronics into a startling number of other fields: ships and submarines, typewriters and cash registers, computers and calculators, steel and wood office furniture, surgical instruments and X-ray equipment, motion-picture cameras, spacesuits, paper mills, book publishing, food preparation and electronic cooking, and so on. For these conglomerates, great growth was quickly

---

[7] For a somewhat dated, but nonetheless intriguing account of the widening of the product line of Minnesota Mining, see "Minnesota Mining in Motion," *Fortune*, March 1949, p. 95ff.

[8] "Things Go Better With Coke," *Sales Management*, April 16, 1965.

achieved, as Litton, for example, grew from $3 million in sales in 1954 to $1.5 billion by 1967.[9] Not until 1969 did the glamor of the conglomerate and its disregard for consistency of product mix finally begin to dim. A collapsing stock market sharpened perspectives toward operational problems often hidden under the financial manipulations of "wheeling and dealing" in a rising stock market—and operating efficiencies were often found wanting.

Product Expansion Versus Contraction

Product proliferation has characterized the market. The proliferation of car lines, models, and options has been a major reason given by automobile industry spokesmen for the failure to achieve a "foolproof" car.[10] But the push for more and more distinctive goods continues; the urbanologist Jane Jacobs sees mass production already being replaced by "differentiated production." Levi Strauss and Company, the maker of "Levi's," for example, used to make millions of pairs of virtually identical work pants; now it has moved to a fast-changing, high-fashion sportswear with many styles and colors.

In the process of widening the product mix, the need to prune products, to weed out the deadwood, is often neglected. And a firm's profits and marketing efficiency may be reduced, since inventory must be maintained and management and sales efforts, which might better be diverted to making healthy products more profitable, are occupied instead with weak ones. Often the blame for retaining such products may be placed on corporate inertia: positive efforts are required to review and eliminate weak products. Frequently vested interests are involved, however, and it may be organizationally disruptive to eliminate some products, since management and personnel might have to be moved around or laid off.

Judgment must be used in eliminating unprofitable products. Perhaps temporary conditions account for this weakness. Marketing efforts may not be effective and a change in marketing strategy or a product modification may rejuvenate. Sometimes a product which is yielding little profit may actually be rounding out the rest of the line, so that the firm's other products are benefited. Occasionally, customer goodwill may be at stake, and in the interest of better serving certain customers, a low-volume product may continue to be carried. In short, it is advisable to have a periodic product-review system to evaluate any weak products.[11]

As we noted in the last chapter, during a period of raw material

---

[9] "For Corporations the Game is Growth," *Business Week*, September 30, 1967, p. 107.

[10] *Washington Post*, January 11, 1969, p. 2.

[11] Philip Kotler, "Phasing Out Weak Products," *Harvard Business Review*, March–April 1965, pp. 107–18.

shortages and burgeoning inflation, product pruning and *demarketing* may be more appropriate strategies than product expansion and differentiation.

THE PRODUCT LIFE CYCLE

Products tend to go through different stages, to be affected by different competitive conditions, and to require differing marketing efforts at different points in time if sales and profits are to be effectively realized. The length of a product life cycle can vary from a few weeks to decades. The stages comprising the life cycle have been variously described; for our purposes we will divide a product's life into four stages—introduction, growth, maturity, and decline. Figure 10-1 depicts representative life cycles for a typical consumer goods product, and for a fad or high-fashion item.

Notice how abruptly the sales peak for a fad item, and the violence of the decline, compared with a nonfad good. Once the decline begins for a fad or high-fashion item, it is usually impossible to reverse or even greatly slow it. A firm is better advised to turn its efforts to other products at this time.

Obviously, the stages comprising the product life cycle are seldom equal in duration, nor are they similar for all products and all firms. A company with vast resources, like Procter & Gamble or

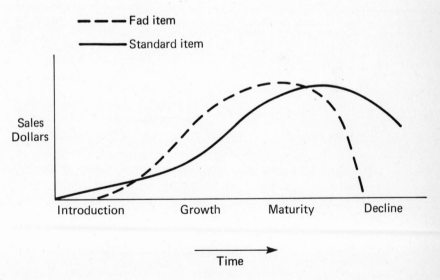

Figure 10-1 Product Life Cycle—Sales

General Foods, can shorten the introductory and growth stages by great infusions of promotional efforts. Some products, often because they are not compatible with certain social and cultural norms, may develop their sales very slowly. An example of this was the acceptance of cigarettes by women, a long, slow process in the 1920s and 1930s, despite substantial promotional efforts directed to this large segment of the total market.

The decline stage of a regular product (nonfad and nonfashion) can sometimes be reversed, and even another period of growth inaugurated, by some innovation or modification of product characteristics, of packaging, or of marketing techniques. Different segments of the market may be cultivated, or different promotional appeals developed. Or new uses might be found. In the last chapter we described such bolstering of a faltering product as *remarketing*.

The classic example of the remarketing of a product—and in so doing, giving it an exceptionally long life cycle—is Listerine. Originally marketed as a mild antiseptic, a plateau of sales maturity was converted to a new era of great growth by simply promoting the idea and use of Listerine as a mouthwash. As another example, radio manufacturers extended the life cycle of radios by such new uses and modifications as miniature transistor, clock, and auto radios. Figure 10-2 shows how the life cycle can be changed by effective marketing.

Eventually it would seem that all products must face decline and abandonment. The need for the product may disappear as technology changes. A better or less expensive product may be developed to fill the same need—plastics are replacing wood and metal

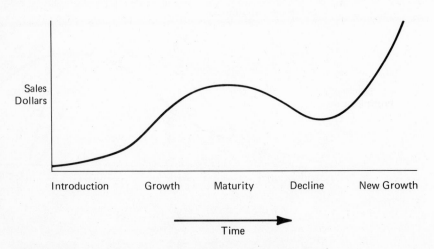

Figure 10-2. Product Life Cycle—Effect of Remarketing

in many instances. A competitor may do a superior marketing job and gradually force a product to be abandoned.[12]

Characteristics of Each Stage

The competitive environment, type and extent of marketing efforts, and profitability differ depending on the stage. We will examine the three factors of profit, promotional efforts, and competition, as a product passes through the life cycle.

Profit Characteristics. Figure 10-3 depicts profitability of a typical product during its life cycle. Most products are not profitable when first introduced. Sales volume is generally low, but growing; substantial promotional and personal selling efforts and perhaps many free samples are needed to give the product a good start. Therefore, immediate profits must be sacrificed for future expectations. This is one of the tragedies of new product failures, since many never enable a firm to recover costs. Note also in Figure 10-3 that profits tend to peak late in the growth or early in the maturity stage. While sales are stabilizing at a high level, competition is becoming keener and prices may have to be lowered and promotional and service costs increased. It is not unusual for sales to increase while profits are decreasing.

Promotional Characteristics. There is considerable variation in the extent of promotional efforts by companies and by products over

[12] See Donald K. Clifford, Jr., "Leverage in the Product Life Cycle," *Dun's Review and Modern Industry*, May 1965, p. 62.

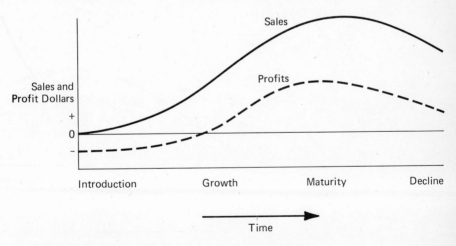

Figure 10-3. Typical Product Life Cycle—Profits

their life cycle. Some products may be introduced with massive expenditure of advertising in the mass media; others may be more gradually developed through the use of selected media and salespeople inducing dealers to stock. (These two contrasting promotional approaches are known as *pushing* and *pulling* respectively. We will describe them in more detail in the next chapter.) Figure 10-4 presents a middle-of-the-road approach to promotional expenditures over the life cycle. After heavy initial efforts, expenditures tend to level off—meanwhile sales are climbing rapidly—but then as competitors enter the field, promotional expenditures are again accentuated as the firm tries to promote its differentiation.

The type of promotional effort also changes over the life cycle. In the introductory, or pioneering, stage, a seller must stimulate *primary* demand (demand for the type of product) rather than *selective* demand (demand for a particular brand). As the type of product becomes increasingly well accepted and as competitors hasten to enter the market, the promotion of brand name becomes of crucial importance if brand share of the market is not to erode. Later, in the decline stage, promotional efforts are mainly used to keep the brand name before the public, and expenditures can be substantially reduced.

Competitive Characteristics. Figure 10-5 illustrates the typical competitive development for a product market. Often the firm introducing the new product has little or no early competition. However, as sales develop and as profits begin to be generated, competitive firms hasten to enter (unless entry is extremely difficult because of patent protection, production and facilities requirements). As severe competition ensues during the maturity stage, the marginal firms will be weeded out. More competitors drop out during the decline, as other opportunities look more attractive. The surviving sellers may be

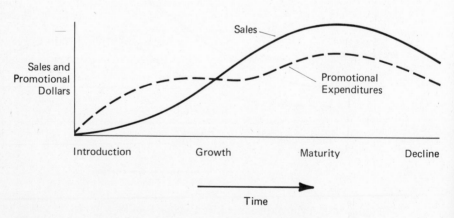

Figure 10-4. Typical Life Cycle—Promotional Efforts

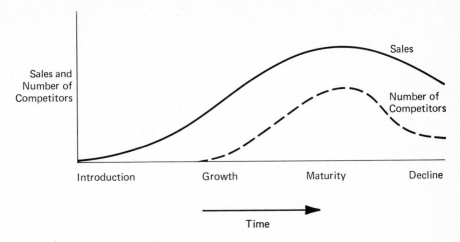

Figure 10-5. Typical Product Life Cycle—Competition

able to maintain a profitable operation for some time, owing to reduced competition and promotional efforts, and probably stabilized prices.

Product Life Cycle Shortening

Although life cycles can vary greatly, from the comet rise and fall of certain fad items to the durability of a Listerine, it is probable that the cycle for most products today is significantly shorter than was the case even a decade ago.[13] Technology is rapidly making products obsolete in some areas. Intense competition and a host of new products constantly entering the market contribute greatly to the shorter life cycle: as new products proliferate, often accompanied by saturation TV advertising, consumer confusion intensifies and brand loyalty tends to erode. Patent protection is seldom sufficient to protect most products, since minor variations are usually possible which can enable a competitor to obtain another patent. Failing this, the time taken to go through the courts often precludes any effective protection.

The shortened life cycle makes the task of marketing management more challenging than ever. The interest of many companies in diversification is partly an attempt to spread the risks so that an unforeseen death of a major product (or the cancellation of a government contract) will not be too catastrophic. But the trend toward

[13] William E. Cox, Jr., "Product Life Cycles as Marketing Models," *Journal of Business,* October 1970, pp. 375–84; "The 'Life Cycle' of Grocery Brands," *Nielsen Researcher,* November 1, 1968.

diversification also poses greater threats to existing products since new and powerful competition may suddenly come from outside firms moving into the industry. Indirect competition can also be a factor, with other categories of products also exerting some competitive influence, for example, tea and wine may compete with coffee, or plastic and aluminum with some uses of steel.

The threat of shortened product life cycles heightens the urgency of more firms to be constantly working on new product ideas. We will discuss this crucial aspect of marketing later in this chapter.

The Effect of Nostalgia on a Product Life Cycle[14]

For certain products nostalgia, or yearning for things of the past, has an interesting effect on the life cycle. For example, the first issue of *Action Comics,* which cost 10 cents in 1938, recently sold for $1,800; and the first issue of *Playboy* magazine has long been a collector's item. Figure 10-6 shows what might be called the nostalgia tail in a product life cycle.

What are the marketing implications of the nostalgia market? Phonograph record manufacturers have often reissued old recordings under discount labels, but many people would rather pay premium prices for the original masterpieces. Another strategy would be to keep a portion of early inventories from the marketplace, to be released some years in the future rather than cleared out at reduced prices in order to make way for the new. Franklin Mint, a large minter of coins, tokens, and medals, purposefully limits production

[14] This section is adapted from Donald W. Hendon, "Bicentennials Come and Go, but the Nostalgia Market Is Here To Stay, Perhaps in a Product Life Cycle 'Pigtail,'" *Marketing News,* July 4, 1975, p. 7.

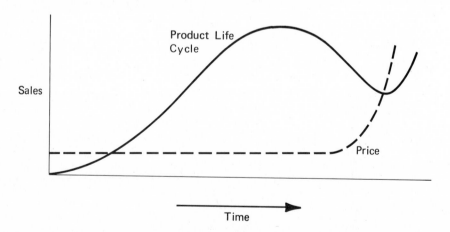

Figure 10-6. Product Life Cycle with Nostalgia Tail

in order to ensure the sales of its products at higher prices and to enhance appreciation prospects.

Is nostalgia just a passing fad? Some marketers believe that nostalgia has become institutionalized and will even increase in importance for certain products. But we need to determine better what types of goods are susceptible (or can be made susceptible) to nostalgia, and how marketing efforts can most effectively be directed to capitalize on this.

Fashion Goods

Consumer goods in which style or fashion is important generally have a predictably short life cycle, at least for women's fashions (men's fashions seem to stay around for a somewhat longer time). Women's shoes, dresses, and coats epitomize fashion goods.

Technically there is a subtle difference in the words *style* and *fashion*. *Style* is a characteristic method or mode of expression, while *fashion* is the currently accepted style in a given field. Thus styles of housing, or ready-to-wear, may be in or out of fashion. *Fad* generally refers to a short-lived but intense fashion and is often found in areas other than ready-to-wear, such as children's products. Hula hoops and monster and Batman items are examples of fads. An interesting question regarding fashions is whether the public can be "forced" to adopt a certain style. The midi skirt brought this issue to culmination.

MARKETING
MISTAKE

Trying to "Force" the Midi
Perhaps the classic failure of marketers to "decree" a fashion happened with the midi length in 1970. After the popularity of the above-the-knee mini skirt, the garment industry deemed it time for a change—after all, change is the essential ingredient for the garment industry: it provides ever-recurring demand.

So, *Women's Wear Daily*, the newspaper of the garment industry, and high-fashion New York department stores beat the drums for the new midi length. Stores even compelled their employees to wear the ankle-length skirts. But in vain. In this instance, American women refused to be swayed by "fashion creators." Indicative of the intense negativism the midi conjured up, a New York columnist wrote:

> So the next time a girl walks down the street in a midi
> skirt, she should know what many men feel . . . it tells
> us that she is frightened of her own judgment, a slave

of commercially inspired tastemakers, and a woman whose mind must be certainly as dull as the blah years of the 1950s, which inspired her clothing.

SOURCE: "Fashion: Does the Midi Look Spell E-D-S-E-L?" *Forbes*, September 15, 1970, pp. 28–34.

For thought and discussion:
What are marketing implications of fashion independence by women?
What factors may account for the shunning of the midi?
Do you expect such independence to be a permanent part of the fashion scene now?

Marketing of fashion goods is fraught with risk. For this reason (and because consumers are willing to pay high prices for the appearance of fashion), high fashion items usually command the highest markups and produce the highest per-unit profits. Since the typical fashion life cycle is short—perhaps only one season, such as fall or spring—mistakes are not easily rectified and a manufacturer or store may err, either by not having enough of a popular fashion, or by overestimating the popularity and consequently being forced to take severe markdowns. Marketing research usually is not of great help in predicting the success and potential of various styles since the life cycle is so short. Consequently, this aspect of marketing management often relies heavily on intuition and the intangible "feel for the market," which is usually developed by considerable experience.

Planned Product Obsolescence and the Controversy

Planned obsolescence is associated with frequent model changes and replacement primarily for the sake of profit. Automobile, appliance, and clothing industries typify this. Critics have assailed this as the consequence of an economy that produces more goods than we need and must therefore use such devices to persuade us to buy more.

Technological obsolescence, in which significant improvements make prior products outmoded, is hardly subject to such criticism. If a new computer, a new airplane, or an electric typewriter supplants in efficiency older products, this is progress.

Obsolescence can be a feature of the product itself. In order to build replacement business, an appliance or an automobile may be designed to last only a few years. Our cars soon require major repairs, our TV sets are prone to failures—eventually the recurring costs of repair make it necessary to invest in a newer model. But despite such apparent examples of built-in obsolescence, it is doubtful that many firms deliberately design obsolescence. This would be a dangerous strategy, since a firm would be vulnerable competitively to the firm offering more durable products. We should recognize also that the costs of building longer life into many products would make them prohibitively expensive for the mass market.

The frequency of styling and model changes, especially of U. S. cars, is perhaps unnecessary. Volkswagen achieved notable success with a marketing strategy centered around consistent styling (with the only year-to-year changes being "hidden" product improvement). Today there is less prestige and status in owning the newest model car, but many people still want something new, and manufacturers do find sales stimulus in the presentation of new models. Moreover, older models are not wasted—the secondhand or used market, especially for cars, is a viable part of the American scene.

THE QUESTION OF BRANDING

A brand is "a name, term, symbol, or design intended to identify the goods or services of a seller and to differentiate them from those of competitors." The brand or trademark is the part of the brand appearing as a symbol (a "logo") or as distinct lettering or coloring.[15] Brands are an integral part of the marketplace and they play a vital role in motivating marketers to the most efficient operating and in aiding consumers in their decision making. To understand better the social and economic function performed by brands, consider the Soviet experience.

The Russian marketing emphasis originally was anonymity in production, with production goals established and controlled almost solely in quantitative terms. But the consequent lack of incentive for quality eventually brought intentional product differentiation: each factory was obliged to identify itself on the good with a "production mark"—essentially, a brand—whereby superior goods could be identified with those sought by consumers.

Table 10-2.
Advantages and Limitations of Branding

For the Consumer

Advantages
Consistency and assurance of quality.
Status or prestige from owning certain brands.
Shopping made easier, especially if brand loyal.

Limitations
Too many brands may confuse.
Some brands command premium price which is unjustified.

---

[15] Ralph S. Alexander, Chairman, Committee on Definitions, *Marketing Definitions: A Glossary of Marketing Terms* (Chicago: American Marketing Association 1960), p. 8.

Table 10-2 (Continued)

For the Seller

Advantages

Brand-loyal customers are source of repeat business and furnish some insulation from competition.

Branding is necessary if promotion is to build selective demand.

Branding differentiates a product and prevents easy comparison of prices with competing goods.

Branding enables a firm to build a reputation and facilitates introduction of new items.

For a dealer, having his own brand may enable him to buy products at lower prices, thereby being able to obtain a higher markup and/or charge a lower retail price; he may also be able to have a closer control over quality and product features.

Limitations

Responsibility for maintaining a consistent quality—dissatisfied customers can identify the brand owner.

Some products do not easily lend themselves to differentiation and branding, such as certain raw materials (cotton and coal), nails, clothespins, some fresh fruits and vegetables.

For the manufacturer, the expenses of developing brand recognition and acceptance may preclude the use of a manufacturer's brand, so that the goods have to be sold unbranded or under dealer brands.

For the dealer, having his own brands may involve buying big quantities from suppliers, with the extra costs associated, taking the blame for inferior quality, and having to stimulate his own demand.

Therefore, the rationale for branding is evident. Both consumers and producers benefit from the presence of brands. Table 10-2 presents in outline form some specific advantages and disadvantages of branding.

Choosing and Protecting Brand Names

There are a number of rules of thumb useful in selecting brand names. Simple, one-syllable names, easy to pronounce, are desirable; such names as Tide, Crest, Coke, and Duz meet this standard. If the name can suggest something about a product and its benefits, this is a plus factor. Examples of such names (these do not meet the one-syllable test) are Frigidaire, Beautyrest, Reddi-Whip, and Sunkist. Probably the most important criterion of a good brand name is distinctiveness—it must be memorable and sufficiently different from other brands. For companies expanding and adding new and unrelated products, an all-purpose name may be desirable.

In practice it is difficult to meet all these criteria. Many products have succeeded with names difficult to pronounce or not particularly pleasant sounding, such as Michelob, Smuckers, and Manischewitz. On the other hand, such names as Standard, Universal, National, Ideal, American, and General, suffer from a commonality and lack of distinctiveness.

Finding names for new products is no easy task. More than 370,000 trademarks are registered with the U.S. Patent Office, and the number is growing by 20,000 a year.[16] With such a profusion of brands, dictionaries become all but exhausted, and computers are even being utilized to produce various combinations of syllables which might not be too difficult to pronounce, or look bad in print, or be too similar to existing trademarks. And conflicts occur. General Foods test-marketed a snack product called Pringle's Pop Chips, only to discover that Procter & Gamble was also testing Pringle's Newfangled Potato Chips. Greater risks lurk in the slang of foreign languages. *Time* reports of a leather-preservatives manufacturer who tried to market a product called Dreck—until he discovered that the name means dirt (or worse) in German and Yiddish.[17]

The *Lanham Act* was enacted in 1946 to specify what types of brand names and marks can be protected by law, and provides registration records to facilitate their protection. The Act gives public notice of a company's intent to use a particular trademark, but it does not establish ownership of a mark; a company actually has to offer the trademarked product for sale on a continuing basis and be able to prove that it was the first to use the particular mark. Registering under the Lanham Act is indispensable to protect a trademark to be used in foreign commerce.

A firm with a popular brand name or trademark must beware that it will not become a common descriptive term for that kind of product—a *generic* term—so that the name becomes public property, with the owner losing all rights to it. This has happened with such names as cellophane, aspirin, nylon, linoleum, kerosene, and shredded wheat. Names now on the borderline of becoming generic, and therefore public domain, are Frigidaire, Kleenex, Xerox, Band-Aid, Kodak, and Scotch Tape. Care must be taken in the promotion to indicate that such product names are brand names and not generic.

Private Brands

There are two general types of brands, depending upon who does the branding: dealer brands and manufacturer brands. Wholesalers and retailers often use their own brands—commonly referred to as private brands—in place of or in addition to the branded goods of manufacturers. Manufacturer brands are called national brands because of their widespread promotion; this is sometimes a misnomer since some dealer brands, such as those of Penney's and Sears, also

---

[16] "The Great Rush for New Products," *Time*, October 24, 1969, p. 93.
[17] Ibid.

In this photo, both manufacturer and dealer brands are visible, as well as many different container sizes. Brand proliferation is also suggested; catsup is the only product shown. *Photo by Helena Frost.*

have national distribution and promotion. National or manufacturers' brands include Magnavox, Wheaties, Green Giant, Hart Schaffner & Marx, RCA, and Westinghouse. Dealer brands—those of wholesalers and retailers—also known as private brands, include AMC (major department-store buying group), Towncraft (Penney's men's furnishings), Ann Page (A&P), and Kenmore (Sears appliances).

The private or dealers' brands usually are lower-priced than the nationally advertised brands, reflecting the promotional savings involved. They are made to dealers' specifications and often by large and reputable manufacturers—for example, General Electric makes appliances for J. C. Penney. Sometimes, despite a lower selling price, these dealer brands may actually be made to more rigid and demanding quality standards than those carrying the manufacturers' names.

With private branded goods directly competing with manufacturers' own labeled goods, sometimes at a better price, this question can be raised: why do manufacturers such as General Electric sell some goods to a retailer under the retailer's brand? A major reason is that manufacturers may utilize more effectively their production facilities and prevent idle plant capacity. The manufacturer can always rationalize that if he refuses business with the private-label seeker, someone else will not refuse, and the competition will not be eliminated. Many manufacturers are too small and lack the resources and know-how to enter the marketplace effectively with their own brands.

A caveat is in order, however, especially for small manufacturers. If a significant proportion of output is going to a certain middleman's brand, there is risk. The dealer is in a powerful position and may exert pressure for price reductions or better quality; there is the threat, always implicit and sometimes explicit, to take business to another manufacturer. Usually a manufacturer has to be content with a lower per-unit profit than if selling under his own brand. However, despite drawbacks to manufacturers, there is usually no lack of firms willing to meet the private-label wants of retailers and wholesalers.

And many large dealers want their own brands. They can often obtain a higher per-unit profit since they are buying goods at more favorable terms. They have better control over repeat business, since satisfied customers can repurchase the item only through the particular dealer. A major incentive for private-brand development occurred when discount stores in their period of rapid growth undercut traditional retailers on many nationally branded items. Often unable to match the lower prices of the discount merchants, other retailers turned to private brands—especially in appliances and items where price comparisons were most easily made—thereby giving them a differentiated product and some insulation from price competition.

While in most stores, nationally advertised brands account for the largest proportion of sales, this proportion is steadily decreasing. Some large chain retailers offer mostly goods carrying their own brand.[18] As retailers find that customers accept their lower-priced private brands, they are eager to push these with better displays because of their better markups. Many consumers today seek out private brands as an attractive alternative to the higher prices of manufacturers' brands carrying the heavy burden of mass advertising expenditures. As an example of the price difference sometimes found between dealer and nationally advertised brands, in 1974 a 14-oz size of Listerine was selling at 79 cents in many drugstores. A private brand with similar ingredients listed and virtually the same taste was also available at these same stores for 88 cents a quart bottle (32 oz). A manufacturer can delude himself into thinking his advertised brand conveys more customer loyalty than it really does, and become vulnerable to price competition.

Two segments of the consumer market are heavily loyal to nationally advertised brands: the upper-lower class or working-class group, and the black ghetto dweller. Some researchers attribute this

---

[18] "A&P's Own Brand of Consumerism," *Business Week*, April 11, 1970, p. 32; "The Public's Crush on Private Labels," *Time*, October 4, 1971, pp. 79–80.

to these groups' feeling of uncertainty and lack of skill in the marketplace.[19]

Brand Strategy

A strategy consideration for multiproduct companies is whether to use a *family brand* for all products, or to have separate brands for each individual item or each group of products.

Libby, Heinz, Campbell, General Electric, and Johnson effectively use one brand for all products. It is simpler and less expensive to introduce a new product under the family brand than to try to develop customer acceptance for a new and different brand. The reputation of the company enfolds any new products introduced under the company's brand name. The image of the company itself may be enhanced as additional products—hopefully, forward-looking—continue to enter the marketplace bearing the common brand of the firm.

On the other hand, Procter & Gamble, Lever Brothers, Sears, and Penney's use a separate name either for each product or for each group of similar products. They feel that these products can be promoted more aggressively if they carry their own names. Different quality levels may best be reflected with different brands, as A&P uses Ann Page, Sultana, and Iona to denote different price classes. If products are sufficiently different, such as crackers and laundry detergents, a family brand might be unwise. General Foods, Lever Brothers, and Procter & Gamble find further justification for individual brands in that intrafirm competition may be spurred by the different company brands competing with each other; if business is lost, it may well be lost to another brand of the company.

Sometimes a manufacturer finds it desirable to use different brands to distribute goods through different channels, such as to department stores and to price-cutting discount stores; thereby price comparisons cannot be made and both channels are satisfied. This opportunistic approach will be discussed more fully in the next chapter.

NEW PRODUCT PROBLEMS AND OPPORTUNITIES

Risk of Market Failure

We have previously discussed the high rate of market failure of new products. Even the prestigious International Business Machines Cor-

---

[19] Lee Rainwater, Richard P. Coleman, and Gerald Handel, *Workingman's Wife* (New York: Oceana Publications, 1959); R. A. Bauer, S. M. Cunningham, and L. H. Wortzel, "The Marketing Dilemma of Negroes," *Journal of Marketing*, July 1965, pp. 1–6.

poration can stumble and introduce new products that fail to live up to expectations. In the brief span of 18 months, IBM quietly dropped four major products: microfilm equipment, offset duplicators, voting machines, and production-control systems.

MARKETING
IN
ACTION

Ollie's Burgers—Engineering a New Product Success

James Y. Brown, Jr., in 1964, bought Colonel Sanders' "secret recipe" and his 600 chicken franchises for $2 million. Eight years later he sold Kentucky Fried Chicken to Heublein for $245 million. Then he bought Lum's, a financially distressed fast-food chain that specialized in beer and hotdogs. He brought Lum's into the black, but believed that really to vitalize it, he needed to find the "hamburger of all hamburgers."

Accordingly, he sent his top executives on a nationwide search. Their eventual recommendation was a hamburger sold at Ollie's, a seven-stool hole-in-the-wall in Miami Beach. This, with a special grill designed to seal in the juices, and a special sauce, sells for $1 at Ollie's.

In order to tap a potentially promising segment of the market— the lunchtime office worker downtown—Brown leased a corner in downtown Louisville, Kentucky, and spent $30,000 to build a 9-ft. by 12-ft. modular building that was designed to look like a trolley car (normally, a Kentucky Fried Chicken unit costs $250,000, while a McDonald's unit is about $400,000). If the location had not worked out, the "trolley" could have been moved for less than $10,000. But the first year, the original Ollie's Trolley had sales of $250,000 and made a net profit of $75,000. Other units were quickly opened and another fast-food chain is in the ascendancy.

SOURCE: "From Colonel Sanders to General Glickenhaus," *Business Week*, November 9, 1974, pp. 134–40.

For thought and discussion:

No marketing research was apparently done for this new "concept" introduction. Subjective judgment only was relied upon. What rationale can you give for entering the market without a better research base?

What kind of marketing research—if any—would you have recommended?

IBM went into microfilm, the most significant of the four discontinued products, without a definitive marketing plan. It had the technical competence, and the expectations had been to generate more volume for aperture cards (IBM tab cards that contain chips of film). "It was like the razor blade manufacturer who makes razors to produce more razor blade business."[20] But IBM was unable to buck successfully the 3M Company and Eastman Kodak, who were already factors in this market. While even a company priding itself on highly efficient management can err when it comes to new products, the speed of the decisions to cut these unprofitable products reflects probably the greater efficiency.

MARKETING
MISTAKE

Du Pont's Corfam Failure

Du Pont introduced Corfam in 1964. It was a leather substitute used in shoes and was ballyhooed as an innovation as important for shoes as nylon was for stockings. The product had uniformity, durability, water repellency, and resistance to creasing or cracking. Reaction was enthusiastic: by the end of 1964 many major shoe manufacturers were using Corfam in their shoes and plans were underway for worldwide marketing. In 1966 Du Pont continued to report that demand exceeded production capacity. How could such a product be a failure?

But it was. Profitwise, Corfam had always lagged. Cheaper competitive products resulted in falling prices. What Du Pont failed to foresee was the willingness of people to put up with less durable shoe materials for rapidly changing styles. Furthermore, many people found Corfam to be uncomfortably hot in the summer. Early in 1971, Du Pont dropped Corfam after losing about $100 million since it was introduced.

SOURCE: "Exit Corfam," *Barron's*, March 22, 1971, p. 1.

For thought and discussion:

How could this mistake have been prevented?

Do you think Du Pont gave up too soon?

Rewards of New Product Success

Despite the substantial risks that accompany the introduction of most new products, rewards can be great. Let us take the early days of the snowmobile as an example of such success.

In five years—1965 to 1970—the use of snowmobiles in the United States and Canada rose from 15,000 to 700,000. Snowmobiling became the fastest-growing winter sport, and a $400 million industry. With such growth, spectacular individual success stories abounded. In 1967, an engineer made a few snowmobiles in his garage; in December 1969, his Couparral Company was acquired by Studebaker-Worthington for over $3 million. Rodco, Inc., sales grew

[20] "When Products Fail IBM's Tough Test," *Business Week*, December 20, 1969, pp. 20–21.

from 500 units to 12,000 in three years. Bombardier, Ltd., a Canadian firm, sales rose from $12.9 million in 1965 to well over $100 million for 1969, with earnings topping $15 million.[21]

As is often the case with significantly different innovations, small companies and individuals first developed the product. Big firms with their research departments and their engineers hesitated. Only after the trend was fairly well established did they become eager to enter the market, buying out the brash innovators (usually at a very good price). But sometimes the timing is bad—the trend upward begins to level off, perhaps too many firms are attracted, and a violent shakeout occurs. This happened to the snowmobile industry, as over 50 manufacturers vied to supply a demand already saturated.

Perhaps the ultimate competitive challenge for any firm is to enter a market successfully and wrest a substantial share of it away from an already strongly entrenched competitor. In chapter 9 we saw how Honda did this by appealing to an entirely different segment of the motorcycle market. Now we will look at a classic example of successful penetration by direct frontal assault.

---

[21] "A Red-hot Winter for Snowmobiles," *Business Week,* January 10, 1970, pp. 34–35.

MARKETING
IN
ACTION

The Attack on Crisco

In 1936 Procter & Gamble's Crisco shortening dominated its field; it was the only nationally advertised product of its kind; its brand name was a household word as the result of years of aggressive promotion. A 1936 national survey of households found Crisco named as the brand of shortening used by 58 percent—no other brand was named by as many as 8 percent of the women surveyed. Up to this time no threat to Crisco's dominant position was in sight.

But by the end of 1936 this picture was changing and Crisco's leadership was threatened. Lever Brothers launched Spry with a whirlwind introductory campaign that is still considered a classic in merchandising efforts. During 1936, nine million homes were visited by Spry sampling crews who left free cans of Spry, cookbooks of Spry recipes, and coupons worth 10 cents on the purchase of Spry. The result? For 1937, Spry sales reached $12 million compared to $25 million for long-established Crisco, and in subsequent years the margin between the two brands narrowed considerably.

The success of Spry was the result of almost five years spent developing and perfecting before a factory was even built to make the product. Initially, marketing research efforts were made to determine if Crisco had any product limitations which might represent competitive opportunity. Depth interviews were made with Crisco users and generally revealed that Crisco was considered an excellent product but did have some shortcomings: there was an occasional lack of uniformity in color, flavor, and consistency; if not kept refrigerated, it turned rancid, while if too cold, it was hard to use in recipes. At this point, consumer research guided technical research in the product development; no attempt was made to enter the shortening market until a new product had been developed which had clear-cut advantages over Crisco.

Speed was emphasized in the promotional planning so that the new product could quickly reach the maximum number of housewives. This was deemed essential, since a slower-moving campaign would have given Procter & Gamble time to improve Crisco and thus dull the definite advantages which spearheaded Spry's entry into this market.

Perhaps the bigget credit for the successful penetration of Spry is attributable to the executives of Procter & Gamble. They ignored the five years of product research backing the introduction of Spry, the extensive research, even the building of a whole new factory.

SOURCE: Adapted from Richard D. Crisp, *Marketing Research* (New York: McGraw-Hill, 1957), pp. 285–87.

For thought and discussion:
Under what conditions would you recommend a frontal attack be used in gaining competitive entry?

When would you recommend such a frontal attack not be used?

Steps in New Product Development

A new product is the culmination of a process, a series of steps beginning with the generation of ideas and proceeding to the commercialization or full-scale marketing of the product. In this process, product ideas pass successive hurdles during which many are eliminated from further consideration. Figure 10-7 illustrates this sequence.

Ideas for new products or product improvements can come from a variety of sources. Customer suggestions and complaints may be a fertile field. Some companies bring groups of consumers together to discuss the merits and shortcomings of products. In many companies, research and development departments are geared to a never-ending effort to find practical new products. Competitors can sometimes be a significant source of product ideas. Some large companies pursue a policy of waiting for competitors to innovate; only after someone else has taken the risk and succeeded will they enter the market, either with a similar product or by means of acquisition of a smaller firm. Salesmen, top management, various staff personnel, all may be sources of product ideas.

Given a large supply of ideas, the remaining steps in the new

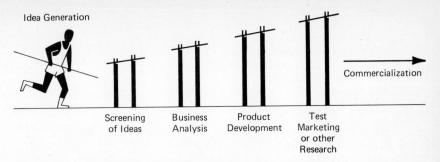

Figure 10-7. Hurdles for New Product Ideas

product development process will necessarily deal with reducing from further consideration those obviously unfit or impractical, and those at variance with company objectives and resources. If the idea does not fit in with existing production facilities, marketing structure, and manpower and executive resources, it would hardly receive further consideration unless there were mitigating circumstances, such as unusual potential. Sales and profit potential, and present and future status of competition are further factors to be weighed before the green light is given leading to final production, market testing, and product launching. Many companies find a checklist or rating scale useful in weeding out product candidates and in deciding which are worth further consideration.

MARKETING TOOL

Rating Scale for Evaluating New Product Ideas
In developing a new-product idea rating scale, the following factors may be deemed important:

Demand—extent of existing or latent demand
Marketing compatiblity—how well the proposed product fits in with existing products, promotional techniques, and distribution channels.
Durability—probable life cycle of the product and the likelihood of severe competitive intrusion
Production capability—how well product fits in with existing production capabilities
Growth potential—long term sales growth prospects
Some firms will assign different weights to these factors, assuming therefore that some are more important than others. For example, these may be the assigned weights:

Factor	Factor Weight
Demand	.20
Marketing compatibility	.25
Durability	.10
Production capability	.30
Growth potential	.15
	1.00

With these factors and factor weights agreed upon, various new product ideas can be assessed accordingly, and those with the highest ratings receiving the go-ahead for further development and research.

Now both the decision on the factors and their relative importance, and the rating of particular product ideas, rest on the subjective judgment of the executives concerned—their estimates of future possibilities. And these "guesstimates" can be wrong. But such a rating scale provides for a more organized and systematic approach to the evaluation; normally this produces better results than relying entirely on hunch or intuition.

SOURCE: Partially adapted from Mark E. Stern, *Marketing Planning: A Systems Approach* (New York: McGraw-Hill, 1966), p. 53.

For thought and discussion:

According to the above weighted factors, which product would more likely receive the go-ahead: (1) a product with modest expected demand, but which would fit in well with present production and marketing capability, or (2) a product with estimated strong latent demand, but which would require different production facilities and different distribution channels?

Do you think this is a wise ordering of priorities? Why?

Product development can take a surprisingly long time. One researcher investigated the elapsed time between the start of development and large-scale or national distribution for forty-two products. Some of these findings are shown in Table 10-3.[22] This suggests that many firms need to widen their perspectives, that they need to be looking ahead, not one or two years, but five to ten years in their new product ideas.

However, many firms today are finding that they can no longer afford the luxury of slow, careful development and introduction of new products. In 1972, some 6000 new products were introduced in drug and grocery channels alone, more than twice the number ten years before. There is an urgency to get the product on the market ahead of competitors, but this often leads to new product failure.[23]

[22] Lee Adler, "Time Lag in New Product Development," *Journal of Marketing,* January 1966, p. 17.

[23] "New Products: The Push Is On Marketing," *Business Week,* March 4, 1972, pp. 72–77.

Table 10-3.
Elapsed Time Between Date Development
Started and Large-Scale Distribution

Product	Years	Product	Years
Frozen foods	15	Frozen orange juice	2
Fluoride toothpaste	10	Minute rice	18
Strained baby foods	1	Dry dog food	4
Instant coffee	22	Automatic washer	12
Liquid shampoo	8	Plastic tile	6
Filter cigarettes	2	Electric toothbrush	4
Zipper	80	Soil conditioners	12
Television	55	Electrostatic copying	15
Transistors	16	Liquid detergent	1
Roll-on deodorant	6	Dry soup mixes	19

Source: Lee Adler, "Time Lag in New Product Development," *Journal of Marketing*, January 1966, pp. 17–21.

Product ideas and marketing opportunities sometimes lie in strange directions. Imagination and the willingness to take some risks may be unexpectedly rewarding. An example of this is the successful reviving of an old product, a cast-off of Bristol-Myers Company. Ipana toothpaste had been heavily promoted in the 1920s and into the 1940s; it had carved out a sizable share of the market, using the theme warning against "pink toothbrush." In time other brands supplanted Ipana, and Bristol-Myers dropped it.

Then in the late 1960s, a small firm in Minnesota obtained the rights to use the Ipana name, package, and formula from Bristol-Myers. Not attempting to compete with the promotional efforts of the behemoths of the industry, this firm spent nothing on advertising, believing that the name would still have sufficient memorability and acceptance with the older generation to gain a niche in the marketplace. And without the vast sums spent for advertising of most toothpaste marketers, the selling price could be attractive. The firm was so successful that it expanded its product line: Ipana mouthwash was introduced at promotional prices to go along with the revival of Ipana toothpaste.

IMPLICATIONS OF PRODUCT PROLIFERATION

Implications for the Firm

The rush for new products and the resulting dynamics of the marketplace are placing new demands on executives. Conservatism can penalize and even jeopardize a firm. The erosion of brand loyalty, which results when new products proliferate, lessens the security of almost every firm and its brands. But this creates opportunities for other firms.

Profusion of new products does lead to marketing inefficiencies —not only from the sheer number of product failures, but also from higher promotional and distribution costs. But the other extreme poses far less desirable consequences. AT&T, the largest corporation in the world, as a government-regulated utility is entrusted with the national communications system. In its monopoly and utility status, and without the incentives and problems created by a competitive environment, its marketing function has atrophied. New products and services slowly and grudgingly win management approval. For example:

> Although Bell Laboratories invented the transistor in 1948,
> it took 10 years for the device to win general approval for use
> in equipment. And only recently has solid-state circuitry
> begun to replace the system's electromechanical equipment.
> Bell expects it will take 40 years to complete the changeover
> to electronic exchanges. New products or services are viewed
> with the same caution. Where most companies would be
> overjoyed at finding a winner, AT&T managers speak of the
> difficulties of satisfying the "avalanche effect": if an innovation
> is made anywhere in the system, it must be made everywhere.[24]

Implications for Consumers

Consumers are confused by the competing claims, the barrage of "New!" products, and their own inability to appraise them. New products may represent progress, improvements in our standard of living, and the advances of science and technology, but one may question whether all "new" products are meeting any real needs. David Ogilvy in *Confessions of an Advertising Man* says,

> The two most powerful words you can use in a headline are
> Free and New. You can seldom use FREE, but you can always
> use NEW—if you try hard enough.

A good part of product proliferation reflects this desire to come up with some teasing modification that can legitimately carry the caption, "New!" But there now is evidence that some consumers are satiated by "newness" claims, and hence discount them.[25]

More substantial improvements are needed. Not all product im-

---

[24] *Business Week*, December 27, 1969, p. 48.

[25] Michael L. Dean, James F. Engel, and W. Wayne Talarzyk, "The Influence of Package Copy Claims on Consumer Product Evaluations," *Journal of Marketing*, April 1972, pp. 34–39.

provements need be innovative features; a return to basics might be an improvement in some areas—a return to reliability and good craftsmanship, for example. Then there is the New Products Action Team, Inc., which is

1. Searching for a buyer for Instant Elephant breakfast-food kernels, which pop into animal shapes when milk is added.
2. Concocting scents for leather products and other goods— "The biggest lure after sight is smell," says their president.[26]

QUESTIONS AND PROBLEMS

1. What advertising strategies are apt to be used when a product is in the maturity stage of its life cycle? Why?
2. What effect does planned product obsolescence have on the marketing mix?
3. Should a product be discontinued when little or no profit is being made on its sale? Explain.
4. How is the risk of product decisions different in retailing than in manufacturing? What are the implications of this?
5. Decisions on branding:
   (a) If a retailer, what factors should you consider in deciding whether or not to have your own brand?
   (b) If a manufacturer, what factors should you consider in deciding whether to manufacture under distributor brands?
   (c) If you decide to use your own brand, should you have (1) one brand for all products, (2) different brands for different products?
6. Why do you think so many products turn out to be market failures? Can you think of some practical remedies for correcting this extreme failure situation?
7. Most products nowadays have very short life cycles. Yet there are a few that have life cycles of decades. Can you name some of these long-lived products? What do you see as accounting for such atypical longevity?
8. How would you systematize: (a) the screening of new product ideas, (b) the phasing out of weak products?

Project

Make a list of five products aggressively marketed today that you think will have disappeared five years from now. Make another list of five products which you think will still be used ten years from now. Explain your rationale.

[26] *Time*, October 24, 1969, p. 92.

Exercise in Creativity

How many new product ideas can you come up with in the areas of (1) personal grooming, (2) small kitchen appliances, (3) sporting goods, and (4) specialty packaged foods?

Role-playing Case

You are the brand manager for a line of cosmetics that has been on the market for six months. As brand manager you are responsible for the advertising, packaging, dealer participation, and, to a small extent, the pricing. Sales, while growing slowly, have not reached plan. Today you are called to the marketing manager's office.

"Marge," he says, "We need to come to a decision on your 'Nocturne' items. The boss wants to ax them—as you know we're losing money on the brand. But I wanted to get your views first."

"Jerry, I think we should stick with the brand a while longer."

What rationale would you present for continuing with these poorly performing products? Support your recommendations as strongly as possible.

CHAPTER 11

CHANNEL OF

DISTRIBUTION

DECISIONS

How a firm is to distribute its products—the channel of distribution —is a major decision for any firm, and a major problem for the small unknown firm seeking to gain market entry. We consider in this chapter the factors affecting distribution for both consumer and industrial goods. Aspects of channel conflict and channel cooperation are examined. Finally, deficiencies of certain channel arrangements are scrutinized. Important terms are:

intensive distribution   **consignment**
selective distribution   **pushing strategy**
exclusive distribution   **pulling strategy**
symbiotic relationship   **channel leadership**
derived demand   **vertical marketing system**
                                    routinization

THE MARKETING CHANNEL

The sequence of marketing institutions—retailers, wholesalers and other middlemen—for a product moving from producer to ultimate consumer or industrial user is the channel of distribution. (The channel does not include the transportation agencies or the banks and other nonmiddlemen who are not involved in buying and selling negotiations. It should also be noted that when a product is altered or transformed, as a raw material transformed into a finished product, a new channel is started.)

A channel may be considered as having "levels" and "length." Each institution (beginning with the producer) that takes ownership of a product as it moves to the consumer or industrial user is a *level*. The length refers to the number of these levels, irrespective of the

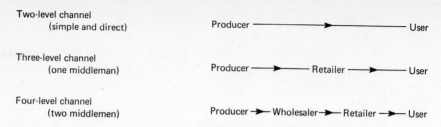

Figure 11-1. Alternative Marketing Channels

physical distance over which the item may be moved.[1] Figure 11-1 depicts some of the less complex channels of varying lengths.

The simplistic channel utilizing no marketing intermediaries characterized the primitive barter economies at the dawn of civilization and is prevalent in the remote regions of the world today. Yet it is not inappropriate to an advanced economy, provided the producer is willing and able to assume the functions normally performed by middlemen, and if the nature of the product and that of the customer is such as to encourage direct distribution. Books and phonograph records may be sold by mail directly to consumers. Vacuum cleaners are sold door-to-door by the manufacturer's own sales force, as are cosmetics, brushes, pots and pans, and a number of other products. Other manufacturers have their own retail outlets: Firestone, Sherwin-Williams, and Bond Clothes are a few examples of this.

Many industrial products—goods bought by manufacturers for use in producing other goods—use direct channels. A high unit value, complexity of product requiring technical expertise which only the manufacturer can provide in selling and servicing, and the importance of firm delivery-time commitments, motivates this form of distribution. Such factors necessitate the direct channels used by IBM for their computers and systems hardware.

The inclusion of a single middleman—a retailer or wholesaler—between the producer and consumer is a common channel. In such a three-level channel industrial wholesalers may be used by some manufacturers, such as in building materials and maintenance supplies. Many large retailers buy directly from manufacturers, at least for some products. They seldom satisfy all their requirements in this way, however. Even the largest retailer may underestimate merchandise needs and find it advantageous to replenish some items from a nearby wholesaler, rather than be out of stock, and consequently lose sales, until a shipment can be received from a distant manufacturer.

[1] Louis P. Bucklin, "The Marketing System and Channel Management," in Frederick D. Sturdivant et al., *Managerial Analysis in Marketing* (Glenview, Ill.: Scott, Foresman, 1970), pp. 565–67.

Distribution from producer to wholesaler to retailer to consumer (the four-level channel of Figure 11-1) is probably the most common one in the United States. As we have seen earlier in the discussion of wholesalers and their services, there are ample reasons for this utilization of the additional channel member, the wholesaler. The retailer is able to get better service, buy smaller amounts (thus reducing inventory costs), and obtain quick replenishment of stock. The manufacturer can deal with a few wholesalers rather than a host of retailers, and thereby reduce selling and distribution costs.

These are the common "basic" channels of distribution. Usually channels are much more complex than this: a single product may be distributed directly to some customers (perhaps the larger ones), while it may pass through the hands of a number of intermediaries to reach other customers. Generally the channel arrangement reflects the best way to reach certain target customers who may have diverse requirements and customs. Figure 11-2 shows the complex marketing channels used by a specialty electrical-goods manufacturer. The different markets for the several product lines require using different types of intermediaries with varying profit margins and often separate sales forces in the manufacturer-middleman interface.

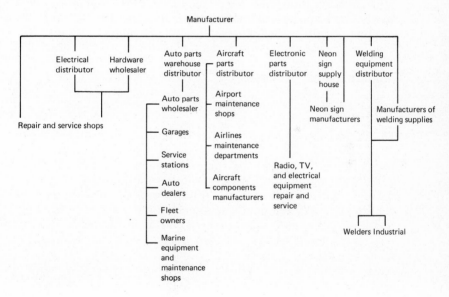

Figure 11-2. Complex Marketing Channel for a Manufacturer of Electrical Wire and Cable

Source: Edwin H. Lewis, "Distributing Electrical Products in a Dynamic Economy," *Electrical Wholesaling*, June 1958, pp. 97–119.

The Channel as a System

The marketing channel is best thought of as a system through which a product moves, rather than as fragmented, uncoordinated independent marketing institutions. While it is true that most channels are composed of independent firms, they need to operate in a spirit of cooperation, coordination, and with actions directed to mutual advantage. This suggests that competition is interchannel rather than intrachannel: various channel systems are then competing against each other.[2] For any system there is a need for some leadership (which may be assumed by the producer, or by a powerful retailer, or less frequently, by a wholesaler), and for integrated efforts, and for controls to provide the feedback for any corrective actions needed. We will discuss in more detail channel of distribution decisions and problems: channel administration, the possibility of channel conflict and the need for cooperation, the factors affecting choice of channels, and other related matters.

Channels evolve to cater to the particular needs of their producers and consumers. Producers and buyers have differing marketing capabilities; consequently, diverse channels may develop even for the same product. As long as the additional costs of a longer channel can be offset by other efficiencies, a channel system is viable. This suggests then that the employment of a lengthy channel is not evidence of marketing inefficiency—as some critics would maintain —which would be best corrected with the elimination of middlemen. The lengthy channel rather may reflect the sophisticated evolution of the marketing institutions best able to meet the needs of their producers and customers.

Channel Alternatives

The manufacturer has a number of alternatives for getting his products into the hands of final users. Success can come in different trappings as is evident in the relative performance of the Revlon and Avon companies. These two firms market similar products but through entirely different marketing channels: Revlon uses the conventional consumer goods channel, going through middlemen and retailers, with heavy consumer advertising; Avon sells directly to final consumers through its own door-to-door sales force, and uses relatively small amounts of consumer advertising. Sales in 1974 for Avon reached $1,260 million, for a five-year annual sales growth rate of 15.4 percent; Revlon's revenues were $609 million, with an annual sales growth rate of 9.8 percent.[3]

[2] This essentially is suggested by William P. Dommermuth and R. Clifton Andersen. "Distribution Systems: Firms, Functions, and Efficiencies," *MSU Business Topics,* Spring 1969, pp. 51–56.

[3] Figures compiled from *Forbes,* May 15, 1975, pp. 163, 164; and January 1, 1975, p. 174.

From these figures it might seem that Avon has the more successful approach to distribution and that Revlon might be wise to change its policies and distribute directly to consumers. However, it is doubtful if the door-to-door method of selling cosmetics and related products to housewives could furnish enough potential for two large and aggressive firms. And Revlon, with its strong brand identification developed by mass advertising, and its entrenched position in most major retail firms, has exhibited a consistent growth pattern and one likely to continue.

MARKETING
IN
ACTION

Successful Change of Traditional Channel—Hoover

Felix Mansager started with Hoover in 1929 as one of its many door-to-door salesmen. The company and its vacuum cleaners had prospered through the decades, and Mansager was one of the best salesmen. But it became obvious to him that the company was spending more time hiring than selling: turnover of salesmen was as high as 60 percent in one year. Furthermore, door-to-door selling precluded broadening the product line: a salesman could only carry so many samples of merchandise to demonstrate—and vacuum cleaners were bulky.

Eventually Mansager was promoted to sales manager of the North and South Dakota territory, after World War II. And he gave up door-to-door selling and formed a group of dealer-supervisors to oversee and train retailers. The plan worked so well that it was expanded nationwide.

Not surprisingly, Mansager became Hoover's president. Today more than 50 products are marketed, ranging from electric fondue pots to washing machines. And door-to-door selling has been abandoned.

SOURCE: "The Challenger from North Canton," *Forbes,* June 15, 1972, p. 60.

For thought and discussion:
Do you think distribution methods for encyclopedias should also be changed?
Why or why not?
How about Avon? Fuller Brush?

IMPORTANCE OF CHANNEL DECISIONS

Channel decisions must rank among the most important marketing decisions of a firm because (1) the channels chosen intimately affect every other marketing decision, and (2) they involve the firm in relatively long-term commitments to other firms.[4] For example, a high-priced, high-quality product offering, and especially one requiring some servicing, can usually best be marketed through a carefully selected and supported dealer network. The type and extent of advertising to be employed depends, at least partially, on the cooperation needed or expected from the middlemen and dealers—sometimes a massive infusion of advertising is needed to induce them to carry the product and in sufficient assortment. The size and quality of a manufacturer's sales force depends on whether it is selling to wholesalers, retailers, or final consumers.

Channel decisions tend to be relatively permanent. They are not easily or quickly changed. The relationships built up with other members of the channel may be broken, but often not without some erosion of public and brand image; furthermore, there may be a disruptive influence on the other members of the channel who begin to view their positions as tenuous and consequently begin the search to establish relations with competitive firms. Even very large and financially strong companies such as General Motors would incur severe financial strains and perhaps legal difficulties in changing channels: the task of buying out its 18,000 independent dealers or of supporting them in some other endeavor would be a monumental undertaking.

Consequently, compared to decisions about price, product features, packaging, promotional efforts, and other marketing decisions, those dealing with channels must be regarded as long term and capable of only gradual modification. Yet with the dynamics of the marketplace, channel decisions must constantly be reevaluated for their fitness in the probable future environment.

During periods of major retail institutional changes, channel reevaluation becomes more important. Traditional and existing channel arrangements may be less able to compete effectively with the "innovistic competition," and other possible opportunities may begin to emerge. In these circumstances, relationships may need to be severed, despite a long and mutually beneficial experience and one of amity and trust. When the discount houses were in their period of greatest expansion a decade or so ago—and were anathema to traditional retailers—existing channel arrangements were jeopardized and many manufacturers faced a dilemma regarding their distributors.

In the late 1950s and early 1960s, discounting experienced a period of rapid growth: sales rose from practically zero in 1955 to $4.5 billion in 1961.[5] With such growth, the attractiveness of doing

[4] Philip Kotler, *Marketing Management* (Englewood Cliffs, N.J.: Prentice-Hall, 1967), p. 386.
[5] Charles E. Silberman, "The Revolutionists of Retailing," *Fortune*, April 1962, pp. 99–102.

business with discounters became almost irresistible. But the avowed policies of the discount merchants—to discount from list price and to underprice conventional retailers—made it virtually impossible for most manufacturers to do business with the new "rebels," and still retain their old customers. No department store could tolerate having its same brands and products offered by the discount store at 20 percent less. It could either match the discounter's price and lose money since operating expenses and overhead were higher, or it could risk the lost sales and, more importantly, the ill will of its customers who could see in the price comparisons the tangible benefits of buying from a discount store.

Manufacturers were thus in the quandary: whether to forsake the old and familiar, for the unknown and militantly aggressive. One solution was that of Fieldcrest Mills (see Marketing in Action box). While discount stores were growing rapidly, their future was not clear and many were shaky financially. A manufacturer with a recognized quality image risked this by offering his goods to discounters.

MARKETING
IN
ACTION

Doing Business with Discounters, and Old Customers Too:
The Fieldcrest Solution
Fieldcrest manufactured high-quality linens and bedding—towels, bedspreads, sheets, etc.—sold primarily in the best department and specialty stores under the "Fieldcrest" label. It was not willing to sacrifice this business and this quality image. Consequently it developed another brand and a different packaging to sell to discounters and called it "St. Mary's." The merchandise mix was changed slightly so that the highest-priced items were not included in the St. Mary's line, but otherwise the goods were basically the same.

In the early 1960s the antagonism of regular merchants for discounters was so intense that Fieldcrest found problems in the intermingling of the two groups of buyers in its New York display offices. Accordingly, a separate "back-room" display office was established for the discount merchandisers. And the company continued to pursue business with both types of retailers, using ostensibly different products. The success of the strategy is reflected in sales more than doubling from 1958 to 1964 (growing from $66 million to almost $135 million), while profits tripled (from $6 million to $18 million during these 6 years).

For thought and discussion:
Do you see any drawbacks to the Fieldcrest strategy (a) from the viewpoint of the manufacturer, (b) from the viewpoint of the discounter?

Services Expected from Channel Members

In determining the amount of service to be provided by distributors and dealers, a manufacturer must weigh the relative merits of *breadth of coverage* and *depth of coverage*. It is generally impossible to have both, and some compromise must be made. Breadth refers to the number of outlets desired, the intensity of distribution: the more outlets, the greater breadth or intensity. Depth pertains to the amount of service expected of the middleman.

Incompatibility between the two basic approaches exists because the middleman logically expects to receive more profit for his efforts if he provides more services. More profit generally translates into some protection from competition, some preferential treatment. This usually takes the form of limited distribution, offering the brand and product only to a few wholesalers and retailers, and giving them rather exclusive rights to distribute in a certain area. Consequently, for those products requiring extra effort on the part of middlemen, because of service or other aspects of the product, breadth of distribution has to be sacrificed for depth.

Intensity of Distribution

The greater the intensity of distribution—the breadth—the greater the market exposure, provided that the middlemen furnish at least the minimum of service needed to display the product. The degrees of market exposure can be viewed along a continuum, ranging from intensive, selective, to exclusive distribution:

Degree of Market Exposure:
Intensity of Distribution

Exclusive	Selective	Intensive

Number of outlets ———→

In an *intensive distribution* the product or service is available through as many wholesalers and retailers as possible. They are urged simply to carry the product. Little selling effort is expected (although there may be some inducements offered—through display materials, racks, and the like—for the dealer to display the product prominently). The dealer usually has no service responsibilities, and probably does not promote (except through counter display).

In *selective distribution* the producer limits the use of middlemen to those he considers to be the best available. These may be the largest, those with the best service standards, the most effective sales organization, and the best reputation. A manufacturer needs at least one outlet in every major trading center, and he may seek more in order to have adequate market coverage. Provided the product is a wanted item and brand, he will probably not use all the intermediaries willing to carry it. In return for the "privilege" of having the particular brand and the lessening of competition because of limited distribution, the dealer is expected to provide more service, carry a more complete inventory, do some promoting himself, provide market feedback, and so on. Also, the manufacturer can expect to have less price cutting than under a more intensive form of distribution, since competition between dealers will be limited. There should be a much closer working relationship and rapport on the part of the producer and the dealer, simply because they depend on each other. This is sometimes referred to as a *symbiotic relationship* in that, while dissimilar, they work together for mutual advantage.[6]

At the extreme of selectivity is *exclusive distribution*. Here distribution of products is severely limited and the distributor is provided the fullest protection from competition and has exclusive rights within a territory. Maximum service and control is expected by the manufacturer. Sometimes promotional and service facilities may be jointly developed, and in many other respects a close relationship is fostered.

With most products—except those highly specialized where very limited markets exist—a manufacturer is faced with the problem of developing the best middlemen and the right number to maximize his market exposure without unduly sacrificing the depth of services that may be required. Probably more mistakes are made on the side of too few outlets than too many (although most middlemen would disagree with this). Lack of sufficient salesmen and time to contact desirable dealers, or their commitment to competing brands, contribute to this.

Another factor that operates to limit the number of outlets is the manufacturer's desire for greater control. Fewer outlets mean more direction over the pricing, promotion, service, training, and merchandising of the market intermediaries. Therefore the exclusive arrangement—while it may provide insufficient market coverage for many products—facilitates more control by the producer. Some manufacturers in their quest for the greatest direction over their channels have even attempted to distribute their products through their own warehouses and retail outlets so as to achieve vertical integration. Usually some compromise has to be made between sufficient market coverage and adequate, if not perfect, controls.

Classification of Consumer Goods and Intensity of Distribution

Related to the intensity of distribution is the classification of consumer goods into convenience, shopping, and specialty items. Refer

[6] For a discussion of other aspects of symbiotic relationships, see Lee Adler, "Symbiotic Marketing," *Harvard Business Review*, November–December 1966, pp. 59–71.

again to Table 10-1 for a brief description with examples of these consumer goods categories. These should not be viewed as discrete groups, and consumers differ: one product might be considered a shopping good by one customer, while another more loyal to the brand would insist on it, so that it would be a specialty good. Nevertheless, they should be considered in choosing a distribution strategy.

Classification of Consumer Goods

Specialty	Shopping	Convenience

Propensity to exert shopping effort

←———   ———→

more   less

Then it becomes logical to consider intensity of distribution and type of consumer goods and to combine the two models:

Classification of Consumer Goods Related
to Intensity of Distribution

Number of outlets:	Exclusive	Selective	Intensive
Type of goods:	Specialty	Shopping	Convenience

Therefore products that fall in the realm of convenience goods need to achieve intensive distribution if adequate market exposure is to be achieved, and if full potential is to be realized. Goods that fall more in the shopping or even more, in the specialty category, can probably be most advantageously distributed with fewer outlets, perhaps even with an exclusive distribution.

CHARACTERISTICS OF INDUSTRIAL DEMAND AND EFFECT ON CHANNELS

Thus far in the chapter we have been primarily concerned with consumer goods and their channel implications. Industrial goods may pose different channel requirements.

Industrial goods are those purchased for business use rather than for direct consumption; they are either used up in the production of other goods, or become part of the product being produced or assembled. Industrial goods can be classified as: installations, accessory equipment, raw materials, component parts, and operating supplies. (See Table 10-1 for a brief description and examples of these categories.)

Nature of Industrial Demand

The industrial market has a limited number of buyers compared to the consumer market: approximately 11 million versus 200 million consumers, if we include the intermediate customers—those who buy goods for resale to others (such as wholesalers and retailers), and various institutional buyers. This market is even more limited when we consider that most industrial demand is highly specialized, for example, the seller of shoemaking equipment can expect demand to exist only on the part of shoe manufacturers. Furthermore, the greatest buying power lies in the hands of a few firms and their representatives, since a little less than 10 percent of manufacturing firms account for about 80 percent of this business.

The industrial market is also geographically concentrated: the steel industry is mostly located in the Pittsburgh, Cleveland, and Chicago areas, the textile industry predominates in a few southeastern states, aerospace on the West Coast, and so on. Even the retail sector is relatively concentrated since buyers in the central offices of a relatively few chains and buying associations account for the largest volume of retail purchases.

Several other characteristics of the demand differentiate it from the consumer market. Industrial goods are often described as having a *derived demand*. This means that they are dependent on the demand for consumer goods. For example, sales of steel are partly dependent on sales of automobiles and appliances: about one fifth of steel output goes to the automotive industry. Therefore producers of industrial goods may have a strong interest in ultimate consumer demand and even direct some advertising through consumer media.

Many industrial goods face a relatively *inelastic industry demand*. Consequently, changes in prices will have little effect on sales. This phenomenon is partially explained as the consequence of derived demand. Usually the price change of one component going into a single consumer product will not appreciably affect the final price, and therefore will have little effect on final demand. Another factor inducing inelasticity of demand is the postponability of many industrial purchases, especially those involving capital goods, such as machinery and equipment. Demand for these is more dependent on expectations regarding future business than on price changes.

While industry demand is often inelastic (within a reasonable range) for many industrial goods, individual firms may face a decidedly more elastic demand vis-à-vis the other firms in their industry. This is especially true if products are relatively homogeneous, and if there are only a few producers (an oligopolistic market structure). If one producer were to lower his prices, customers would shift to him unless competitors matched his price reductions. In actuality, prices of all firms in such an industry tend to stabilize at a similar price level, with any price changes quickly followed.

Demand in the industrial market tends to be widely fluctuating —much more so than for consumer goods—not only for capital equipment, but also for accessory goods and even raw materials. This is partly a result of the build-up and reduction of inventories of retailers and wholesalers depending on their sales expectations. Because of the erratic nature of the industrial goods market, forecasting demand is difficult; the peaks and valleys of business may lead to a more conservative approach to expanding facilities and sales personnel, and may encourage a firm to seek diversification in order to gain greater stability.

Effect on Marketing Channels

The characteristics of the industrial market structure and demand make it possible to contact the buyers personally, through sales representatives, rather than by mass media. Marketing channels tend to be shorter than for consumer goods. More use is made of direct channels from the manufacturer to the industrial user, eliminating any middlemen, particularly in the case of most installations, parts and fabricated materials, and even much of the accessory equipment.

Usually such products involve a high cost, and require technical expertise in tailoring to the customers' needs and facilities. The industrial market itself usually is rather concentrated, thus facilitating direct contacts Many of these customers are large and prefer to deal directly rather than through an intermediary. The erratic nature of certain aspects of industrial demand also predispose toward short direct channels, since a complex channel structure might be jeopardized in lean years. On the other hand, some smaller manufacturers may use brokers and other agents for their distribution to industrial users, in lieu of developing their own sales force.

FACTORS AFFECTING CHOICE OF CHANNEL

The major factors or constraints influencing the channel decision are the following:

1. Customer characteristics
2. Characteristics of the producing firm
3. Product characteristics
4. Environmental characteristics

Customer Characteristics

Whether a product is intended for the consumer or industrial market is a major determinant of channel composition. Most industrial users prefer to deal directly. If customers, whether retail or industrial, are large, they will probably insist on direct, short channels. Large retail chains and department stores often wish to bypass the wholesaler.

The geographical dispersion of customers affects the channel alternatives. If customers are widely scattered—as, for example, small retail firms—this may make a simple producer to retailer channel impractical because of the heavy expenses involved in contacting and distributing; some type of middleman will almost certainly be required. Customer preferences must be considered. Some will be reluctant to deal with middlemen and prefer to buy directly from manufacturers; others may prefer the convenience and the local services and rapport of nearby middlemen.

Product Characteristics

Earlier in this chapter we considered certain consumer goods characteristics that affect the breadth of coverage and the length of the channel. Other influencing product attributes are: the complexity of the product, its perishability, the degree of fashion, the bulkiness, unit value, service requirements, and the frequency and regularity of purchase needs.

Complex products, such as data processing equipment and many kinds of machinery, require a high degree of technical selling knowledge and expertise in installation which only the manufacturer usually can provide. Perishable items—fresh seafood, dairy and bakery products—because of the dangers involved with delays and repeated handlings, may require more direct marketing. Middlemen, when used (as when many small producers are involved) may be selected because of their special storage facilities. High fashion items, such as women's ready-to-wear, usually require direct, fast distribution, because of the transitory nature of demand for such products. Bulky products are more effectively moved through the use of brokers, agents, and drop shippers who make sales contacts, but do not handle the goods.

Usually the lower the unit value of a product, the longer is the channel of distribution. Many of these goods fall into the convenience goods category which, as noted earlier, is characterized by a longer channel than shopping or specialty goods. A product with substantial service requirements may necessitate direct distribution. Where customers purchase small quantities on a frequent basis, the high cost of filling such orders leads manufacturers to rely chiefly on wholesalers.

Characteristics of the Producer

A manufacturer is influenced, and often constrained, by the resources, both financial and managerial, the reputation, the breadth of the product line, and the particular policies of his firm. A financially strong company needs middlemen less than one with limited resources. Similarly, a firm with strong marketing know-how and experience may be reluctant to rely heavily on middlemen to do the marketing job. A firm with a good reputation—and to some extent this is a function of the size of the firm in its industry—can acquire better middlemen than less well known or smaller producers.

Breadth and diversity of product lines should influence channel decisions. A producer with a broad product line may want to deal directly with customers since each of his salesmen can offer a variety of products and reasonably expect a substantial total sale from each call. A firm with a limited or narrow product line may find the costs of making a sales call about the same whether one item or twenty are shown, but the total sale will of course be less. Consequently, the disadvantageous cost/sales ratio may induce such a limited-line producer to use a longer channel and some intermediaries. For example, a firm offering as many products as General Foods may deal directly with customers; one with a smaller line could not afford it. A widely varied product mix may require complex channels to reach all the target markets.

Company policies and executive preferences also determine channel decisions. For instance, a policy of heavy advertising may enable a firm to acquire stronger dealers; a policy of uniform retail prices leads to a more limited distribution to sellers willing to cooperate in maintaining list prices; a policy of fast delivery and service may affect the choice of intermediaries and the number of functions they are required to perform. Choice of channel depends to a considerable extent on how much control the producer wants over the channel members. If more control is desired over dealer prices, inventory levels, promotional efforts, and service effectiveness, then a shorter channel with fewer outlets which can be screened and supervised by the producer's sales representatives becomes necessary.

Environmental Factors

The nature and competence of available middlemen and retailers can constrain the choice of channel. The most desirable may not be available because they are already carrying competitive products, or because their demands for special treatment or prices are not attractive. Economic, political, and legal factors sometimes affect channel decisions. During periods of depressed economic conditions, the temptation often is to shorten channels and bring goods to the market at the lowest possible prices, even if some services have to be neglected.

Exclusive-dealing contracts may be subject to charges of illegality (under the Clayton Antitrust Act of 1914, which states that exclusive sales or lease contracts are unlawful if their effect "may be to substantially lessen competition or tend to create a monopoly . . .") when the manufacturer's sales volume or the volume done by the exclusive dealers is a significant percentage of the total business of the area. There may also be some legal question if the manufacturer attempts to set a limitation for the dealer's handling of competitive products. Therefore, large firms that attempt to tie their dealers tightly and restrict their freedom of action vis-à-vis competitive products may be acting illegally. Small firms trying to gain a position in a market through agreements to sell only one retailer or wholesaler in a given territory, and with no limitations on competitive products, should not be affected.[7]

Channel Selection Problems for New Producers or New Products

The new firm, or the established firm attempting to market a new, unrelated line of products, frequently faces problems in the selection of the best channel members. It is only natural that the more aggressive established middlemen and dealers already have a strong relationship with established producers. They are naturally reluctant to assume distribution for a competitive brand, and an unknown one at that. The manufacturer in such a dilemma is often forced into higher-cost and less efficient distribution methods. Several options are available, with none a clear winner:

1. Manufacturers may attempt to bypass reluctant middlemen with stronger efforts by the company sales force directed to retail buyers.
2. They may invest heavily in promotion in an attempt to win consumer interest and, thereby, dealer acceptance of the product.
3. A manufacturer may be content to accept whatever channel members can be induced to handle the product, no matter how marginal they may be, in the expectation that better middlemen can eventually be persuaded to accept the product. In the endeavor to gain some middleman support, it may be necessary to offer higher profit margins, and even sell on consignment (whereby the manufacturer keeps title of the goods until they are sold by the dealer, thereby bearing all the risks and inventory costs).
4. The manufacturer may consent to selective and even exclusive dealer arrangements, as a further incentive to attract outlets. The risk of using this method to gain initial distribution is the ill will engendered when the manufacturer later wants to broaden the market and gain more exposure, and attempts to terminate the exclusive arrangements.

[7] Some of the implications of exclusive-dealing legislation and interpretation are given in Leonard J. Konopa, "Exclusive Dealing Arrangement in Marketing," *Business Topics,* Summer 1964, pp. 63–72. More recent court cases which bear on exclusive-dealing arrangement and which serve to raise greater doubts and cautions regarding the legality in any given situation are described in these sources: "Antitrust Verdict Rocks the Stores," *Business Week,* July 26, 1969, p. 29; S. Powell Bridges, "The Schwinn Case: A Landmark Decision, *Business Horizons,* August 1968, pp. 77–85. Shelby D. Hunt and John R. Nevin, "Tying Agreements in Franchising," *Journal of Marketing,* July 1975, pp. 20–26.

Difficulty in Gaining Market Entry—Lestoil

A small unknown firm has difficulty attracting channel members to carry his product; essentially, market entry may be denied him. The problem is especially acute when the principal competitors are large and well-established firms. This problem faced the maker of Lestoil for over twenty years.

In 1933, Jacob Barowsky had perfected an all-purpose liquid detergent superior in cleaning power to anything on the market. He began bottling the product, which he called Lestoil, in his kitchen.

Barowsky was able to gain industrial orders in modest quantities, but could not get into household kitchens. The power of such competitors as Procter & Gamble and Lever Brothers over grocer shelf space left no room for Lestoil. Not discouraged, he ran newspaper ads, sent out cents-off coupons, canvassed neighborhoods handing out samples (and often housewives even refused to take the samples).

By 1953, industrial sales were $450,000 a year, but there were few household sales, and for these he was spending $3 in merchandise samples and advertising for every $1 in sales. Finally, in 1954, Barowsky gave a last desperate whirl at advertising—this time on TV. He laid out $10,000 for spot advertising on just one station in his home town. But sales miraculously picked up. So he added two nearby stations and allocated $50,000 more for TV advertising. By the end of 1954, $90,000 of Lestoil had been sold for home use.

Now he began expanding TV advertising city by city, saturating each area with commercials, but because of limited funds the movement toward nationwide distribution was slow. But by 1958, sales had topped $35,000,000, and he was budgeting $10,000,000 for advertising. Now at last dealers were eagerly putting Lestoil on their shelves.

SOURCES: "From Gravy Stains into the Gravy," *Fortune*, April 1959, p. 238; and *Advertising Age*, April 4, 1960, p. 31 ff.

For thought and discussion:

What other methods could Barowsky have tried to gain market entry?
Do you think they would have been more successful?

Therefore channel problems, particularly those of attracting enough suitable channel members, may be among the biggest impediments to entry in some fields. As an example of the difficulties a new firm may encounter in developing an effective channel and dealer relationship, picture the plight of the unknown candy-bar manufacturer attempting to wrest counter and display space from the well-known brands. The task may be so formidable that other distribution approaches may have to be developed, such as distributing through vending machines, through institutions such as hospitals and schools, even through Girl Scouts and clubs interested in fund raising. The fact that traditional channels may be relatively closed does not preclude a new firm from gaining entry via an innovative avenue.

PUSHING AND PULLING CHANNEL POLICIES

Most firms, even major ones, have some difficulty in gaining the support of dealers for the new products. In the effort to gain shelf space and dealer cooperation, a manufacturer has two strategies: "pushing" and/or "pulling" the product through the channel system. Major consumer goods firms frequently use both strategies simultaneously; firms not so well endowed must choose one or the other.

A *pushing* strategy refers to efforts to induce middlemen to back the product, to stock it, to give it adequate shelf space and display attention, and in any other ways to encourage their customers to try the new product. A successful pushing strategy depends on good working relations with the distributor, but usually added incentives must be provided. Manufacturers' salesmen can be persuasively demanding; display and other dealer aids may be provided; perhaps an extra margin for profit must be offered and returned-goods privileges stressed so that the dealer feels a minimum risk. Perhaps this will provide adequate incentive for sufficient dealer efforts, although other promotional possibilities may have to be considered, such as free goods, advertising allowances, setting up dealer displays, and the like.

A *pulling* strategy focuses primary efforts at the consumer end, rather than the dealer end. Coupons may be offered, free samples distributed, and the mass media employed to generate consumer demand. If such a strategy is successful, the reluctant middlemen, who have been effectively bypassed, will be forced to stock the product to meet the demands of their customers.

Generally a pulling strategy involves considerably heavier promotional expenditures than does the pushing approach. Furthermore, there is always the danger of some dealers resenting having something forced on them. However, this is usually soon mitigated if the new product proves saleable and can contribute to dealer profits. Also, any possible dealer resentment can be minimized by keeping them informed of the promotion so that they can anticipate demands if it proves successful. Usually a small firm is prevented from using a full-fledged pulling strategy because of limited resources. Distribution of free samples—if the product is perceptibly superior—may help pull it through the channels, even without much advertising. However, pushing, through extra dealer discounts or display aids, is generally the more feasible for the small firm.

The ability of large firms to utilize both approaches simultaneously gives them a powerful advantage in getting their new products quickly into the channel system. This thrust coming from these major firms accounts for a good part of the product proliferation prevalent in today's marketplace.

CHANNEL INTEGRATION AND LEADERSHIP

Channel Integration

Conventional channels of distribution have been described as fragmented networks in which loosely aligned and relatively autonomous manufacturers, wholesalers, and retailers have customarily bargained aggressively with each other, established trade relationships on an individual transaction basis, severed business relationship arbitrarily with impunity, and otherwise behaved independently.[8]

The symbiotic relationship mentioned earlier, in which dissimilar firms work together for mutual gain, would seem to be a deterrent to the extreme of unilateral, arbitrary action by the individual members of a channel. Cooperation would seem to develop naturally, without conscious effort on the part of any party, since all stand to gain from the exploitation of a joint opportunity. It is to the manufacturer's advantage to aid his wholesalers and retailers wherever possible. He can supply training aids, promotional material, such as advertising mats and displays; he can help with servicing problems and the handling of customer complaints; financial help and flexible credit arrangements may be supplied to enable the distributor to stock up in advance of a big selling season, while ample warning of price reductions and even protection against price changes can help a channel function smoothly and with a cooperative spirit. It is reasonable to expect the retailer and wholesaler to be motivated to promote and merchandise the product in its best light, and also to furnish feedback up the channel so that any difficulties can be corrected and more customer satisfaction result.

Despite the strong incentives for cooperation, conflicts may arise from actions either on the part of the producer or the middlemen. E. H. Lewis has noted:

Manufacturers may create conflict and upset the channel balance by such actions as selling to a middleman's customers, thus

---

[8] William R. Davidson, "Changes in Distributive Institutions," *Journal of Marketing,* January 1970, p. 7.

competing directly with him; by making heavy demands on middlemen, such as requiring large and varied inventories, special promotional support, extensive service facilities, burdensome payment terms, etc.; by refusing to protect middlemen against model changes and price changes; by making goods available to a middleman's competitors, perhaps to firms of a different type.

Middlemen, especially large-scale retailers, can create conflict by demanding large discounts, special promotional allowances, and more favorable pricing terms. They may also demand special shipping arrangements, quicker deliveries, protection against price changes, etc.[9]

Channel Leadership

The need for an integrated and coordinated channel system where all members work together to maximize the total system effort is obvious and an important incentive for the development of channel leadership to supply the unifying planning and stimulation.

The position of leadership of the various channel members usually varies depending on their size and general market power. Small retailers and wholesalers are not in a position to lead; even though they furnish access to the market, it is limited because of their size, and thus their bargaining position is less than that of large firms at any level in the channel.[10] Small manufacturers, however, may be channel leaders if they have a desired product and can therefore exercise control by offering or withholding it from various middlemen.[11]

Large manufacturers, large retailers (especially chains), and some large wholesalers who have established strong private brands and wholesale-sponsored voluntary chains are the more common exercisers of channel leadership. The power of a General Motors or a Ford can be almost dictatorial regarding prices, discounts, bonuses, warranty reimbursements, and even inventories. At the other extreme, the market power of a Sears, a Penney's, or an A&P is indisputable, even with large manufacturers. Smaller manufacturers whose entire output may be marketed under the private brand of a big retail chain may be dependent on the retailer even to the design of the product.

Sometimes the market power of a big retailer and a big manu-

[9] Edwin H. Lewis, *Marketing Channels: Structure and Strategy* (New York: McGraw-Hill, 1968), pp. 64–65.

[10] For a more complete discussion of potential market leaders, see Robert W. Little, "The Marketing Channel: Who Should Lead this Extra-Corporate Organization?" *Journal of Marketing,* January 1970, pp. 31–38.

[11] Neil H. Borden, *Acceptance of New Products by Supermarkets* (Boston: Division of Research, Graduate School of Business Administration, Harvard University, 1968), p. 13.

facturer may be almost evenly balanced. The concentration of power in some markets by a few retail chains may be awesome, especially in the grocery market. A study of market concentration in six market areas found a few retail chains controlling from 63 to 93 percent of the grocery market in each of these metropolitan areas.[12] Consequently, these retailers can pick and choose from the offerings of many manufacturers and substantially influence the success of the manufacturer in that area. On the other hand, the strong product franchise of a manufacturer—such as a Gillette or a Colgate—will hardly permit exclusion from the shelves of an appropriate retail outlet.

Some generalizations have been offered to help summarize the channel leadership role:

1. The strong retailers are in the best position to lead channels because the value to the manufacturer of market access far exceeds the value of one more product to the retailer's merchandising mix.
2. The more product sources are available to the retailer within a channel system, the more the locus of power will tend to shift to the retailer.
3. Reciprocally, the wider the manufacturer's product line, the greater his economic significance to retail organizations and the greater his potential power.[13]

TRENDS IN CHANNEL STRUCTURE: VERTICAL MARKETING SYSTEMS

Competition in the marketplace takes place not merely between individual retailers or individual manufacturers, but more correctly, it takes place between different channel systems. The better-directed and better-coordinated channel efforts will generally prevail over fragmented and independent efforts, provided, of course, that there is no great discrepancy in the other aspects of the marketing mix, such as the product features, the price, and the promotional efforts.

The need for better organized and controlled channel systems is resulting in "vertically organized marketing systems" becoming the dominant distribution mechanism. With efforts coordinated to eliminate unnecessary duplication and to make each channel member responsible for a specific part of the physical goods and information flow, more powerful marketing efforts can be exerted.[14] One writer

---

[12] Ibid., p. 10.

[13] Little, "The Marketing Channel," p. 36.

[14] For more discussion of this, with examples, see D. J. Bowersox and E. J. McCarthy, "Strategic Development of Planned Vertical Marketing Systems," in Louis Bucklin, ed., *Vertical Marketing Systems* (Glenview, Ill.: Scott, Foresman, 1970).

describes three forms that such vertical systems may take: corporate, contractural, and administered.[15]

Corporate systems refer to the vertical integration which has long been part of the marketing scene. Penney's and Sears integrate back up the channel into some types of manufacturing. Firestone and Goodyear integrate forward and own their own retail outlets. There are advantages to this in that tight control and firm adherence to policies is assured. Inefficient middlemen or marginal producers will be eliminated, and it may be possible to make certain economies not possible through an independent system. However, the investment required—especially of funds which might better be used in more familiar operations—and the lessened flexibility to adjust to changing marketing conditions temper somewhat the desirability of corporate vertical integration.

Contractual systems include wholesaler-sponsored voluntary chains, retailer-cooperative associations, and franchising arrangements. These systems involve voluntary but contractual integration of retailers and some other members of the channel, but not necessarily the complete channel. A study suggested that 35 to 40 percent of all retail trade is accounted for by some form of voluntary chain, cooperative, or franchising organization.[16] Some of these contractual systems are very old, such as the automobile dealer franchises; others are new, as are fast-food franchises and the Ethan Allen furniture franchise stores. (We have described franchising in more detail in chapter 3). The buying power and the increasingly sophisticated management controls are making these contractual systems viable and expansive.

Administered vertical systems refer to categories of merchandise which are vertically organized, rather than being a complete store operation. Comprehensive merchandising programs, where the manufacturer has control over displays, promotions, and prices, are being developed by some manufacturers, such as Scott for lawn products and Villager in young women's apparel. Research has indicated that such vertically coordinated programs are growing rapidly.[17]

OVERVIEW OF CHANNELS: THEIR EFFICIENCY AND THEIR PROBLEMS

The careful selection of market intermediaries and the cultivation of a spirit of cooperation and good communication encourages the effi-

[15] Much of this section is based on Davidson, "Changes in Distributive Institutions," pp. 7–9.

[16] Ibid., p. 8.

[17] Ibid.

ciency of marketing and the satisfaction of consumer product needs at the lowest possible price. Middlemen are viable only when their existence is economically sound; the service they perform must be worthwhile and economical or other channels will arise to do it better.

There is a high degree of interdependence among all channel members; a weak link, be it retailer, wholesaler, or manufacturer, lessens the success of all members of the channel. Channels must be kept flexible; they must be able to adjust to changing conditions; they should provide a sufficient level of market penetration. A manufacturer of ski equipment seeking as broad a market as possible would make a mistake to establish channels that include only department stores and ski shops at the retail level. Discount stores, major trading stamp companies, even some multiproduct hardware stores, might be possible outlets.

Routinization in the Channel

The nature of the relationships along the channel is one of both stability and fluidity.[18] Being fluid or flexible, any business firm or any consumer can shift purchases from one source to another, in other words, adjust to changing requirements and competitive offerings. At the same time, there is a consistency and a continuity of contacts, ". . . a mutual affinity that grows up between two persons or firms in business which causes them to prefer to deal with each other rather than with someone else."[19] The process of seeking out new customers and persuading them to buy (which often involves heavy promotional efforts and repeated sales calls) contributes to some of the major costs of marketing. Therefore, when a continuity of contacts can be achieved, the transaction is more easily undertaken, costs are reduced, and the factor of *routinization* enters. Such stability of channel relationships can, however, impede progress and improvement if too inflexible. For example, if a manufacturer is content to continue doing business with dealers who are conservative and not vigorously expanding—or if a dealer is content to continue buying from a manufacturer whose production efficiency and product improvements are not keeping pace with competition—then routinization becomes a costly burden.

Communication and Service Deficiencies of the Channel

An important contribution to efficiency is the flow of communication up and down the channel: dealers can provide feedback of market conditions and consumer reactions to other members of the channel;

[18] Edmund D. McGarry, "The Contactual Function in Marketing," *Journal of Business*, April 1953, pp. 96–113.
[19] Ibid., p. 106.

the manufacturer can furnish product and servicing information. Unfortunately the channel structures have not always provided adequate communication nor given the product-service satisfaction desired by customers.

Positive actions that the members of the channel team can take to improve communication and service are another aspect of *responsive marketing:*

1. Clear guidelines can be established as to which member of the channel is responsible for corrective actions regarding product service and defective products under various circumstances.
2. Where a certain problem is beyond the responsibility of the member first contacted (usually the retailer), a definitive communication network is desirable for getting the problem to the channel member responsible for the correction or adjustment.
3. Where servicing problems are complex and difficult to correct—such as inadequate facilities, poor stocking of parts, poorly trained service employees—joint efforts of manufacturers and dealers can be employed constructively to ease the problem.
4. Better training of dealer salespeople so as to instruct customers in proper use of products can help eliminate mishandling and decrease the number of service problems.

In the quest for sales, adequate service and adjustment policies may be disregarded, at least by some members of the channel. But all members are hurt when the actions of one, whether a retailer or a manufacturer, are not geared to the customer satisfaction that results in repeat sales and loyalty.

QUESTIONS AND PROBLEMS

1. In view of the large size of many manufacturers and retailers, and the ability of these large firms to buy and sell in quantity directly from each other, how can the existence of wholesalers be explained?
2. What is consignment selling? Why would a manufacturer agree to do this? Would you consider this a powerful marketing strategy?
3. Why would a manufacturer want anything less than the most widespread distribution he can obtain?
4. What factors determine who controls the channel of distribution or is the channel captain?
5. What are "push" and "pull" strategies? Discuss the implications in regard to (a) channel selection, (b) size of firm, (c) type of promotional effort.

6. Why do we find wholesalers relatively little used in the marketing of high fashion wearing apparel? Would not retailers' needs be better satisfied by being able to obtain these goods more promptly through wholesalers than by going to the manufacturers?

7. What can a manufacturer do to stimulate wholesalers to perform a more aggressive job of promoting the manufacturers' products?

8. What do we mean by routinization, and what are the benefits of it? Do you see any limitations?

Project

Select two companies manufacturing similar goods for similar customers. (Two such pairs of companies, for example, are Avon and Revlon with cosmetics, and Bond Clothes and Hart Schaffner & Marx for men's clothes.) Investigate their distribution strategies. Are the strategies similar? Different? How successful do you judge the respective strategies to be? What conclusions can you draw from the two examples?

Exercise in Creativity

As a small manufacturer you have developed a candy bar that a majority of some 30 people who taste-tested it declared to be of superior flavor. How would you undertake to wrest a place for this on dealer shelves, amid the host of well-known, heavily advertised brands of the major manufacturers? Be specific and creative in your recommendations, and support them as fully as possible.

Role-playing Case

You and a silent partner own a small men's clothing store near a college campus. You carry several well-known brands of suits, slacks, and shirts. Today the sales representative of your major slacks supplier comes in while you are busy with a customer. He looks around, jots down a few notes, and approaches you after the customer has left.

He greets you pleasantly, then says, "Bill, I see your stock of our new slacks is not very complete. Have they been selling that well?"

"Don, our customers don't go for such a conservative style, so we thought it best just to sample the new number."

"Bill, if you're going to have exclusive handling of our brand in this area, you have to carry an adequate stock of all our numbers. That's not what I say—that's home office dictates."

How would you respond to this veiled threat? What can the manufacturer do if you don't stock the new number in larger quantity? Is this likely to happen? What factors are likely to affect the outcome of this controversy?

CHAPTER 12

MARKETING

COMMUNICATIONS:

ADVERTISING

The pervasiveness of advertising is apparent to anyone who can see or hear. In this chapter we consider advertising as one element in the *promotion mix* (along with sales promotion and personal selling). The goals, types, management, and development of advertising campaigns are considered and evaluated. Finally, we look at the role of advertising in our society. Important terms are:

institutional advertising	positioning
reminder advertising	objective and task method
rational appeals	carryover effect
advertising media	pretesting
promotion mix	posttesting
	affirmative disclosure

PERVASIVENESS OF ADVERTISING

The sheer number of advertising messages confronting consumers daily is staggering.

> Every day 4.2 billion advertising messages pour forth from 1,754 daily newspapers, millions of others from 8,151 weeklies, and 1.36 billion more each day from 4,147 magazines and periodicals. There are 3,895 AM and 1,136 FM radio stations broadcasting an average of 730,000 commercials per day; and 770 television stations broadcasting 100,000 commercials each day. Every day, millions of people are confronted with 330,000 outdoor billboards, with 2.5 million car cards and posters in buses, subways, and commuter trains, with 51.3 million direct mail pieces and leaflets, and with billions of display and promotional items.[1]

[1] Leo Bogart, *Strategy in Advertising* (New York: Harcourt, Brace & World, 1967), p. 2.

Only a small proportion of these messages actually intrude upon our consciousness. The people sampled in one study totaled the ads that they were aware of during half a day with the aid of hand counters that they carried around with them. The researchers called the figures resulting from this procedure a measure of "sensitive attention" rather than "exposure." The respondents also filled out cards with their detailed reactions to unusual advertisements. The readings on the counters were then doubled to project a full day's response. The average was 76 ads reported per day; 12 of these (16 percent) were considered sufficiently singular to warrant classification on the cards. Of the 12 so categorized, 4.4 were considered "informative," 4.2 "enjoyable," 2.8 "annoying," and 0.6 "offensive."[2]

Although the people in the study were exposed to thousands of advertisements in different forms, they recorded being aware of only 76 in a day—and these people were actually *looking* for advertisements. Most ads were ignored, while some were noticed particularly for their offensiveness. The typical family is confronted with 1,500 advertising messages every day[3]; 76 ads amounts to 5 percent; with 12 having sufficient impact to be recorded and classified, the percentage drops to less than 1 percent. The results of this study, conducted for the advertising industry, should be frightening to most marketing executives whose firms are spending millions for advertising. The study points out the need for messages of more impact. But how is this to be achieved amid the daily barrage from all sources and media? More creativity and originality are needed, but not so easily achieved: there is a limit to how far an advertiser can go in being original and distinctive without being offensive or without distracting attention from the product itself. As total expenditures continue to increase and more products compete for attention, a monotonous similarity of advertising results, and the impact on consumers continues to lessen.

[2] "The A.A.A.A. Study on Consumer Judgment of Advertising," American Association of Advertising Agencies, May 1965. This research was initiated by A.A.A.A. researchers William Wellbacher and Donald Kanter, and conducted by the Opinion Research Corporation.

[3] John S. Wright and Daniel S. Warner, *Advertising,* 2d ed. (New York: McGraw-Hill, 1966), p. 3.

MARKETING MISTAKES

Monotony of Advertising Claims

The lack of distinctiveness and impact of some of today's advertising can be seen in the following series of product claims for ten different heavy duty detergents:

1. "It's concentrated . . . gets your whole wash cleaner than any powder can . . . puts its strength where the dirt is."

2. "Fortified with whiteners, water softeners, more cleaning boosters than any powder detergent . . . gets clothes lots cleaner looking with lots less bleaching."
3. "I notice that my clothes smell clean . . . new, improved . . . adds new freshness to the cleanest wash you can get."
4. "A brand new heavy duty detergent formula with more brightening powder than ever before . . . and its safe suds level assures you of super whitening power, too."
5. "Has lower suds for best washer protection . . . cleans best of all . . . protects best of all . . . get new action . . . new liquid, too!"
6. "Has extra strength . . . has five extra laundritives to get the toughest wash clean clear through."
7. "Avoid machine failure with safe sudsing . . . the detergent recommended by every automatic manufacturer . . . unsurpassed cleaning . . . works hard cleaning."
8. "Famous blue magic whitener will wash so white you can actually see the difference . . . and when your white things are this deeper, fresher white, you can be sure your whole wash is right."
9. "Combines high suds cleaning power with low suds washer protection."
10. "When it's whiteness you're after, reach for the one with the bleach."

Do you beieve that a person exposed to the above examples can be expected to distinguish the claims of one advertiser from all the others? Is it any wonder that many advertisements do not even register on the listener's consciousness? All these detergents claim to be better, new, or different, but they all say the same thing in the same dull way.

SOURCE: Leo Bogart, *Strategy in Advertising* (New York: Harcourt, Brace & World, 1967).

For thought and discussion:
What creative ideas do you have for making detergent advertising more distinctive?
Can you think of any fresh approach?

How to make advertising more effective and memorable remains a stimulating challenge. And despite success stories, one can well raise the question in view of the lack of impact of many advertising messages: Why advertise at all?

Why Advertise?

Imagine yourself a manufacturer of a consumer product which you do not advertise. What are the likely consequences if you face competition from other firms? Without advertising to inform the public of your product, you will have a difficult time winning brand recognition and brand acceptance. Without advertising it will probably be difficult to persuade dealers to carry your products, especially if competitive brands are well known.

Now you may say: "My salespeople provide all the information and persuasion my product needs. And it is a good product; it practically can sell itself." With industrial products, true, the salesperson's role is often the prime method of communicating with customers—although even here advertising can pave the way and make the job easier. But with consumer goods, advertising can reach far more people than even the most energetic salesperson ever could. No matter how good a product, unless enough people know about it and enough dealers carry it, sales will be few.

Unless you are content for your firm to remain small, or are willing to sell your output under a dealer's brand (as a private brand), thereby sacrificing some independence and flexibility, you will probably find yourself turning to advertising.

The Power of Massive Advertising

However much advertising may suffer from lack of creativity, still the massive use of advertising is a powerful competitive tool. We will illustrate with two examples.

**MARKETING
IN
ACTION**

The Success of Bristol-Myers via Advertising
In 1954 Bristol-Myers was a relatively small company with sales of $62 million, mostly from penicillin drugs and a handful of consumer products sold through drugstores ("Ipana for the Smile of Beauty . . . Sal Hepatica for the Smile of Health"). By 1965 sales had jumped to $265 million and earnings from 35 cents a share to $2.18 a share, a 500 percent increase.

The factors behind this growth are varied. A much broadened line of products, often achieved by careful acquisitions, was a significant factor. Such well known products as Bromo-Quinine, Fitch Products, 4-Way Cold Tablets, Clairol, Drano, Endust, and O'-Cedar were among the products and brands added. The company epitomized the prevalent philosophy of proliferating with new products. By 1965, 30 percent of sales came from products less than five years old. Often these were practically the same as the old products, but with different names and advertising appeals.

And massive advertising, especially on TV, was the key to Bristol-Myers' marketing strategy. By 1965, expenditures for advertising had reached $109 million. Only Procter & Gamble, General Motors, General Foods, and Ford—all billion-dollar corporations—spent more for advertising. High volume, heavily advertised products, usually selling for under $2, and ones that were used up reasonably quickly and had to be bought again, were the candidates for the advertising. By concentrating on products highly profitable to operators of discount stores and supermarkets, and capitalizing on the trend to self-service, Bristol-Myers assured its products plenty of prime shelf space. The results reflected the successful strategy of going with products highly promotable, and spending vast sums to do so.

SOURCE: "A Little P&G—But Different," *Forbes*, January 15, 1966, pp. 38–39.

For thought and discussion:
What percentage of Bristol-Myers' sales were advertising expenditures in 1965?

How does this compare with its expenditures in later years (see Table 12–7)?

What factors might have led Bristol-Myers to cut down on the percentage of sales budgeted to advertising?

MARKETING
IN
ACTION

The Might of Procter & Gamble versus Scott Paper
In 1879 Scott entered the household paper products market and in time became the undisputed leader of this over $1.2 billion market which consists primarily of toilet paper and paper towels (and more recently, of disposable diapers).

In 1957 Procter & Gamble entered this market on a small scale when it acquired Charmin Paper Mills, a largely obsolete operation in Wisconsin. By 1971, Scott's share of household paper products had shrunk to 40 percent, while newcomer Procter & Gamble had garnered 25 percent and was relentlessly increasing its market share. How did Procter & Gamble do it?

The credit rests chiefly with the overwhelming advertising which P&G threw at Scott. For example, in 1971, P&G spent $13.5 million advertising its paper products (in terms of its total advertising expenditures of $265 million, this was no big deal). For the same year, Scott stretched its resources to spend $6 million advertising its paper products.

In 1966 P&G started pushing Pampers, its disposable diaper. In so doing, it beat Scott to the market by two years: babyScott Disposables finally came on the market in 1968. But being late with a product not noticeably better than Pampers (and some mothers thought it not as good), and without the advertising resources to push as hard as its competitor, almost preordained a market failure. And in 1971, Scott was forced to discontinue its disposable-diaper line at a cost of $12.8 million.

SOURCE: "How Procter & Gamble Put the Big Squeeze on Scott Paper Co.," *Wall Street Journal,* October 20, 1971, p. 1, 25.

For thought and discussion:
If Scott's disposable diaper had been notably superior to that of Procter
    & Gamble, do you think the results would have been different?
Is there any way Scott could have countered the massive advertising
    thrust of P&G?

PROMOTION AND PERSUASION

Promotion involves selling—selling a product, a service, perhaps a person (a political candidate), an organization (a charity), or an idea (fight water pollution). Promotion is generally considered to be the all-inclusive term for (1) advertising, (2) personal selling, and (3) sales promotion and other selling devices. This chapter primarily concerns advertising; the next, sales promotional techniques and personal selling.

    Persuasion is the object of most promotional efforts today. It may be defined as an active attempt to influence people to action or belief, involving some overt appeal to emotion or reason. Advertising, then, is persuasion by means of mass communication media; personal selling is persuasion through interpersonal contact. Persuasion is not bad, though sometimes its label carries an aura of deception or distortion. It has been pointed out that "all successes in business, in industrial production, in invention, in religious conversion, in education, and in politics depend upon the process of persuasion."[4]

THE PROMOTION MIX

Early in this chapter we examined some possible goals of promotional and advertising efforts. It is generally a mistake to use such a vague goal as "to increase sales." This may be the ultimate objective, but efforts can be more effective if particular goals are well defined and clearly specified. Furthermore, an advertising campaign or series of promotional efforts should be built around a central theme. The ads in the campaign should be integrated with the other sales promotional efforts (such as point-of-purchase displays and premiums) and

[4] Clyde R. Miller, *The Process of Persuasion* (New York: Crown, 1946), p. 16.

with the efforts of the sales force. This is known as the promotion mix. The promotion mix or blend consists of three ingredients:

Advertising
Sales promotion
Personal selling

These may be likened to a pie in which the various ingredients can be blended in any number of ways. For example, see Figure 12-1. In most firms, advertising and personal selling take up the major part of the budget. One study found different ratios of advertising to personal selling by type of product: for example, food products used a preponderance of advertising, while certain types of industrial equipment used mostly personal selling.[5] But generally both must be employed in some form and to some degree. Rarely will a single input into the promotional program suffice, but to a substantial extent, the various promotional elements are substitutes for one another. More advertising might make the job of the salesperson so easy that a lower-paid and lower-quality sales staff could be employed. But the job, even for top-flight people, might be inordinately difficult, especially in a highly competitive situation, without advertising to smooth the way.

The study concludes that:

The development of a satisfactory sales-promotion mix by an individual company requires continuous study of the market and the competitive situation in it. The optimum mix probably

[5] Edwin H. Lewis, "Sales Promotion Decisions," *Business News Notes,* University of Minnesota, No. 12 (November 1954).

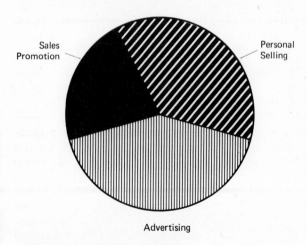

Figure 12-1. The Promotion Mix

is seldom attained, but companies must continue to experiment with the several methods of sales promotion and to use them in various combinations in order to make their sales efforts more effective.[6]

While it is difficult to attain an optimum mix—and a firm would have no sure way of determining if the optimum were reached—there are some guides that help in the allocation. Neil Borden, in a classic study of advertising thirty years ago, identified five criteria that influence the effectiveness of advertising efforts:

1. The primary demand trend for the product should be favorable—that is, the market demand for a product should be on the upswing.
2. There should be considerable opportunity to differentiate the product, since then the company has something specific to say or features to point out.
3. The product should have hidden qualities—advertising can then be effective in bringing these qualities to the attention of buyers.
4. Emotional buying motives should exist for the product, and advertising can stimulate buying action by appealing to these motives—certainly nails, or salt, would not fit this criterion.
5. The company must have sufficient funds to support an advertising program adequately.[7]

There are a number of other factors which should affect the promotional mix, such as the nature of the product, the stage in the life cycle (we discussed this in chapter 10), the promotional strategy of competitors, the nature of the market, and, of course, the size and resources of the firm. There is often no one best mix.[8]

GOALS OF ADVERTISING

The general goal of advertising is to increase sales, either immediately or in the future, and to do so profitably. But of course the same thing can be said about any marketing decision or, for that matter, practically any decision of a business firm. So more specific goals should be established. One expert distinguished 52 different goals that might be established for a single advertisement or for a company's entire advertising program. Some of these are:

[6] Ibid., p. 5.
[7] Neil H. Borden, *The Economic Effects of Advertising* (Homewood, Ill.: Irwin, 1942), pp. 424–28.
[8] For a discussion of the dearth of research dealing with the promotional blend itself, see J. B. Haskins and W. C. Hugli, Jr., "Evaluating the Effects of Company Promotional Activities: A Neglected Area for Research and Management Attention," *Journal of Marketing*, October 1969, pp. 66–68.

Build morale of a company sales force.

Announce a special reason for "buying now" (price, premium, etc.).

Reach people inaccessible to salespeople, such as top business executives and professional people.

Enter a new geographic market or attract a new group of consumers.

Build familiarity and easy recognition of package or trademark.

Correct false impressions, misinformation, and other obstacles to sales.

Persuade prospect to visit a showroom, ask for a demonstration.

Introduce a new product or a new price schedule.

Build goodwill for the company and improve its reputation by rendering a public service through advertising.

Place advertiser in position to select preferred distributors or dealers.

Expand the industry's sales.[9]

The choice of advertising media, the allocation of advertising dollars, and the type of copy or message to use would differ, of course, according to the goal.

From examining the above sample of advertising goals we can see that the consumer is not always the only target, and is often not the most important target, for certain promotional objectives. Three external targets for promotion are usually possible (the internal morale building for salespeople and/or executives will be considered a concomitant target): (1) consumers, (2) channel members, such as wholesalers and retailers, and (3) the public at large, and indirectly, their elected representatives and governmental officials.

The consumer is the main target for promotion and the object of the billions spent for TV, radio, newspaper, and magazine advertising. But sometimes a firm can achieve better results by directing persuasion to present and/or potential channel members, to convince them that they ought to carry a certain product or should devote more space or selling efforts toward it. Small manufacturers with little-known products often must of necessity do this because of the prohibitive expense involved in using the mass media for a widespread consumer market. This is, of course, another way of distinguishing a pushing from a pulling strategy.

One class of advertising having a somewhat different target is *institutional*, public relations, or corporate advertising. The objective is to create a favorable image by the general public toward the firm. A major deterrent to this institutional advertising is that the results of such efforts are intangible and the effects on sales generation rather remote.

[9] Russell H. Colley, ed., *Defining Advertising Goals* (New York: Association of National Advertisers, 1961), pp. 62–68.

Advertising can be categorized by the following opposites:

Product ——————————— Institutional
Direct action ————————— Indirect action, and reminder
Emotional ——————————— Rational
Primary demand ————————— Selective demand

In *direct-action* advertising, the goal is to persuade the reader, viewer, or listener to act at once to buy or order products or services, or else to send for additional information. Probably the strongest examples of such advertising can be found in the many retail "sale" ads which almost scream "urgency"—"rush to buy or the sale will be over or the stock depleted!" *Indirect-action* advertising has a longer-range goal, pointing out product virtues and attempting to engender a favorable attitude so that when the customer is ready to buy he or she will buy that particular brand. Much advertising is necessarily of this kind, since for many products such as cars, airline vacation travel, or cameras it would be presumptuous for the advertiser to expect the listeners to take immediate action.

A type of indirect-action advertising is *reminder*. The intent is simply to keep the product's name before the public, such as with signs or ads which say, "Coca-Cola." Of course, such advertising can be useful only when a product has already achieved wide acceptance.

Advertising can be categorized by the type of appeal predominating, that is, whether emotional or rational. Books on advertising have long stressed the desirability of appealing to emotional motives —such as romance, pride, or fear.[10] Probably most of us, after exposure to an evening of TV commercials, will agree that this can be overdone or crudely done. Appeal to rational motives, such as dependability, durability, stress on specific product features, and "reason why" copy is too little encountered.

Primary-demand advertising, sometimes called pioneering advertising, is directed to building demand for a product category, rather than for a specific brand. It is often used in the early stages of a product life cycle, when information about the product is needed to spur initial industry sales. Later, as a product receives more acceptance, and more competitors are attracted to the industry, then *selective-demand* advertising (which stresses a specific brand rather than a general product category) becomes commonplace. An example would be the microwave oven. At first advertising stressed the features of the new product; more recently distinctions are made between brands. Primary-demand advertising is sometimes sponsored by trade associations on behalf of all their members, such as the Tea

---

[10] For example, Melvin S. Hattwick, *How to Use Psychology for Better Advertising* (Englewood Cliffs, N.J.: Prentice-Hall, 1950), Chaps. 2, 6–7.

This sign is an example of reminder advertising. It tells nothing about the product and so can be used only for well-known brands. *Photo by Helena Frost.*

Institute which has long been advertising to persuade Americans that tea drinking is enjoyable.

ADVERTISING MEDIA

Table 12-1 shows the volume of advertising expenditures in the United States by media, and the trend for the last twenty years. Of particular interest is the phenomenal growth of TV, rising from 3 percent of advertising volume in 1950 to 18.3 percent in 1969. However, newspapers still remain the single largest medium, while direct mail (sometimes referred to as "junk mail") is also substantial. Let us now examine the advantages and limitations of the various media.

Table 12-1.
Annual Volume in Advertising in the United States by Media
(millions of dollars)

Media	1955 Amount	1955 Per-cent	1960 Amount	1960 Per-cent	1965 Amount	1965 Per-cent	1969 Amount	1969 Per-cent	1974 Amount	1974 Per-cent
Newspapers	$3,088	33.6	$ 3,703	31.1	$ 4,435	29.4	$ 5,850	29.9	$ 7,910	29.8
Television	1,025	11.1	1,590	13.3	2,498	16.5	3,858	18.3	4,850	18.3
Direct mail	1,299	14.1	1,830	15.3	2,271	15.0	2,680	13.7	3,920	14.8
Magazines	729	7.9	941	7.8	1,198	7.9	1,375	7.0	1,525	5.7
Radio	545	5.9	692	5.8	889	5.9	1,270	6.5	1,790	6.7
Miscellaneous* .	2,508	27.4	3,176	26.7	3,830	25.3	4,532	24.6	5,240	19.7
Total	$9,194	100.0	$11,932	100.0	$15,120	100.0	$19,565	100.0	$25,235	100.0

* Includes transportation advertising, outdoor advertising, weekly newspaper advertising, point-of-purchase materials not covered in direct-mail expenditures.
Source: *Statistical Abstract of the United States 1965*, pp. 774, 848; *1970*, p. 757. 1974 figures from *Advertising Age*, December 16, 1974, p. 23.

Newspapers

The typical newspaper circulates in a limited and well-defined area, and this offers advantages to the advertiser interested in geographical selectivity. Since almost everyone reads the newspaper, an intense coverage of the local market can be obtained. Newspapers offer great relative flexibility, since ads can be inserted or removed with only a few days' notice; this makes it feasible to feature prices in most newspaper ads. Circulation costs per prospect are low, and since most metropolitan areas have daily newspapers, messages can be presented frequently. But there are several significant limitations to newspaper ads. The paper has a short life—nothing is quite so stale as old news—so it is not likely that advertising will have much influence beyond the day of publication. Newspapers are hastily read: most studies indicate that the average reader spends between twenty and thirty minutes on the paper.[11] Therefore a message has to make an impression quickly or not at all. Finally, newspapers, being printed on pulp paper, do not have the quality of reproduction and color that can be achieved in magazine ads. This can be a disadvantage for some car and food ads where the illustration has an important role to play. As seen from Table 12-1, while the relative dominance of newspaper advertising expenditures has slipped some, it is still substantially above any other medium.

[11] S. Watson Dunn, *Advertising, Its Role in Modern Marketing*, 2d ed. (New York: Holt, Rinehart, and Winston, 1969), p. 451.

This is an advertisement for advertising. It appeals to marketers wanting to reach a particular segment, in this case, teenage girls, and it also provides information about the market. *Courtesy Seventeen Magazine.*

Magazines

While magazines rank only fourth among the media in total dollar revenue, more manufacturers advertise in magazines than in any other medium. There are particular advantages to magazines. Perhaps the most striking is their selective readership: most magazines appeal to some groups and not to others, such as hunting and fishing magazines, skiing, boating, and automobile magazines, and those appealing to "hi-fi" buffs.[12] Manufacturers of such products can direct their

[12] The mass-market magazines, such as *Life, Look,* and the *Saturday Evening Post* went out of business, while the specialized magazines are doing well: "The Hot Magazines Aim at Special Targets," *Business Week,* May 2, 1970, pp. 64–74; "What Finally Crippled the Cowles Empire," *Business Week,* September 25, 1971, pp. 122–25.

messages to that segment of the total market which represents the most potential and thereby have a minimum of waste circulation. Magazines also offer a high degree of geographic selectivity. For example, it is possible to purchase one or more of 70 state and regional editions of *TV Guide,* 42 for *Time* (see Table 12-2 for the various regional, metropolitan, and demographic editions of *Time*), and 10 or more for such magazines as *Better Homes and Gardens* and *Ladies' Home Journal.*

Magazines are read in a leisurely fashion, compared with newspapers. Some, such as *National Geographic* and *Fortune,* may be kept for years; they are often found in doctors' and business reception rooms, thereby having a much wider readership than mere circulation figures would indicate. Most magazines are printed on

Table 12-2.
Regional, City, and Demographic Editions of Time

Regions	Metropolitan	Demographic
Eastern	Group I:	Doctors
East-central	Atlanta	Educators
Southeast	Boston	College students
Florida	Chicago	
West-central	Cleveland	
Texas	Detroit	
Southwest	Los Angeles	
Pacific Southwest	Minneapolis/St. Paul	
California	New York	
Northern California	Philadelphia	
Southern California	Pittsburgh	
Pacific Northwest	San Francisco	
	St. Louis	
	Washington/Baltimore	
	Group II:	
	Buffalo	
	Cincinnati	
	Denver	
	Hartford	
	Houston	
	Kansas City	
	Miami	
	Milwaukee	
	New Haven	
	Phoenix	
	Portland, Oregon	
	San Diego	
	Seattle	
	Tampa/St. Petersburg	

Source: *Standard Rate and Data,* January 27, 1975.

good paper and provide excellent reproductions, especially for color ads. Advertising in some magazines undoubtedly lends prestige to the product, or an aura of quality and reliability. But there are some limitations to magazines. They lack flexibility: changes cannot be made for several weeks before publication date, a factor which discourages the use of price in most ads. The infrequency with which magazines reach the market, compared to other media, can also be a drawback.

**MARKETING
IN
ACTION**

Standing Up for Principles—*Audubon* Magazine
The temptation facing advertising media is to willingly accept prospective advertisers—after all, the name of the game is sales, and who would turn away business? Of course, in the clear instance of deception bordering on fraud, then a newspaper, magazine, or radio station may refuse such business; and in TV, industry codes prohibit advertising certain products, such as fire arms and hard liquor (fire water).

The National Audubon Society, which publishes *Audubon* magazine, probably takes the award for being the most dedicated to principles, even at the expense of sales. Strongly espousing conservation and protection of the environment, the magazine decided to reject advertising for Japanese and Russian products because Japan and Russia refuse to halt harvesting of increasingly scarce whales. This is no minor decision for the magazine: Japanese advertisers alone had provided 18 percent of its revenues, some $250,000, in 1973.

SOURCE: Reported in "Matter of Principle," *Wall Street Journal,* June 27, 1974, p. 1.

For thought and discussion:
Do you agree with this decision of *Audubon*?
What effect do you think it will have on the killing of whales?

Direct Mail

Direct mail permits the most selectivity of any media, since it reaches only that part of the market the advertiser wishes to contact. It is more personal than other media. It has the greatest flexibility, since messages can be tailored to the particular characteristics of the audience, and best timing can be assured. A multiplicity of advertising messages are sent through the mails, from postcards and sales letters to four-color brochures and thousand-page catalogues. The mailing list is a vital part of the direct-mail campaign since the people addressed should really be prospects. A firm may compile its own list from company records and billings or various directories. A number of firms, or "houses," specialize in offering lists of almost every type breakdown imaginable. For example, the following lists can be obtained:

200,000 new births each month
200,000 Northern guests in Southern and West Coast hotels
12,000 women heads of Protestant fund-raising organizations
78,000 buyers of sex information books
20,000 race track system players
10,000 millionaires
112,000 members of golf and country clubs

Direct mail offers particular advantages to smaller firms that cannot afford mass-media advertising, since they need spend only what they can afford or have productive capacity to handle. You can see how the quality of the mailing list—the extent of duplication and the accuracy of addresses—is important to success. Customer resistance, since there is no editorial or entertainment material, is often a problem; undoubtedly much of this material is thrown away without being read or even opened.

Television

As Table 12-1 shows, television has grown the most rapidly of the major media. It offers the great advantage of appealing through both the eye and the ear, thereby permitting demonstration as well as explanation. It offers tremendous impact, as millions can be viewing a program and its commercials at one time. Messages can be repeated as often as an advertiser can afford, and great flexibility of presentation is possible.

On the other hand, television is extremely costly. One minute on a top-rated network program can cost upwards of $100,000. Added to this are the costs of developing a commercial—rehearsals, filming, reshooting, dubbing, scoring, animation, printing—and these can add up to many more thousands. The J. C. Penney Company made a record buy in terms of the amount of TV time filled by a single advertiser on a single night when it sponsored most of the election coverage on the three major networks in 1972. This one-night TV blitz cost the chain about $4 million, including the production cost for many new commercials.[13]

However, TV spot costs for any single station—as contrasted with network coverage for all stations—can vary widely and even cost under $100 for some of the shows with lower audience ratings.[14]

Table 12-3 shows the leading U. S. television and magazine ad-

[13] As reported in *Advertising Age,* November 13, 1972, p. 1.
[14] "You Can't Afford Prime Time? So Try Selling Direct on TV," *Advertising Age,* October 16, 1972, pp. 64–68.

Table 12-3.
Leading U. S. Advertisers in Television and
General Magazines in 1973

Advertiser	Network TV*	Advertiser	General Magazines
Procter & Gamble	$129,293,000	General Motors	$30,823,000
American Home		Philip Morris	26,175,000
Products	70,562,000	R. J. Reynolds	25,051,000
Bristol-Myers	70,483,000	Ford	24,480,000
General Foods	63,956,000	Brown & Williamson	21,934,000
Sterling Drug	62,625,000	Sears Roebuck	19,772,000
General Motors	48,087,000	Distillers Corp-	
Ford	43,577,000	Seagrams	19,077,000
Gillette	43,334,000	Bristol-Myers	18,337,000

* The figure for TV expenditures does not include the amount spent on Spot TV advertising which is also appreciable but not as much as for network TV.
Source: *Advertising Age,* July 15, 1974, pp. 82–83.

vertisers for 1973. We can learn from this which products are perceived to be best adapted to these two quite different advertising media. It is apparent that TV is most attractive to low-price, repeat sale, mostly convenience goods manufacturers, while magazines are strong with distillers and tobacco companies (who have been banned from TV and radio); the automobile manufacturers use both media.

Radio

TV did not cause the demise of radio, as many had predicted, although radio did lose ground between 1950 and 1955. It reaches audiences at relatively low cost: a one-minute radio spot announcement may cost as little as $10. Radio is very flexible geographically, so that a national firm can pick the areas where it wants to concentrate efforts; the commercial itself can be changed or modified up to broadcast time. Radio also permits the advertiser to practice segmentation or audience selectivity, since many stations concentrate on particular types of listeners, such as teenagers, blacks, country-music devotees, classical music enthusiasts, the Spanish-speaking group, etc. However, radio audiences tend to be extremely fragmented, with many radio stations being present in most parts of the country. There is another disadvantage that radio shares with TV: the transient nature of any presentation—the message is not available for reference or for rereading.

Outdoor or Billboard

This medium has sales volume of a little more than 1 percent of total advertising expenditures in all media. Billboards have been freely

Outdoor advertising comes in many forms other than the billboard.
Bus and subway ads are examples, as is this unusual use of a city
trash basket. *Photo by Helena Frost.*

criticized by those concerned with beautifying the nation's highways
and by some safety advocates who think such advertising is distracting. It is a highly flexible, low-cost medium, and is excellent for the
reminder type of ad. However, copy must be limited and much detail
avoided if the message is to be comprehended in the brief period of
passing the sign. Usually there is substantial waste circulation so that
costs per prospect may be quite high. The automobile companies
have been the major users of outdoor advertising.

Finding Alternative Advertising Media

As of January 2, 1971, cigarette commercials were banned from TV
and radio; the $250 million that had been spent annually for com-
mercials was now forced to seek other outlets. At first it was thought
that the tobacco companies would be unable to find enough effective
media to use up the money they formerly spent on TV and radio, but

in fact, they found a myriad of new and original ways to advertise, along with the expected increase in magazine, newspaper, and billboard advertising. Some companies sponsored sports events both to reach the large crowds attending, and to draw some notice in printed news reports of the contests. Philip Morris, for example, sponsored a Powder Puff derby for women air racers. Reynolds concentrated on auto races in the South, where racing is most popular, with the Alabama 500 becoming the Winston 500. In the early days of the ban, more "far out" ideas were studied: one "dedicated" smoker volunteered to walk clear across the United States with a Camel sign on his back, and an inventor offered the use of a device that could project the word Winston on clouds or buildings.[15]

Many tobacco marketing experts believed that the day of the new cigarette brand was over, that without TV it would be impossible to launch a new brand. But by 1974 the industry had recovered from this attitude. A flood of new cigarettes—some 27 new brands and brand extensions—were introduced.[16] The loss of the medium of TV had apparently been satisfactorily compensated for by other media.

DEVELOPING THE ADVERTISEMENT

Probably in no other aspect of business does creativity come more into play than in the development of the advertisement. And this process will probably continue to defy the sophisticated mathematical and computer-based tools that offer potential for many other aspects of decision making. But, as observed at the beginning of this chapter, imaginative thinking, the discovery of new relationships, is far from evident in much advertising today—the thirteen undistinguished messages about the detergents being a case in point.

If an ad is to accomplish its purpose, if it is to be effective, it must first attract attention. After being noticed, it must hold interest long enough for the message to be read and for a desire to be stimulated. And finally, the ad should induce the reader to some kind of action, perhaps a purchase, but more probably, instilling a favorable image of the product. This has popularly been known as the AIDA concept: attention, interest, desire, action.[17]

The creative elements of an ad—this might be termed the *creative mix*—consist of verbal and nonverbal symbols. The verbal symbols include the headline and the main body of the message—the

15 "Cigarettes, After the Blackout," *Time*, March 22, 1971, pp. 73–74.
16 "A Deluge of New Cigarettes," *Business Week*, November 23, 1974, pp. 114–16.
17 M. S. Heidingsfield and A. B. Blankenship, *Marketing* (New York: Barnes & Noble, 1957), p. 149.

copy. Nonverbal symbols are the illustration(s), layout (the physical arrangement of all the elements in the ad), typography, trademarks, the relative amount of white space, and the possible use of color. In particular, the blend of copy and illustrations must be utilized in the most effective way possible within the framework of the AIDA concept.[18]

There is seldom one best way to combine these elements in an ad. But some combinations are better than others, and studies have long been made to determine the better of two or more ads. Some advertisers, before committing an advertisement or a commercial to a nationwide audience, attempt to measure the relative effectiveness of various ad formats so that the better can be used.[19] Certainly the media to be used and the audience must be carefully considered. An advertisement in *Fortune* can carry a different—and probably longer —copy from that of an advertisement in a newspaper. But the creative mix still remains an art, and one that does not lend itself to easy measurement or easy prediction.

Positioning

The term *positioning* is the new buzz word of the advertising industry. Essentially it means promoting a product so that it is not going head-to-head against an entrenched competitor, but rather is placed or positioned in a new sector or segment of the market. It is easier to explain this concept with several examples. Seven-up has been able to position itself successfully as the "Uncola," an alternative to the cola drink; Schaefer beer as the one beer to have when "You're having more than one," clearly aimed at the sports fans (Schaefer sponsors television coverage of the New York Knicks, Rangers, and Mets) and guzzlers; *Sports Illustrated* as the third newsweekly; Nyquil, as a "night-time cold medicine."

The idea behind positioning is not new; it simply represents an effort to find a new segment of the market, a unique niche not tightly controlled by a competitor—in other words, a distinctive appeal. Positioning represents more a state of mind, or image, than different ingredients or attributes. And such a state of mind is derived from advertising, much more than from product planning and design. Accordingly, the success of the advertising campaign in positioning a product so that it does not compete directly with another product,

---

[18] There are a number of guides for creating attention and interest. While they are beyond the scope of this book, most advertising texts cover them. For example, see C. H. Sandage and V. Fryburger, *Advertising Theory and Practice,* 7th ed. (Homewood, Ill.: Irwin, 1967); Maurice I. Mandell, *Advertising* (Englewood Cliffs, N.J.: Prentice-Hall, 1968); Philip Ward Burton, and J. Robert Miller, *Advertising Fundamentals* (Scranton, Pa.: International Textbook, 1970).

[19] For example, see Philip Ward Burton, ed., *Which Ad Pulled Best?* (New York: Decker Communications, 1969).

but rather has a different emphasis, becomes important.[20] One might well ask, however, Is this not what advertisers have always tried to do—to be different, distinctive, memorable?

Organizing for Advertising

The creative aspects of advertising may be handled entirely within the firm, as is often the case with large retailers who have their own layout people, copywriters, and artists. Most of these retailers use the local newspapers, sometimes daily, and close communication must be maintained with the buyers whose merchandise is being featured. The short lead time of newspapers enables last-minute changes to be made in pricing, in feature items, and other details; the uncertainties of deliveries from manufacturers, the actions of competitors, weather, and other factors often necessitate such last-minute changes. Furthermore, displays, signs, informed salespeople, and adequate stocks all must be coordinated if the full impact of the advertising expenditure is to be achieved.

Many large manufacturers, in addition to having their own advertising department, use an advertising agency. The department acts as liaison, approves agency plans and advertisements, and prepares and administers the advertising budget and certain other advertising and sales promotion activities; the agency provides the creative expertise needed.

Advertising agencies are independent firms that specialize in the technical aspects of advertising in the mass media. Some of the functions most agencies have are those relating to planning and budgeting, copy, art, media selection, research, client contact, and even public relations. Since agencies have a number of clients, they usually have gathered far more creative talent than that which the advertising department even of a large manufacturer might be able to muster. They are often able to bring fresh perspectives and a desired objectivity to a client's particular promotional problems and needs. Relations between an agency and a client are very easy to terminate; therefore, an agency has considerable motivation to do an effective job.

As an example of the ease with which an advertising agency can be fired, Miles Laboratories, makers of Alka-Seltzer, in December 1970 dumped the Doyle Dane Bernbach agency and shifted the $22 million account to Wells, Rich, Greene. What makes this rather startling is that 1970 witnessed the most memorable TV commercials of the year from Alka-Seltzer: the "Spicy Meatball Man," and the "Poached Oyster Bride." These had won both professional awards

[20] For a sample of the many articles on positioning, see "Why is Schaefer Beer the One Beer to Have When Having More . . . ?" *Wall Street Journal*, December 13, 1972, p. 1 ff.; " 'Positioning' is a Game People Play in Today's Me-too Market Place," *Industrial Marketing*, June 1969, pp. 51–53; Jack Trout and Al Ries, "The Positioning Era," *Advertising Age*, April 24, May 1, and May 8, 1972.

and "popular chuckles as the best of their breed."[21] The reason for the switch was that Alka-Seltzer's sales had dropped somewhat. Of course, no one will ever know whether the drop might have been much worse without these commercials.

Agencies receive about two thirds of their income from media commissions—commissions paid by the media—and the balance from client fees and other charges. An advertiser may thus be able to use the services of an agency for much less than might otherwise be expected. There is a trend toward agencies' broadening their scope of service, to become more complete marketing agencies, helping with such activities as over-all marketing strategy planning, marketing research, sales promotion, product development, and packaging.[22]

Advertising Management Problems

The more creative problems—development of an advertising theme and the specific advertisements and commercials—can well be left to specialists in the advertising department or agency to propose, subject to management approval. But there are other problems confronting management. These problems and decisions may eventually be helped by a computer technology and mathematical model building. Some crude models have already been devised that presage greater help in the future, but their immediate help is negligible. We will examine four problem areas:

1. How to determine the amount of advertising to buy
2. How to allocate advertising expenditures by media
3. How to time or schedule advertising
4. How to measure the effectiveness of advertising

Setting the Advertising Budget. There are four common methods of budgeting advertising expenditures.

"Affordable" Method. Some companies plow everything they can into the promotional program after allowing enough to meet other expenses. Such a method of budgeting has a curious aura of "plucking at straws." Yet it can be reasonably effective for the new company hoping to establish a niche in the market and needing as much short-term impact as possible. How much can be afforded is subject to various interpretations by executives with different points of view. Without some other rationale for setting the advertising budget, it is likely that, before long, efforts elsewhere will be undermined.

Percentage-of-Sales Method. A widely used method of budgeting

---

[21] "Advertising: A Case of Indigestion," *Newsweek*, December 21, 1970, p. 81; also *Time*, "Nice Work, You're Fired," December 21, 1970, p. 66.
[22] "Why Ad Agencies Make Good Marketing Partners," *Printers' Ink*, November 11, 1960, pp. 68–69.

advertising is to do so on a specified percentage of sales, either current or anticipated. It is quite simple to do, and does give some order to the budgeting process. It has several crucial, if theoretical, weaknesses. Advertising and promotion essentially are being viewed as the *result* of sales, when they really *cause* sales. This method often typifies the complacent firm, one using historical spending patterns, when a more aggressive approach, or one tailored to a product-by-product or territory-by-territory approach, has much more to recommend it. Furthermore, a firm is committed to a decreasing advertising budget when sales are declining, either because of a recession or other circumstances, when a better course of action might be to maintain or increase the level of promotional activity until the sales decline can be corrected.[23]

Follow Competition. A major firm in the industry or industry averages may be followed in order to maintain competitive parity. This is a weak method that implies that other firms know better what they are doing (when they probably do not), and that it is best to stabilize industry spending. But the needs and goals of a firm, and its resources, may be quite different from those of its competitors.

Objective and Task Method. By setting objectives and determining what tasks and costs are involved in reaching these objectives, a more logical approach to advertising spending should be made than under the previous three methods. This approach is growing in popularity and it is compatible with the longe-range planning and better-defined objectives that are beginning to characterize business today. A major flaw is the difficulty of correctly estimating how much and what kind of promotional efforts are necessary to reach a certain objective. For example, if brand preference is to be increased by 10 percent, it is difficult to determine what expenditure will be required —lacking as we do any definitive measure of the relationship between advertising costs and advertising effects—and the answer will be affected by factors over which the firm has no control, such as competitive actions. Despite this weakness, the objective and task method is a substantial improvement, mostly because it builds up desired appropriations by products and by territories. But the difficulties remain in estimating payoffs of alternative advertising budgets; this accounts for many firms' continuing use of simplistic approaches to budgeting advertising.

It is generally conceded that advertising expenditures eventually reach a point of diminishing returns. Figure 12-2 illustrates hypothetically a promotion-sales curve. Up to a certain point, increasing expenditures may increase sales more than the additional expenditure; then a decreasing rate of sales return is yielded; finally, negative returns may even result.

[23] A. C. Nielsen, Jr., "Many Measurements Available to Increase Advertising Effectiveness," *Medial Scope,* September 1965, p. 72.

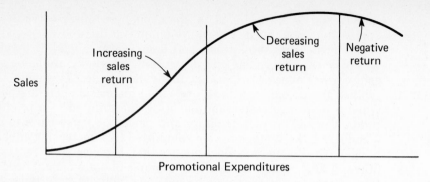

Figure 12-2. Hypothetical Promotion-Sales Curve

Several factors logically account for such a decreasing return. The most likely prospects are reached by the initial efforts, and those less susceptible because of loyalty to other brands and other preference or economic reasons remain. Perhaps the most effective media have been exhausted. Perhaps the extent of learning about the product and brand was effectively maximized earlier, so that more promotional input produces little additional learning. And there is always the possibility in heavy "saturation" campaigns of generating negative attitudes on the part of some consumers.

Allocating Advertising Expenditures by Media. With the total advertising budget and plan determined, the allocation decision presents further difficulties because of the many available alternatives: How much should be spent on TV, radio, newspapers, magazines? Which magazines? How many issues of each should be purchased? And many similar questions.

The various major media have their strengths and limitations. Some obviously are being used more by certain manufacturers than others. For example, the automobile manufacturers are strong users of magazines where the reproduction and color enhance the presentation of the product. Polaroid cameras, whose demonstration is important, are best advertised on TV. The type of customer a firm wants to contact—the target audience—also affects the media decision. The interests of the *Fortune* reader are far different from those of the *Modern Romances* reader, or of the average person watching network TV. Cost of the various media categories is an important consideration for many firms. The small firm can hardly afford the cost of network TV; even a general-purpose magazine may be too costly or too wasteful. Perhaps direct mail, or a special-interest magazine, or radio spots are the only feasible choices. Therefore, the allocation decision is influenced by at least these three factors:

1. The media's effectiveness in presenting the product.
2. The target audience's media habits.
3. The relative costs among media alternatives.

For the specific decision on which magazine or TV program, most media buyers evaluate according to some criterion of cost per audience reached. For example, magazines are rated by a *cost-per-thousand criterion,* newspapers by *milline* rates (the cost of putting one agate line of advertising before a million persons), and radio and TV by *cost per commercial minute per thousand.* The cost-per-thousand rates for a black-and-white page in several leading magazines are shown in Table 12-4.

While the *Reader's Digest* would seem the best buy—being the lowest cost per thousand circulation and audience reached—the more selected readership of the *New Yorker* and *Business Week* would make these much more attractive to some advertisers.

Mathematical models have been developed that purport to improve media selection. However, there are many variables and alternatives involved in these decisions, and the models so far tend to be artificial in the weighting of the various factors and the constraints. Judgment and imagination still need to be used for these decisions.

Timing of Advertising. Timing can make the difference between a successful campaign and a mediocre one. Major decisions are necessary to determine how concentrated and how continuous the advertising should be during a period. If used throughout the period, the impact at any given time may be less than desired; on the other hand, a strong, concentrated advertising effort at the beginning may have impact, but lack of funds remaining may prevent lasting effects. Mathematical models have also been developed for these decisions. For example, one model attempts to relate optimal timing patterns to the degree of advertising carryover and the amount of habitual

Table 12-4.
Advertising Rates

Magazine	Total Paid Circulation	Cost for One Black/White Page	Approximate Cost per Thousand Subscribers
Reader's Digest	18,817,325	$52,915	$ 2.80
New Yorker	486,917	5,900	12.00
Business Week	751,831	10,690	13.50

Source: Approximate cost per thousand subscribers compiled from circulation and cost figures per *Standard Rate and Data,* January 27, 1975.

brand choice.[24] Certainly if advertising has a strong *carryover effect* (that is, may influence sales a week or a month hence), then there should be a greater lead time. If a firm is advertising ski equipment and it has been determined that a fairly long carryover effect is present, then ads might be effective well before the start of the winter season.

Measuring the Effectiveness of Advertising. Measures of advertising effectiveness cannot be divorced from research to improve ads, although in this section we will be more concerned with over-all measures of this effectiveness and the problems encountered. Table 12-5 depicts the common measures of effectiveness, both for individual ads and overall.[25]

Table 12-5.
Methods of Measuring Advertising Effectiveness

Measures for Individual Ads	
Pretesting	Evaluating different ad candidates before the ads are run, in order to choose those perceived to be best.
Checklists	Advertiser checks prospective ads against a list of elements that should be in an advertisement.
Consumer juries	Reaction to prospective ads is obtained from a selected group of consumers.
Objective methods	
Eye-movement camera	Records attention value of particular parts of an ad by eye movement.
Psychogalvanometer	Instrument to measure emotional reaction to ads.
Perceptoscope	Instrument to measure dilation of pupil of eye.

[24] Alfred A. Kuehn, "A Model for Budgeting Advertising," in Frank M. Bass et al., eds., *Mathematical Models and Methods in Marketing* (Homewood, Ill.: Irwin, 1961), pp. 302–53; David B. Montgomery and Glen L. Urban, *Management Science in Marketing* (Englewood Cliffs, N.J.: Prentice-Hall, 1969).

[25] For more detail on these measures, refer to any advertising text, several examples being: James F. Engel, Hugh G. Wales, and Martin R. Warshaw, *Promotional Strategy* (Homewood, Ill.: Irwin, 1967), chaps. 22–24; S. Watson Dunn, *Advertising, Its Role in Modern Marketing,* 2d ed. (New York: Holt, Rinehart, and Winston, 1969), chap. 32. Most marketing research texts devote one or more chapters to these subjects, such as: D. J. Luck, H. G. Wales, and D. A. Taylor, *Marketing Research,* 3d ed. (Englewood Cliffs, N.J.: Prentice-Hall, 1970), chap. 18; Jerry E. Drake, and Frank I. Millar, *Marketing Research: Intelligence and Management* (Scranton, Pa.: International Textbook, 1969), chap. 19.

Table 12-5. (Continued)

Tachistoscope	Mechanical device to measure perception.
Concurrent testing	Primarily used to measure radio and TV listenership at the time of the program.
Nielsen Audimeter	Electronic recorder attached to radio or television set which records when the set is operating and what programs (stations) are tuned to.
Coincidental surveys	Telephone surveys to solicit responses as to what programs are being listened to or viewed.
Posttesting	Measuring advertising impact after the ad is run.
Coupon returns	Responses to coupons and offers; sometimes used as a *split-run*, in which two or more versions of an ad are published in the same issue of a publication.
Recognition or readership tests	Ascertaining from a group of consumers how much was recognized and read of an ad.
Aided recall	Specific ads are shown to aid recall.
Unaided recall	Little aid is given.
Diary method	Primarily used to obtain radio and TV listening and viewing information by cooperating consumer groups.
Sales tests	Measuring results in direct sales generation.
Mail order sales	Can measure ad pull specifically in mail order sales generated.
Retail sales	Rough measures of ad pull can be obtained by tally of advertised item sales in 1–3-day period.

Measures for Advertising Campaigns

Attitude change	Surveying consumer attitudes toward a company, its brand and products; the assumption is that favorable attitudes predispose people to buy the product.
Sales tests	Attempts to relate sales to advertising under some degree of controlled conditions.
Test market measurements	The effectiveness of an advertising campaign is gauged by relative sales in test and control markets.

Table 12-5. (Continued)

Consumer diaries and pantry checks	Ascertaining product purchases by co-operating consumer groups.
Store inventories	Determining product sales by inventorying cooperating retail stores.
Quasi-measures of sales effectiveness	Using company marketing performance as a rough guide for determining advertising effectiveness, but where the results of such cannot be directly credited to advertising.
Accounting records. Sales records. Market-share reports. Distribution studies.	

Evaluating Overall Advertising Effectiveness

While the effectiveness of individual advertisements and advertising campaigns can be evaluated, and sometimes fairly definitively, evaluating overall effectiveness must be more conjectural:

> Although partial measurement of results is nearly always possible, one is seldom able to measure all of the effects of advertising. At times, some of the results are so slow in materializing that they cannot easily be traced to specific advertising efforts. These results must be measured over long periods of time, during which marketing factors other than advertising may influence them. At other times, the results of advertising are quite subtle and elusive, making measurement most difficult. And advertising frequently produces results that are neither sought after, expected, nor perhaps even noticed. Therefore, if management insists on complete measurement of advertising results or nothing, it will almost surely have to accept nothing.[26]

When a firm spends millions of dollars, it wants some indication of the results of these efforts: To what extent did the advertising really pay? The ultimate purpose of advertising effectiveness studies is a search for a causal relationship between independent (the advertisement) and dependent (the result of the advertisement) variables. But as the middle column of Table 12-6 shows, there are many uncontrollable variables that can affect the outcome, in addition to the relative quality of the respective advertisement. Looking at the dependent variables in the last column, it is most desirable to determine the causal relations between the advertising variables (in column 1) and the sales variation, or the change in market share

---

[26] Harry Deane Wolfe, James K. Grown, and G. Clark Thompson, "Measuring Advertising Results," *Studies in Business Policies, No. 102* (New York: National Industrial Conference Board, 1962), p. 9.

(column 3). This can seldom be done. The next choice is the measurement of variations among purchasers, such as buyers versus nonbuyers, or changes in brand loyalty, or frequency of purchase. But more often, effectiveness studies center on such things as attitude, knowledge, or awareness of the product or the message, since the more desirable outcomes are difficult or impossible to relate to the advertising inputs.

Table 12-6.
The Advertising System

Independent Variables		Dependent Variables
Controllable (Alternative Advertising Strategies)	Uncontrollable States of Nature	Advertising Outcomes (in Descending Order of Measurement Desirability)
Variations in	Variations in	Variations in
1. Media	1. Competitors' activities	1. Sales
2. Message	2. Consumers' tastes	2. Market share
3. Money	3. Dealer push	3. Purchasers
	4. Displays	4. Distribution
	5. Distributors' activities	5. Momentum
	6. Effective distribution	6. Attitude
	7. Out of stock	7. Knowledge
	8. Personal selling	8. Awareness
	9. Pricing	9. Playback
	10. Product differentiation	
	11. Product performance	
	12. Promotions and deals	
	13. Publicity	
	14. Public relations	
	15. Retailers' activities	
	16. Trade shows	
	17. Weather	

Source: Roy H. Campbell, "A Managerial Approach to Advertising Measurement," *Journal of Marketing,* October 1965, p. 2.

Most presently used evaluative methods simply tell which ad is the best among those being appraised. But even though one ad may be found to be more memorable or to create more attention than another, that fact alone gives no assurance of relationship to sales success.[27]

[27] See Clarence E. Eldridge, "Advertising Effectiveness: How Can It Be Measured," *Journal of Marketing,* January 1958, pp. 242–43; and Gail Smith, "How GM Measures Ad Effectiveness," *Printers' Ink,* May 14, 1965, p. 19.

Despite the many decades of advertising-effectiveness research, we still have not progressed very far, as you can see. But advertising industry spokesmen are optimistic that a new era is beginning when results of advertising will be predicted in advance and measured with accuracy. The president of one large agency has forecast that mathematical techniques and computers will give predictability in results that can be measured in profit and loss statements, and that new managements will insist on this.[28] Despite such optimism, it is doubtful that such will be reached in the near future. Such an outcome would have traumatic effects: "waste" advertising would be virtually eliminated and expenditures greatly reduced; marketing undoubtedly would become more efficient, but advertising agencies and the media would likely disappear.[29]

Now let us shift our focus from the techniques and problems of advertising from the firm's viewpoint to its social aspects.

ADVERTISING AND SOCIETY

Advertising has been the focus of more criticism than any other aspect of marketing or of business. It was an issue long before anyone had heard of consumerism. John Kenneth Galbraith, one of the more eloquent critics of advertising, wrote:

> a relentless propaganda on behalf of goods in general. From early morning until late at night, people are informed of the services rendered by goods—of their profound indispensability . . . Even minor qualities of unimportant commodities are enlarged upon with a solemnity which would not be unbecoming in an announcement of the combined return of Christ and all the apostles. More important services, such as the advantages of whiter laundry, are treated with proportionately greater gravity.[30]

[28] Speech, January 25, at the 1970 convention of the International Newspaper Advertising Executives, Atlanta, Ga., by Neal W. O'Connor, president of N. W. Ayer & Sons, and quoted in the *Washington Post,* January 26, 1970, p. D9.

[29] For additional discussion of advertising effectiveness measures and their productivity, see John E. Morrill, "Industrial Advertising Pays Off," *Harvard Business Review,* March–April 1970, pp. 4–14; David A. Schwartz, "Measuring the Effectiveness of Your Company's Advertising," *Journal of Marketing,* April 1969, pp. 20–25; and Roy H. Campbell, *Measuring the Sales and Profit Results of Advertising: A Managerial Approach* (New York: Association of National Advertisers, 1969).

[30] John Kenneth Galbraith, *The New Industrial State* (Boston: Houghton Mifflin, 1967), pp. 218–19. For a perspective in examining the criticisms of Galbraith and others regarding advertising, see John A. Howard and Spencer F. Tinkham, "A Framework for Understanding Social Criticism of Advertising," *Journal of Marketing,* October 1971, pp. 2–7.

Advertising lends itself to deception and exaggeration. Some would say it permits manipulation. Most people, marketers and the general public alike, concede that too much money is spent on advertising.

Let us see what companies and products bear the brunt of advertising, and what constraints are being placed on advertising today. Finally we should look at advertising on balance—the faults, and the benefits.

Expenditures for Advertising by Companies and Product Categories

Table 12-7 shows the top ten advertisers by total expenditures as well as these expenditures as a percent of sales. You can see from this that the big automobile companies are fairly conservative in their advertising, even though the total dollars spent make them some of the largest advertisers. Procter & Gamble, by far the biggest spender, still budgets a relatively moderate percentage for advertising. On the other hand, the medium and large-size drug and cosmetic firms allocate a substantial percentage of sales to advertising. Interestingly, no beer or liquor firms are represented in the top ten, and only one tobacco firm.

Table 12-7.
Top Ten National Advertisers in Total Expenditures, 1973

	Advertising Expenditures	Advertising as Percent of Sales
Procter & Gamble	$233,567,000	6.0
General Motors	158,379,000	0.4
General Foods	133,267,000	5.6
Ford	127,187,000	0.5
Bristol-Myers	124,440,000	9.0
American Home Products	122,838,000	6.9
Sears Roebuck	99,161,000	0.7
Colgate-Palmolive	96,770,000	4.4
Sterling Drug	93,069,000	11.6
R. J. Reynolds	84,074,000	3.6

Source: Advertising expenditures from *Advertising Age,* July 15, 1974, pp. 82–83. Advertising expenditures as a percentage of sales computed from sales data of *Forbes,* May 15, 1974.

Table 12-8 shows the percent of sales invested in advertising by certain industry groups. Soaps and related products, and drugs, show the highest percentage expenditures for advertising.

Table 12-8.
Percent of Sales Invested in Advertising
By Product Classification, 1971-1972

Selected Industries	Percentage
Soaps and related products	8.95
Drugs	8.41
Watches and clocks	5.27
Bottled soft drinks	4.68
Tobacco manufacturers	4.47
Malt liquors	4.27
Optical, medical, and ophthalmic goods	3.35
Household appliances	2.05
Motor vehicles	0.70
All industrial and service groups	1.08

Source: *Advertising Age,* September 30, 1974, p. 76.

Constraints on Advertising

As noted in chapter 4, media and the advertising industry itself exert pressures against deceptive advertising and advertising which may be of questionable ethics; codes of ethics have been more prevalent in advertising than perhaps any other aspect of business.

In recent years the Federal Trade Commission has been taking a militant stand against ads that smack of deception or of unsupported claims. The FTC has several alternatives in dealing with such unsatisfactory advertising:[31]

Cease and desist orders
Affirmative disclosure
Corrective advertisements
Counter-commercials

Cease and desist orders are issued to terminate a questioned advertising practice, and may involve fines. For example, the maker of Geritol was fined $812,000 for advertised claims challenged by the FTC.[32]

An *affirmative disclosure* order may be issued when the FTC thinks an advertisement has not provided sufficient information to the consumer to permit an informed decision. For example, Kenrec Sports, Inc., was ordered to disclose certain limitations to its swim-

[31] Robert E. Wilkes and James B. Wilcox, "Recent FTC Actions: Implications for the Advertising Strategist," *Journal of Marketing,* January 1974, pp. 55–61. For a discussion of some of the problems in defining "deception in advertising," see David M. Gardner, "Deception in Advertising: A Conceptual Approach," *Journal of Marketing,* January 1975, pp. 40–46.

[32] "Legal Developments in Marketing," *Journal of Marketing,* July 1973, pp. 82–83.

ming-aid device, namely that it was not a life preserver and should always be used in shallow water.[33]

Corrective advertising may be required in order to eliminate the "residue" effects of misleading advertising in prior advertisements. The first such order was against ITT Continental Baking Company, and required 25 percent of the media budget for one year to be given to FTC-approved corrective advertisements that Profile Bread was not the effective weight reducer that prior advertisements had represented. The makers of Ocean Spray Cranberry Juice were also required to correct possible misrepresentations of their product as having the food energy of orange or tomato juice, and 25 percent of the budget was specified for this purpose.[34]

Counter-commercials have been proposed to counteract product claims and advertising themes which are controversial. Free time might even be given those who wished to present counter positions. The antismoking commercials on TV (before cigarette ads were banned from TV and radio) are an example of such counter-commercials.

As we noted in chapter 5, the FTC is also pressuring advertisers to back up their claims. For example, it asked for scientific data to back up claims such as these:

A McLean's toothpaste ad that says a major dental clinic claims McLean's gets teeth "whitest."

Warner Lambert Company's inference that Listerine helps in the prevention of colds.

Bristol-Myers' claim for Excedrin that a clinical study shows that "two Excedrins work better for the relief of pain than twice as many aspirin tablets."

Ford Motor Company's claim that its LTD is "quieter than some of the world's most expensive cars."

Some of the "proofs" were not very convincing, to say the least. For example, in an inquiry by the Senate Monopoly Subcommittee about the claim that Excedrin tablets are more effective than aspirin, this was described by an expert witness as true, but only because the Excedrin tablet is larger.[35] The justification for the Ford statement was a 5-year old test with nine older foreign cars, including a 1963 Daimler with over 37,000 miles.[36] *Responsive marketing* would suggest more forthrightness in advertising.

[33] "Legal Developments in Marketing," *Journal of Marketing,* October 1972, p. 69.

[34] Robert F. Dyer and Philip G. Kuehl, "The 'Corrective Advertising' Remedy of the FTC: An Experimental Evaluation," *Journal of Marketing,* January 1974, pp. 48–54.

[35] "Nothing, Says FDA, Beats Aspirin," *Washington Post,* June 23, 1971.

[36] "FTC Airs Auto Firms' Ad Data," *Washington Post,* October 14, 1971, p. A6; "Auto Ads: What FTC Learned," *Business Week,* October 16, 1971, p. 30.

Comparative advertising has been encouraged by the FTC as an information boon to the consumer, and some advertisers have seized on it as an effective marketing technique. In comparative advertising the advertiser names the competitors and tells why the product being advertised is better than they are. By stressing some of the services that its credit card offers that bigger competitors such as American Express do not, Carte Blanche added 105,000 new cardholders—45,000 more than in any previous year. Avis, with its "We Try Harder" challenge to Hertz Corporation, moved from an anonymous and distant second to a widely recognized competitor.[37]

However, the practice of naming competitors' names in advertisements is controversial. Lawsuits and countersuits are developing. For example, Sperry Rand's Remington division sued Schick for $6 million because of Schick's ad claims regarding its electric razor; and Schick sued Sperry Rand for $6.5 million because of Sperry Rand's counter-ad claims. Some advertisers see the credibility of all advertising being damaged by claims and counterclaims which name names.[38]

Advertising on Balance

As with most social issues, the role of advertising is not clear-cut, neither wholly good nor entirely bad. There is perhaps too much advertising, much of it consisting of claims and counterclaims and stressing trivial differences, so that the net effect on the average person becomes one of disregard. Some advertising is in bad taste, some insults the intelligence, other advertising is aggressively intrusive in an attempt to gain attention. Then there are the billboards that obliterate the view on the nation's highways. And some advertising— fortunately, not a great deal—is deceptive and downright fraudulent.

We should recognize that advertising is hardly as powerful a tool as its critics assume. One advertising expert notes:

> I think it cannot be said too many times that the public may buy a product on faith, on what the advertising says it will do; but it buys it the second time only on confirmation, on performance, on what the product actually does in use.[39]

Much advertising is entertaining, is pleasant, performs a service in informing about new products and features, and finances much of the entertainment we enjoy. Furthermore, it can be a spur to the

[37] "Naming Names of Rivals in Ads is Catching On But Spurs Controversy," *Wall Street Journal*, December 26, 1973, pp. 1, 17; "Comparative Ads Get Hit in First Big Test, Over Schick Campaign," *Wall Street Journal*, December 31, 1973, p. 11.

[38] Ibid.

[39] Walter Weir, *On the Writing of Advertising* (New York: McGraw-Hill, 1960), p. 40.

economy and lead to lower prices and more rapid realization of mass production for new products.

Therefore, on balance, advertising is a desirable and necessary part of our society. The Soviet Union has been forced, reluctantly but firmly, to embrace this device of a capitalistic society in order to maintain reasonable quality standards and to stimulate the economy. And, despite our protestations at repetitious commercials, would we not sorely miss advertising in its absence?

QUESTIONS AND PROBLEMS

1. Evaluate the power of advertising to change attitudes and behavior.
2. Can a business succeed without advertising? Discuss.
3. How do you determine the effectiveness of institutional advertising?
4. How can a firm determine how many sales dollars resulted from a given ad or from an entire campaign?
5. Discuss the kinds, uses, and potential of research for advertising decisions.
6. Explain how promotional objectives are affected by the product life cycle.
7. Discuss the disadvantage the small firm faces in being unable to match the expenditures of big firms. What recourse does such a firm have? How effective is this likely to be?
8. In trying to determine the amount to spend on advertising for a given period, the objective and task method is usually offered as the most sophisticated and logical. What limitations do you see in this approach that precludes its wider acceptance?

Project

Find in the Standard Rate & Data Service the cost per thousand for Redbook, Time, and Playboy for a single-page black and white, one-time ad. Also note the circulation and the audience.
Which periodical of the three would you choose for advertising
— a resort in Jamaica
— dog food
— flowers as gifts
What is your rationale for this advertising media decision?

Exercise in Creativity

Kato is a small local brewery in a small city. It has been in existence for 70 years, but now finds its viability threatened by several large national beers that are advertising heavily in the home town. (These national brands sell for about 5¢ a bottle or a can more than Kato beer.)

Develop a promotional plan to counter the competitive inroads, recognizing that Kato's advertising budget must necessarily be limited.

Role-playing Case

You have been given the responsibility for the marketing efforts of a relatively new line of furniture (introduced nine months earlier) by a major manufacturer. Sales had risen satisfactorily shortly after the introduction, but now had tapered off at a rather disappointing level. You believe that increasing the advertising budget by 30 percent for the next quarter will substantially improve sales results.

How would you support a recommendation to top management for such a substantial increase in the advertising budget? (Make any assumptions necessary, but keep them reasonable. You may also expect top management to ask how you would spend the increased advertising dollars.)

CHAPTER 13

MARKETING COMMUNICATIONS: SALES PROMOTION, PACKAGING, AND PERSONAL SELLING

Sales promotion techniques and personal selling efforts complement and reinforce advertising. The blend of these three activities constitutes the promotion mix. In this chapter we look at the ingredients of sales promotion: displays, packaging, sales incentives such as trading stamps and games, and their effectiveness. The latter part of the chapter is devoted to personal selling—its importance, its challenges, and its place in the promotion mix—and then we look at the role of sales management. You will encounter these terms:

gamesmanship
point-of-purchase displays
coupons
missionary salesmen
detail men
market log

manufacturers' representatives
call rate
order-call ratio
  (batting average)
sales quotas

SALES PROMOTION

Sales promotion covers a wide range of techniques, such as demonstrations and exhibitions, samples, premiums, coupons and cents-off deals, games and contests, trading stamps, displays, store and window signs, and packages and package inserts.

One common (and very old) example of sales promotion is the use of premiums in cereal boxes. With young children, one wonders whether brand, taste, or nutritional value of the cereal is nearly as important as the particular premium inside the box: the ring, the toy, or the baseball card.

In recent years, sales promotion strategies have proliferated. Trading stamps and games have waxed and waned. Reflecting the growth of self-service, packaging and point-of-purchase displays have become important as "silent salesmen." Increased emphasis on sales promotion is partly due to changes in marketing strategy (such as more self-service), but it also hints at the sobering conclusion (from the view of the advertiser) that advertising alone is not able to do the job.

Sales promotion has been called the "plus" ingredient in the marketing mix.[1] This suggests that it is helpful but optional. At one time it was perhaps true that the absence of sales promotion might have no visible effects. This is no longer the case today. The use of trading stamps, coupons, and premiums virtually forces competitors to come up with something similar; otherwise, business shifts to those firms offering extras and more excitement. And in the impersonality of the supermarket shelf, the attractive display and package become powerful selling tools.

Point-of-Purchase Displays

With the trend in retail stores to self-service, advertisers must depend on displays to remind consumers of the advertising they have seen. As described in chapter 6, an effective display for a product can boost sales. We know that the actual decision to buy in the store hinges on the consumer's attitude toward the brand (and, of course, any prior experience in using the product), with advertising helping to mold attitudes. But in many instances the consumer does not feel strongly about any particular brand. This being the case, an attractive and striking package, good shelf position, and any point-of-purchase display may be the final influences and sales generators: the brand that makes the last impression—at the point of purchase —makes the sale.

Any kind of display that can be used either in a retailer's window or inside his store is point-of-purchase advertising. The variety ranges from banners and easel-back cards to mannequins, merchandise stands or racks, to turntables or expensive mobile displays to in-store demonstrations. A display should be designed to meet the needs of the retailer who will use it, while at the same time presenting the best image of the product and brand. The bigger problem,

---

[1] Albert W. Frey, *The Role of Sales Promotion* (Hanover, N. H.: Dartmouth College, 1957), p. 2.

This point-of-purchase display stresses urgency ("Buy Now") but also gives information about the service contract available with the lawn-mower. *Photo by Helena Frost.*

however, is enticing the retailer to use the display material even though it is furnished free by the manufacturer.

All advertising is susceptible to waste, but display materials are particularly so. Many signs and displays are buried in stockrooms and never used, or used ineffectively in poorly located windows, or not for the intended purpose. Moreover, usually the smaller dealers —those who generate the least sales volume—are the most willing to use manufacturer-supplied display material. The major retailers are often more discriminating. Therefore, the manufacturer frequently finds that, even when his material is being used, the potential sales volume is not worth the cost.

Undoubtedly one of the more successful manufacturers in point-of-purchase promotion has been Hershey Foods Corporation.

MARKETING
IN
ACTION

Can Point-of-Purchase Display Do the Whole Job?—
The Hershey Story

Hershey Foods Corporation (until 1968 the name was Hershey Chocolate
Company) was the foremost exponent of the use of point-of-purchase
display to the exclusion of almost all other promotional devices. It has
been described as "a rare marketing phenomenon: a company that
managed to turn a retail product into a national household word,
without resorting to mass promotion."

The Hershey Company was started in 1903 by Milton Hershey, who
was the first candymaker to produce small, inexpensive bars. Rather
than using mass media advertising, Hershey focused his efforts on the
small retailers that carried his product. Hershey bars were primarily
impulse items, placed near the cash register, so point-of-sale advertising
was stressed. World War II resulted in Hershey's market being greatly
expanded as chocolate became a "D ration" for the military. After
World War II, the growth in supermarkets and discount outlets induced
the company to shift its distribution efforts from retailers to larger
wholesale jobbers. But the point-of-sale advertising was continued with
posters and vending machine stickers. Promotional efforts were mostly
directed to encouraging dealer support. Special discounts were offered
jobbers and retailers, advertisements placed in trade journals, and some
local newspaper ads of retailers partly paid for by Hershey. Therefore,
Hershey traditionally spent money for promotion, but mass media
advertising was conspicuously absent.

By the late 1960s, however, there were signs that Hershey's strategy
needed revamping. Profits had been slipping since 1966 and market
share, at least in the wholesale confectionery market, had been eroding.
Increased competition by conglomerates moving into the candy field
became an even bigger problem.

Hershey, after over 60 years of operation, in late 1969 began
launching a mass consumer advertising campaign in the United States.
Hershey candy and Instant Cocoa mix were featured on regional television
in seven medium-size cities.

SOURCE: "Hershey's Sweet Tooth Starts Aching," *Business Week,* February 7,
1970, p. 99.

For thought and discussion:

As a marketing consultant, what arguments would you give Hershey
    for continuing with mass media advertising? How would you suggest they
    determine its effectiveness?

As another marketing consultant (one with a different viewpoint),
    what arguments would you give Hershey for discontinuing mass media
    advertising and again relying primarily on point-of-purchase efforts?

Packaging

The container or wrapper for a product, the package, is generally regarded by consumers as part of the product. The package can add greatly to the appeal of the product, or it can detract from it. Marketers have discovered that a well-designed package, one with certain convenience features (such as easier pouring or handling), can prop up demand for a mediocre product, or can provide an element of differentiation which might not be possible otherwise. But more than this, good packaging can be a significant part of the promotional strategy and the point-of-purchase efforts.

For products distributed through self-service outlets, such as supermarkets where products must compete with as many as 7,000 other items, the role of the package assumes greater importance. It can enhance the image and present subtle selling appeals at that most decisive moment of choice. Even after the sale, the package can continue the selling job. The cigarette package, in particular, is displayed to other people each time the smoker extracts one of its twenty cigarettes; the package design then needs to be distinctive, and even prestigious:

> With television denied the tobacco companies, they are turning to catchy packaging to help market their new brands. For example, Lorillard Corporation's Zack has a package that looks like blue denim; Brown & Williamson's Tramps carries Charlie Chaplin's "Little Tramp" image; Liggett & Myers' St. Moritz is billed as the "first gold band, luxury length, filter cigarette."[2]

Then there is the example of a manufacturer of frosting mix for cakes who thought he had improved the package by changing the illustration, only to find that the brand's market share was cut in half.[3]

Strategies in Packaging. Basically, the package is a protective device. It must protect against transportation and handling damage, against exposure perhaps to sunlight or moisture, and certainly against contamination by insects, rodents, and other external objects. So the old cracker barrel and other bulk containers have long since been replaced by packaged items which are not only more sanitary but fresher. This object of packaging is taken for granted today by most marketing departments. However, production and shipping departments may not always give sufficient attention to the need for protection: crumbled cookies and broken crackers continue to confront consumers, while retailers and wholesalers battle both transportation companies and manufacturers over goods damaged in shipment. Sometimes overly rough handling is the cause, but in other cases better packing and containers might have prevented the damage.

[2] "Where There's Smoke," *Wall Street Journal,* October 3, 1974, p. 1.
[3] Dik Warren Twedt, "How Much Value Can Be Added Through Packaging?" *Journal of Marketing,* January 1968, p. 58.

Convenience is also generally recognized as a necessary function of the package. But the situation here is often a little more visible and is more of a plus factor than is the protection function which usually only arouses attention when something goes wrong. In efforts to devise more convenient features for their package and gain thereby an initial, if temporary, advantage over their competitors, manufacturers have introduced aerosol spray dispensers, no-drip spouts, flip-top and pull-tab closures, self-applicators, boil-in-bag packages—and the search continues.[4]

Packages have even been designed for other uses after the original contents are consumed—this is called *reuse packaging.* Peanut butter, jelly, some cheeses, and even tea may be offered in containers that can be used for cookie jars, fruit-juice glasses, or drinking tumblers. It is a common practice of cereal manufacturers to design their packages so that they can be used as cut-out toys and thereby appeal to youngsters. Products that may be purchased as gifts, such as candy, liquor, cigars, cigarettes, and perfume are often marketed in gift wrapping.

Multiple packaging—placing several units in one container—is popular. Experience has shown that the consumer is as likely to take several units as one, and multiple packing therefore encourages multiple-unit sales and higher consumption. The six-bottle carton of soft drinks or the six-pack of beer are common. Even men's underwear is packaged in units of three. Retailers and wholesalers, of course, like this method of packaging because unit-handling costs are reduced and sales increased. Consumers have generally gone along with multiple-packaging without protesting, although they may recognize that this is a not very subtle way of persuading them to buy more at a time. But perhaps multiple packaging can be carried too far, can become primarily a vehicle of manufacturer and dealer interest, so that the consumer's wishes become disregarded and unheeded. One especially wonders at this, when, in order to replace a broken shoe string, one must purchase three pair.

Criteria of a "Good" Package. To evaluate an existing or proposed package, four criteria have been suggested:[5]

1. Visibility
2. Informativeness
3. Emotional appeal
4. Workability

Visibility refers primarily to how well the package and its product identification stand out from competing products and brands when, for example, displayed on the supermarket shelf. Laboratory

[4] Phyllis Daignault, "New Dimensions in Convenience Packaging," *Sales Management,* January 17, 1964, p. 25.

[5] This section is partly based on Dik Warren Twedt, pp. 59–61.

instruments and attitudinal measurements have been used in testing various designs. An effective package must indicate clearly and quickly what it contains and any important instructions for use. The emotional appeal of a package—the image it conveys, whether "expensive," "old-fashioned," "for young people," and so on—can be assessed by psychological scaling techniques such as the semantic differential, or by projective tools such as word association tests. The workability criterion refers to the more standard functions that a good package should perform: its protective features, ease of opening and closing, storability. In the quest for a package that conveys an emotionally favorable image and one that is distinctive, informative, and persuasive, the practical needs should not be forgotten. Consumers particularly resent packages that are destroyed by being opened.

While effective presentation to consumers must carry high priority in packaging decisions, requirements of dealers and middlemen cannot be disregarded. Particularly is this important for self-service operations such as supermarkets and vending machines. Here size of container is important. Sizes must be uniform with those of similar products; otherwise shelf space may be inadequate or require redesigning. An expensive foul-up occurred with the packaging of Royal Crown Cola in an attractive new aluminum can which was carefully designed to fit supermarket shelves, but proved to be too tall for vending machines.[6] Size selection, better pictures of the product itself and possibly the product in use, shipping cartons tailored to the needs of retailers in quantity packed, descriptive information, and ease of opening and marking are other important packaging considerations in better meeting the needs of middleman customers.

Misuses of Packaging. Deceptive packaging and labeling, and containers that are purposely misleading, have been the cause of bad publicity for marketers and have resulted in both state and federal laws designed to curb the worst abuses. The consumer has long faced a proliferation of weights and sizes of packages in the supermarket. Congressional attention was focused on potato chips, as just one example; they were sold in packages containing 71 different quantities under 3½ pounds.[7]

The difficulties facing housewives in picking the best buys for their money in a typical shopping trip have been documented on several occasions. In one such test, conducted by California's Consumer Council, 5 housewives were given a list of 14 packaged-good items —common staple foods and household necessities—and asked to make their selections solely on the basis of quantity and cost. Among 246 possible choices for the 14 items, these housewives, possessing

---

[6] "RC Cola's Package 'Too Tall to Vend,'" *Printers' Ink,* May 12, 1967, pp. 56–57.
[7] Philip A. Hart, "Comments on S.985—The Fair Packaging and Labeling Bill," Washington, D.C., undated, mimeo., p. 2.

better-than-average educations and spending more than the average amount of time, succeeded 36 times and failed 34 times to pick the most economical items. In the case of 2 of the 14 products, all five were bewildered by the assortment of prices and package sizes—for example, there were 14 different packages of white rice, not one in a one-pound package; of 10 cans of tuna, none was one pound or one-half pound, and 7 were fractional ounces—and not one housewife succeeded in picking the best buy.[8]

There are production reasons for confusing packaging (such as economies gained using standard-sized packaging for varying goods), but too much has been continued without regard for changing consumer attitudes. The concern of consumers resulted in the Fair Packaging and Labeling Act of 1966. Although this is a weak law, in that industry is encouraged to draw up its own standards,[9] more drastic regulation could come.

Another area of public interest concerning packaging is pollution. In a decade when the national attention is focusing on our environment, the contribution of packaging to this situation is not small: 35 million tons a year are added to the nation's refuse, which is about 20 percent of the total refuse. Cartons, paper wrappers, 26 billion glass bottles and jars, and almost 50 billion metal cans represent the intrusion of packaging on our environment.[10] While some of these metal cans are tin—which rusts in 10–15 years—many are aluminum and can last practically forever. Marketers will have to begin to grapple with this and similar environmental problems, or public pressure will again raise the specter of increased regulation and perhaps severe penalties.

Sales Incentives

Sales incentives include premiums, games, contests, trading stamps, cents-off deals, and scattered other sales stimulation devices. We will examine these under three broad categories: coupons and price deals; games and contests; and trading stamps. Such devices are by no means new, although the last decade has witnessed a proliferation and, especially with games and contests, a spate of new and ingenious ones. Unfortunately the interest and excitement which some of these can furnish the consumer in her shopping experience have been palled by the sheer abundance, and also by unpleasant revelations of, in some cases, a paucity of winners despite inflated claims.

[8] Reported in E. B. Weiss, "Marketers Fiddle While Consumers Burn," *Harvard Business Review*, July–August 1968, p. 48.

[9] Dik Warren Twedt, "What Effect Will the 'Fair Packaging and Labeling Act' Have on Marketing Practices?" *Journal of Marketing*, April 1967, pp. 58–59.

[10] "Science Yells for Industry's Help Against Pollution," *Business Week*, January 3, 1970, p. 63.

At the present time, the government is moving toward legislation aimed at curtailing some of these incentives. Truth-in-games and truth-in-premium laws are not remote possibilities.

The Objectives of Sales Incentives. Sales incentives can be either short-term, designed to create an immediate impact on sales and competitive position, or long-term with the objective of producing brand and/or store loyalty. Price deals, most games and contests, are the former; trading stamps would fall in the latter category and are less promotional vehicles of manufacturers than of retailers (except where the manufacturer owns or leases retail facilities and the use of the brand, as with gas stations). Sometimes these incentives are an offensive part of marketing strategy, aimed at winning new markets and inducing consumers to switch brands; more often nowadays, sales incentives are defensive measures, with most competitors in a given area being forced to resort to stamps, or various games and giveaways, in order to combat the efforts of others and prevent an erosion of market share.

Most sales incentives are easily and fairly quickly duplicated. For example, if one firm in a given market area decides to give trading stamps to its customers, consumer acceptance of something "free" may generate enough extra business that other firms may be forced to take counteraction. Several alternatives are possible: (1) prices may be reduced slightly with the price savings widely publicized as due to lower costs of operation than competitors who are giving stamps; (2) a special contest or giveaway may be quickly developed in the hope that it will be sufficiently attractive to customers to mitigate their switching; or (3) the firm may join the ranks of firms giving stamps—probably a different brand of stamp will be used, such as King Korn instead of Green, since the stamp companies are reluctant to give their stamps to direct competitors.

The impact of lower prices is seldom very significant since any increase in prices induced by higher costs of using stamps can be disguised while the more visible "specials" remain as competitively priced as ever. If trading-stamp competition is matched, either by contests or giveaway promotions, or by adopting trading stamps, the result is that the competitive environment tends to stabilize—the initial advantage gained by the first firm to use stamps is largely overcome. All firms in the market area, then, find themselves with about the same market share as formerly, *but* with increased costs of doing business: the cost of the sales incentives, whether stamps, games, or something else.

Trading Stamps. Trading stamps made their biggest gains in the United States in the 1950s and 1960s, but the idea has actually been around for a long time. The Sperry and Hutchinson Company (S&H Green Stamps) started issuing stamps in 1896, and there have been recurring cycles of enthusiasm and disinterest since before World War I.[11]

Supermarkets have been the predominant distributors of stamps, distributing between 60 and 70 percent of all trading stamps, and this has induced other types of retailers to also use them. For example, many noncompeting stores, such as gas stations, drugstores, and various specialty stores and services, may distribute the same stamps as the nearby supermarket to some mutual benefit, since consumers are inclined to buy from stores offering the same stamps as the ones they are saving.

Why were trading stamps so attractive to supermarkets, and why do they seem less so today? Allvine, in pointing out the increasingly competitive environment of supermarkets and the homogeneity of operations, suggests that these characteristics of stamps made them appealing to supermarkets:

1. A supermarket chain could, to a degree, differentiate itself from its competitors by distributing a stamp for which it had exclusive rights in the grocery field.
2. The value of merchandise that shoppers could obtain with trading stamps was greater than a cash discount from a supermarket equal to the cost of the stamps.
3. A trading stamp program was a desirable way for many shoppers to save routinely for practical purchases or occasional indulgences.
4. A trading stamp program seemed to be a way with which a large monolithic chain organization could gain some advantage over the looser-knit system of independent supermarkets.
5. A synergistic effect was created when a strong system of noncompetitive stores distributed a particular trading stamp.[12]

Costs of stamps to retailers generally range around 2 percent of sales. However, as more retailers began giving stamps, the effectiveness decreased. Retailers began turning to stamp promotions, extra stamp giveaways, such as weekend specials of bonus stamps with a certain minimum of groceries purchased, or bonus stamps for buying certain featured items. In 1964 and 1965 the extra stamp giveaway ratio was close to 50 percent, that is, 50 extra stamps were given to every 100 regular stamps.[13]

Faced with a market saturation of stamps so that any initial competitive advantage was dissipating, and involved in the growing

[11] Harold W. Fox, *The Economics of Trading Stamps* (Washington, D.C.: Public Affairs Press, 1968), offers a definitive study of trading stamps, both historically and economically.

[12] Fred C. Allvine, "The Future for Trading Stamps and Games," *Journal of Marketing*, January 1969, p. 46.

[13] Ibid., p. 48.

trend toward bonus stamps and the consequent higher costs associated with stamp programs, supermarkets began turning away. A not insignificant prod in this direction was the "housewives' rebellion" in the fall of 1966 over high food prices and the stamps and games which were perceived as contributing to higher prices.[14] Furthermore, surveys were showing consumers to be less enchanted with saving stamps and playing games.

**MARKETING
IN
ACTION**

The Winter of Trading Stamps—S&H Green Stamps

The S&H Green Stamp Division of Sperry & Hutchinson, the giant in the trading stamp industry, encountered difficulties beginning in 1970: earnings fell 13 percent in that year. Food stores contributed 55 percent of stamp revenues, but this had been dropping as rising food costs, coupled with the short supply of some food items, forced supermarket chains to eliminate all frills in an effort to keep food prices from rising even higher. Furthermore, the gasoline shortage in 1973 played havoc with stamp sales to service station dealers, the second-largest customer segment.

S&H attempted to find new business to compensate: car-rental offices, truck-refueling stops, private-aircraft refueling depots, bowling alleys, even fast food chains. It also promoted the use of stamps as incentive sales awards given to salesmen or dealers as prizes for their sales performance. But these can hardly counteract the lost supermarket and service station business.

However, even though sales were faltering, trading stamps remain exceedingly profitable. One facet of this profitability is the one-year lag between the time S&H sells the stamps and when the housewife redeems them. This "cash float" was $250 million in 1972, and most of this is invested in stocks and bonds.

SOURCE: "A Sticky Time at Sperry & Hutchinson," *Business Week*, March 20, 1971, pp. 102–06; and "The Green Stamps Sing the Blues," *Forbes*, September 1, 1973, pp. 44–45.

For thought and discussion:

Is there any way that S&H might have saved some of its lost supermarket and service station accounts?

Is this lost business likely to be permanent? Why or why not?

Although the popularity of stamps among conventional users is declining, stamps will probably remain on the marketing scene; their

[14] "Housewives Skewer High Food Prices," *Business Week*, October 22, 1966, pp. 42–43.

premiums and the satisfaction they offer the strong acquisition instinct of customers continue to attract a sizable segment.

Gamesmanship. Games and contests developed as a reaction to trading stamps. They are time-limited events (originally running from six to eight weeks) during which customers attempt to collect particular sets of game slips which qualify them for prizes. With the game slips distributed free with a purchase, the object is to encourage customers to purchase more frequently and more consistently in order to acquire more game slips and thus have a better chance of winning.

The initial use of games by supermarkets seems to have started about 1963,[15] but the popularity mushroomed a few years later with the testing by several food chains of "Let's Go to the Races" and "Bonus Bingo." By late 1966, Allvine reports, chains representing about 35 percent of food sales were simultaneously using games[16] with such similar names as:

Super Bingo	Post Time
Make Money	Cash Bingo
Merry-Go-Round	TV Bingo
Let's Go to the Races	Billfold Bingo
Double $5 Bingo	Surethingo
Bonus Bingo	Sweepstake

The games proved easy to imitate and competitors all began to use them. As long as a competitor was involved with a game, other firms were reluctant to drop theirs. And the games were costly, especially for the small independent gas station dealer forced, in many cases, to buy large batches of lottery cards (thereby giving a nominal profit to the oil companies selling the cards to their dealers) which increased overhead without appreciably increasing sales.

However, was not the consumer benefited? Undoubtedly gamesmanship gave an aura of excitement to the marketplace which was lacking before. For some, the chance to win something for nothing, the element of a lottery where blind luck made the winner, was attractive, and this was not limited alone to those who frequented race tracks and bingo parlors. But even the excitement of expectation can wane when many stores offer similar promotions and where experience begins to reveal few winners. In the end, the perceived lack of winners and bad publicity with innuendos of rigging, jaded consumer enthusiasm.[17]

In a drive against deception and promotional games, the Federal Trade Commission proposed a complaint against McDonald's

---

[15] "Games for Cash Are New Super Lure," *Grocery Beacon,* April 22, 1963, p. 16.

[16] Allvine, p. 48.

[17] "Why Gas Stations Keep Up Games," *Business Week,* September 21, 1968, pp. 62–66; and "End Gas Games, Atlantic Richfield Executive Urges FTC," *Advertising Age,* March 24, 1969, pp. 1, 114.

"$500,000 Sweepstakes." McDonald's was charged that only $13,000 in prizes was awarded (rather than $500,000), with some winners denied prizes, while other misrepresentations also occurred. For example, McDonald's advertised that participants were given a reasonable opportunity to win the stated prizes, when in reality chances were one in 1.9 million to win a first prize. McDonald's also claimed that 15,610 prizes had been purchased for winners, when in fact prizes were bought only after the sweepstakes ended, and in a much smaller number. The Federal Trade Commission seeks to require that all prizes be distributed as represented, and that the number and approximate retail value of prizes be disclosed clearly, as well as the odds of winning each prize.[18]

Coupons, Price Deals, and Premiums. Trading stamps and games have generally been a sales promotion tool of retailers, but coupons and cents-off deals offer greater flexibility. Both giant manufacturers and neighborhood pizza shops can use coupons effectively, and distribution can be in the hundreds or in the millions. A coupon is simply a document that entitles the holder to so many cents off the purchase price of the particular product. These coupons can be distributed by mail, inserted in newspapers and magazines, or even placed on a product, as for example in a jar of instant coffee. Welcome Wagon and various other organizations to welcome newcomers often distribute coupons from local merchants as inducements to visit their stores and services.

Most deals are temporary price reductions used to attract consumers to a product, often a new or improved product. Not all price deals involve coupons, but the coupon is effective because it highlights the actual price discount the consumer is receiving. Nielsen has reported that the face values of coupons ranged from a low of 5 cents to a high of 39 cents, with the average being 12 cents.[19]

Besides price deals, premiums or special gifts may be offered to make purchase of the particular product more attractive. Sometimes trade incentives are directed to retailers. Special cost discounts or allowances are offered in the expectation that the reduction will be passed to consumers, and that larger displays and features will be used. Such trade incentives are not always without flaw, however: the dealer may pocket the price difference and continue his usual selling methods. For this reason, more attention is being centered on the use of coupons. And Nielsen notes that of the 20 leading manufacturers in the food industry, 14 are among the top 20 couponers.[20]

The objective of a price deal is to sell more of the product, both

---

[18] Described in "Legal Developments in Marketing," *Journal of Marketing,* January 1971, pp. 83–84.

[19] A. C. Nielsen, Jr., "The Impact of Retail Coupons," *Journal of Marketing,* October 1965, p. 13.

[20] Ibid., p. 11.

during and after the promotional period. The assumption is that if the consumer can be persuaded to try the product, he or she may continue using it; therefore, there will be some longer-term carryover effect of the deal. One researcher, in studying price deals, made these generalizations:

> Off-season price reductions were more profitable than those used during the height of seasonal demand.
>
> A high frequency of price promotions tends to make consumers overly price conscious, so that sales at regular price are adversely affected.
>
> Price dealing is more effective for new brands than for established ones.
>
> Deals do not seem to be a good way to counter new brands offered by competitors.
>
> No brand is invulnerable to price-deal competition if it has basic marketing problems; a price-deal promotion is never a cure for marketing problems.[21]

Price deals, whether using consumer coupons or trade incentives, have been most important with low-priced, frequently purchased, nondurable products. These are most usually found in supermarkets and drugstores where retailing has become most impersonal.

The value of coupons as a research tool can be utilized by coding the distributed coupons for various sets of data, such as: area code, product description, and face value of the coupon. Analyzing the returns of coupons with the various face values, for example, can enable the researcher to determine the optimum cents-off impact relative to profitability. The area code can help pinpoint areas in which redemption is weak and lead to more intensive research to discover why.[22]

Despite their popularity, price deals (and the related premium or special gift offers) present problems. Most of these efforts are mutually neutralizing. A competitor can easily retaliate and match the effort, either immediately or in the near future. There is always the possibility that the deal will "steal from future business." In other words, the consumer may be induced to stock up now to avoid buying later at the regular price. A typical sales pattern shows sales rising above normal during the period of the deal, then falling below normal for some period of time after the deal. Consequently the total effectiveness may be suspect, especially if lower per-unit profits resulting from sales during the period do not lead to a substantial total sales gain.

---

[21] Charles L. Hinkle, "The Strategy of Price Deals," *Harvard Business Review,* July–August 1965, pp. 75–85.

[22] *28th Annual Review of Grocery Store Trends* (Chicago: A. C. Nielsen, 1962), pp. 12–13.

Another disadvantage of promotion deals which is not always recognized, can be termed *channel resentment.* Coupons or price deals usually require some extra handling by dealers. Unless sales can be seen as substantially improved through the deal (and usually any improvement is not that conspicuous), it may be viewed as merely an extra burden.

Sometimes a firm finds itself in the predicament of relying over-much on deals, perhaps to boost fading sales. Nothing can be less fruitful. Virtually the only justification for coupon or premium deals, except for introducing a new product, is as an occasional once- or twice-a-year fillip. To do so more often lessens the possibility of many goods being sold at regular price; customers and dealers will merely defer purchases until another "deal" is offered. A firm faced with such a vicious cycle might be better off dropping the product (unless regular demand can again be gained) and devoting marketing efforts to something new.

Effectiveness of Sales Incentives. In the beginning of this chapter we noted that advertising, despite ever-increasing expenditures, is declining in relative importance in the marketing mix, while sales promotion devices are becoming more prominent. One expert confirms this and suggests further that:

> advertising alone is no longer able to do the job. . . . Marketers are finding it necessary to rely more and more heavily on promotions—which in a great many cases are neither fundamental, nor business-building, nor of long-lasting effectiveness.[23]

Thus he casts doubt both on the effectiveness of advertising and of promotions (except on a short-term basis). And in examining some of these sales incentives—especially stamps, and games and contests—their effectiveness must be questioned. Another study shows that such incentives appeal only to a small part of the market (about 15 percent) who would be influenced to change brands or who might be attracted by "gimmicks." Furthermore, this 15 percent segment tends to include:

1. A high percentage of low-income families.
2. A high percentage of shoppers with extremely low brand loyalty.[24]

The first group have limited disposable income and are not the best target market for many products, while the second group are

---

[23] Clarence E. Eldridge "Advertising: Its Marketing Role," *Marketing Insights,* April 3, 1967, p. 10.

[24] E. B. Weiss, "Today's Sophisticated Consumers are Killing Off Incentive Promotions," *Marketing Insights,* February 9, 1970, p. 15.

expert shoppers whose very expertise in shopping for incentives dilutes the effectiveness of incentives for long-term gain. The rest of the total market is virtually immune to such appeals because of their greater affluence or sophistication.[25]

It is doubtful that sales incentives will disappear, however. A certain segment of the consumer market will continue to support stamps and the firms that offer them. And with games, the temptation to gain an initial advantage, however short-lived, undoubtedly will be attractive to some marketers.

PERSONAL SELLING

A significant problem in marketing is how to attract more good people into selling. Selling suffers from its reputation as a low-prestige, disagreeable job. Such a perception is far from realistic. In this chapter we will try to present a more positive and realistic picture of the salesperson's role in society.

Importance of Selling

Selling is an ancient occupation. Trading companies and salesmen were present in Mesopotamia in 2500 B.C. and Phoenician salesmen sailed the Red Sea and the Persian Gulf in 1500-1200 B.C.[26] In a much later age, itinerant salesmen and trading post agents brought early commerce to large parts of North America long before the land was tamed and settled.

Today, selling furnishes employment for a large number of people. There are many different kinds of selling jobs requiring a diversity of competence, education, and special skills and training. The newsboy is a salesman, as is the auctioneer, and the stockbroker. Other sales categories defined by the U.S. Census are hucksters and peddlers; real estate agents and brokers; advertising agents; demonstrators; insurance agents, brokers, and underwriters; and salesmen and sales clerks of manufacturers, wholesalers, and retailers.[27] The number of persons engaged in selling is about 5 million, which is some 25 to 30 times as many people as employed in advertising.

At the retail level the shift to self-service has reduced the number of clerks, particularly in grocery, discount, variety, and some drugstores, but personal selling is probably gaining in importance with manufacturers. A survey of 400 presidents of large corporations indicated that: (1) personal selling is becoming a popular route to the top in a company, (2) sales jobs have increased in number and im-

[25] Ibid.

[26] Stanley C. Hollander, *Sales Devices throughout the Ages* (New York: Joshua Meier, 1953), p. 6.

[27] U.S. Department of Commerce, *Census of Population, Detailed Characteristics.*

portance, and (3) expectations are that this increase in importance will continue.[28]

For many companies that are small or have inadequate funds to carry out an effective advertising program, personal selling is the essential ingredient in their marketing operation. Even when advertising is present, a salesperson is usually needed to follow up and secure the buying action: advertisements are generally limited to attracting attention and arousing some desire; they generally do not produce the buying action by themselves.

Challenges of Selling

In the discussion to follow, we will primarily focus on the higher-level sales positions, those involving a maximum of creativity and a minimum of routine. Such positions demand skill in selling, and the idea that good salespeople are born, not made, has sometimes surfaced, along with the notion that good managers are born, not made. Both are fallacious. An extroverted and aggressive personality may achieve some short-term sales success in the absence of other abilities. But the carefully trained man or woman who is well motivated and organized will usually come forth with better performance and long-term development.

Motivation. A person with a high degree of motivation can find selling unusually rewarding and stimulating. Success in sales jobs requires hard work, initiative, and persistence. A highly motivated person may revel in the opportunity to work long hours, and to see this directly reflected in performance and pay. In few other types of work can the fruits of one's efforts be so clearly revealed and so directly rewarding.

Freedom of Action. Many sales positions require people who can work effectively on their own with minimum supervision (outside of occasional sales meetings, and certain sales and customer reports). This can be very attractive to the self-starter. While some salespeople succumb to temptations (afternoon movies may attract some), this creates greater opportunities for others. Perhaps the man or woman interested in security is more comfortable when closely supervised in the factory or office, but for the person constricted in such an environment, the freedom of selling offers both a comfort and a challenge.

Company Representation. Because the salesperson is the major and often the sole contact that a customer has with the company represented, this places a significant responsibility on the conscientious person. By his or her actions, by the impression left, the company

[28] "Top Executives Rank Salesmanship Tops," *Sales Management,* March 18, 1966, p. 120.

can be benefited or harmed; achieving goodwill is a major responsibility. Misinformation, a disregard for service and complaints, pressure on a customer to become overstocked, a personal life at variance with accepted patterns, or efforts at bribery—any of these can destroy goodwill, perhaps permanently. However, representing the company to customers and the general public can bring with it good training for more important jobs in the future.

Stepping-stone to Advancement. Not all salespeople aspire to become managers and executives. And there is not necessarily a close relationship between great success in selling and successful managing. However, most college graduates do aspire to get into management. The sales route represents one of the fastest and most effective paths to top management in a firm because of the vital dependence of a company's operations on sales: without sales, there is no need for staff experts, production workers, and the like. Some attributes of a promising salesperson have been described as follows:

1. He works endlessly on his sales presentation. He is always prepared to meet the objections of his prospect and varies his presentation to meet the situation.
2. He sells across the board. He knows which items carry the best margin and pushes them while not neglecting the remainder of the line.
3. He has a nose for new customers. He never stops building his clientele.
4. He follows a definite pattern of territory coverage, thereby minimizing the time he spends enroute to calls.
5. He apportions his contact time between accounts in proportion to the potential business available from them.
6. He knows the value of reports and does not neglect this aspect of his job.
7. He services his customers' customers. He does not stop working once the order is in his pocket.
8. He works cooperatively with the credit department. He knows that it is useless to sell goods if they are not paid for at the proper time.
9. He is an intelligence agent in the field for his company, continually on the alert for competitive developments, new products, new merchandising ideas, new uses for the product, and trade gossip.[29]

It has been estimated that almost a million copies of books dealing with selling are marketed in the United States every year.[30] Many of these bear provocative titles such as *The Power of Enthusi-*

[29] William C. Dorr, "The Salesman Who Will Make 'Manager,'" *Sales Management,* May 20, 1960, pp. 47–48.
[30] Daniel Seligman, "The Latest Secrets of Selling," *Fortune,* June 1956, p. 123.

astic Selling, and *1,000 Ways a Salesman Can Increase His Sales.* Selling is still an art and not a science, although sales skills can be greatly improved by analysis and training. The intangibles involved in face-to-face interaction defy complete systematizing and planning: the "canned" sales talk that some companies insist their salesmen use is seldom effective with all customers in all situations. Therefore, the intuition, the "feel" of a situation, the empathy for the customer, and a strong ego drive to make a sale become important traits of the good salesperson.[31]

MARKETING
IN
ACTION

Selling Success Can Lead to Entrepreneurship

Gwendolyn Claytor was a day-care teacher in Atlanta. This was to change in May 1971 when she came across an importer who was stuck with $40,000 worth of wigs. She offered to sell them for a percentage of the profit. This she did in one month, netting herself $14,000. She took this money and invested it in more imported wigs, and opened stores in Atlanta and Pittsburgh to sell these wigs. In her first year of operation she had sales of $1.5 million. A year later she had eleven Oriental imports stores in six cities. She had further plans to buy wig factories in Hong Kong and to franchise ten more stores. Her career as a day-care teacher had ended abruptly.

SOURCE: "Discriminating Woman," *Forbes*, July 1, 1972, p. 56.

For thought and discussion:

What personal characteristics would you say accounted for Gwendolyn Claytor's success?

Are these characteristics more likely to be found in a salesman, a financial analyst, a manager, or a marketing researcher?

Types of Selling Jobs

Sales jobs can be grouped as (1) order getting, (2) order taking, and (3) supporting. *Order getting* concerns developing new business; it is sometimes called "creative selling." Usually the highest level of salespeople, and the best paid, are order getters. Much selling is

---

[31] The latter two qualities are offered by David Mayer and Herbert M. Greenberg, "What Makes a Good Salesman," *Harvard Business Review*, July–August 1964, pp. 119–25. There is, however, some conflicting evidence that the highly structured canned presentation can be a more effective tool for the salesman than the flexible approach geared to the customer and the situation: Marvin A. Jolson, "The Underestimated Potential of the Canned Sales Presentation," *Journal of Marketing*, January 1975, pp. 75–78.

order taking, that is, the more routine completion of sales made to the same customers. Where the sales job primarily or entirely consists of order taking, a lower-paid, less-experienced or less-competent person may be perfectly able. However, order getting, if successful, may become order taking. And this is good. Marketing costs, as we have seen before, tend to be lowered when transactions can be reduced to routine, as is possible with well-established connections between buyers and sellers.

Supporting salespeople generally do not try to secure orders; their objective is to provide specialized services and cultivate goodwill. There are two types of supporting salespeople: missionary salespeople and technical specialists. *Missionary salespeople* are employed by manufacturers to work with dealers, perhaps to develop point-of-purchase displays, train dealer salespeople to better sell the product, provide better communication between distributor and manufacturer, and in general, aggressively promote the manufacturer's brand. The *detail men* used in the drug industry to call on doctors and other professionals might also be called missionary salespeople. They leave samples and explain applications and research information about new products with the objective to encourage prescriptions for their brand.

Technical specialists—engineers and scientists—assist regular salespeople. Sometimes certain products require a higher degree of technical expertise than a regular salesperson can be expected to provide, or perhaps a certain piece of equipment needs to be tailored to the particular requirements of the customer.

Sales personnel are most commonly classified by types of employer and type of customer. Table 13-1 presents this classification with the most common characteristics of each type. The manufacturer's salesperson selling to other industrial users often represents the highest quality of salesperson—months of preparation and discussion with top executives may be necessary to achieve a single sale. Selling to dealers (wholesalers and retailers) may require a fairly high-level person, but the work tends to be more routine and less creative. Missionary salespeople working with dealers usually are involved in work which is not very creative nor particularly rewarding; often turnover is high in these jobs, although some firms use the missionary positions as part of the management-training program.

Manufacturers' sales representatives who sell directly to consumers—door to door—are involved in some of the most difficult and frustrating types of selling, especially where the product is relatively high-priced, such as encyclopedias. Often the caliber of salesperson is not very high, training is minimal, the pay is on a straight commission (based on a percentage of sales, so that if nothing is sold, there is no pay); under such conditions, the marginal producers are quickly eliminated and only the more able (which often translates to those more aggressive and more adept at "high pressure") are likely to long remain —and these may do quite well.

Selling for wholesalers and retailers usually is low-level, non-creative. Wholesalers' sales forces, for example, sell mostly from

Table 13-1.
Types of Selling Jobs

Selling for Manufacturers

Selling to industrial users
  Caliber of salesperson:
    Usually the highest.
  Type of selling:
    Creative; order-getting; may involve selling expensive installations.
Selling to wholesalers
  Caliber:
    Reasonably high caliber.
  Type of selling:
    Creative; but probably also will have major involvement with training wholesalers' salespeople, handling complaints, and in general, servicing the accounts.
Selling to retailers
  Caliber:
    (1) Similar to that for selling to wholesalers.
    (2) Not particularly high caliber if used for missionary purposes.
  Type of selling:
    (1) Similar to that for selling to wholesalers.
    (2) Missionary, concerned with building goodwill and helping with displays, etc.
Selling directly to consumers (door-to-door)
  Caliber:
    Usually not very high.
  Type of selling:
    Creative, and often very difficult.

Selling for Wholesalers

Selling to retailers (and/or manufacturers)
  Caliber:
    Not particularly high.
  Type of selling:
    Primarily order-taking, and selling from catalogs.

Selling for Retailers

Selling to consumers
  Caliber:
    Generally low; however, salespeople for "big ticket" items, such as automobiles, appliances, carpeting, and men's clothing may be high caliber.
  Type of selling:
    Could be creative, but often more order-taking.

catalogs and are order takers. Retail selling often requires little skill or experience and is a first job for many young people. But there are exceptions. Some retail selling, especially for such high-priced items as cars, appliances, expensive clothing, and the like may require high-caliber salespeople and be highly creative and rewarding.

The type of product is a major influence on caliber of selling. Often, but not always, there is a direct relationship between the price of an item and the competence and compensation of the effective salesperson involved: the Fuller Brush man versus the encyclopedia salesman; the cleaning supplies salesperson versus the computer salesperson; the variety-store clerk versus the furniture salesperson. Selling intangibles—insurance, mutual funds—is generally conceded to be the most difficult type of selling since the salesperson is dealing with ideas and future needs, rather than tangible, immediate, need-satisfying products. Accordingly, such salespeople are often rigidly screened and highly trained and rewarded.

Personal Selling in the Promotion Mix

Personal selling, being one element of the promotion mix, along with advertising and sales promotion, is best used in combination with the other elements: for example, advertising can create buyer awareness of the product, but the salesperson is more effective in actually closing the sale. A recent study of industrial goods companies found that, in dealing with professional buyers or purchasing agents, a salesperson has an advantage if the reputation of his company has been built up by institutional advertising. The representative of a well-known company, one with a good reputation, has a better chance of getting a favorable first hearing for a new product and of getting early adoption of that product than the salesperson of a less well known company.[32] While this initial advantage can be dissipated by a poor sales presentation, it represents a substantial argument for the use of advertising, even where the nature of the product or the type of customer requires that personal selling be the most important ingredient of the promotion mix.

Personal selling needs to carry the bulk of the promotional load under certain conditions. When the product is complex and/or has a high unit value, it is of vital importance. If the product has to be demonstrated or specially tailored to the customer's requirements, a salesperson or perhaps an "engineering consultant" is needed. One can hardly imagine purchasing a car by mail order or self-service. Nor would a sewing machine or television set—where demonstration, and possibly a trade-in is involved—likely be bought without the help of a salesperson.

A small company often has limited funds for advertising; there-

[32] Theodore Levitt, "Communications and Industrial Selling," *Journal of Marketing*, April 1967, pp. 15–21.

fore, the major component of the promotion mix may have to be personal selling, despite the many more customers that might be reached with mass advertising. The use of salespeople gives the flexibility to expand and contract as dictated by company resources and market conditions; especially is this true when they are paid mostly or entirely on commission.

With a concentrated market, as are many industrial markets, personal selling is more practical than in widespread markets since the size of the staff can be relatively modest. Most contact with industrial users or dealers is done through sales personnel, perhaps supported by advertising but not replaced by it.

Advantages of the Salesperson in the Promotion Mix. The salesperson has certain important advantages over the mass media. He can develop, modify, and maintain the intercommunicative relationship with the buyer to the fullest extent. He can adapt his message to the particular interests and requirements of the buyer. By observing nuances in facial expressions, tones of voice, and manner, he has immediate feedback as to the effectiveness of his message and can modify his presentation accordingly. Furthermore, he is a person, and can attract or repel customers on the basis of his personality, or because it is felt that he needs the business. The very fact that a prospective buyer has taken up the salesperson's time may exert a subtle pressure to consummate the sale.

Often, relatively lasting relationships may be built up between salesperson and customer. If confidence and rapport can be established, future sales are more easily made; little selling effort may subsequently be required for such customers, and more time can be devoted to prospecting and winning new customers. Occasionally such customer loyalty can be built up that a salesperson when changing companies takes some of his customers with him.

A salesperson can make a further contribution by furnishing feedback from the market. In face-to-face contacts with final customers, he is advantageously placed to gather information, both good and bad, about the company's products, methods of doing business, and any present or potential changes in the environment. Ideas for product improvements may come in this way; changes in competition can be promptly brought to the attention of management. Some firms overlook this valuable source of market information, or else there is no systematic procedure established to encourage it. One writer suggests that a "market log" be used to record all developments in individual markets that might be relevant to an understanding of the firm's sales experience:

> The log would include information about changes in the company's own prices; special offers that were made and the responses to those offers; reports on changes in competitors' prices; statements by customers and by noncustomers to

salesmen; and information on the amount and form of competitors' sales efforts, including copies of their advertisements, indications of additions to their sales forces, and any concerted sales programs initiated by them.[33]

Most of this information would be gathered by the people in the field and the market log would serve as a vehicle for the systematic compilation and analysis.

Limitations of the Salesperson in the Promotion Mix. Sometimes a company may choose not to have its own sales force. It may rather work through *manufacturers' representatives* (independent agents who sell a number of noncompeting, but complementary products, usually on a straight commission basis); it may decide to market all of its goods through one or a few major retailers or wholesalers under their brand (private branding), in which case the major executives of the company may be involved in maintaining contacts and rapport with the monopsonistic (meaning one buyer and many sellers) buyers; a firm may do all its marketing through mail order by catalogs, direct mail brochures, and other forms of promotion.

Personal selling is costly. In ten years the average cost of an industrial sales call has more than doubled to over $66 in 1973;[34] and an average of six calls may be required to sell a customer.[35] Desire for economies (as well as increasing difficulty in getting and keeping good people) contributed to the development of self-service stores and eliminated the sales clerk. And the suggestion has even been made that at least in the retail store the absence of a salesperson may increase sales:

> The mere presence of the salesman prevents large numbers of persons from looking at things that they are not seriously interested in, because of the presumed social obligation to buy. . . . Lack of such pressure in the self-service store allows the shopper to look around at his leisure, incurring no social debts. . . . Such leisurely perusal of merchandise seems to do as good a job of suggestive selling as many experienced salesmen, and accomplishes more than the mediocre sales clerk at less expense.[36]

For nonretail selling, it may be difficult or impossible for a salesperson to determine who the decision makers are, much less talk

---

[33] Alfred R. Oxenfeldt, *Pricing for Marketing Executives* (San Francisco: Wadsworth, 1961), p. 64.

[34] "Toward Higher Margins and Less Variety," *Business Week,* September 14, 1974, p. 99.

[35] McGraw-Hill Research, *Laboratory of Advertising Performance* (New York: McGraw-Hill, undated).

[36] W. T. Tucker, *The Social Context of Economic Behavior* (New York: Holt, Rinehart, and Winston, 1964), pp. 76–77.

to them. And the task may be complicated by the anti-salesperson attitude of some executives: "Some executives may have status so superior to the salesman that they would suffer a loss of status merely by talking to him."[37] In these cases, advertising, especially in trade journals, may be the only practical way of reaching and influencing these people. It may be necessary to "open the door" for the salesperson.

Developing Sales Effectiveness: Selection of Salespeople

Developing and keeping good, effective salespeople is a never-ending problem with most firms. A poor salesperson not only may not make a sale that another, more able one would, but as the representative of the company may diminish its reputation and alienate certain prospective customers so that they are almost irretrievably lost. This problem is not new:

> More than 35 years ago, the insurance industry embarked on an intensive program to solve the problem of costly, wasteful turnover among its agents. Estimates at that time indicated that there was a turnover of better than 50% within the first year and almost 80% within the first 3 years. After the expenditure of millions of dollars and 35 years of research, the turnover in the insurance industry remains approximately 50% within the first year and 80% within the first 3 years.[38]

(It might be noted here that the insurance industry has spent part of these millions of dollars on psychological tests to measure aptitude for selling insurance, and is today the largest user of such tests for screening sales applicants.)

The costs of sales turnover and of poor selling are huge, if incalculable; the wastes of personal selling must approach those of advertising. Marketing and society are burdened by this unproductivity. Besides the costs of lost sales and alienated customers must be included the expenses of recruiting, selecting, training, and supervising those who fail; the salaries and travel and expense money paid the ineffective producers must also be counted as waste. And why do we still have this—after all these years? Our selection tools are imprecise, crude, often invalid: we still do not know what makes one person able to sell and another not.

Two main tools are used to select from among candidates for sales jobs: interviewing and testing. In some cases an applicant may be ruled out before getting this far in the selection procedure, perhaps because of obvious deficiencies in personal appearance or on

[37] Edgar Crane, *Marketing Communications* (New York: Wiley, 1965), p. 206.
[38] Mayer and Greenberg, "What Makes a Good Salesman," p. 119.

an application form. Generally, the interview and testing will comprise the major weeding-out devices.[39] Of course, if recruiting has been so disappointing that there are few applicants for the sales jobs, then a firm is put in the dilemma of hiring the available, rather than the able.

The Personal Interview. It has been stated that the interview is the "most used and least scientific" of the several ways of selecting employees.[40] Without doubt, many worthy candidates are turned away as a result of the interview, while others are hired with the results noted before. Research studies done many years ago found that interviewers themselves cannot agree on how applicants should be ranked.[41]

A number of common pitfalls reduce the dependability of the interview. The personal bias of the interviewer may influence the decision on the basis of some personal mannerism or characteristic. Some sales managers still have the mistaken notion that a salesperson should be male and at least 6 feet tall (all the better to dominate the customer, so the belief goes). Sometimes the total worth of a person is judged on the basis of a specific trait—the "halo effect." A tendency toward stereotyping may also adversely influence the interview: for example, all long-haired men may be seen as unreliable and nonconformist. Such biasing factors may not be intentional, or even conscious, but they may affect judgment.

Lack of rapport is a common failing of the interview. It may result in too much tension or in a general lack of communicativeness. Applicants for sales positions would generally be expected to perform fairly well in the interview situation. For example:

> The man's poise and self-control under the strain of an interview
> may be noted along with his ability to dominate or lead a
> conversation. Aggressiveness, initiative, imagination, courtesy,
> tactfulness, a sense of humor, and enthusiasm can come out
> when the applicant is talking.[42]

But these traits seem to be developed and observed more easily under certain situations and with certain personalities than under other conditions, at least for some job applicants. And the applicant who is at ease and is a good talker may by no means be the best for the job.

[39] For a description and rationale for another tool for selecting retail and other salesmen, the weighted application blank, see Robert F. Hartley, "The Weighted Application Blank Can Improve Retail Employee Selection," *Journal of Retailing,* Spring 1970, pp. 32–40.

[40] Roger Bellows, *Psychology of Personnel in Business and Industry,* 3d ed. (Englewood Cliffs, N.J.: Prentice-Hall, 1961), p. 228.

[41] H. L. Hollingworth, *Vocational Psychology and Character Analysis* (New York: Appleton, 1929), pp. 115–119.

[42] William J. Stanton and Richard H. Buskirk, *Management of the Sales Force,* 3d ed. (Homewood, Ill.: Irwin, 1967), p. 171.

To overcome at least partly some of the weaknesses inherent in the interview, various modifications, such as patterned interviews, nondirected interviews, interview boards, and interaction interviews are sometimes used.[43]

Use of Tests. More than half of all companies make some use of psychological tests in hiring salespeople, with nearly all nonusers being small companies having a sales staff of fewer than fifty.[44] A great many tests are available and some are vigorously promoted. The various tests used can be classified as:

> *Intelligence and Mental Ability*—measure language usage and comprehension; abstract reasoning; problem-solving ability.
> *Interest*—measures vocational interest.
> *Sales Aptitude*—measures special aptitudes purported to be needed for selling: for example, may attempt to measure knowledge of salesmanship, or social intelligence.
> *Personality*—attempts to measure various personality traits, such as stability, gregariousness, self-confidence, aggressiveness, dominance.

The primary value of these tests is to weed out the obvious misfits, but ideally these should have already been eliminated from consideration; the use of tests can be an expensive way of distinguishing marginal candidates. The ability of tests to predict sales success is limited. Many tests are easily faked. In applying for a job, a person will usually try to tell the potential employer whatever he thinks the employer wants to hear:

> Given a certain amount of intelligence, the applicant will know that he should say he would "rather be a salesman than a librarian," regardless of his real preference. He knows that he should say he would "rather be with people than at home reading a good book," that he prefers "talking to a P.T.A. group to listening to good music," or that he would "rather lead a group discussion than be a forest ranger."[45]

A serious conceptual weakness of psychological tests is that they attempt to appraise personality or aptitude as a series of traits, such as aggressiveness or sociability rather than the total person. Most tests are so constructed that if a person rates high in one trait, he will necessarily be low in something else.

Two researchers in recognizing the traitological nature of most

---

[43] For further description of these interview modifications, refer to almost any personnel management or sales management book, particularly, Bellows, chap. 11, and Richard R. Still and Edward W. Cundiff, *Sales Management,* 2d ed. (Englewood Cliffs, N.J.: Prentice-Hall, 1969), chap. 7.

[44] Still and Cundiff, p. 217.

[45] Mayer and Greenberg, "What Makes a Good Salesman," p. 122.

tests, see two basic qualities, empathy and ego drive, as being essential in good salesmen.[46] Empathy is the ability to feel as others do, to sense their reactions and adjust as necessary. Ego drive is the particular incentive that powers a salesperson to make a sale to enhance his ego, to fulfill a personal need, not merely for the money to be gained. The good salespeople possess both of these qualities in balance, and early empirical evidence suggests that the measurement of these two alone (through the use of special psychological tests) has greatly improved prediction of success in different selling jobs.[47] There is other behavioral science research which suggests that some types of salespeople may be more successful when similar to their customers in physical, attitudinal, and behavioral patterns.[48]

Therefore, some progress is being made in the development of better selection tools. Obviously there is a long way to go. Overreliance on any selection device—whether interview, testing, or various other tools—may well be dangerous.

Developing Sales Effectiveness: Managing the Sales Force

With the selection task completed, other aspects of sales management concern training, compensating, supervising, motivating, and evaluating the sales force.

Training. The traditional belief that salespeople are born, not made, has been thoroughly discredited. Good selling can be developed by proper training, coaching, and experience. Some firms, however, prefer to let a person "prove" himself in the field first, before going to the time and expense necessary to give him intensive training. (This is somewhat akin to throwing a person into the water to see if he can manage to keep himself afloat before giving swimming lessons.) Formal training may vary from a few days (or even less) to several years, depending on such factors as: complexity and cost of the product, type of customer, education and experience of the salesperson, extent of turnover of sales force, and company preference.

If the product is technically complex and/or has a high selling price, generally more expertise is needed; in addition, the opportunity lost in even one missed sale makes it imperative that salespeople be well trained and able. At the other extreme, the products sold by the Good Humor man and the Fuller Brush salesman, being

---

[46] Ibid, pp. 119–25.

[47] Ibid.

[48] Frederick W. Webster, Jr., "Interpersonal Communication and Salesman Effectiveness," *Journal of Marketing*, July 1968, pp. 7–13; Franklin B. Evans, "Selling Is a Dyadic Relationship—A New Approach," *American Behavioral Scientist*, May 1963, p. 79; and J. A. Belasco, "The Salesman's Role Revisited," *Journal of Marketing*, April 1966, pp. 6–8.

of low unit value and requiring no technical know-how, can be sold fairly well by untrained people.

Training programs usually need to cover such general areas as: (1) company policies and operating procedures, (2) knowledge both of the firm's products and those of its major competitors, and (3) selling techniques. The training may be centralized in the home office, or it may be decentralized to branch offices, sales clinics, or on the job.

Most firms have found that the training process should be continuous. Typically, after the initial period, meetings and clinics are held periodically for refresher training, disseminating new information, and for morale and motivation purposes. Salespeople can become stagnant or discouraged, and such periodic meetings and exposure to other, perhaps more successful, individuals, can if properly engineered (and not overdone) be highly stimulating to the sales organization.[49]

Compensation. There are three basic methods of paying salespeople: (1) straight salary, (2) straight commission, or (3) a combination of salary and commission. The advantages of the latter in offering some of the strengths of the other two without suffering from their full limitations, has made some type of combination plan the most widely used method of compensating a sales force.

A straight salary plan normally offers the greatest security and least incentive for the salesperson, while the straight commission is the other extreme, providing maximum incentive and minimum security. This is shown in the continuum below, which also shows the combination plans as being a middle ground, a compromise between maximum and minimum security and incentive.

Straight Salary	Various Combination Plans	Straight Commission
Security ←		Incentive →

Besides offering maximum security, which tends to minimize turnover, a straight salary enables management to exercise better direction and control since the salespeople are not dependent on sales for their pay. Therefore if some missionary work is needed or a credit check advisable, or if a new employee needs to be coached by an experienced one, these duties can be assigned without generating dissatisfaction. Customer goodwill is often best cultivated where incentives for sales are lower pitched than under a substan-

[49] See Joseph W. Thompson and William W. Evans, "Behavioral Approach to Industrial Selling," *Harvard Business Review,* March–April 1969, pp. 137–51, for sales training in the industrial area.

tial commission plan. Drug salespeople (or detail men) who contact doctors and other professional people are usually paid on a straight salary (with perhaps a bonus arrangement based on territorial sales) since part of their job is missionary in purpose, and since customer goodwill must not be jeopardized. New salespeople are usually paid a straight salary as are those opening up new territories, and those selling technical products involving lengthy negotiations.

The principal limitations of the straight salary method—lack of maximum incentive, and a fixed cost not related to sales revenue—are certainly overcome by using a straight commission, but security and control tend to be sacrificed. In order to attain some balance between incentive and security, a multiplicity of combination plans are being used: a base salary and commission or bonus arrangement are proportioned in various ways.[50]

A good compensation plan should be simple and economical to administer, it should provide management with reasonable control over the sales force (which the straight commission usually does not), it should be flexible, fair, and should provide an incentive. Furthermore, it may need special tailoring to meet special compensation objectives of the company, such as encouraging teamwork, servicing of accounts, prospecting, and the like. Not all of these objectives are compatible. There is seldom an optimum plan for all salespeople under all conditions, but if a plan does not permit the attracting, motivating, and retaining of good people, then it is seriously flawed.

Supervision. A direct relationship usually exists between the type of compensation plan and the amount of supervision. People paid substantially by commission often are expected to seek their own prospects and their management of time is their own primary concern. Where salespeople are expected to call on and service many accounts and are paid mainly by salary, then substantial supervision is more the rule. Sometimes routes and calls are planned in minute detail by management. That such planning and supervision can sometimes be defeating is illustrated in the following:

> The story is told about a salesman who thought he literally had to make 12 prospect calls a day. At 4:45 p.m. he was still talking with the eleventh prospect, who was getting increasingly interested in the company's products. "Tell me more, young man," said the prospect. "I'm sorry, sir," replied the salesman. "There are only 15 minutes left, and I must leave to make my last call."[51]

---

[50] Richard C. Smyth, "Financial Incentives for Salesmen," *Harvard Business Review,* January–February 1968, pp. 109–17; F. E. Webster, Jr., "Rationalizing Salesmen's Compensation Plans," *Journal of Marketing,* January 1966, pp. 55–58.
[51] Philip Kotler, *Marketing Management* (Englewood Cliffs, N.J.: Prentice-Hall, 1967), p. 525.

A number of methods, direct and indirect, are used in sales supervision. The supervisor may accompany the salesperson on some of his calls to help solve problems, to coach him in better methods, and to encourage and motivate—this often is the most effective method of supervision, but it is also costly and often not practical. Consequently, correspondence, the telephone, periodic sales meetings, and the ubiquitous report are more commonly used devices to guide and supervise.

An integral part of most sales jobs, and one frequently criticized, is the report on activities, such as number of calls made, new prospects called on, miles traveled, and number of orders taken. Such reports encourage planning by the salesperson and furnish a means to evaluate performance and to focus supervisory attention on areas needing improvement. These reports can also furnish systematic information about happenings in the field, such as competitive activities and reactions of customers, which are needed for marketing intelligence and to keep abreast of changes in the marketplace.[52]

Supervision is also exercised by indirect or automatic devices such as compensation plans, sales quotas, territorial assignments, expense accounts, and various evaluation procedures. These act to limit efforts and to provide incentives and opportunities in accordance with policies established by management. For example, the method of compensation and the sales quota can guide salespeople to emphasize certain product lines, various classes of customers, or certain order sizes; the size of the territory may mean skimming the cream of the market or, if it is small, actively cultivating all potential buyers.

Motivation. Most of the aspects of sales management previously described can, if properly treated, act to provide incentive and motivation. Often in practice these tools are seen as insufficient, and additional incentives are sought. The nature of the selling job with its triumphs and frustrations, the traveling and being away from home, the tendency for salespeople to become apathetic as they sell the same merchandise to the same customers, and the need to stimulate a feeling of group identity and competition with other members of the sales staff, makes individual and group incentive programs often a useful supplement to whatever standardized incentives may be provided by compensation plans and supervisory efforts.

Three methods of special stimulation are commonly used, either singly or in combination: conventions, contests, and honor awards. Not all firms can effectively use such special incentives: where overemphasis on sales could harm goodwill and long-run customer relations, then these should be viewed with caution. And generally these

[52] Van H. Robertson, "Sales Force Feedback on Competitors' Activities," *Journal of Marketing*, April 1974, pp. 69–71.

incentive programs do stress short-run results—if contests are to be won or honors achieved in a given period. Selling of life insurance, automobiles, and food products seems to thrive on special incentives.

Conventions are usually held yearly and may be national or regional in scope. They often serve many purposes, bringing salespeople together for sometimes badly needed interpersonal contact among themselves and with company executives. In the process, the sales force can be informed of new products, policies, and management changes. Training in new selling techniques may be introduced. Inspirational talks usually have a place in all such meetings, and may sometimes be the dominant purpose of the convention.

Contests may provide special, short-term incentives. Two surveys found that 74.4 and 66 percent respectively of the firms questioned used contests.[53] These can take a variety of formats, some off-beat, others more straightforward. Rewards may be based on individual effort or on group achievement. They may be in cash, in merchandise, or may involve a vacation or trip for the family. Any sales contest should provide each person with a chance to win a prize—if only the top producers win all the prizes, the incentive value for the average and poor salesperson is nil.

Special recognition and *honor awards* for salespeople who have done an outstanding job—perhaps "Salesperson of the Month"—is an easy and effective way to stimulate. The major limitation is that a few tend consistently to receive all the honors. A common practice is to publicize the sales performance of every salesperson relative to the others; those lower on the list may be motivated to do better.

Measuring Sales Effectiveness. While salespeople may espouse the independence and the relative freedom from close supervision that typifies many selling jobs, they cannot escape—nor should they want to—being measured for their relative effectiveness. Any evaluation procedure tends to work to the advantage of the able, though it should pinpoint the weak (who may be strengthened by better guidance made possible by singling out those areas where improvement is needed). Therefore, an evaluation process, if systematic, objective, and well defined, should help improve the over-all performance of the sales force.

Unlike many jobs where quantitative measures of effectiveness are difficult or impossible to develop, so that overreliance must rest on subjective, qualitative judgments, the salesperson's job permits objective, quantitative performance measures. However, the sales job is multidimensional, and a number of performance measures should be used to evaluate the full effectiveness.

[53] Albert Haring and Malcolm L. Morris, *Contests, Prizes, Awards for Sales Motivation* (New York: Sales and Marketing Executives, International, 1968); "What's Wrong with Sales Contests," *Sales Management,* September 10, 1967, pp. 34–35.

Measuring Performance of Salespeople

The following tools or measures of selling performance are available.
They are best used in combination. Evaluating sales performance on only
one or a few of these measures would disregard some important aspects
of performance.

Tools	Explanation
Sales volume alone, or in relation to quota	Most commonly used measure, but tells nothing about profitability of business generated.
Gross margin of goods sold	Measures profitability.
Call rate—number of calls made per day	Generally the more calls made, the more sales; a measure of hustle, but not necessarily of effectiveness.
Batting average—order-call ratio	A measure of effectiveness, especially in dealing with certain customer groups.
Average number of orders per man-day	Tells nothing about size of orders.
Average order size	Best used in conjunction with the average number of orders per man day.
Salespeoples' expenses and expense ratios	Can determine cost per call, per order, and direct selling expense ratio to net sales.
New accounts	A measure of customer generation, which may be a salesperson's most important contribution.

The most common objective measure is also the most simple: *sales volume produced.* The salesperson who consistently makes the most sales is thereby the best one. However, the use of this yardstick alone is seldom a sufficient measure except for certain sales jobs where salespeople are expected to find their own customers without territorial restraint, such as is often the case with insurance, mutual funds, and real estate sales. In the more common selling situation, in which territories are assigned, the lack of complete equity in territorial assignation often makes gross sales comparisons unfair. One territory may have more potential—perhaps more population, more stores, larger accounts. In metropolitan New York City, for example, a person might produce in a day as much business as another, perhaps in the North and South Dakota territory, could do in a month.

Therefore it is often necessary to develop sales quotas for each person based on a determination of territorial potential. A measure of relative sales performance—the *ratio of sales to quota*—becomes the better yardstick. But even this usually proves lacking. It tells nothing about the salesperson's contribution to profit, since he may be concentrating his efforts on the lower-profit items which are often the easiest to sell. It also provides no recognition of the person's customer relations; he indeed may be generating large sales by the use of pressure tactics which will have a detrimental effect in the long run.

Gross profit in dollars is a better measure of effectiveness, especially where diverse products with differing gross margins are marketed. However, even this has some flaws since territorial potential may differ and intensity of competition in certain territories may prevent peak sales in some product categories.

It can be seen then that a salesperson's true worth to a firm is not always so easily determined—gross figures are seldom a sufficient measure. It is better to use a number of quantitative measures in combination since only in this way can the many facets of sales performance be reviewed and compared in perspective. A balanced picture is generally more desirable than a strong showing with certain yardsticks and weakness in others.

Other measures of performance commonly used include:

Number of calls made per day
Sales batting average, or order-call ratio
Average number of orders per man-day
Average order size

While the call rate may vary according to customer density, its use when compared with other salespeople in similar territories can be quite revealing: a rate below the norm may indicate that a representative is not putting in a full day, that he is spending too much time with each customer, or that he is losing too much time in waiting to see prospects; on the other hand, a large number of calls made per day may indicate inadequate time and attention given to each customer.

The batting average, which denotes the number of orders received compared with the number of calls made, can be an important indicator of a salesperson's ability to locate good prospects and to close a sale. This, when used with the call rate, can pinpoint problem areas which might deserve further training or attention.

The average number of orders per man-day should be closely compared with the average order size. This may reveal that a person is getting too many small, unprofitable orders even though total volume may be satisfactory. While this may be due to the customers being fewer than average in the particular territory, it is more likely due to neglect in selling all the items in the product lines or in suggesting sufficiently large quantities to customers.

For thought and discussion:

In what ways might a salesperson "pad" his performance to look better?
How might such padding be detected?
If a salesperson has a below-average number of orders per man-day, but
    above-average new accounts, what might you as sales manager
    conclude about his performance?
What other data might you want to have in making his evaluation?

The job of selling is challenging; that of sales management is even more so. The sales manager must avoid supervising too closely, but must motivate people to strong and effective efforts; a sense of enthusiasm and team spirit can make a sales force unbeatable.

Responsibilities. The sales manager is directly concerned with the profitable generation of sales in the territory or region of his assignment. This of course has to be the most vital responsibility in this echelon of management, since without the production of sales at an adequate price and volume to produce sufficient profits, the company itself is in jeopardy. This basic obligation or responsibility can be better appreciated by looking at specific responsibilities. The sales manager needs to develop a *sales organization* that can most effectively carry out the company objectives. Lines of authority should be clearly demarcated, compensation should be equitable in line with responsibilities and performance, and a unified and coordinated sales effort must be fostered. The sales manager must interpret and adapt company *sales plans* to his particular territory or division. It is his responsibility to develop detailed programs to generate the profitable sales volume so that established goals can be met.

Management of sales personnel consumes the greatest amount of attention. The human element, and the necessity to develop and motivate the salespeople, will to the major extent determine the success and promotability of the manager. All the elements of sound management and supervision have a role here. But the sales manager's job often involves a more challenging type of supervision since the average salesperson is more independent, more temperamental, and has less physical constraints (such as proximity to supervision, time clocks, and other checks) than counterparts in other places in the organization.

The sales manager must work closely in the development and use of *controls* designed to evaluate the performance of the organization as a whole and individually. Sales and expense budgets, salespeople's reports, customer reactions, all must be studied so that suitable corrective actions can be applied as needed.

The sales manager serves as a *communication link* between the customers (the market) and higher company executives. Attitudes of customers (especially any changes), actions of competitors, and any other exogenous factors which have real or potential impact must be transmitted. For example, a worsening situation regarding product quality or service should be quickly relayed to those in the organization in a position to act on such problems. The sales manager serves as the company official to customers and prospective ones. It is important that a favorable image be imparted.[54]

---

[54] See Leslie M. Dawson, "Toward a New Concept of Sales Management," *Journal of Marketing*, April 1970, pp. 33–39; Derek A. Newton, "Get the Most

Opportunities. Opportunities in sales management usually are significantly greater than for executives at the same level in other parts of the organization. The responsibility for direct and profitable sales generation makes this position most important to the success of the enterprise, and higher compensation often results. The capable sales executive may quickly move up in his or her organization and attain a top executive position.

Requirements. The characteristics of an effective sales manager have changed from those of a few decades ago. Then it was thought that the best salesperson made the best sales executive; any training was carried out by the sales manager demonstrating his "successful" techniques to the not yet so successful salespeople. An intuitive approach to most matters, an unbounded self-confidence, an exuberant personality, usually sufficed.

Times have changed. It is now quite generally agreed that the best salesperson may not make the best sales executive: some sales ability is necessary of course if the salesperson is to be given the chance to be an administrator. And if the manager is to evaluate the performance of the salespeople, and even more, understand their problems and be able to propose viable solutions, he or she must have reasonable sales proficiency. This also is necessary if the staff is to have the confidence in its superior which makes for an integrated, smoothly running team. The ability to motivate is probably nowhere more important than for the sales staff—unless it is the athletic coach trying to exhort his team to "Win one for the Gipper!" While to some extent this ability is intuitive, it is strongly influenced by effective selection, training, and compensation of the sales force.

Another requirement of the successful sales executive is that of creativity or imagination. Constraints in field selling are relatively less than in most other aspects of business. Imagination often is desired in selling if a product is to be most effectively presented to meet the particular needs of a customer. And the sales manager has considerable flexibility in seeking creative ways to sell the company's products, through special promotions, campaigns, contests, displays, etc.

Ethical aspects. The nature of selling—the interpersonal relations and the generally private settings where it takes place—can be conducive to dishonest practices. The pressures to produce sales, if sufficient, can lead to false and exaggerated claims, high pressure and various methods of inducing a feeling of urgency. (Salesmen for real estate developers sometimes create this with two-way radio cars from which "urgent" queries of central communications headquarters

---

"Out of Your Sales Force," *Harvard Business Review,* September–October 1969, pp. 130–43; and R. O. Loen, "Sales Managers Must Manage," *Harvard Business Review,* May–June 1964, pp. 107–14.

can be made as to whether such and such a lot has been "sold yet.") Probably no other aspect of marketing lends itself to quite as much abuse as does personal selling. Claims and methods that most advertisers would hesitate to use because of the greater visibility of advertising and its tangible elements may be advanced in the face-to-face buyer-seller confrontation.

The sales executive who desires to be socially responsive and to maintain high ethical standards must be on guard against "pushing" the sales staff for sales production "at any cost." Far better is the development and maintenance of long-term cemented customer-seller relations. But, especially where a sales force is not stable, either because of growth or turnover, and where company emphasis is on constant sales growth, sales abuse may occur. Good, honest marketing techniques and responsive standards of conduct should not be sacrificed for immediate gain, inflated quotas, and overaggressive management pressures. Otherwise, consumers are disadvantaged, and the status and prestige of selling as a career is jeopardized.

QUESTIONS AND PROBLEMS

1. How can you justify the increasing interest in packaging today?

2. What makes "gamemanship" so attractive to some marketers? What is the source of the current disillusionment with games?

3. How can a manufacturer stimulate his dealers to use the point-of-purchase materials that are lavishly furnished?

4. What are problems associated with coupons or premiums? Design a program using these promotional devices for (a) an existing deodorant, (b) a new food product.

5. From your own experience, can you categorize those consumers you think are most attracted to trading stamps? Would your characterization of consumers vary for those interested in games, contests, and premiums? Do you think these market segments are large? Are they stable?

6. What methods can marketers use to determine when an optimum mix of the promotion factors (essentially advertising and personal selling) has been reached?

7. What reasons can you give for the best salesperson's often not being the best candidate for a sales manager's position? How about the mediocre salesperson? Can you make any generalizations as to what type of person you would look for to fill a sales management vacancy?

8. A traditional view of selling is that "salespeople are born, not made." Evaluate this idea in terms of its validity and implications in (a) selecting, (b) training, (c) motivating sales personnel.

Project

Check with the placement department of your school and find out how many companies are looking for people to go into sales jobs. Determine:

What percentage of all jobs being recruited are sales jobs
What salary levels are relative to other categories of job
What the next promotion is above the sales job

Exercise in Creativity

In opening a new men's clothing and sportswear store near a college campus, what sales promotion techniques might you want to consider? Design a promotion program for the initial opening and for the next three months, assuming that limited funds preclude most other advertising efforts.

Role-playing Case

You have just been appointed to manage the major appliance department at Lauter's Department Store. Sales have been declining for several years in this department, mostly because of strong competition by Sears, Penney, and three discount stores.

"Russ, it is imperative that our salespeople be motivated to push our appliances. Now you know we have nationally advertised brands, which our competitors don't have. More aggressive selling should be the answer." The general merchandise manager pauses, and looks at you intently. "I'm giving you complete freedom to motivate your people any way you can—within reason, of course. I'll be watching your sales results."

How would you motivate your salespeople to be more aggressive? Be as specific as possible.

Do you see any potential problems?

CHAPTER 14

PRICE AS A COMPETITIVE TOOL

Price can be a powerful tool for generating demand. In many cases, however, the power of price as a competitive tool is disregarded, while efforts are directed more to mass promotion of sometimes negligible product differences. In this chapter we examine the pricing structure, especially as it relates to competition, and various pricing objectives. We consider a number of price policies that face firms: for example, the discount structure, leader pricing, and product-line pricing. Differences in pricing to the government are also described. Finally we look at the importance of price (low price) to consumers in general. Important terms include:

administered pricing	price lining
price leadership	leader pricing
kinked demand curve	demand-backward pricing
nonprice competition	skimming pricing
product-line pricing	penetration pricing

THE PRICE SYSTEM

Types of Price Making

There are three broad areas of price making: (1) market pricing, (2) administered or inverted pricing, and (3) government-controlled pricing.

Market Pricing. In market pricing, supply and demand determine the prices a seller will get. He has no control over his prices, because if he asks for more than other suppliers his goods will remain unsold. Such a condition exists rather rarely, as many producers and a homogeneous product are required if market pricing is to prevail.

The stock market, commodity exchanges, and some agricultural products where the government is not a factor in regulating and maintaining price floors are the major instances of market pricing.

Administered Pricing. Attempts to create differentiation through branding and promotion result in some degree of distinctiveness for most goods. The greater the differentiation, the more administration or control the seller has over price. (Sometimes this is called *inverted pricing,* because the seller rather than the natural market determines prices.) The retailer of gasoline has little pricing freedom; competitors will quickly match his price if he reduces it, and a gas war may result (when there is no petroleum shortage). At the other extreme, cosmetics manufacturers have great pricing discretion because their products are perceived by consumers to differ from each other.

However, administered prices are still affected by demand. Sometimes the seller's control over his prices leads him to forget this, as Detroit found out in late 1974 and 1975.

**MARKETING
IN
ACTION**

Administered Prices—in Detroit

For 15 months, from 1973 to late 1974, Detroit auto makers repeatedly increased the selling prices of their cars. This was a time of burgeoning inflation, with material and labor costs rising. Furthermore, new government standards for safety and pollution control added other costs. And the auto makers also incorporated certain more expensive equipment, such as radial tires.

During this time, the average price of a new car increased by $1,000. And suddenly sales plummeted 25 percent. Now auto makers offered cash rebates for a limited time in order to reduce massive inventories of unsold cars. And they began stripping their cars of expensive equipment. But the damage had been done, and the auto industry led the rest of the nation into a severe recession.

SOURCE: "Detroit's Dilemma on Prices," *Business Week,* January 20, 1975, pp. 82–83.

For thought and discussion:

Can you suggest another pricing strategy the auto industry might have pursued during a time of rapidly rising prices?

In a recession do you think widespread and deep price reductions would significantly boost auto sales?

Why or why not?

What do you think would be the effect of such price reductions on profits?

Government-Controlled Pricing. In certain sectors of the economy, neither the natural market nor the seller directly controls prices. For public-utility industries—those deemed essential to the welfare of society—statutes have prescribed that the government regulate prices. The transportation industry and electric utilities are examples. During wartime or during a period of severe inflation, government control of prices may extend to many other areas as well.

Market Structure and Its Effect on Administered Prices

Economists recognize many types of market structure; for our purposes one major type—which characterizes much of our economy—will be discussed here: oligopoly. A common definition of an oligopoly is an industry in which up to four firms control more than 50 percent of sales. This defines many of our major industries, such as autos, steel, oil, chemicals, electronic equipment, and such consumer product industries as drugs, soap and detergents, refrigerators, laundry equipment, household paper products, and television picture tubes.

In some of the major raw materials industries, the products of the different producers are perceived as having equal quality or value. This condition has major pricing implications. Since buyers consider the products to be similar in quality, they are hardly likely to choose a more expensive product. Consequently each seller must closely watch the actions of competitors, and any price deals or reductions are likely to be quickly matched.

More common is the situation where each seller offers a product that buyers perceive as having some difference in quality and performance. The distinctiveness of these products may vary greatly and in some cases be even imaginary. For example, most cigarettes have minute product differences, but sometimes strong preferences can be developed by advertising: one advertiser's copy reads, "I'd rather fight than switch." The freedom of a seller in setting a price depends not only on the degree of difference he is able to convince customers exists with his product, but also on the importance of this difference to customers. For example, an orange-colored toothpaste may be different from other toothpastes, but it is doubtful if many of us would pay extra for such a trivial difference.

The seller's desire to have more control over prices, especially in an upward direction, accounts for the strenuous efforts to build product differentiation and brand image. However, except in a few unusual instances, actions of competitors cannot be disregarded; a degree of product differentiation does not permit insularity. Thus, pricing freedom exists only within certain boundaries or constraints, beyond which a firm cannot go without business erosion. Whenever firms in an industry are few in number, the actions of one will likely affect the others.

Price Leadership

Oligopolistic market structures are characterized by price leadership, in which a large firm in the industry changes its prices and the rest of the industry follows. Typically the large firm leads only in raising prices, not in reducing them. Reductions generally take place more gradually under the guise of extra discounts or special allowances. Often small firms initiate such reductions, hoping that their increased business will not be viewed seriously by the larger firms wishing to protect a more profitable price structure.

Why do the other firms in an industry follow a large firm acting as a price leader? The answer most simply is that this is an easy way to set prices, and one that usually assures good profits. Accounting systems of the followers need not be as extensive as that of the leader because a price high enough for the leader will be high enough for all, and the spotlight of public criticism of price hikes can fall on the leader. Some threat of retaliation may occur if any smaller firms refuse to go along with the price increases by the rest of the industry. Often there are common costs in the industry, and when they change they change for all. An example of this would be the response to a new labor contract based on industry-wide bargaining, which results in the increased costs being passed on to customers.

Sometimes price changes are followed so quickly that collusion may be suspected. This would be illegal according to the Sherman Antitrust Act. But it is doubtful that collusion plays any significant role. The penalties are too severe, and it is not necessary in most instances. Price changes in major industries are usually widely publicized; even if they are not, feedback to salesmen from customers usually provides the information needed. Usually the other firms in the industry welcome a leader's move to higher prices; they seldom resist it.

The price leader's role is not, however, without some drawbacks. Over a period of time the leader may enjoy a smaller share of the market. The "umbrella" effect of profits being maintained at a good level is incentive for smaller firms to increase capacity. Sometimes the price leader's timing is bad, and government and public opinion may take issue with the price increases. The most notable example of this was the confrontation of President Kennedy with United States Steel described in chapter 5.

A model can be used to depict the rationale for price leadership and uniformity among major firms in the typical oligopolistic situation. Figure 14-1 shows the demand curve facing the individual firm in such an industry. Note the decided "kink" at the midpoint, with the lower portion being relatively inelastic (that is, a change in price will have little effect on demand and sales), while the upper portion of the line is relatively elastic (with a change in price substantially affecting demand and sales). In other words, if the firm were to raise

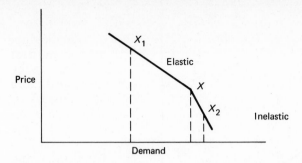

Figure 14-1. Demand Curve for Individual Firm in Oligopolistic
Market Structure

its price above X, the equilibrium price of the industry, to point X_1, demand would slacken (unless the other firms followed such a price rise); if the firm attempted to reduce its price below the equilibrium price to X_2 in an effort to gain a larger share of the market, the other firms would probably follow quickly in order to prevent erosion of their business. The net result of a lowered price would be an insignificant increase in sales accompanied by less profit. Consequently, prices tend to become relatively rigid and price as a competitive tool is little used; emphasis instead is on various aspects of nonprice competition, such as service, warranties, delivery, credit terms, all possible efforts to obtain greater product differentiation, and so on. In this situation then the price leader "leads" the other firms in the industry to a new higher equilibrium price when deemed desirable.

The Attraction of Nonprice Competition

The great limitation in using price as a competitive tool, from the sellers' viewpoint, is that competitors may retaliate and a price war ensue. Not only may no seller benefit from such a situation, but prices may even settle permanently at a lower level.

The distinction between price and nonprice competition is illustrated in Figure 14-2. The object of the nonprice competition is to increase sales without cutting the price. This is possible if the demand curve is shifted to the right, perhaps by increasing advertising and other promotional activities and/or by developing attractive product features and improved quality.

For example, referring to Figure 14-2, if the manufacturer of a particular brand of electric razor wished to sell 50,000 razors, he could lower his selling price to $17; on the other hand, by additional expenditures for a promotional program he may succeed in shifting the demand curve to the right, to D'D', and thereby sell 50,000 at the originally contemplated price of $20. In actuality, of course,

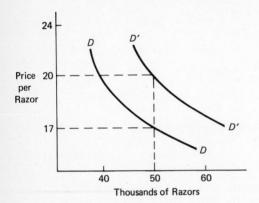

Figure 14-2. Shift in Demand Curve for Electric Razor

these demand curves are not so clear, and the results of a promotional program or other nonprice efforts are unpredictable.

Some advantages of nonprice efforts are obvious. Cutthroat competition is generally prevented. Goodwill on the part of customers and dealers may be more lasting than from a price cut, which is transient. Anyone can copy a price cut, but some nonprice features are more difficult to match. For example, if enough consumers can be convinced that a certain brand has "exclusive taste," then this is not easily countered by competition and not without a long and expensive promotional campaign.

Certainly some methods of nonprice competition are easily duplicated and mutually neutralizing in their impact. This is one of the drawbacks of trading stamps and games. Similarly, more liberal guarantees and warranties are easily duplicated and can lead to increased costs in the industry. But enough alternatives are possible that nonprice competition is attractive to sellers.

PRICING OBJECTIVES

A 1950s' Brookings Institution study of the pricing goals of twenty large companies is still widely cited; although it might be updated, there is little to suggest that the findings would be much different today. The main goals cited by the companies were:[1]

1. Obtain target return on investment or on net sales.
2. Stabilize prices.

[1] A. D. H. Kaplan, Joel B. Dirlam, and Robert F. Lansillotti, *Pricing in Big Business* (Washington, D.C.: Brookings Institution, 1958).

3. Maintain or improve a target share of the market.
4. Meet, follow, or prevent competition.
5. Maximize profits.

It is interesting that maximizing profits as a pricing goal was cited least often by these large firms, despite the assumption of economists in their price theory models that this is the major quest of firms. Maximizing as a goal is frustrated by imperfect knowledge of costs and demand, and the desire to deter competition, expand the market quickly, soften wage demands, and perhaps prevent government scrutiny.

A target rate of return was the most popular pricing goal, one influencing not only price setting but also product development, since a product might not be cleared for production unless it could be projected to meet the targeted return rate. Even departments and divisions might be discontinued or sold if they consistently failed to meet target return goals. These were the targets of some of the firms surveyed:[2]

Firm	Target Rate of Return (Percent)
General Motors Corporation	20 (after taxes)
General Electric Company	20 (after taxes)
Sears, Roebuck & Company	10–15 (after taxes)
Aluminum Company of America	20 (before taxes)
International Harvester Company	10 (after taxes)
United States Steel Corporation	8 (after taxes)

The objectives of price stability and of meeting or following competition lead to the price leadership situation. Fear of price wars and desire for price and profit stability help account for the popularity of these goals.

On the other hand, improving market share represents a more aggressive pricing goal. Strongly competitive prices and price cutting may be employed vigorously to this end, as well as heavy promotional efforts. And a disequilibrium may result in the industry with drastically changed market shares.

But the "growth at any cost" syndrome is seldom a comfortable objective; it involves disruption, invites retaliation, promotes extreme pressures for results. Usually such goals are found in smaller "eager" firms, the "tigers" of their industry; they are also characteristic of new industries. Large firms may even try to limit their share of the market because they fear government intervention if they become too large. General Motors, with about half of the domestic automobile market, might well be forced to dispose of some of its divisions were its market share to become much larger.

[2] Ibid., pp. 130–52.

Pricing objectives are general determinations of what a marketer expects to accomplish with a pricing system. Price policies are more specific guides to action. In this section we will consider the more common types of pricing decisions demanding established policies.

One Price Versus Variable Prices

Most U.S. producers and retailers have adopted a one-price policy: all customers of the same type, purchasing similar quantities, are offered the goods at the same price. The opposite of this is a variable-price policy in which each customer is treated separately so that different prices may be charged each. In some foreign countries bargaining or haggling is the rule; shopping becomes a real challenge to both buyer and seller. Usually a variable-price policy exists where businesses are small, where products are not standardized, and where the practice is traditional.

A variable-price policy imposes severe impediments to marketing efficiency. Our system of mass merchandising with large and efficient retailers could not exist were each transaction negotiated individually and at considerable length. The time involved in shopping would be formidable, and marketing expenses much higher than now.

However, variable prices are not limited strictly to foreign markets. With used products, from automobiles to furniture, negotiation is common. Even in the purchase of new products where a trade-in is involved, it is not uncommon. The car buyer who does not attempt to bargain and who accepts the dealer's initial offering price may often be disadvantaged to the more sophisticated purchaser. This type of policy—charging different buyers different prices for the same product—may be considered illegal under the Robinson-Patman Act when involving selling to middlemen and dealers; it is not illegal when selling to the *final consumer*.

Flexible prices may allow some adjustment to competitive conditions, but on balance it is difficult to defend. Customers may resent paying more than others for the same item; costs of selling are higher because of the time involved in bargaining; and perhaps the greatest limitation is that offering price cuts on the part of salesmen becomes the easy and quick solution to closing the sale, and insufficient effort is directed to making more profitable sales.

Geographic Prices

The question of who is to pay the freight or how it is to be split between buyer and seller offers a number of pricing alternatives. Table 14-1 presents the more important of these rather technical options. For many products freight is a significant portion of the total cost. The decision about freight costs can vitally affect the geographic limits of a firm's market as well as its competitive strength. Furthermore, this influences such other major decisions as where to locate production facilities, warehouses, and sales branches.

Table 14-1.
Geographical Price Policies

F.O.B. Pricing
Characteristics:
  The seller states the price minus the shipping charges which the customer must then assume. (F.O.B. means "free on board" at the transportation agency.)
Implications:
  Tends to establish a geographic monopoly for a given seller since freight rates preclude distant sellers from competing effectively with local producers.

Uniform Delivered Price
Characteristics:
  Same delivered price quoted to all buyers regardless of location. This is sometimes called "postage stamp pricing." Used mostly for nonbulky, lightweight products.
Implications:
  The intent of this policy is to enable a seller to compete in distant markets.

Zone Delivery Pricing
Characteristics:
  A modification of uniform delivered prices, with such quoted for each zone or segment of the country. Most often used by hardware and food manufacturers.
Implications:
  Tends to stabilize prices within an area, and simplifies computation of transportation charges when shipments are made to thousands of customers.

Freight Absorption Pricing
Characteristics:
  Freight charges are omitted, or absorbed by the seller, wholly or partially.
Implications:
  Particularly beneficial to producers having heavy fixed costs who need to expand the geographic limits of the market in order to cover better these fixed costs. Absorbing freight charges permits them to compete in entirely new markets.

Basing Point Pricing
Characteristics:
  Freight charges are calculated, not from the point of production, but from certain cities designated as basing points by all competing sellers in

Table 14-1. (Continued)

an industry. This method is quite common with homogeneous industrial-type products, such as steel, cement, plate glass, and heavy chemicals.

Implications:
This is controversial and can be criticized as leading to price rigidities; it has collusive overtones; it discriminates against local buyers (who must still pay freight—"phantom freight"—from the designated basing point city, even though the factory is nearby).

Discounts and Promotional Prices

Discounts and promotional prices represent a deduction from the list or catalog price. Discount decisions are important because in many industries list prices are relatively stable due to fear of competitive reaction and price wars. However, discount policies may be varied as conditions warrant, and may be used to cater to different segments of the market. For example, trade or *functional discounts* are offered to different members of the channel in some relative proportion to their functions served: that is, a merchant wholesaler may receive a larger discount than a drop shipper.

While some discount policies are traditional and widely followed throughout an industry—for example, *cash discounts* allowed—other types, such as *promotional* and *seasonal discounts,* are more varied. The legality of certain types, such as *quantity discounts* and some promotional allowances, is sometimes suspect, and care must be taken to make them equitable to all customers. Otherwise, a firm may be in violation of the Robinson-Patman Act specifically designed to thwart unfair price discrimination. Table 14-2 shows the various types of discounts.

Table 14-2.
Types of Discount Policies

Cash Discounts

Characteristics:
A typical cash discount is stated as "2/10, net 30," which means that a 2 percent discount is offered as a reward for payment during the first ten days, with the face amount of the bill due by the thirtieth day.

Purpose:
If this policy is successful, the selling firm can reduce its resources needed to support customer credit, can minimize bad debt losses and collection expenses.

Functional and Trade Discounts

Characteristics:
These discounts are offered to different members of the channel of distribution and in varying relative amounts according to service or function performed; for example, the wholesaler will get a greater discount

Table 14-2. (Continued)

than the retailer (usually as an extra discount), thus rewarding him for his extra service.

Purpose:

One obvious purpose is to make handling of the product attractive to various middlemen; in addition, the list price is visible (offering retailers an opportunity to sell "below list"), but the true cost is hidden unless the current trade discount schedule is known.

Promotional Discounts and Allowances

Characteristics:

Such discounts are offered to encourage promoting special sales and activities by the buyer. Perhaps the encouragement may be in the form of a special discount from list price; sometimes it may be in the form of free goods, promotional aids and materials supplied by the seller, or the manufacturer may pay part of the cost of an advertisement placed by the retailer which features the manufacturer's products.

Purpose:

While the obvious purpose is to obtain local advertising beneficial to product sales, certainly a concomitant purpose is to achieve a better relationship between the manufacturer and his channel members.

Seasonal Discounts

Characteristics:

With certain seasonal products, such as air conditioners, toys, and sporting goods, these are commonly used, and may consist of a special discount given to customers who place orders during the slack season.

Purpose:

Off-season orders enable the manufacturer to level off his production schedules, avoid the peaks and valleys of sales and production, and make better use of his facilities.

Quantity Discounts

Characteristics:

There are two main types of quantity discounts: cumulative and non-cumulative.

Cumulative quantity discount

This is available to purchasers based upon the total quantity ordered over a period of time, usually a year, regardless of the number of orders used to obtain this quantity.

Noncumulative quantity discount

Certain prices are stated for particular product quantities ordered at one time, and applicable only to that order.

Purpose:

These discounts are granted as rewards for volume and loyalty, and to encourage additional sales effort on the part of the purchasers. The legality of quantity discounts, especially the cumulative, can be questioned, since the large-size purchaser is advantaged over the smaller, without the cost savings necessarily being commensurate with the discount allowed.

Product-line Prices

When a firm has a variety of products—as most do today—pricing policies become somewhat more complex. The interrelationships of the various products must be considered. For example, how should different sizes be priced? For one product, men's suits, the various sizes are all offered at the same price, yet a 36 short is less costly to make than a 46 long which requires much more material. Here custom and the fact that there is no difference in utility among the various sizes have acted to preclude price differentials. But turning to different-sized containers for a product such as toothpaste, we see substantial price differences. There are three different approaches to product-line pricing:

1. Relate prices to differences in costs.
2. Set price in proportion to differences in sizes.
3. Set prices so as to maximize profitability of entire line.

While the first two approaches make sense logically and are geared to relative equality in the unit-profit percentage for each size or quality category, they fail to consider the nature of elasticity of demand for the various sizes, and the need for competitive pricing. When relative markups of individual items in the line are allowed to vary, several strategy considerations are possible. Sometimes the smallest size will be priced at a very low markup so as to attract consumers to try the product. By custom, we have been conditioned to expect the greatest price savings when we purchase the largest size; in other words, the price per ounce should be lowest with the larger sizes. But this has not been always true: with detergents in particular the larger sizes have sometimes been higher per ounce than smaller sizes of the same brand.

Where different products in the line reflect quality differences, a common pricing policy is to price the lowest-quality item very competitively in an attempt to combat or ward off competition. Sometimes it may be necessary to price certain items below total costs in order to round out the line, to improve its over-all attractiveness, or to satisfy the needs of certain customers. The highest unit markups are often charged on the highest-quality items, the "top of the line." The assumption here is that the customer who can afford the most expensive product is not particularly price conscious and is willing to pay something extra for the prestige of owning the best. An inelastic demand curve is therefore thought to apply to these high-quality items, so that, within a relevant range, a difference in price will not appreciably affect demand. Figure 14-3 illustrates this.

With such an inelastic demand curve facing a luxury item, lowering the price, even drastically from X_1 to X_2 in the example, will only succeed in increasing demand slightly, from Y_1 to Y_2.

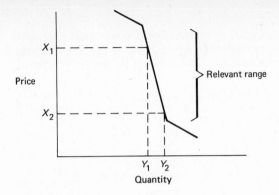

Figure 14-3. The Demand Curve for Luxury Items

Protection Against Price Declines

We have seen that reluctance to reduce prices characterizes many industries today. A lessening of demand, brought about perhaps by a recession, does not mean lower prices, as economic theorists would postulate. Part of the reason for this behavior is that costs, especially of labor, have a habit of going up regardless of the business cycle. A further factor causing reluctance to reduce prices is the effect on middlemen and dealers. Declining prices mean reductions in the value of inventories of wholesalers and retailers, placing them in a position of facing an immediate loss, the extent of which varies with the amount of goods carried. To minimize such potential losses, the natural reaction of dealers, when price levels begin to fall, is hand-to-mouth buying, maintaining minimum stocks of goods, and reordering small amounts frequently. This in turn affects the profitability of manufacturers who face declining total order quantities but probably an increased number of orders to be processed.

Certain brands have a reputation of holding their prices; yet when conditions become serious enough, some reductions may have to be made if a firm is to maintain a semblance of competitiveness. To combat the natural tendency of dealers to pare stocks, *price guarantees* have developed. Under such a guarantee the manufacturer promises his wholesalers and retailers that if he cuts prices during a certain period he will give a rebate and thus protect them from inventory losses. Where a manufacturer is producing seasonal goods and seeks to encourage dealers to order in advance of the season, such a price guarantee may be most important.

Naturally, there are some disadvantages to price guarantees. A manufacturer forced to drop a price faces a substantial loss while dealers have heavy inventories. If a manufacturer anticipates a price drop, he may ask for a higher initial price to compensate for a later rebate; in other words, the cost of the rebate is added to the cost of goods. Under most situations price guarantees lead to price rigidity and a reluctance to drop prices, even when market conditions may warrant this, because of the rebates which would result.

Price Maintenance Policies and Fair Trade Laws

Manufacturers are sometimes interested in controlling the retail prices of their products to protect the prestige of the brand. Sometimes retailers themselves will exert pressure on manufacturers to prevent other retailers' selling below a "list price."

The depression days of the 1930s saw state fair-trade laws proliferate, with the intent of protecting small retailers. These laws permitted the manufacturer, if he wished, to set the minimum resale price (in some states the manufacturer set the exact price) at which the product would be sold at retail. A controversial feature of these state laws was the "nonsigners" clause. Under this, when a manufacturer signs a fair-trade contract with one retailer in a state, every other retailer in the state is bound by this same contract.

In the heyday of fair trade all but three states had enacted such laws, but since 1950 it has been collapsing. Certain provisions, especially the nonsigners clause, have been legally questioned. But an even bigger detriment is that enforcement is left up to the individual companies, and many manufacturers have shied away from the expense of enforcement. Less than 10 percent of retail sales have ever been covered by fair trade, with the retail druggists long the greatest proponents of it. Some fourteen states set the minimum prices for farmers selling milk to dairies and stores selling milk (at one time 32 states regulated milk prices, but many of these laws have either been repealed or ruled unconstitutional). The results have been predictable: high retail prices, and weak incentives for dairy companies to reduce costs.[3]

If a manufacturer wishes to have prices maintained, he may exert pressure on retailers for this by:

1. Refusing to sell to price-cutting retailers.
2. Withholding advertising allowances and the like.
3. Offering the goods to retailers on consignment, whereby the manufacturer keeps title to the goods until they are sold.
4. Entering fair-trade contracts.
5. In extreme cases, opening retail outlets.

If the brand is a desirable one from the retailer's point of view, and if the manufacturer uses an exclusive distribution pattern, then

[3] For example, Pennsylvania has such regulation of milk prices. In Spring 1971, the state-fixed price for a gallon jug of milk was $1.21; just across the Ohio line where there was no such regulation, a gallon jug of milk was selling for $1.02. For more elaboration of this, see "In Pennsylvania, a Man Can Be a Lawbreaker for Selling Milk Cheap," *Wall Street Journal*, May 24, 1971, pp. 1 and 4.

the pressures to maintain price or the enforcement of fair-trade contracts are feasible. Lacking this, the final price to consumers is largely beyond the control of the manufacturer, even in fair-trade states.

Retail Pricing Policies

A number of pricing policies originate at the retail level and affect manufacturers indirectly. In this section we will discuss price lining, leader pricing, odd pricing, and various aspects of what might be called psychological pricing.

Price Lining. Price lining is a common phenomenon of retail pricing. All products of a given type are priced at varying intervals regardless of small differences in costs. For example, one store might offer sportshirts at these price lines: $3.95, $5.95, and $12.95. Products from a number of different manufacturers carrying different costs would then be grouped under the most appropriate price line.

This strategy simplifies buying for both customers and the retailer. Price choices are limited and there usually are clear differences between price lines. The retailer can better recognize sales trends, plan and select the merchandise assortment, promotions, and displays, than would be possible under a myriad of prices. Furthermore, the desired image of the store—that is, whether of a promotional, a quality, or a medium-priced store—can be more systematically planned and maintained.

The danger is that a store may not offer the best price lines to appeal to its customers, or that the spread between may be so great that customers want items at prices in between. A period of rising costs causes problems in obtaining profitable merchandise of sufficient quality to fit the regular price lines, without constantly changing prices. Some products have traditional prices difficult to change. For example, with the 5- and 10-cent candy bars, manufacturers have reduced sizes in order to continue maintaining these prices while faced with increased costs—almost to the point of the "disappearing bar."

Leader Pricing. Leader pricing is a type of promotional pricing in which certain popular items are advertised at a very low price—sometimes even below cost, in which case they are known as *loss leaders*—in order to attract customers into the store. The expectation is that customers attracted by the leader item will stay to purchase other regular-price items, resulting in increased sales and profits.

As a promotional device, leader pricing can be effective if the items are carefully chosen, well known, and ones which are frequently purchased by most people. However, abusive practices sometimes result, such as "bait-and-switch" advertising. Sometimes the firm offering the most attractive "leaders" may have other prices marked up a little higher than justified.

Some 25 states have *Unfair Practices Acts,* usually dating to the 1930s, to regulate leader pricing and to prevent severe price cutting at the retail level especially on the part of chains and other large retailers. However, these laws have generally been unenforceable because of the large number of retailers and the difficulty in determining the real cost of doing business. Some states have declared these laws unconstitutional; other states require proof that leader pricing is being used to "destroy competition." Generally these laws have little impact today.

Odd Pricing. Most retail prices are set at odd amounts, such as 49 cents, 98 cents, $5.95; rarely does one encounter an item selling for such even amounts as 50 cents, $1.00, $5.00, or $10.00. Why is this? What is the almost universal attraction of odd prices by retailers?

Originally, odd prices were developed as a control device for retail clerks. By having to make change, they had to ring the cash register thus recording the sale (otherwise, the dishonest clerk might pocket the money without ringing the cash register and thereby not record the sale). However, today it is generally believed that odd prices sell better than even prices. Thus, $1.98 may be perceived as being substantially less than $2.00. There is little confirmation of this psychological value of odd prices, but the practice has persisted and become traditional.[4]

Other Aspects of Psychological Pricing. Leader pricing can be considered a type of psychological pricing in that the genuine price-attractiveness of the leader item(s) is thought to convey an aura of good values for the whole store. And odd prices are considered to be psychologically more attractive to customers. Since there is the tendency to judge quality by price, the interesting phenomenon sometimes occurs that an item may sell less at low prices than at a high price. One textbook cites an instance of aspirin being tried out at different prices, 19 cents, 29 cents, 39 cents, and 49 cents, with the greatest sales resulting at 49 cents.[5]

The Price-Quality Relationship. Considerable research has focused on how consumers perceive the price-quality relationship. Apparently customers do fear that at a low price, quality must suffer. Figure 14-4 illustrates the demand curve in such a situation.

Intuitively this seems rather obvious, and certainly in some instances a high price may be an attracting rather than a repelling force.[6] However, can this perceived relationship be generalized, that is, does it apply to all products and purchase situations?

[4] For studies about the value of odd prices, inconclusive though they may be, see Edward R. Hawkins, "Methods of Estimating Demand," *Journal of Marketing,* April 1957, p. 433.

[5] P. D. Converse, H. W. Huegy, and R. V. Mitchell, *Elements of Marketing,* 5th ed. (Englewood Cliffs, N.J.: Prentice-Hall, 1952), p. 207.

[6] For an elaboration of this, see Benson P. Shapiro, "The Psychology of Pricing," *Harvard Business Review,* July–August 1968, p. 16.

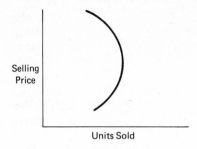

Figure 14-4. Demand Curve of Items Susceptible to Prestige Pricing

A number of studies have supported this relationship.[7] Other recent research suggests that this perception may not be so generalized.[8] Still other findings lead to the conclusion that price-quality relationships may operate within limits: below a certain price a product may be perceived as too cheap; then there is an upper limit in which the product is regarded as too expensive. But for a middle range of prices, higher ones may be seen as indicative of higher quality, and be more attractive to those consumers interested in better quality.[9]

Calculation of Retail Markup Percent. Most retailers prefer to express markup percentages on a retail price base, rather than on a cost base. The alternative formulas are as follows:

$$\text{Markup percent on retail} = \frac{\$ \text{ markup}}{\$ \text{ selling price}}$$

$$\text{Markup percent on cost} = \frac{\$ \text{ markup}}{\$ \text{ cost price}}$$

The difference is the denominator used, whether the cost price to the retailer or his asking or selling price. The following example shows this calculation and also the relative comparison between a markup on retail and a markup on cost:

[7] For example, D. S. Tull, R. A. Boring, and M. H. Gonsior, "A Note on the Relationship of Price and Imputed Quality," *The Journal of Business,* April 1964, pp. 186–91; J. Douglas McConnell, "The Price Quality Relationship in an Experimental Setting," *Journal of Marketing Research,* August 1968, pp. 300–03; and James E. Stafford and Ben M. Enis, "The Price-Quality Relationship: An Extension," *Journal of Marketing Research,* November 1969, pp. 456–58.

[8] David M. Gardner, "Is There a Generalized Price/Quality Relationship?" paper presented at the American Marketing Association Fall Conference, September 1, 1970, Boston, Mass.; also David M. Gardner, "An Experimental Investigation of the Price/Relationship," *Journal of Retailing,* Fall 1970, pp. 25–41.

[9] Kent B. Monroe and M. Venkatesan, "The Concepts of Price Limits and Psychophysical Measurement: A Laboratory Experiment," in Phillip R. McDonald, ed., *Marketing Involvement in Society and the Economy* (Cincinnati: Proceedings of the American Marketing Association, 1969), pp. 345–51.

Selling price	$8
Cost to retailer	4
Dollar markup	4

Markup percentage (from above formulas)

$$\frac{4}{4} = 100\% \text{ markup on cost}$$

$$\frac{4}{8} = 50\% \text{ markup on retail}$$

Table 14-3.
Markup Equivalents

Markup on Retail (percent)	Markup on Cost (percent)
20.0	25.0
25.0	33.3
33.3	50.0
40.0	66.7
50.0	100.0
60.0	150.0
75.0	300.0

Table 14-3 presents some markup equivalents. Note that markups on cost percentages are always greater than the respective markups on retail equivalents. Furthermore, markups computed on a retail (selling price) base can never reach 100 percent, while on a cost base that can readily be exceeded.

There are several reasons for the prevalence of the markup on retail. An obvious one is that profitability sounds considerably less than if the cost base is used; consequently if a customer should encounter the markup percentage, it would not seem as extreme. However, for planning and control purposes most operating ratios are expressed as a percentage of sales, and it seems more natural to do so with markup figures also. Sales and selling price information is more readily available than that on costs which is usually determined only periodically at inventory computation time. And most comparative trade statistics are expressed on a sales base.

PRICE DETERMINATION

Relationship of Costs, Competition, and Demand

The role of costs in pricing tends to be exaggerated, despite the avowed objectives of some large corporations to attain a designated target return. Yet costs are important and form a yardstick for measuring profitability and for any consideration of what is a fair markup.

The difficulty in working with costs is that there are several costs—each having different behavior as output increases—which are relevant.

Fixed costs are those basic to the operation. These do not change as production changes. Therefore, the more units produced, the more these fixed costs can be spread, so that the cost per unit decreases. Examples of fixed costs are property taxes, interest paid, and executive salaries. On the other hand, *variable costs* result from variations in production and will increase as output increases, although not always in proportion. Examples of variable costs are labor and material. *Total costs* are the combinations of fixed and variable costs at different production levels. The relationship of fixed and variable costs and the effect on total costs is shown in Figure 14-5.

There are several other ways of looking at costs that also are pertinent to the pricing and markup decision: average costs, marginal costs, and sunk costs. *Average costs* are computed by combining all expenses incurred—including both fixed and variable costs—and dividing the total by the number of units produced. This gives an average cost per unit and this is most commonly used in pricing computations.

However, the more relevant costs to be covered are marginal costs. *Marginal costs* are the added expenses incurred in producing and selling one additional unit. For example, if the cost of producing and selling 200 units of a particular item is $12,000, and the cost for 201 units is $12,040, then the marginal cost is $40; any price above $40 would make some contribution to profit. But it can be seen that this is below average unit costs, which for 200 units would be $60 (12,000 ÷ 200). Therefore, marginal costs should set a minimum limit on price, below which a firm would incur a financial loss. But the price can sometimes be profitably set below average costs.

The reason for this phenomenon is that average costs usually are high when small quantities are produced because the fixed costs

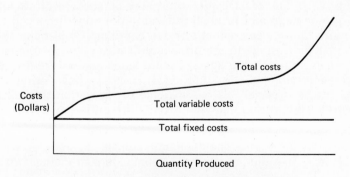

Figure 14-5. Relationships of Total Fixed Costs, Total Variable Costs, and Total Costs

are spread over relatively few units; marginal costs—the costs of producing additional units—then may be less than average costs. However, when output is well above capacity, production becomes less efficient as more wear and tear on machines is incurred, less efficient workers have to be hired, and perhaps overtime with its increased costs is necessary. Under these conditions, marginal costs may be greater than average costs and a firm may need to appraise carefully the desirability of seeking further sales near-term, unless very attractive prices can be obtained.

While marginal costs, then, should represent the floor below which a firm cannot go in its pricing (without losing money on every unit sold), obviously all orders cannot be priced to cover only variable costs or the total sales of a firm would leave fixed costs uncovered. But there are occasions when a firm may validly seek to cover only its marginal costs: keeping a plant running and labor employed during slack times and thereby avoiding costly shutdowns, would be such occasions.

Sunk costs are outlays which have already been made; they cannot be revoked or canceled. A common example here is research and development expenditures aimed at product improvement. Sometimes such expenditures result in valuable discoveries, sometimes not. Usually such costs already "sunk" should be ignored in making decisions about price and output.

However, prices should not be determined by cost alone. Costs frequently are difficult to allocate, especially for multiproduct firms. Adequate cost data about cost-volume relationships is frequently lacking. Especially with new products, the inability to estimate sales volume accurately at various selling prices also presents problems in cost estimation.[10] But perhaps the biggest fallacy in the emphasis of cost as a factor in pricing is that it is a one-sided approach. Unless the consumer is willing to pay the prescribed price, there will be no sale. Furthermore, the influence of present and potential competition can seldom be ignored in safety.

Competitive Influences. Despite what may be successful attempts to achieve some degree of product differentiation, few firms can charge much more than close competitors are charging. Consequently there is an upper limit range to the price any firm can charge. We can call this a range rather than a specific point since, unless the firm is in a homogeneous oligopolistic situation, it does not have to meet competitive prices precisely. It has a range of discretion depending on the degree and attractiveness of the differentiation perceived by consumers.

Demand Considerations. The economic concept of price elasticity of demand describes the sensitivity of consumers to changes in price.

[10] For an elaboration on the nature of costs, see Robert N. Anthony, "What Should 'Cost' Mean?" *Harvard Business Review*, May–June, 1970, pp. 121–31.

If a small change in price substantially affects unit sales, then the price elasticity of demand is high. However viable this concept may be in theory, in practice it is often difficult to determine specifically enough to be practical. Furthermore, the sensitivity of consumers to price seems to vary in unpredictable ways. Some customers place a higher value on convenience, service, and quality than on small price savings. Therefore the concept of price elasticity seldom can be used to predict accurately the effect of a proposed price change on sales volume.

Demand-backward pricing is commonly used by producers of some consumer goods. Here the producer aims for a particular *retail* price or price range at which he estimates good demand exists, and then works backward, subtracting typical costs and margins of channel members to arrive at the approximate price he can charge and the amount he can spend on production and marketing. The previously mentioned example of candy-bar manufacturers trying to maintain the 5- and 10-cent retail price is an example of demand-backward pricing.

Now let us look more closely at an important tool for marketers, one which takes into account both costs (fixed and variable) and demand in trying to arrive at an optimum pricing decision.

**MARKETING
TOOL**

The Breakeven Analysis
An important tool for many marketing decisions is the breakeven analysis.
It is valuable in making go/no go decisions regarding new products,
new ventures, new strategies. It is useful in determining which of several
alternative decisions is best, and this is how we will examine it here.
A breakeven analysis can be graphically shown as follows:

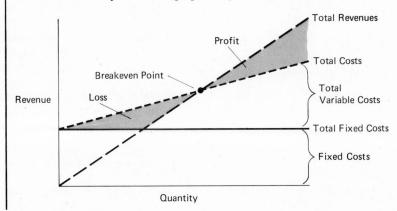

Below the breakeven point, losses will be suffered; above it, the product or venture becomes profitable.

Example: Let us take a hypothetical new product, a dog food. It is estimated that at (a) 39¢ a can, sales will be 1 million cans; at (b) 49¢ a can, sales will be 350,000 cans, and at (c) 29¢ a can, sales will zoom to 3 million cans. Fixed costs, which include new machinery and planned promotional efforts are planned at $200,000. Variable costs—the cost of labor and ingredients—will be 10¢ a can. Dealer margins will be 33% of selling price. What is the best price for the manufacturer given these conditions?

Formula:

$$\text{Breakeven Point (in units)} = \frac{\text{total fixed costs}}{\text{per-unit contribution to fixed costs}}$$

Under (a)   39¢ − (33% x 39¢)   =   26¢ selling price (revenue) for manufacturer per can

Less   10¢ variable costs

16¢ contribution per can

$$BE = \frac{\$200,000}{16¢} =$$ 1,250,000 cans to break even
1,000,000 cans estimated sales at 39¢

250,000 cans *less* than breakeven

Under (b)   49¢ − (33% x 49¢)   =   33¢ selling price for manufacturer

Less   10¢ variable costs

23¢ contribution per can

$$BE = \frac{\$200,000}{23¢} =$$ 870,000 cans to break even
350,000 cans estimated sales at 49¢

520,000 cans *less* than breakeven

Under (c)   29¢ − (33% x 29¢)   =   19¢ revenue per can

Less   10¢ variable costs

9¢ contribution per can

$$BE = \frac{\$200,000}{9¢} =$$ 2,222,222 cans to break even
3,000,000 cans estimated sales at 29¢

777,778 cans over breakeven

Therefore, strategy (c), the 29¢ price, would be the only viable pricing alternative, given these conditions and estimates.

Now you can see some problems with this analysis. First of all, we are assuming that fixed costs will remain constant at all sales volumes. More realistically, some increases may occur, such as more salesmen needed at the higher sales volumes. We are also assuming that variable costs will remain constant at all outputs—that variable costs are a straight line, whereas these tend to vary somewhat beyond the middle range of sales volumes (as in Figure 14-5). Finally, the estimates of demand may or may not be valid. Supposedly they were obtained by a market test, dealer opinions, consumer surveys, past history, and/or executive consensus of judgment. But we still are on risky ground when it comes to predicting demand accurately.

Therefore, while breakeven analysis does not remove all the problems in making price decisions, it does permit a systematic evaluation of profit consequences given certain reasonable conditions. As such it can be a valuable tool indeed for marketing managers.

For thought and discussion:
In the above example, if variable costs were 16¢ and fixed costs were $100,000, would this change the decision?

Skimming and Penetration Pricing

Two basic and opposite approaches may be taken in pricing a new or changed product. A relatively high price may be charged (a *skimming price* aimed at taking the "cream" of the market), or a relatively low price (a *penetration price*). For more mature products the market situation usually is too competitive to permit such options.

The temptation in introducing a highly differentiated product is to use a skimming price that will yield maximum profit per unit sold. This is also a rather easy approach to pricing since the price may be lowered later if the initial one proves unattractive to consumers. Furthermore, skimming permits a natural approach to market segmentation: the high initial price attracts the upper portion of the market, those consumers interested in highest quality and perhaps in the prestige of having something distinctive; later as production expands, the price periodically can be reduced to appeal to other segments.

There are, however, limitations to skimming. Usually it is most practical when a firm either faces a relatively inelastic demand curve, in which sales will not be appreciably affected by price, or else has a limited market. If the price elasticity of demand is at least moderate, greater total profits may be gained by pricing lower, and expanding production. But the major deterrent to skimming is competition. A high price encourages competitors to enter the market because they see good profit opportunities where prices are held at a high level and productive capacity expands slowly. If imitation is easy, then a skimming price may be forced down quickly and competitors become firmly entrenched.

Ballpoint pens are an example of skimming: they were introduced at around $15; after a few years they were available well under $1. Polaroid has also used a skimming approach with its cameras, but Polaroid's pricing policy was supported by adequate patent and technological protection. Ballpoint pens, by contrast, were easily imitated, the market was not technologically or legally secure, and competitive entry was quickly established.

Conditions favoring penetration pricing are more common. Such a policy assumes an elastic demand, with sales increasing substantially if prices can be lowered; therefore a large market must also be expected. By gaining maximum sales, a firm has the opportunity to build an unassailable position. A penetration pricing situation is a necessity if the initial product differentiation is not ample, or is easily copied, or if there is no elite market which would take higher-priced offerings. While penetration pricing with its low unit profits may force a firm to accept some losses at first, the expectation is for economies of scale and reduced costs as volume expands.

What Is a Fair Markup?

While firms usually are constrained by demand and competition, occasionally a substantial innovation or an economic situation of scarcity may raise the "ceiling of pricing choice." If competitive entry is not likely in the short run, a firm might want to price as high as the market will bear:

Some ethical questions arise in such a situation:

−Is a businessman entitled to charge all he can get or should he moderate his price demands and be satisfied with more modest profits?
−Should a businessman desist from price increases in order to minimize the threat of inflation?
−Should the answer differ depending on whether the product is a drug essential for health, or something not involving health and welfare?

The tenets of a free enterprise system support the right to charge the most profitable price. Rewards are thereby created for innovation without which the economy would languish. One pricing expert notes that

one could also justify the right of the businessman to charge as much as he pleases, because he is not protected against the necessity of charging a price that yields him no profit at all. Equity would seem to require that he be protected against loss if he is to be prevented from reaping high profits when he might get them.[11]

But it seems desirable to use restraint in raising prices in order to prevent or lessen inflation. And there is some point at which the price of a drug essential for the health of certain persons becomes unfairly priced.

PRICING TO THE GOVERNMENT

Government procurement practices present different complexities and opportunities to marketers. Many branded items are routinely purchased—products such as tires, gasoline, school supplies, construction materials, data processing equipment and supplies—and represent additional sales volume (perhaps at lower profit margins) with little or no marketing adjustments needed. But bidding and negotiated contracts are unlike normal marketing practices.

Where competitive *bidding* is involved—as it often is for staple products and those in continuous demand—various suppliers are invited to submit sealed bids with the lowest price usually being accepted. Where the larger production base made possible by additional business from government enables a firm to reduce its unit cost, then there is incentive to submit as low a price as possible. However, there may be additional costs involved with government business due to higher quality control standards demanded, somewhat different specifications needed, and more comprehensive and frequent reports required.

Many contracts are *negotiated* rather than using either the bidding process or purchasing on the open market. Usually negotiation is necessary when:

1. The product(s) needed is complex and not easily described
2. Research and development is needed
3. No other firm is in a position to readily design and produce the needed item

More than 80 percent of military procurement has been made through negotiation rather than sealed bids.[12]

Such procurement is made outside the market system, and is noncompetitive in the sense that price is seldom the determining variable. Of more importance is the technical competence of the

[11] Alfred R. Oxenfeldt, *Pricing for Marketing Executives* (San Francisco: Wadsworth, 1961), p. 15.
[12] U.S. House of Representatives, Committee on Appropriations, *Hearings on Department of Defense Appropriations for 1963,* Part 4, 87th Cong., 2d Sess., 1962, p. 19.

firms under consideration, their financial responsibility, facilities available, security considerations, and performance on previous contracts. And influence and favoritism can sometimes be important, especially at the local level, but even at the federal level: retired generals and admirals are eagerly hired by many defense-oriented firms because of their personal contacts.

Negotiated contracts may be subject to audit and renegotiation, especially if the contractor makes an excessive profit. On the other hand, cost overruns have shocked Congress and the public in recent inflationary years. These contracts negotiated on a "cost-plus" basis have missed their estimates by awesome amounts. As one example, a short-range attack missile (SRAM) originally estimated to cost $421 million grew to $1.47 billion.[13] How could responsible estimates, both on the part of defense contractors and Pentagon brass, miss the mark so badly?

---

[13] "Cost Plus and Then Some," *Forbes,* January 1, 1970, pp. 172–77.

MARKETING
IN
ACTION

Doing Business with the Government—The Lockheed Dilemma
Lockheed has been the nation's biggest defense contractor as well as one of the best managed and most technically competent. During World War II it mass-produced 20,000 combat planes, mainly P-38 fighters. In Korea, its F-80 Shooting Stars ruled the skies. Later it built the U-4 spy plane and the F-104 fighter, the latter being the mainstay of NATO's air defense. Its Agena rocket was used in more than 250 space launchings, and the Polaris submarine-fired missile—completed two-and-a-half years ahead of schedule—was an essential part of our nuclear deterrent. The more advanced Poseidon missile, at its test firing in the summer of 1970, induced a Russian tracking ship to almost collide with a U. S. destroyer as it raced to pick up some telltale debris.

After such a history of successful development of sophisticated products, the contract to build the military transport C-5A, the world's largest plane, seemed relatively simple. But the weight of the plane caused major new technological ground to be broken, while inflation and other factors led to a 40 percent cost overrun, one of $1.6 billion. Of this, Lockheed stood to lose $500 million. Furthermore, the Air Force cut orders for the giant cargo aircraft. Lockheed experienced other problems with its defense contracting as well. For example, its Cheyenne hybrid craft, capable of hovering like a helicopter or flying at 250 mph, developed defects and one crashed; this resulted in the contract being canceled and $124 million in unreimbursed costs.

While economic and technological problems led to Lockheed's difficulty, political factors compounded the problems. The C-5A was the first and most disastrous of the TPP (total-package procurement) contracts, in which a contractor had to bid on the whole contract from designing to final production, thereby attempting to forecast costs before the product had even been invented. Air Force deviousness toward a congressional committee investigating military spending also hurt, as it hardened congressional opposition to costly military programs.

SOURCES: "Lockheed Hits Heavy Head Winds," *Business Week,* February 14, 1970, pp. 46–48; "Target, Lockheed," *Barron's,* August 17, 1970, pp. 1, 12.

For thought and discussion:
With Lockheed facing bankruptcy—by the narrowest of margins and accompanied by great controversy—Congress authorized the federal government to assist or "bail out" Lockheed. Discuss the pros and cons of such government assistance for a private firm.

SRAM, like many other contracts where cost overruns were plentiful, was awarded under *total-package procurement* (TPP). Under TPP, a single fixed-price contract was awarded for the total job—research, development, production, testing, etc. But it proved virtually impossible to estimate at the beginning of some of these contracts, before even any research had been done, what the cost of the total package would be. The temptation was to underestimate when in doubt.

THE CONSUMER AND PRICES

How important is price to the consumer, and how may consumers be better equipped to compare prices? The first question cannot be answered with any degree of certainty, but there do seem to be some trends. We have already seen in chapter 6 that emotional buying motives, such as desire for status, fulfillment, or security, may be present. Moreover there are rational reasons for buying other than price, such as convenience, quality of goods, or courtesy.

On the other hand, two studies described in chapter 6 found that the largest group of shoppers were "economic," that is, primarily interested in getting the most for their money.[14] The rapid growth of discount stores in the 1950s and 1960s may be attributed to such a concern for lower prices. More recently, relentless inflation has made even middle-class consumers very price-conscious, and it may be that firms will be forced to reconsider price as a competitive strategy.

The second question, how may customers be assisted in com-

[14] G. P. Stone "City Shoppers and Urban Identification," *American Journal of Sociology,* July 1954, pp. 36–45; Housing Research Center, *Houses Are for People,* Cornell University, Research Publication No. 3.

Table 14-4.

Benefits and Drawbacks of Unit Pricing

	Benefits	**Drawbacks**
To Customers	Permits more knowledgeable buying. A customer can determine from posted prices which size or brand has the lowest price per ounce, pound, or standard unit.	Some time and effort is needed to check unit prices. Some customers do not consider the savings of a few pennies worth the extra effort. Quality—which is at least partly accounted for by unit-price differences—is an intangible thing and may be seen as nullifying the significance of unit prices.
To Retailers	A retailer can better promote the price advantages of private brands over nationally advertised ones. If a store adopts unit pricing before its competitors do, it may earn a reputation as a socially concerned retailer.	Costs are somewhat increased, but rather modestly compared to initial estimates.

paring prices, brings up the question of unit pricing. In recent years there has been public pressure for unit-pricing legislation. This, at either the local, state, or national level, would require retailers to post prices by the ounce, pound, or other standard measure. Of course, shoppers then would be able to make instant price comparisons to determine which sizes and brands were the better values.[15] Table 14-4 shows the benefits and drawbacks of unit pricing both for customers and for retailers.

At first some retailers strongly opposed unit pricing. For example, New York City led the way in enacting unit-pricing legislation, and retail groups there sought to have the law declared illegal. The opposition focused on the extra costs and effort involved in complying with unit pricing. However, more reasoned study of the issue has found that retailers also benefit from unit pricing, as shown in Table 14-4. In any case, *responsive marketing* would suggest doing

[15] Recent research and articles on unit pricing and its effect on consumer purchasing habits include: J. Edward Russo, Gene Krieser, and Sally Miyashita, "An Effective Display of Unit Price Information," *Journal of Marketing,* April 1975, pp. 11–19; Hans R. Isakson and Alex R. Maurizi, "The Consumer Economics of Unit Pricing," *Journal of Marketing Research,* August 1973, pp. 277–85; and Michael J. Houston, "The Effect of Unit-Pricing on Choices of Brand and Size in Economic Shopping," *Journal of Marketing,* July 1972, pp. 51–54.

Typical unit pricing labels are shown here. They enable the consumer to compare prices of different brands and different sizes. *Photo by Helena Frost.*

whatever is necessary to give consumers better information in the marketplace.

QUESTIONS AND PROBLEMS

1. Do you think a marketer should charge all that the market will bear, even when this may yield exceptional profits? Would your answer vary if the product is a drug essential for the health of some people?

2. How might a company's pricing strategies differ depending upon whether a product is in the pioneering stage or maturity stage of its life cycle?

3. What is product-line pricing? How can this be used as an effective tool of marketing strategy?

4. Skimming and penetration are pricing strategies. Under what circumstances would you consider using these?

5. Assume that a manufacturer wants to introduce a new consumer product. What factors would he want to consider in deciding upon a pricing policy for this product? Organize your answer around the following:
   a. characteristics of the product;
   b. costs of production and marketing;
   c. financial needs of the firm;
   d. present and potential competition.

6. Price leadership has been present in many industries in the United States. Define price leadership and explain why it has arisen in certain industries. Why have the "followers" been willing to go along with the price leader? What role does collusion play in price leadership?

7. What is demand-backward pricing? Illustrate how it might be used by a manufacturer of men's shirts.

8. The degree of control over their own prices which sellers are able to secure varies widely in the United States. Illustrate these variations in control and explain why these variations exist. Why do many firms prefer to compete on a nonprice rather than a price basis?

CHAPTER 14 / PRICE AS A COMPETITIVE TOOL

Project

Investigate a unit of each of the major supermarket chains in your cities to determine if they have unit pricing. If so, how simple is it to interpret? From observation, what percent of customers appear to be using it? Does the chain promote the use of unit prices in newspaper ads and display signs?

Exercise in Creativity

Develop as many ideas for nonprice competition as you can for:
    a. a hamburger
    b. toothpaste
    c. beer

Role-playing Case

The Whirlpool Corporation had a major pricing problem with the development of its unique "Trashmasher," a kitchen appliance smaller than a dishwasher, which could compress a week's trash (in the ordinary household) into one small bag. Since nothing similar had ever been on the market, the attempt to fashion the best price had little basis for comparison.

    As the Whirlpool executive responsible for setting the price of the Trashmasher, how would you make this determination? What factors would you consider?

CHAPTER 15

PHYSICAL DISTRIBUTION AND MORE EFFICIENT MARKETING

Without the physical means to move goods from seller to user, marketing activity breaks down. Physical distribution involves transportation, storage, inventory control, and location of facilities. Each is examined in some detail, as well as in interrelationship in a total-cost concept. Key terms include:

carload and LCL rates	public warehouses
containerization	distribution center
common carriers	inventory control
piggyback service	total-cost concept
class rates	physical distribution manager

The term *logistics* is sometimes used to describe the management of physical distribution. The word was originally used in a military context to describe the process of transporting and supplying troops and equipment in order to have sufficient strength to meet demands. In the marketing sense, logistics or physical distribution concerns moving, placing, and balancing products with respect to a particular goal. In short,

> Physical distribution involves the coordination of activities to place the right quantity of the right goods at the desired place and time.

IMPORTANCE OF PHYSICAL DISTRIBUTION

We sometimes take the distribution of goods for granted, but the importance of physical distribution is made clear when we look at certain countries where distribution and handling facilities are inefficient and backward.

A failure of distribution can compound the problems of economic development. For example, markets at the village level in India:

> Village markets are very poorly equipped; most of them are uncovered and lack storage, stalls and drainage facilities. The quality of roads linking most of these markets to towns and wholesale markets is also so poor that often only a bullock cart can travel on them and even then only with considerable difficulty. Some markets lack roads completely. Hardly any of these markets have telephones, telegraphs, or even postal facilities. Producers within a radius of five or ten miles gather in these markets to sell their small agricultural surpluses.[1]

A lack of good logistical facilities and organization is nowhere more crucial than in food distribution. Food is more complex than most other products because of danger of spoilage, the bulkiness of most produce, and the requirement of widespread distribution. Even competition for food by insects and rodents poses problems: 50 percent of the grain harvested in Somalia is eaten by such before it can be transported to the table.

Until recently the problem of the chronic food shortage of some countries was seen entirely as one of production: the need to produce more crops. Recent breakthroughs have been made in producing nitrogenous fertilizers more efficiently, and in developing new strains of wheat and rice that produce substantially higher yields than traditional varieties.[2] But:

> While increased production will mean more food available for market, the amount actually reaching the consumers depends on . . . the marketing system in developing countries. On the one hand, if it does not serve the interests and needs of the producer (if his additional production does not move to market and brings him no additional earnings), there is a disincentive to higher production. On the other hand, if the marketing system does not bring the food to the consumer when he needs it and at prices he can afford, then higher production will have little effect on the war on hunger.[3]

The problems are complex and permit no simple solution to world hunger, but improvement in physical distribution—both trans-

---

[1] Uma J. Lele et al., *Developing Rural India* (Ithaca, N. Y.: Cornell University Press, 1968), p. 243.

[2] Martin Kriesberg, "Marketing Food in Developing Nations—Second Phase of the War on Hunger," *Journal of Marketing,* October 1968, p. 57.

[3] Ibid., pp. 56–57.

portation and storage—would make a large contribution to the underdeveloped economies of the world.

ACTIVITIES INVOLVED IN PHYSICAL DISTRIBUTION

The basic activities involved in the process of physical distribution are: transportation, storage, inventory control, and location of facilities. Although these will be discussed separately, they are interrelated and should be considered in combination; in other words, the process of physical distribution should be integrated and coordinated. Often this means that a compromise must be made between enhancing the opportunity for profitable sales volume and minimizing the cost involved. The most economical method of moving goods may not get the right quantity of the right assortment of goods to the right place on time; sometimes more expensive means of physical distribution, such as air freight, may be necessary.

Differing executive perspectives may impede integration of distribution, however. For example, production executives desire long production runs that minimize unit manufacturing costs, but raise inventory and storage costs; financial executives are critical of heavy inventories and will push for minimum transportation costs; a traffic department typically concerns itself with freight rates and seeks lowest ton-mile charges, often to the exclusion of other considerations; and the sales department constantly presses for broad assortments of goods available at locations near customers, or lacking this, the use of the fastest mode of transportation so that service and delivery will be most attractive to customers. Incompatible as some of these objectives may be, they must be resolved if the efficiency of the physical distribution process is to be maximized.

PHYSICAL DISTRIBUTION: UNTIL RECENTLY
A NEGLECTED ASPECT OF MARKETING

As important as the physical aspect of distribution is, it has not been the subject of serious marketing concern, at least until recently.[4] Perhaps some of the reason for this neglect was the belief that physical distribution could not be improved, a belief that held sway until computers and quantitative techniques became popular.[5] Now we know that this aspect of marketing permits operational efficiencies more than do others, since most of these problems and their solu-

[4] One of the early articles drawing management's attention to this aspect of marketing was that of Peter Drucker, "The Economy's Dark Continent," *Fortune*, April 1962, pp. 103–04.

[5] Donald J. Bowersox, "Physical Distribution Development, Current Status, and Potential," *Journal of Marketing*, January 1969, p. 64.

tions are tangible, easily defined, and capable of being systematically and quantitatively analyzed.

Transportation and storage account for about half the total cost of marketing.[6] The sheer dollars involved in storage and movement of products to market is awesome: estimates some years ago ranged between \$50 and \$75 billion annually in the United States, and if inventory-carrying and order-processing costs are included, as high as \$100 billion.[7]

In addition to the sheer magnitude of expenditures for physical handling of goods, there are other reasons why this aspect of marketing deserves attention:

1. Trend toward a short-order economy. Reducing inventories through more frequent ordering of smaller quantities puts greater demands on the distribution process if customer service requirements are to be met.
2. Increasing assortment of goods. An increasing variety of models, styles, colors, packages, and price variations of goods increases inventory problems of obsolescence, stock availability, and imbalance.
3. Pressures for lower prices. Beginning with the discount store and the marketing of consumer goods, and now carrying over into industrial goods distribution, pressures for lower prices have forced the development of new, more direct, and more efficient channels of distribution.
4. Limits on pricing flexibility. Governmental pressures against price differentials and discounts, unless they can be justified by differences in costs, have been an incentive for many companies to determine their actual distribution costs where formerly they relied on broad national cost averages.
5. Physical distribution as a tool of competitive marketing strategy. By outperforming competition on customer service and product availability, and sometimes by lowering distribution costs, a strong competitive advantage can be achieved.[8]

TRANSPORTATION

Transportation provides place utility. It is basic to any marketing system since, unless goods are brought to where they are needed or desired, or unless reasonable convenience of purchasing is provided, the other marketing efforts are wasted. The United States, of course,

[6] Paul D. Converse, Harvey W. Huegy, and Robert V. Mitchell, *Elements of Marketing,* 7th ed. (Englewood Cliffs, N.J.: Prentice-Hall, 1965), pp. 13–14.
[7] Wendell M. Stewart, "Physical Distribution: Key to Improved Volume and Profits," *Journal of Marketing,* January 1965, p. 66
[8] Adapted from Stewart, "Physical Distribution," pp. 65–70.

Table 15-1.
Distribution of Intercity Freight Traffic in the United States
in Millions of Ton-Miles

Year	Total Ton-Miles (millions)	Percent of Total				
		Rail-roads	Trucks	Inland Water-ways	Oil Pipe-lines	Air Carrier
1930	524,350	74.3	3.9	16.5	5.3	—
1940	618,592	61.3	10.0	19.1	9.6	—
1950	1,062,637	56.2	16.3	15.4	12.1	.03
1960	1,320,200	43.8	22.2	16.2	17.7	.05
1965	1,620,800	43.5	23.1	16.0	17.3	.10
1968	1,845,000	42.0	21.5	15.5	21.0	.16
1972	2,077,000	37.8	22.6	16.3	23.1	.18

Source: *Railroad Facts,* Chicago: Association of Western Railroads, 1961, p. 5; and *Yearbook of Railroad Facts* (Washington, D.C.: Association of American Railroads, 1966), p. 39. The 1972 figures are from *Statistical Abstract of the United States,* 1974, p. 547.

has well-developed rail, highway, and air facilities. This has contributed to the development of our high standard of living with its availability of all kinds of products at acceptable prices. Perhaps just as important is the unhampered freedom of goods to move throughout our country: there are no border checks or inspections at each state line.

The various modes of transport are relatively familiar to us all. The trend in their relative importance, however, reveals new patterns which may be significant in the future. Table 15-1 shows these trends, as measured by ton-miles of domestic intercity freight traffic. Several things are worth noting from this table. The consistent and steady growth of total ton-miles indicates the increasing task and importance of this marketing function: more goods have to be moved. The steady decline of the railroad share of this business, and the concomitant increase in trucking suggests that the railroad business is in need of an overhaul. While the tonnage carried by air freight is minuscule, air may well be a more important factor in the future—not for bulk goods, but for finished and specialized goods. (If the table showed dollar value of goods moved, rather than tonnage, then air freight would show up much stronger.) Let us now look briefly at the characteristics and particular strengths of these various modes.

Railroads

Railroads are best adapted for long hauls of bulk products, low in value relative to weight, such as coal, sand, petroleum, and agricultural products. More than 99 percent of the tonnage shipped by rail consists of carload shipments.[9] *Carload rates* are generally less than one half of the *less than carload (LCL) rates,* because of the easier loading and handling costs involved.

The decline in the railroads' relative share of total freight, which has contributed to a general decline in railroad profits in recent years, has resulted in various defensive measures being taken. Some computerization and automation of rail facilities has been effected, while specially designed refrigerator cars, hopper cars, livestock-handling cars, and the like have increased freight handling and loading efficiency. Other efforts and improved services now offered by railroads are described in Table 15-2.

[9] *Railroad Facts* (Chicago: Association of Western Railroads, 1961), p. 26.

Table 15-2.
Recent Improvements in Railroad Services

Piggyback

Characteristics
Carrying truck trailers on specially designed flatcars.

Advantages
Provides the flexibility of trucking by offering portal-to-portal service, and may cost less than trucking. For example, shipping a loaded truck trailer from the Midwest to the West Coast by rail costs about half that of using highways. By using a combination rail plus truck movement there is no need for constant loading and unloading.

Pool Cars

Characteristics
"Pooling" small shipments of groups of shippers in a single area so that they can be shipped as a full car.

Advantages
This combining of shipments permits greater speed of delivery and the utilization of lower carload rates.

Fast Freight

Characteristics
"Fast freight" service for perishable or high-value items, with certain trains organized for such expedited service.

Advantages
This can be competitive in speed with trucks; however, shippers and receivers must be located near rail lines for this advantage to be realized.

Diversion in Transit

Characteristics
Allowing redirection of carloads already in transit.

Advantages
Gives flexibility to the shipper who can make last-minute decisions

according to demand-and-supply conditions; especially useful for perishable agricultural commodities which may be shipped in the general direction of the market without the specifics designated until later.

Transit Privilege

Characteristics
Permitting raw materials to be shipped from their original source to a processing plant and then on to users at a lower "through" rate, as long as this is in the same general direction. Especially important to the flour-milling industry.

Advantages
Cost savings and expediting of processing and physical handling.

Transloading Privilege

Characteristics
Parts of an original carload shipment can be delivered to two or more destinations. This is done by moving the full car to a close point to the various destinations and then reloading the parts of the shipment into "less than carload" size deliveries.

Advantages
Makes LCL (less than carload) size deliveries more feasible in cost and time.

Piggyback service, in which truck trailers are hauled on railroad flat cars, merits additional discussion. (Truck trailers are also placed on ships and barges and on air cargo planes, and this is known as "fishy-back" and "birdy-back" respectively.) The importance of this innovation can be seen in the amount that railroads are spending to improve piggyback facilities. The Rock Island Lines, for example, opened a $1-million piggyback terminal in Houston, permitting trailers coming into the terminal to be unloaded immediately and taken directly to the customer's door. Trailers and containers can be loaded or unloaded in two minutes by means of a mobile crane with a lift capacity of 90,000 pounds. Second-morning delivery is offered to Houston from points as far away as Chicago.[10] Over long distances, piggyback service is faster than movement over highways, since it is not affected by traffic or road conditions or driver rest stops.

Trucks

Despite the defensive efforts of railroads to improve service and prevent erosion of demand, trucks have made major inroads. And trucks offer certain important advantages. They are very flexible and can transport goods wherever there are roads and usually in much less time and with less danger of breakage than rails. Trucks are a

[10] "Common Carrier Capabilities," *Transportation & Distribution Management,* March 1970, p. 27.

particularly vital mode of transportation for moving small lots of goods for short distances, and can often charge even lower rates than railroads in these circumstances. It is doubtful if railroads will be able to wrest much of the present freight handling away from trucks. However, for bulk goods moving more than short distances, the rails have a nearly unassailable position, except for the inland waterways.

In their efforts to be more efficient, and in the process compete even harder against railroads, truckers perennially attempt to increase the payload a vehicle can carry. This is not easy since some states, particularly in the East, are reluctant to permit large trucks on the public highways. But encroachments continue to be made that may presage developments to come and depict the effectiveness and self-interest of pressure groups in a pluralistic society.

As an example, the Florida Sunshine Parkway, a toll road running from central Florida to Miami, in 1967 began permitting "double bottom" truck-trailers up to 110 feet in length. The railroad industry and the American Automobile Association have opposed these giant trucks, the AAA because of the hazard to road safety, the railroad industry because trucks are already more efficient than the railroads would like them to be. So far, the Florida Trucking Association has the stronger lobby, and the question is whether other states will follow the lead of Florida in legalizing bigger trucks.[11]

Waterways

Water transportation is the lowest-cost method and is widely used for bulky products such as steel, iron ore, grain, sand, coal, and so forth—products also important to railroads. Barges ply the inland waterways, ore boats the Great Lakes, and with the completion of the St. Lawrence Seaway in 1959, ocean transport can reach 2,300 miles into the heartland of the United States.

Water transport, although the least costly method, is usually the slowest, and therefore is limited to nonperishable goods. It also has seasonal limitations because winter ice completely stops shipping, not only on the navigable rivers, but even on the Great Lakes. Rather surprisingly, the St. Lawrence Seaway has never generated the tonnage predicted for it. Unit trains (entire trains hauling one commodity, such as iron ore or grain) have come close to matching the costs of shipping on a laker in the Seaway, and can do it three or four times faster.[12]

Containerization (containerized freight). Containerization is an innovation in ocean shipping—it also is being used by other transportation modes—that may revolutionize physical distribution over long distances. Modular-sized containers geared closely to order size, and

[11] "Big-rig Truckers Roll Into Battle," *Business Week,* March 21, 1970, p. 136.
[12] "Dollar Dilemma on the St. Lawrence," *Business Week,* May 23, 1970, pp. 78–79.

Containerization, which began with shipping, has spread to other forms of transportation. *Courtesy American Airlines.*

even truck trailers, are being carried on ships, some of which are specially designed "container" ships.

Substantial advantages are offered. Piece-by-piece handling of individual items is eliminated as is the need for checks at transfer points. Labor per unit of cargo thus can be dramatically reduced; this means less time in port and a faster turnaround for ships, thereby avoiding skyrocketing port handling expenses. Packing can be done at the producer's plant, with the contents remaining sealed to the consignee's door, resulting in less theft, less breakage, and consequently lower insurance rates.

Actually, not all of these benefits have been realized. The issue of containerization has brought serious labor strife to some ports; dock workers fear it will cause their extinction. Theft has not been entirely eliminated; the entire crate may now be taken instead of a smaller lot. And if the container is improperly packed, damage can be severe in transit (but not realized until opened at the buyer's premises). Standardization of containers also presents problems.

Universal standards have been prescribed for better handling and storage, but some customers reject the stipulated standard sizes as not fitting their needs. Furthermore, containers are costly and sometimes have to be returned to the point of origin for reuse.

Nevertheless, containerization already is becoming a major factor. A 50-acre container complex has been built in Los Angeles. By 1969, 38 container ships were operating in the North Atlantic alone. (This may not seem particularly significant until one learns that a single container ship is the equivalent of six "break-bulk" vessels—the standard freighters.) Ports around the world are investing heavily in new facilities to speed up handling of containers and to attract the container-ship "armada."[13]

Pipelines

Natural gas and petroleum are transported primarily by pipeline, especially from Texas to the Midwest. The Alaska pipeline now under construction will greatly increase the volume of oil moved in this way. This is a less costly transportation mode than railroads, but more so than water transportation. Accordingly, the East Coast market for petroleum products is served by ships.

Air Freight

Shipping by air is the most expensive method of transporting products; it is also the fastest. High-value, low-weight goods and those of a perishable nature (such as lobsters and high fashions) are likely candidates for air shipment; replacement industrial parts—emergency shipments—are rushed by air, with auto parts the largest category of such industrial items. Even produce such as California strawberries and asparagus, and Hawaiian papayas, are moving more frequently by plane.[14] Table 15-3 shows the top ten commodities moved by a major airline in 1969 and 20 years before. In 1949 the top ten commodities accounted for from 80 to 90 percent of freight traffic; in 1969 the top ten accounted for about 50 percent.[15]

Facilitating Transportation Agencies

Several other means of transporting goods often are important for small shipments. Parcel post mail is used extensively for such prod-

[13] For articles on containerization, see: "Containers Widen Their World," *Business Week,* January 7, 1967, pp. 88–90; "Whither Containers: Full Speed Ahead via All Trade Routes," *Business Abroad,* July 1969, pp. 31–34; "Global Container-port System Taking Shape," *Via Port of New York,* November 1969, pp. 12–30; "Containerization on Review at America's Container Capital," ibid., July, 1969, pp. 2–6.

[14] "Air Cargo Sees a Higher Ceiling," *Business Week,* May 13, 1967, pp. 106–10.

[15] *1970 Air Transport Facts & Figures* (Washington, D.C.: Air Transport Association of America, 1970), p. 6.

Table 15-3.
Ten Top Commodities Moving in Domestic Air Freight
(based on revenue ton-miles)

1949	1969
1. Cut flowers	1. Auto and motorcycle parts
2. Baby chicks	2. Printed matter
3. Amusement and coin-operated vending machines	3. Nonelectrical machinery
4. Machine parts	4. Electrical machinery
5. Auto parts	5. Clothing
6. Heating equipment and parts	6. Cut flowers
7. Blood plasma	7. Metal manufactures
8. Fresh vegetables	8. Appliances
9. Mushrooms	9. Strawberries
10. Fish oil	10. Plastics

Source: *1970 Air Transport Facts & Figures* (Washington, D.C.: Air Transport Association of America, 1970), pp. 6–7.

ucts as costume jewelry and toiletries, in which the weight and size are small. Railway express and air express services are available for small shipments where fast delivery is needed and where the freight cost is low in relation to the value of the goods.

Freight forwarders are often used for small shipments. They are transportation wholesalers—they do not own their own transportation facilities—and their main function is to accumulate small shipments from various shippers into carload and truckload quantities, thereby obtaining lower transportation rates. They are particularly important for goods in the export market.

**MARKETING
IN
ACTION**

Handling Small Shipments—United Parcel Service, Competitor of the U. S. Postal Service
The small-shipments problem has plagued American business because few carriers have been willing to take on such shipments without exorbitant prices. The Post Office Department (now the U. S. Postal Service) has catered to such "freight nobody wants," with its parcel post service. So also does United Parcel Service (UPS), a privately owned commercial trucker. After paying $45 million in federal income taxes in 1973 (the U. S. Postal Service pays no taxes and indeed had a deficit of $1.5 billion, including subsidies, for the same period), UPS had a net profit of $57 million.

UPS offers rates competitive with parcel post, but additional services are offered. For example, a pickup driver calls automatically each day at the shipper's premises without regard to the size of the business; a weekly service charge entitles the shipper to this call each day whether or not any packages are to be sent out. Next-day delivery is provided within 150 miles with prompt service to more distant points. Deliveries are made directly to the premises of the consignee whether he is located on an upper floor, in a basement, an office, or any other location. If for any reason a delivery cannot be completed on the first call, a second and, if necessary, a third attempt is made without additional charge.

In addition, the so-called "Blue Label Service" is available cross country. This combines regular UPS pickup and delivery plus cross-country transit by jet. "Blue Label Service" is available at rates not much higher than insured ground parcel post.

SOURCES: *Transportation & Distribution Management*, April 1972, p. 22; and "Break Up the Post Office," *Barron's*, November 25, 1974, p. 7.

For thought and discussion:

In what ways would you surmise UPS is more efficient than the Postal Service?

What obstacles do you think prevent the Postal Service from obtaining such efficiency?

Transportation Rate Structure

Transportation rates of common carriers, such as railroads and major truck lines, present some of the most complex aspects of transportation. A *common carrier* must maintain regular service and accept merchandise from any shipper, being franchised by a government regulatory body which usually must give permission for service or rate changes. *Contract carriers* are less regulated, do not maintain regular schedules, and work under contract for a particular shipper for an agreed charge and length of time. With thousands of types of products moving between thousands of points of origin and destination, goods for rate determination are grouped according to bulk, weight, value, and difficulty of handling.

Most manufactured goods move under *class rates*, of which there are some 10,000 rail freight classifications. Ton-mile charges are less as the length of haul increases because terminal handling costs remain about the same regardless of distance. Complications arise in applying these rates as thousands of new rates are filed with the Interstate Commerce Commission each year, and a slight change in description may move a product from one class to another.

Commodity rates have been developed for most heavy and bulky goods which move in large volume—goods such as sand, gravel, iron ore, lumber, grains, and other agricultural products. Commodity rates are usually lower per ton-mile than class rates because of the lower value of products shipped. A *blanket rate* is a special type of commodity rate in which the same rate applies regardless of distance carried, the objective being to encourage greater distribution and consumption of the particular commodity. California citrus fruit comes under the blanket rate structure, with the same charge to all points east of an arbitrary line drawn roughly north and south from Denver, Colorado. Thereby, California fruit can be marketed on the East Coast at the same cost as in the Midwest. In order to meet truck competition, railroads have granted *exception rates*—special lower charges—in certain territories. Railroads move about 85 percent of their freight under commodity rates, 5 percent under class rates, and 10 percent under the special or exception rates.

These rates are quoted for carloads (CL), truckloads (TL), and less than carload (LCL), and less than truckload (LTL). Carload and truckload are considerably lower per item (often less than half as high) than the LCL and LTL rates. This reflects the additional time and effort involved in combining the shipments into a rail car or truck. This substantial difference often makes it advantageous to ship goods by carload quantity to wholesalers and/or branch warehouses located close to markets, before distributing in smaller quantities to individual customers.

With the maze of transportation rates, the different alternatives available for shipment, the many exceptions (and the possibility of negotiating for still more exceptions), and the continual flood of rate changes (more than 150,000 rates changes are made annually), the task of plotting the most efficient mode and route of transportation is difficult, yet presents opportunities for cost savings.

STORAGE

Storing provides time utility: goods are held between the time of production and the time of final use. Naturally a cost is incurred whether the goods are stored in public warehouses or whether the producer or buyer stores in his own warehouse or other facilities. But despite the cost and risk factors involved, storing offers certain advantages.

Reasons for Storage

Storage may be necessary simply to have enough stock on hand to meet normal buyer demands for colors, sizes, styles, and various quality levels; if a sale is to be made, in many instances the goods must be immediately available or else the buyer will go elsewhere. Storing is also important when production and demand are not compatible. Most agricultural products are harvested only once or twice a year; yet demand is uniform, and storage may enable it to be satisfied throughout the year. An inverse to this situation occurs with goods subject to seasonal demand, such as Christmas cards, skis, bathing suits, and the like. If production runs can be scheduled uniformly throughout the year, lowered production costs may more than offset storage costs. Sometimes storing is necessary because adequate transportation is not available at the time of production. Many commodities shipped by water transportation need to be held until the ice goes in the spring. Rail transportation becomes choked during the harvest season and may necessitate short-term storage. Winter may delay shipments of liquid products, such as chemicals and toiletries, which are subject to danger of freezing en route. Some goods need to be stored until properly aged; cheese, some liquors, and wines are examples of products that gain in value through aging (in this example, storing creates form utility).

Storage may also be used as a marketing tool to reduce costs or to gain higher prices. A firm can often lower unit costs by volume purchasing; storage facilitates this opportunity to buy in such quantities, although the cost savings should be carefully weighed against the consequent increased handling and investment costs. It is not uncommon for products to be withheld from the market in order to get better prices. The federal government has consistently had various programs to stockpile, not only agricultural commodities but also certain metals.

Shifting the Storage Function to the Channel

Contrary pressures and/or incentives are frequently exerted by various channel members to shift the storage or warehousing activities to someone else. Firms near the end of the channel—retailers and some wholesalers—commonly attempt to shift the function back to the manufacturer, by small-quantity buying, or selling from samples (as is common in retail furniture). On the other hand, manufacturers may provide their customers with special inducements to maintain larger inventories, such as quantity discounts, prepaying transportation on large shipments, and terms of sale that make possible delayed payments. The latter is common with seasonal goods, such as toys, in which the retailer may take delivery in the summer, but have 90 days or more in which to pay for the goods.

The ability and willingness to accept more of the storage function can be a powerful competitive tool for a seller. By maintaining a large assortment of goods in advanced warehouse locations, a seller is able to offer quicker service to his customers and also is more likely to have the right goods in stock to meet most demands. This providing of quick delivery with few "out of stocks" may well win out over other sellers who may have better products or do more aggressive advertising. This is particularly true, for example, in the case of college textbook publishers. Books must arrive by a particular date, the beginning of classes, and the company that consistently gets the books to the bookstore on time has a strong competitive edge. We must not make the mistake of assuming that the only effective competition involves product features, pricing, or promotional efforts.

Facilities for Storing

Warehouses are the most typical storage facility for major quantities of merchandise. These may be classified as private or branch warehouses, and public warehouses. *Private warehouses* are owned by individual companies for their own storage and distribution uses. Many of these are designed to store specific products on a continuing basis. A firm needs to approach a decision carefully of whether to maintain its own warehouse(s). This is a substantial fixed cost and one which may limit flexibility if the firm should later see the need or desirability of passing some of the storing function on to its customers; a warehouse no longer needed because of shifting demand or other distribution arrangements is often difficult to lease or sell.

Public warehouse facilities are used by firms that do not need permanent space (perhaps because of seasonal goods), that do not have a large volume of goods to store, or that wish to maintain flexibility. These public warehouses will not only store goods, but will perform other functions as well, such as inspecting, wrapping, and shipping in any size lots ordered. They provide an important financing service also, since warehouse receipts can be used as collateral when borrowing from banks. Furthermore, public warehouses take over the risk function (of course, not that dealing with unsaleability or obsolescence), being responsible for any damage or loss occurring while merchandise is in the warehouse.

Several types of public warehouses should be noted. *General-merchandise* warehouses handle merchandise of all kinds which need no special facilities. *Commodity* and *cold-storage* warehouses are specially designed, the latter for storing perishable goods such as fresh fruits and vegetables, while the former is typified by the huge grain elevators. *Bonded* warehouses are used for storing certain goods subject to particular payments of taxes or duties to the government; imported goods, liquors, and cigarettes require a tax to be paid before any goods are released.

Toward More Efficiency in Storage. Storage facilities and the physical handling of goods present opportunities for greater marketing efficiency. Any stored goods must be handled at least twice: once to place them in the warehouse, and again to remove them. In order to expedite this, modern warehouses are needed, with advanced equipment and carefully designed layouts. The computer offers substantial economies, especially in order handling, by permitting faster order processing and record keeping.

The newest warehouses are single-story with easy entry and exit of many products simultaneously. Single-level designs eliminate the need for elevators and can utilize effectively such advanced equipment as fork-lift trucks, conveyor systems, electric hoists, and hydraulic ramps. Battery-operated motor scooters and even roller-skating order pickers have been found to be practical and time saving. Overtones of science fiction are found in such warehouses, with "man-amplification machines," which combine the "delicacy of human perception with the power of a fork truck" being developed by G.E. and several small companies.[16] Warehouse layout attention is becoming focused not so much on saving space, which usually results in narrow aisles, but rather in speed of handling and finding particular products. Operations research techniques, particularly linear programming, are being used to improve the physical layout of merchandise in warehouses.[17]

Despite this multifaceted approach to maximizing the efficiency of the storage and physical-handling function, inefficient facilities remain: old, multistoried warehouses located on narrow congested downtown streets, with material handling a costly operation, both internally and externally. There is a continual need for marketers to seek more efficient storage and handling. An investment in physical-handling facilities can be as worthwhile as investment in plant and equipment, and in the long run may be a significant competitive tool, increasing sales through lower costs and faster service.

The Distribution Center. The distribution-center concept is a modification of warehousing. Where no storage is needed—that is, where time utility is not a factor—then an integrated system for the flow of products to customers can improve physical-handling efficiency. Essentially, the orientation is different from that of typical warehouses: movement, not storage. As products are assembled at the distribution center, a deliberate effort is made to keep inventories as low as possible and to handle orders as quickly as possible, thereby having a high stock turnover. Order filling and billing is aided by the use of the latest techniques of data processing, inventory-control systems, and materials-handling equipment.

The usual effect of putting the distribution center idea into operation has been to concentrate inventories in fewer places, carefully chosen to serve several major markets, rather than one. As a result, firms have been able to eliminate warehouses. For example, Libby, McNeill & Libby eliminated 214 warehouses and was able to

---

[16] Kenneth Marshall, "The Man Amplifiers are Coming," *Transportation and Distribution Management,* March 1970, p. 23.

[17] Ronald H. Ballou, "Improving the Physical Layout of Merchandise in Warehouses," *Journal of Marketing,* July 1967, pp. 60–64.

greatly improve efficiency and reduce costs with five distribution centers.

INVENTORY CONTROL

Closely related to the storage function is that of inventory. Important as good warehousing and physical-handling facilities are, unless accompanied by an effective inventory-control system, certain flaws will occur and persist: too much inventory, or too little inventory. A balance must be struck between these two extremes. With too high an inventory, unnecessary goods take up storage space, increase the required investment, and face greater risks of obsolescence, price

This photograph shows an inventory control system in a retail store in Canada. Computers compare actual stock with current demand levels, automatically calculate the quantity of each item to be reordered, and record the order data on tape cassettes for daily transmission to the company's head office. *Courtesy Burroughs Corporation.*

declines, destruction, and the like. Naturally, costs are higher and profits lower than under a better-balanced inventory. On the other hand, too little inventory, which manifests itself in "out of stocks" so that customer orders cannot be shipped, results in loss of sales and customer goodwill; if this occurs too frequently, customers may be lost permanently.

Unfortunately, the total amount of goods found in inventory is seldom a sufficient criterion of "in stock" condition and ability to fill customer orders. A heavy inventory of goods—whether in a producer's warehouse, or in a wholesaler's or retailer's stock—more often than not reflects an unbalanced condition: a preponderance of slow-moving items, while fast sellers are "out of stock." An "80-20" rule often holds with inventories: 20 percent of the goods produce 80 percent of the sales. Careful attention and control is needed to assure that the fast-selling 20 percent are replenished in time to meet customers' demands.

The computer has shown great promise in inventory control, both in reducing the size of inventories and in decreasing out-of-stocks. Some manufacturers have data links between sales offices, plants, and distribution and shipping points and are closely coordinating production, warehousing, and shipping. Big retailers with their huge inventories are also finding the computer useful in inventory control. Sears, the largest retailer, has taken the biggest strides with computer technology.

**MARKETING
IN
ACTION**

Inventory Control Via Computer Technology, at Sears
Sears is instituting a $750 million computer that ties together
836 stores, more than 1,200 catalog sales offices, warehouses, and
business offices, plus 1,000 of Sears's largest suppliers. Among other
uses, the system provides instant national sales data for the company's central buyers to assure an optimum product mix in the stores.
As an example of how it works, take a coffeepot:

When the pot is received in the store, an automatic ticket-maker produces a ticket with the coffeepot's color, price, stock number, and department number.

When sold, the coffeepot data is recorded by the salesclerk, and this along with other coffeepot sales data of the day is stored in a minicomputer until nightfall when it is automatically transferred to one of twenty-two regional data centers where the IBM computers process the information. If the day's coffeepot sales lower the inventory below a predetermined point, the computer automatically prints a purchase order. At the same time, the sales data are channeled to Sears's Chicago headquarters where national sales information is compiled.

The system eventually will involve more than 30,000 electronic cash registers, more than 640 minicomputers, and 33 large IBM 370 main computers.

SOURCE: "How Giant Sears Grows and Grows," *Business Week*, December 16, 1972, pp. 54–55.

For thought and discussion:
Do you think there are any kinds of merchandise for which such a computerized inventory system might not be particularly useful?
Would you expect this inventory system to prevent all merchandise "outs"?
Why or why not?

LOCATION OF FACILITIES

Usually the location of a plant or a warehouse has been considered a problem of production: proximity to a labor force and to raw materials was the major consideration. Now it appears that in some cases plant locations closer to particular markets may be more desirable in reducing costs and improving service, and in providing a more optimum assortment of goods. The location of warehouses, in particular, plays a substantial role in physical distribution effectiveness and economy. But before the warehouse location can be determined, a more basic decision must be made: Should the inventory be centralized or dispersed throughout the market?

Centralizing, or concentrating, the inventory in one or a few warehouses usually permits greater efficiency in warehousing and materials handling; inventory can be better controlled, and this usually results in a reduced inventory requirement and fewer "outs." However, if the market is widespread, then transportation charges and longer in-transit time from a single centralized warehouse will make this unattractive to customers.

One solution to problems of concentrating rather than dispersing inventories relates to the 80-20 rule mentioned in the previous section. Where the need for fast service makes branch warehousing desirable, only fast-moving goods would be allocated to these warehouses. Slower-selling goods would then be centralized, being carried solely in the main warehouse. A careful screening of products and a continual analysis of demand patterns may permit better customer service without incurring the needless expense of stocking all items at all locations.

Throughout this chapter, areas have been noted where the physical handling of goods could be improved. Some of these areas have been exogenous to the firm—that is, they are part of the environment in which it functions. For example, trucking may represent a high-cost mode of transportation; yet the slowness of rail may preclude its use until and unless railroads can improve their efficiency.

Improvement in efficiency can be achieved by reducing costs or delivery time, or both. If delivery time can be reduced while costs remain the same, then efficiency is improved; similarly, if costs can be reduced without lengthening delivery time, then efficiency is improved. Ideally, both could be improved, although this is unlikely without a technical breakthrough in transportation modes. But the individual firm, in many instances, has ample opportunities to improve its distribution efficiency. Let us examine some of these.[18]

1. *Revising channels of distribution.* Sometimes a firm is wedded to traditional channels of distribution long after they have become less efficient than others; in any case, a reevaluation of existing and available channels may well be in order for many firms. For example, distributing through certain wholesalers, who over the years have become marginal and not progressive, may add as much as 10 to 20 percent to distribution costs. Sometimes it may be desirable to revamp channels so that major retailers are given direct distribution (without the use of wholesalers), with wholesalers being reserved only for smaller retail outlets. And sometimes the wisest course is to weed out the smaller customers (even though some sales might be lost) and concentrate on those who are more profitable. A distribution cost analysis, which will be discussed in chapter 17, is a necessary adjunct to such a decision.

2. *Simplifying the system.* A producer should always be alert to any possibility for simplifying the distribution system. While this relates to revising the channels of distribution, we are primarily thinking here of eliminating field warehouses wherever possible. The more the physical handling of goods can be reduced, the more cost savings can result, provided that customer service does not suffer unduly as a result. As mentioned earlier, the factors of service and of costs must be carefully weighed.

3. *Reducing inventories.* If some warehouses can be eliminated, less inventory should be needed. However, inventories can be streamlined and inbalances corrected without necessarily eliminating warehouses if their proximity to markets is judged desirable. Careful analysis of rates of sale for the various items carried might well lead to the centralizing of slower sellers with consequent reduction in total inventory.

4. *Packaging considerations.* Packaging design that considers

[18] Part of the following section is adapted from Stewart, pp. 68–70.

transportation, shipping, and storage needs can improve physical-handling efficiency. In particular, package sizes should be uniform wherever possible; sometimes they can be made smaller for easier handling and storage; the product identification often can be more strategically placed and better described.

5. *Receptivity to innovations.* Technological innovations can afford more efficient material handling, as can better space utilization, order processing, and the like. It must however be realized that the use of advanced equipment and procedures is not always justified. For example, not every firm can effectively use a computer; the volume of business may not be sufficient to justify the additional expense incurred. Sometimes the best route to increasing efficiency is simply to analyze carefully and seek maximum efficiency from the present system.

The Total-Cost Concept

In seeking greater efficiency, the total physical distribution system should be considered, with all variables measured in combination with one another.[19] It is not unusual under such a total approach for costs in a particular sector to go up, but the gain in total efficiency is the criterion. Warehousing cost, freight cost, and customer service are all interrelated. The promoters of air freight have been quick to point out that air freight, even though costing substantially more than other modes, may reduce some costs so that the total cost of distribution is not appreciably higher, while delivery is substantially improved. Indeed, if storage can be eliminated by means of air freight, the trade-off of costs may more than justify its use. More generally, strategically located warehouses may offer cost benefits and service improvement which should be considered by many firms.

Figure 15-1 presents a hypothetical example of the benefits in cost savings and service improvement which may result from the judicious use of a warehouse (or a distribution center).

If in Figure 15-1 we take the hypothetical case of a furniture manufacturer selling standardized living room sets to retailers, the cost advantage to be gained from the use of a branch warehouse would be over 20 percent ($50 per set without a warehouse, versus $39 per set with a warehouse), assuming that the average set remained in the warehouse for one month or less. This cost savings might be kept by the manufacturer, or it might be passed on to the retailer in the form of lower price or lower shipping charges. This

---

[19] A sampling of the literature dealing with a systems view of physical distribution is: Alan H. Gepfert, "Business Logistics for Better Profit Performance," *Harvard Business Review*, November–December 1968, pp. 75–84; R. P. Neuschel, "Physical Distribution—Forgotten Frontier," *Harvard Business Review*, March–April 1967, pp. 125–34; J. L. Heskett, "A Missing Link in Physical Distribution Systems Design," *Journal of Marketing*, October 1966, pp. 37–41.

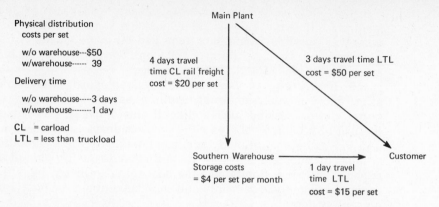

Figure 15-1. Cost and Service Advantages of a Field Warehouse (hypothetical example of set of furniture)

saving is gained by the use of carload rail shipments into the warehouse, rather than less than truckload shipments from the factory to the customer. Perhaps an even greater advantage in generating sales and customer satisfaction would be the shortening of the in-transit delivery time from 3 days to 1 day.

A similar hypothetical model (the correct figures would need to be ascertained for each individual case) might be developed for the use of air freight versus other modes of transportation. Figure 15-2 illustrates such a hypothetical case for a manufacturer of automobile mufflers.

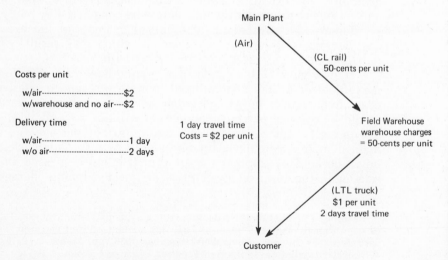

Figure 15-2. Cost and Service Advantage of the Use of Air Freight for Mufflers (hypothetical example)

In this case it is assumed that the manufacturer would need to have warehouse stocks in order to serve his customers satisfactorily. Such a warehouse creates storage and handling costs, inventory costs due to interest charges or investment tied up which could be used profitably in some other way, as well as some risk (fire, theft, breakage). With air freight, a single stock kept at the plant would probably be smaller than combined field stocks, and individual orders quickly filled and sent by air. In the example in Figure 15-2 it is assumed that the relative costs of air versus truck and rail using a branch warehouse would be about the same. However, delivery time is cut in half—from 2 days to 1 day—and this could be an important service consideration with certain items, such as car mufflers.

It must be stressed again that these examples are hypothetical; the actual relative advantages of the various transportation modes and the use of warehouses would need to be calculated for each firm. The point to be made, however, is that distribution costs should be considered for the total system rather than merely for certain sectors of it.

Importance of Customer Satisfaction

It is easy to become wound up in cost structures and the search for greater efficiency in the physical distribution process. But the importance of customer service, however intangible, should not be shunted aside in favor of more "urgent" matters.

Good customer service and its concomitant effect on customer satisfaction may be viewed as a product of these four factors:

1. On-time delivery according to customer expectations and needs.
2. Costs of distribution in a reasonable relationship to competitive modes, and in line with customer expectations.
3. Minimization of damage in transit and handling.
4. Prompt and courteous handling of any service problems that inevitably will arise.

None of these factors should be sacrificed in the quest for faster or cheaper distribution; they form the basis for cemented and mutually satisfactory long-term relationships.

For good customer service there must be sound control. For this control to be effective, procedures should be established for prompt feedback to responsible executives of service problems and customer complaints. Creative efforts are needed in this area. Usually some centralized and standardized procedures need to be established both to obtain service feedback and to handle complaints. One suggestion for such a service-management program is

(1) Define the fundamental elements of service; (2) determine the customer's viewpoint—i.e., what is important to him; (3)

develop a competitive service "package" that incorporates the results of the first two steps; (4) develop a program to "sell" service; (5) market-test the program, and (6) establish performance standards and controls.[20]

Whatever procedures are established, the important point is that customer service and resulting satisfaction must not be ignored or given lower priority than other operational matters.

Physical Distribution Manager

In order to coordinate the total physical distribution process of a firm, a change in organization may be required. The typical fragmentation of physical distribution functions is shown in Figure 15-3. It can be seen that a substantial part of these functions is not even under the control of the marketing department. One survey found that in 43 percent of the firms, the marketing department did not have any responsibility for physical distribution; in most of these firms there was not even any participation in discussions regarding this phase of marketing.[21]

Some companies are unifying these activities under a single manager of distribution, who is frequently responsible to the top marketing manager. Where the physical distribution activity is well organized into a separate administrative group responsible for the planning and operation, marketing and sales personnel are thereby

Purchasing

Inbound transportation

Manufacturing

Inventory management
Packaging and packing
Receiving and shipping
Plant warehousing
Outbound transportation

Control

Order processing
Data processing

Marketing

Field warehouses
Customer service

Figure 15-3. Traditional Fragmentation of Physical Distribution Functions

---

[20] William B. Wagner, "The Complaint Menace," *Transportation and Distribution Management,* March 1971, pp. 15–16. See also Stanley S. Stasch, "Distribution Systems Analysis: Methods and Problems," *The Logistics Review,* March–April 1968, pp. 7–34; P. Ronald Stephenson and Ronald P. Willett, "Selling With Physical Distribution Service," *Business Horizons,* December 1968, pp. 75–85; John F. Stolle, "How to Manage Physical Distribution," *Harvard Business Review,* July–August 1967, pp. 93–100.

[21] Robert E. Weigand, *Business Topics,* Summer 1962, pp. 70–71.

freed to devote more attention to the basic responsibility of demand creation.

Challenges for Logistics Management

The need for greater efficiency in the physical aspects of marketing is real, and many of the solutions are tangible (unlike solutions to many other marketing problems). Some improvements were mentioned: containerization, air freight, modern one-story warehouses and distribution centers, advanced materials-handling equipment, operations research techniques, and the use of computers. More undoubtedly are forthcoming.

But advances have been spotty: some firms have been progressive while others still embrace archaic methods and facilities. Some transportation modes have not been progressive or have been restrained by unions or by regulatory agencies. Labor costs have often risen much faster than efficiency owing partly but not entirely to especially strong unions in transportation. Railroads, in particular, have had difficulty in improving their efficiency. Mergers to avoid duplication of efforts had been touted as a major solution to rail problems. But after the merger with the New York Central in 1968, the largest railroad, the Penn Central, was plagued by "problems of management, problems of coordination, problems of service, and problems of customer dissatisfaction,"[22] culminating in bankruptcy.

There are also challenges in the area of social policy. Trucks and air freight are adding flexibility and speed to the handling of goods. However, there is a limit to how many more trucks and how much larger trucks society can tolerate on our public highways. And air traffic is reaching a point of maximum possible utilization unless facilities and new airports are forthcoming.[23]

QUESTIONS AND PROBLEMS

1. Differentiate between a warehouse and a distribution center.
2. What kind of utility is provided by "storage"? Why is this important? For what kinds of goods?
3. Underdeveloped countries usually are characterized by poor distribution facilities. As a marketer seeking to tap such markets, what positive contribution if any might you be able to make in such a situation?
4. Customer service tends to be a relatively neglected aspect of physical-distribution activity in some firms—that is, any problem or complaints

[22] "High-Cost Money Hurts the Penn Central," *Business Week*, June 6, 1970, pp. 106–07.
[23] John A. Volpe, "To Build a Truly Integrated . . . System," "Presidential Issue," *Handing & Shipping*, Fall 1969, p. 12.

tend to be shunted aside in view of more "pressing" matters. What prescriptions would you make for such a situation?

5. Should the major objective of any physical-distribution function in a firm be to operate at the lowest possible total cost? Discuss.

6. Is it probable that technological innovations or breakthroughs—such as containerization—will lead to a greatly decreased cost of physical distribution and handling in the coming years? Why or why not?

7. The myriad of transportation rates makes it difficult to find the most efficient and least costly route of transportation (while it does frequently present opportunities for cost savings through new evaluations or different approaches). How do you account for these thousands of rates? Can you propose any way to simplify this situation?

8. Explain the philosophy of the total cost concept. What changes from traditional methods of distribution has it motivated?

Project

In the last decade some railroads have faltered badly—Penn Central for example—while others have prospered. Using library facilities, identify successful and unsuccessful railroads, and try to ascertain some of the factors accounting for the difference.

Exercise in Creativity

Develop as many ideas as you can for providing more customer service on the part of (1) railroads (freight), (2) trucks, and (3) buses. Then consider any trade-off in terms of higher costs. Do any of your proposed new customer services still seem desirable?

Role-playing Case

You are the traffic manager for a department store. As such it is your responsibility to expedite incoming shipments of merchandise from vendors, and also to minimize incoming freight charges. Today you are called to the merchandising vice-president's office.

"Matt, have you seen last quarter's freight charges?" (Mr. Begg is not one to waste time on trivial conversation.)

"Yes, I have."

"What explanation do you have for this 150 percent increase over last year?"

"This reflects major increases in freight rates—the rise in oil costs mostly, but also some new labor contracts by transportation workers . . ."

"I see." Mr. Begg strokes his chin. "Do you have any suggestions for us as to how we might lessen these costs?"

How would you answer Mr. Begg?

What would be the implications of your suggestions?

CHAPTER 16

INTERNATIONAL

MARKETING

OPPORTUNITIES

The lure of foreign markets is unmistakable. Besides representing new profit opportunities, they offer challenge and discovery. At the least, production surpluses may be disposed of, but more intriguing is the possibility of creating burgeoning new markets. There are risks in foreign marketing, however, and the complexities of marketing in diverse and foreign environments can be formidable. A firm usually must modify its U. S. strategy if it is to tap what may be a very different market. The following terms will be encountered in this chapter:

licensing	European Common Market
tariffs	dumping
nationalism	cartels
exchange controls	transfer pricing
export subsidies	international trading companies

SCOPE OF INTERNATIONAL MARKETING

World trade has been increasing at an annual average of around 10 percent, compared with a global Gross National Product (GNP) growth rate of 5 percent for the non-Communist nations. In billions of U. S. dollars, the value of world trade for the last decade has been as follows:

1962	$125 billion
1967	191 billion
1972	413 billion

Then in 1973 total exports of all countries leaped 37 percent to $566 billion. While rampant price inflation accounted for a good part of

423

this increase, still, in constant dollars the rise amounted to 13 percent.[1]

Consumers in the United States are, of course, dependent on foreign imports for such things as coffee, tea, and cocoa, chocolate and vanilla, and foods such as pineapples, certain spices, and coconuts. The energy crisis and the oil boycott of 1973–1974 made us realize the importance of imported gasoline and petroleum products. Less obvious are many components of everyday products such as television sets and automobiles, as well as the tin in tin cans.

Important as imports are in maintaining our accustomed mode of living and in providing luxuries, our exports of goods and services as a percentage of GNP have almost doubled, reaching 8 percent in 1973 versus 4 percent average for the years 1963–1967.[2]

INCENTIVES FOR DOING BUSINESS ABROAD

Many parts of the world market offer greater growth and profit opportunities than does the domestic market. For example, the GNP in Western Europe increased 77 percent between the year the Common Market was established, 1958, and 1965; during these same years, that of the United States rose only 51 percent. Rising living standards in Africa and Latin America present attractive growth prospects. In some foreign markets domestic competition is not as aggressive or sophisticated and is vulnerable to market entry by U. S. firms.

Foreign operations have often contributed more than the profits coming from larger domestic operations. For example, B. F. Goodrich Co. generated 28 percent of its sales in 1973 from foreign operations, but 33 percent of its profits.[3]

For some companies the potential for profitable foreign expansion remains undiminished. Coca-Cola has long been a force in overseas markets: in the early 1960s it had generated 35 percent of its sales overseas and 40 percent of its profits. But expansion continues, into the communist bloc and even into the Soviet Union.[4]

Expectation of increasing profits is the major incentive to engage in foreign trade. Export markets can serve as outlets for surplus production or can enable a firm to maximize its production efficiency.

[1] The above statistics are derived from: International Monetary Fund, *International Financial Statistics*, vol. 22, no. 9 (September 1969); and General Agreement on Tariffs & Trade (GATT), as reported in "The Future Shape of Trade," *Business Week*, July 6, 1974, pp. 112–13.   fn

[2] "The Future Shape of Trade," p. 113.

[3] "New Era for the Multinationals," *Business Week*, July 6, 1974, p. 74.

[4] "Coke's Formula: Keep the Image Fresh," *Business Week*, April 25, 1970, pp. 66–74.

Sales and production may be stabilized to cushion the effect of seasonal and cyclical variations.

Probably not the least of the incentives to expand internationally is the desire of a firm to become a world company, to expand the horizons of operation to the farthest limits. The promise of opportunity and worldwide challenge can have great appeal for stockholders, employees, management recruits, as well as customers and suppliers. Undeniably there are risks in individual markets; yet these can often be spread by doing business in diverse markets.

THE FOREIGN ENVIRONMENT

You know of course that the environment for doing business in other countries differs from that in the United States. But firms continue to make mistakes by assuming that appeals and products successful in one country will necessarily be successful in others. Economic and demographic factors will often differ significantly; geographic conditions impose constraints; cultural considerations shape buying behavior and prejudices; and political regulations and the threat of drastic restrictions introduce additional complexities and even severe risks.

Economic and Demographic Factors

Population statistics are imperfect gauges of market potential; economic measures such as GNP and per capita national income also are too broad and may obscure the extent of significant markets. More useful are measures of distribution of income, rate of growth in buying power, and extent of available consumer financing.[5] Breakdowns of occupational categories, especially the percent of population engaged in agriculture, not only indicate economic development, since greater development usually results in a smaller proportion of the population engaged in agriculture, but can help in ascertaining probable needs and wants.

Educational levels and literacy rates are useful in estimating the demand for and acceptance of new products. In addition, the literacy rate should guide packaging and promotional decisions. A firm wishing to introduce a product in a country with a low literacy rate may be forced to rely on package illustrations rather than written description, and may find promotion through newspapers and magazines difficult. But mass promotion may not be ruled out: although Brazil has a low literacy rate (almost 50 percent, and higher in the

[5] John Fayerweather, *International Marketing*, 2d ed. (Englewood Cliffs, N.J.: Prentice-Hall, 1970), pp. 31–35.

interior), millions own TV sets. Furthermore, the widespread dissemination of transistor radios to all parts of the world has opened up an advertising medium in areas where print media are of little value.

Geographical Conditions

Consumer requirements for clothing, housing, food, recreational goods, and many other things differ depending on such geographical factors as climate, rainfall, elevation, and extent of seacoast. Geography can also impose serious logistical problems. Air is the only practical means of transportation to certain parts of South America hemmed in by mountains or jungles. In many parts of the world refrigeration is limited. Electricity is often not widely available, especially in the hinterland.

Cultural Factors

Culture, mores, and traditional ways of doing things influence and shape behavior in foreign markets in ways more subtle than geographical conditions. Packaging sometimes has to be altered to meet existing customs. One firm failed in marketing mayonnaise in Germany because the product was packaged in the jars so acceptable to U. S. consumers; Germans are accustomed to buying salad dressing in tubes. The difficulty of bucking entrenched preferences confronted Hershey in entering the Canadian market in the early 1960s. Despite being number one in the chocolate candy field in the United States, Hershey was able to capture only 1 percent of the market in Canada. The reason? Canadians lean toward European-made light milk chocolate; Hershey doggedly stuck by its traditional darker formula.[6]

Major differences can be found among neighboring countries on virtually the same cultural and economic level. Table 16-1 shows the

Table 16-1.
Average Household Consumption of Beverages (liters)

	Milk	Wine	Beer
France	103	116	28
Germany	100	7	46
Holland	153	2	11
Italy	87	95	2

Source: Le Monde, weekly overseas edition, February 15–21, 1968, p. 7.

---

[6] "Hershey's Sweet Tooth Starts Aching," Business Week, February 7, 1970, pp. 98–104.

International marketing finds familiar products in unexpected settings. *Courtesy Heinz Corporation.*

difference in average consumption of beverages for four Western European countries. The contrast in wine consumption between France and Italy, compared with Germany and Holland, could hardly be greater. These customs are unlikely to change quickly.

While some customs and tastes seem solidly entrenched, others are changing. There is increasing acceptance of ready-to-use foods and of factory-made clothing among Europeans to whom this not too long ago was heretical. And traditionally, people have been food conscious in France and shunned such things as the lowly hamburger. But now hamburger shops are spreading over Europe, gaining initial acceptance among students. The entry of Sears into Latin America led to major changes in ways of doing business in these countries and was an economic boon.

Sears in Latin America

Sears entered Latin America with the same policies and techniques it used successfully in the United States. Merchandise was substantially the same, but most of it was produced domestically rather than being imported from the United States. With only a handful of stores—at first, never more than one store in one city—Sears nevertheless forced spectacular changes in retailing over wide surrounding areas: store modernization; customer credit; changing attitudes toward customers, store personnel, suppliers, and merchandise; modern methods of pricing, of inventory control, of markdowns, of training.

But more important was the impact of Sears on the industrial framework. Selling primarily goods manufactured in these countries, Sears helped establish hundreds of local manufacturers who were assured of a market where formerly there was none. The insistence on standards of workmanship, quality, service, and delivery accelerated more progressive management techniques.

While Sears necessarily had to cater to the richer segment of the population of these countries, the vitality induced in the economy expanded the markets and contributed in no small way to the development of a more prosperous and numerous middle class in Latin America. By 1969, Sears had 74 stores in 10 Latin American countries and Spain. The table shows the growth in these overseas markets.

Growth of Sears in Latin America and Spain

Countries	Number of Stores				
	1945	1950	1955	1960	1969
Mexico	1	3	7	16	21
Brazil		2	3	9	14
Cuba		2	6	7	—
Venezuela			7	9	12
Colombia			3	6	9
Peru				2	2
Panama				2	3
Costa Rica				1	1
San Salvador				1	1
Puerto Rico				6	9
Nicaragua					1
Spain					1
Total	1	7	26	59	74

Source: Moody's Investors Service, Inc.

SOURCE: Peter Drucker, "Marketing and Economic Development," *Journal of Marketing*, January 1958, pp. 253–59; Daniel James, "Sears Roebuck's Mexican

Revolution," *Harper's*, June 1959, pp. 65–70; "Spain's Shoppers Say 'Bienvenido' to Sears," *Business Week*, April 15, 1967, pp. 92–96.

For thought and discussion:

Do you think Sears's successful Latin American policies would be successful in India? in Ethiopia? Why or why not?

Sears has had notable problems in its expansion into Spain. What factors would you hypothesize would account for this?

Political and Legal Aspects and Risks

In many parts of the world today an emerging sense of national self-interest is inducing greater government control of international marketing activities. At the least, governments are leaning toward stricter controls of foreign investment; at the extreme, actual take-overs and nationalization of foreign operations have occurred or are threatened. In other countries where the government has not actually intervened against foreign enterprises, hostile groups have sacked stores and factories. Therefore, the risks for even long-established foreign companies is not inconsiderable in the dynamics of political and social unrest. Government influences may act to impede, encourage, or replace international marketing transactions by local firms.

Government Impediments to Foreign Trade. Impediments take the form of restrictions and/or controls over imports and exports, overseas investment, profit remittance from abroad, and foreign exchange.[7] Both imports and exports may be subject to *licensing,* in which licenses would be granted for only limited amounts of goods. *Tariffs* are taxes on imports. These are generally classed as *protective tariffs,* with the object of keeping goods out of the country, and *revenue tariffs,* primarily to generate tax revenue. *Quotas* and various designated extra taxes may be imposed.

Many countries have imposed restrictions concerning the types and extent of investments which may be made in the country by foreign investors. For example, Sears, in its venture into Barcelona, contracted to stock the store heavily with goods made in Spain, to export merchandise to help Spain's trade balance, and to staff the store mostly with Spaniards.[8] Such restrictions often are part of a national plan for economic development. However, in some parts of the world, particularly Latin America, they apparently reflect a current surge of *nationalism,* as country after country tightens restrictions on foreign investors, moves to protect local businesses, and even expropriates foreign operations. International Petroleum Com-

[7] For a more complete discussion of these restrictions see Paul T. Ellsworth, *The International Economy,* 4th ed. (New York: Macmillan, 1969), Chaps. 14–15, 23.

[8] "Spain's Shoppers Say 'Bienvenido' to Sears," *Business Week,* April 15, 1967, pp. 92–96.

pany, a Standard Oil of New Jersey subsidiary, Anaconda Copper, Gulf Oil, International Telephone & Telegraph, and RCA are examples of major American firms which are being squeezed or have had operations taken over by Latin American countries.

Sometimes a country is justified in its concern about the extent of foreign investment and ownership. There has been a decade-long controversy in Canada about what should be done about massive U. S. ownership of large segments of Canadian industry. Concern about U. S. dominance has even reached the communications industry: Canadian television, which once relied almost entirely on U. S. programming, must now, by federal ruling, be 60 percent Canadian in content.[9] Such a policy is believed necessary to encourage Canadian culture and to prevent too much dependence on the United States.

Exchange controls are sometimes used to restrict international marketing through government control over the supply of, or demand for, foreign currencies. If the seller is prevented from obtaining his own currency in payment, or can obtain only a limited amount, the incentive for trading with such a country is effectively reduced. Related to exchange control are *profit-remittance restrictions*. These concern the remittance of profits of local operations to the parent company located in another country. Impediments in drawing out profits of foreign investment destroys the incentive for such investments.

Governments may actively engage in trade, directly or through agencies under their control, thereby supplementing or replacing private traders. The best examples of this are the Soviet Union and other communist countries where government monopolies handle all foreign trade. But even the United States does some state trading in the stockpiling of strategic materials, and in the purchase and sale of surplus commodities.

Not the least of problems confronting firms seeking to engage in foreign marketing is bureaucratic red tape, which can assume monumental proportions in certain countries. Brazil has been singled out:

> The former president, Costa e Silva, signed more than 4,000 laws and decrees in less than two years. His successors wrote a new constitution that was amended within a day after publication.
>
> A recent law states that foreign manufacturers can buy land for industrial plant expansion, with the approval of "competent authorities," but fails to specify who those authorities might be.
>
> A shipment of Scotch whiskey was held up for months when federal tax inspectors decided that customs officials were using a form with the wrong seal.[10]

[9] "The New Reality: Nationalism," *Time,* December 16, 1974, p. 53.

[10] "We Have More Laws Than We Can Afford," *Business Week,* January 24, 1970, p. 48.

Bribes are the time-honored method for slicing through red tape in less developed countries, but this adds to the expense and complexities and the risks of foreign marketing. Such practices are antithetical to the quest for more efficiency in marketing.

Firms have even been known to interfere in the internal politics of a country in which they are doing business and—radical as it seems—encourage overthrow of the regime. Such was the role of International Telephone & Telegraph Corporation in attempting to meddle in Chilean politics. In so doing, ITT found itself with a bad image on an international scale, which it is now attempting to improve.

MARKETING
IN
ACTION

Improving a Bad Image—International Telephone & Telegraph
Still smarting from the bad publicity of its meddling in Chilean politics, and from additional disclosure that a major executive in Belgium was linked to payoffs to a government official, ITT launched a major promotional campaign in Europe to persuade the public that it is a "responsible corporate citizen with a heart." Over $700,000 was budgeted the first year for the British campaign. Ads appeared in British newspapers and magazines pointing out that ITT subsidiary companies paid nearly $29 million in corporate taxes and contributed more than $26 million to the British balance of payments. Furthermore, ITT executives appeared on radio and TV, the company treated important journalists to expense-paid tours, and a new company magazine called *Profile* was sent to 55,000 selected opinion leaders.

Officially, the ITT campaign was designed to humanize the company: "Most people regard us as a faceless giant. People can't help but be afraid of a company when they don't know anything about it."

SOURCE: "Europe: ITT Tries to Sweeten Its Sour Image," *Business Week,* November 30, 1974, p. 44.

For thought and discussion:
Can you defend ITT's political actions?
How would you evaluate the effectiveness of this image-improving campaign?
How would you defend this expenditure to stockholders?

Encouragement of Foreign Trade. Many countries are interested in restricting international marketing for various reasons—and these are the countries that usually receive the most newspaper attention—but others see it as their best interest to encourage the development and growth of foreign trade. This is recognized as vital to the growth of the domestic economy. Often exports are given special promotional emphasis in an effort to vitalize domestic industries and/or improve the balance of payments. Even public figures, such as the royal family of England, have been used in efforts to promote a nation's products in other countries. *Export subsidies* may be granted to assure the profitability of domestic industries when exposed to international competition. The shipbuilding industry, in many countries, receives such subsidies in order to overcome cost disparities with foreign builders.[11]

Investment by foreigners may be encouraged by offering such inducements as relaxation of government restraints, repatriation guarantees, liberal depreciation, and lower taxes. Even low-cost government loans and grants and subsidies may be available to foreign investors.[12] Sometimes a company's home-country government encourages investment overseas by offering *tax credits,* and especially *investment guarantees.* For example, the Agency for International Development (AID) offers U.S. firms protection against investment losses due to expropriation, war, or currency inconvertibility in more than 60 countries. Loans to business firms, either directly from a national government, or through membership in such international financial organizations as the International Monetary Fund and the World Bank, may be available. Governments may furnish *credit insurance* covering certain commercial risks for exporters and private investors.

Information services are often provided so that firms, especially smaller ones, can make the best international marketing decisions. Trade missions may be sponsored and trade fairs and trade centers operated. Even state governments may be active in promoting international trade. Most governmental efforts to encourage trade are aimed at stimulating the growth of exports. The desirability of this from the home country's or state's point of view can be seen from official estimates for New York State in 1964 that a 10 percent increase in the state's annual exports could provide 50,000 new jobs in manufacturing and service industries.[13]

Supranational Incentives for Foreign Trade. National governments may formally work together to promote international marketing. This may be done through various agreements on certain facets of the trading relationship among countries, possibly dealing with quotas,

[11] For specific examples of government promotional activities, see: "Sweden Brushes Up Its U.S. Image," *Printers' Ink,* April 23, 1965, p. 54; "Mexican Border Towns Lure Gringo Industry," *Business Week,* December 2, 1967, pp. 120–22; "U.S. Woos Foreign Investors," *Clipper Cargo Horizons,* vol. 8, no. 4 (April 1968), pp. 2–4ff.

[12] Franklin R. Root, "Foreign Government Contraints on U.S. Business Abroad," *Economic and Business Bulletin,* Vol. 20, No. 1 (September 1967), p. 28.

[13] Stanley Lichtenstein, "States Win Export Laurels," *International Commerce,* June 1, 1964, p. 2.

tariffs, treatment of certain primary commodities, and the like, seeking to arrive at some commonality of interest or advantage. Of greater implications for world trade have been the more permanent organizations.

The European Economic Community, popularly known as the European Common Market, was established in 1958. It was originally composed of Belgium, France, Italy, Luxembourg, the Netherlands, and West Germany; in January 1973, Britain, Denmark, and Ireland joined. This opened up a large free-trade market and the result has been a breaking down of old nationalistic attitudes, increased employment and investment, lowered prices, and raised standards of living.

Such an economic union seems a strong step toward the goal of a United States of Europe. However, it is not a panacea as far as individual countries and their industries are concerned. For example, where Britain had strong industries these benefited from membership in the Common Market. But in other industries, productivity was low compared to some Common Market countries, placing British firms at a serious disadvantage.

Other multinational economic organizations are the European Free Trade Association (Austria, Denmark, Finland, Norway, Portugal, and Sweden), the Central American Common Market, and the Latin American Free Trade Associations. Although these have not reached the degree of trading uniformity of the Common Market—they have no common external tariffs and generally have some restrictive measures among members—the trend toward formal cooperative associations should contribute to the further growth of world trade.

Another economic union has received wide attention—mostly critical—in recent years. The Organization of Petroleum Exporting Countries (OPEC) quadrupled the price of oil and dramatically upset the balance of world trade and economic stability.

DEVELOPING EFFECTIVE INTERNATIONAL MARKETING

Evolution of Emphasis in Foreign Markets

The movement of a firm to an international role generally proceeds through several stages or levels of sophistication and corporate emphasis. Occasionally a firm will bypass certain of these stages and proceed to a higher level; this happens when early efforts at tapping foreign markets meet with unusual success, or when certain major competitors have led in expanding their markets in this way. These stages may be classified as:

1. Exporting through foreign trade agent middlemen.
2. Exporting through company sales branches or sales subsidiaries.
3. Overseas production, through licensing agreements with foreign firms.
4. Overseas production, through either joint ventures or wholly owned foreign subsidiaries.
5. An integrative multinational enterprise.

For the firm inexperienced in foreign marketing, the logical first step would be to use export-import middlemen who presumably are knowledgeable about the markets the firm is attempting to reach and of the technicalities involved. While there is little risk or investment involved in this approach, unfortunately these middlemen are seldom aggressive and the firm has little control over them.

Consequently the desirability for more active marketing efforts and better control may motivate the firm to set up its own foreign sales branches. This results in training and supervising a distant sales force, one perhaps necessarily comprised of foreign nationals of questionable familiarity with the company and its products, and with company loyalty a relatively unknown factor. Since the firm is still exporting at this point, it may well face the impediments of high tariffs, quotas, and general governmental discouragement.

As the company gains experience in foreign marketing and sees potential increasing, the development of overseas production facilities seems a practical and necessary way of overcoming governmental restrictive trade practices. Licensing foreign manufacturers to produce the goods permits a better market penetration and usually faster service to foreign customers, all this at a minimum investment. Dangers lie in finding reliable licensees and ones who will not turn into future competitors when the licensing agreement expires.

Investment in production facilities represents a further advance in international emphasis. In many countries, nationalistic pressures preclude complete foreign ownership in business enterprises; in these instances a firm may be forced into a joint venture with ownership divided between the American company and the nationals of the country. But rationale for relinquishing some ownership in order to do business is not hard to come by:

> . . . the demand for tires will grow faster out of the U. S. than in it.
> Thirty-five percent of something is a lot better than 100 percent of nothing.[14]

By this stage, an international division has probably been set up, responsible for running all aspects of a company's business outside

---

[14] "New Era for the Multinationals," Business Week, July 6, 1974, p. 74.

the United States. In some cases decentralization becomes so complete that the foreign subsidiaries are run almost as independent organizations.

A final stage may be seen as some sort of retrenchment back from acute decentralization of foreign operations to a more integrative global thinking:

> It has a global perspective. All basic decisions concerning marketing, production, and research are made in terms of the alternatives available to it throughout the world.[15]

Such a multinational company will emphasize pooling of talent and even seek multinational top management.

Marketing Research

Marketing research is needed to decrease the risks of foreign markets. However, there may be two serious impediments: (1) lack of information—only crude estimates of data on population and production may be available, and (2) much of the data may be of questionable reliability and not uniform. Costs tend to be higher, while specialized research services, such as trained interviewers, are often lacking. Furthermore, survey collectors may be viewed with suspicion, especially when they ask about attitudes or opinions.[16]

Of course, in most advanced countries the need for marketing research and the problems and techniques associated with it are similar to those in the United States. In the less developed countries the need, especially in analyzing market opportunities, is the greatest and the most difficult to accomplish.

Often a careful analysis of population statistics in such countries may indicate marketing possibilities. For example, 5 percent of India's 520 million people, or 26 million, have incomes that give them the buying power of the average American, and such a market size represents an affluent market larger than the Canadian market. If marketing research stops only at India's per capita national income, this well-to-do potential consumer market would likely be overlooked.[17]

[15] "Multinational Companies: How U. S. Business Goes World Wide," *Business Week*, April 20, 1963, p. 63.

[16] For some of the difficulties in using marketing research in underdeveloped countries, see Harper W. Boyd, Jr., et al., "On the Use of Marketing Research in the Emerging Economies," *Journal of Marketing Research*, November 1964, pp. 20–23. For a partial solution to some of these problems, see Reed Moyer, "International Market Analysis," *Journal of Marketing Research*, November 1968, pp. 353–61.

[17] Harry A. Lipson and Douglas F. Lamont, "Marketing Policy Decisions Facing International Marketers in the Less Developed Countries," *Journal of Marketing*, October 1969, p. 25.

Product Planning

Marketing in foreign lands often requires some degree of product revision, modification, and/or special tailoring. Necessary product changes may be slight, such as converting to metric weights and measures where the metric system is used. At other times, more basic differences in the requirements of the various markets may necessitate substantial product changes or even specially designed ones. It is no wonder that compact cars are popular in Europe, with the narrow roads and high gasoline prices typical of that area. Sometimes consumers in other countries, because of lower income per capita, cannot afford the standard U. S. product; the marketer must then face the decision of whether to proceed with a stripped-down or lower-quality product or to stay with the standard model that would appeal only to a small upper-class segment.

Products by no means always have to be tailored to individual and sometimes fragmented markets. Coca-Cola best illustrates the success that can come in world marketing with a standardized product having universal appeal. Skol's beer is another example (not yet in this country to any extent) in which a highly standardized product is selling in 36 countries. The product represents a compromise in tastes, being well flavored with hops, having some of the full body of Continental beers, and the high carbonation and paler color of American beers. In the area of wearing apparel, the famous Levi blue jean has been sold worldwide without adapting to special markets. The close identification with the United States West probably has contributed greatly to its universal appeal.

Warren Keegan has identified five alternatives available in multinational product planning:[18]

1. *One product, one message—worldwide.* This, of course, is the strategy described above. Although it can sometimes be strikingly successful, there are probably more failures than successes. For example, Campbell tried to sell its U. S. tomato soup formulation to the British only to find that they prefer a more bitter taste. When Corn Products Company tried to introduce the successful Knorr's dry soups in the United States, they failed, not because of taste but because the American housewife was unwilling to take 15 to 20 minutes longer cooking these soups.

2. *Product extension—communication adaptation.* This strategy is dictated when the same product serves different needs or functions in its various markets. Examples are bicycles and motor scooters which satisfy needs mainly for recreation in this country, but provide basic transportation in many foreign countries. Another example is that of a farm machinery company marketing its suburban lawn and

---

[18] The following categories and certain of the examples are excerpted from Warren J. Keegan, "Multinational Product Planning: Strategic Alternatives," *Journal of Marketing*, January 1969, pp. 58–62.

garden power equipment as agricultural implements in less developed countries. As Keegan points out, this is an effective strategy once its possibilities have been identified, since the product is unchanged, and research and development, tooling, manufacturing setup, and inventory costs associated with additions to the product line are avoided.

3. *Product adaptation—communications extension.* This strategy assumes that the product will serve the same function in foreign markets but with different minor use conditions, such as climate conditions, different types and levels of insect resistance, different scales of measurement, voltage requirements, etc. Oil companies do this, even regionally in this country, by adapting gasoline formulations to meet expected weather conditions. Under this strategy, basically the same promotional efforts and communication would be used in domestic and foreign markets.

4. *Dual adaptation.* Here both the product and the communications have to be changed for the overseas markets. This would be a combination of the market strategies of 2 and 3.

MARKETING
IN
ACTION

"Inventing Backwards"—Product Development in Backward Countries
Real marketing opportunities can exist in neglected segments of the world, segments not advanced enough to use the products of modern technology, but still needing something better than their archaic ways of doing things.

For example, there are an estimated 600 million women in the world who still scrub their clothes by hand. These women had been served by multinational soap and detergent companies for decades, but none recognized the unique need these women had for an improved product, an inexpensive manual washing device.

Finally, the Colgate-Palmolive Company persuaded an inventor to "invent backwards," to apply his talents to inventing, not a better mechanical washing machine, but a better manual device. And so an inexpensive, all plastic, hand-powered washer with the tumbling action of a modern automatic machine was developed and met with enthusiasm in test marketing in Mexico.

SOURCE: Warren J. Keegan, "Multinational Product Planning: Strategic Alternatives," *Journal of Marketing,* January 1969, p. 60.

For thought and discussion:
Can you think of other products which might be "invented backwards"?
What do you see as practical drawbacks of "inventing backwards" in
     product development?

5. *Product invention.* This strategy is forced upon a company when fundamental product changes are needed if a particular foreign market is to be tapped. Perhaps because of lack of purchasing power, deeply ingrained customs, and the like, a new or significantly changed product is the only one with a chance of succeeding. If product development costs are not overwhelming relative to the market potential, this may be a worthwhile strategy.

Pricing

Price frequently does not receive the attention it deserves in foreign marketing. A mere extension of U. S. prices will put many products out of reach of most of the population, since average incomes in most of the world are so much less than in the United States. This is true not only of underdeveloped countries, but also of the countries of Western Europe.

When goods are exported from the United States (rather than being produced in a foreign market under U. S. company auspices), a substantial price escalation frequently results due to additional export channels, import duties, and higher costs of shipping, insurance, and handling. Therefore, an acceptable price at production may inflate to an unreasonable price.

While most of the constraints and considerations affecting domestic price decisions are just as applicable to the foreign setting—that is, considerations of demand, present and potential competition, and costs—there are sometimes political and legal aspects that constrain and cannot be avoided. Many countries—especially industrialized ones—have antidumping restrictions. *Dumping* refers to the practice of selling in foreign markets at prices below those in the domestic market; where legal, this offers a manufacturer a chance to get rid of surplus or poorly selling goods without disrupting the domestic market for his regular goods and without destroying a quality image. Many countries decry such dumping because of its ruinous effects on local manufacturers. Therefore, antidumping legislation essentially puts a price floor on goods coming into these countries.

Changes in the values of currencies can affect prices. For example, when England devalued its currency in an effort to improve its balance of payments, English goods became relatively lower priced in the world markets, while exporters to England were sometimes forced to lower their prices to compete with English producers. Tariffs, import restrictions, and similar regulations inhibit pricing flexibility; in some countries the degree of constraint may depend on the favorableness of the image that a foreign firm has been able to build for itself by good public relations and compatibility.

Customary behavior of foreign middlemen sometimes decreases the effective use of price. Discount stores and supermarkets, similar to those operating in the United States on the basis of low markups and big volume, are still relatively unknown in most parts of the world. The traditional marketing behavior of foreign dealers is to maintain high markups despite low sales volume; price reductions and sales are infrequent and price rigidity prevails. These traditional practices are even incorporated into laws limiting the range of promotional efforts retailers can make. For example, in Germany a store can hold mark-down sales only twice a year, while the Netherlands permits bargain sales only when a store is actually going out of business.[19]

Collective business action that establishes price agreements, division of markets, and various other devices to restrain trade, is widely accepted in most parts of the world. Only in the United States must most business be practiced at "arm's length" devoid of any agreements by competing firms, or else be subject to prosecution under antitrust laws. Consequently, various combinations of firms which act to restrain competition are common in overseas markets. The best known of these combinations are the *cartels*. These are groups of companies producing similar products which have combined usually to fix prices and sales quotas, and sometimes even to centralize selling. Penalties often are assessed against those firms who exceed the designated quotas. The Organization of Petroleum Exporting Countries (OPEC) mentioned earlier is a type of cartel, but one composed of sovereign nations rather than business corporations. Price setting and control of production of a scarce and essential commodity puts this cartel in an unparalleled power position.

Multinational firms sometimes have the opportunity to use abusive pricing practices. The opportunity exists in so-called *transfer pricing,* when a parent company transfers goods to a subsidiary in another country at a particular set price. While the price should reflect market prices, in many cases with unique products there is no competitive market. So the transfer prices can be manipulated. Some governments are now investigating such pricing practices, and profiteering in the international arena may become more hazardous.

---

[19] Fayerweather, p. 77.

**MARKETING
MISTAKES**

Price Gouging via Transfer Pricing—Hoffmann-La Roche
Swiss-based Hoffmann-La Roche is the world's largest pharmaceutical company. Two of its most successful products are the tranquilizers Librium and Valium; these provide some $500 million of the company's $1.2 billion drug sales.

However, the British government's Monopolies Commission has pried open some of Hoffmann-La Roche's secrets and found that the company has been selling the active ingredients of the two drugs to its

British subsidiary for $925 and $2,305 a kilogram. Cost of manufacture: $22 and $50 a kilogram. And Hoffmann-La Roche has been charging far higher prices elsewhere: in the U. S., for example, nearly four times as much for Valium and more than 2½ times as much for Librium.

Hoffmann-La Roche defends itself by saying that its profits "brought benefits to all its customers." It spends over 15 percent of revenues on research and development, and its research budget has been growing at a 25 to 30 percent rate. But now governments of Australia, the Common Market countries, Sweden, and South Africa are conducting their own probes into drug costs; several countries have ordered major price cuts and demanded return of some of the excess profits.

SOURCE: "Swiss Showdown," *Forbes,* June 15, 1973, pp. 36–37; and Investigations Beset Multinational Firms with Stress on Pricing," *Wall Street Journal,* December 19, 1974, pp. 1 and 15.

For thought and discussion:
Can you justify the pricing practices of Hoffmann-La Roche?
Should a firm be entitled to charge all it can get for its products?
Why or why not?

Channels of Distribution

Institutions and distribution patterns vary widely in foreign markets. In some the channel of distribution is long and complex. A firm doing its manufacturing in the United States will generally face a longer channel than if it moves some production facilities overseas, either through direct investment or through licensing. Unless producers can deal quite directly with their final customers, they face the handicap of high transportation costs, slow movement of goods, and complicated packing and documentation. The foreign marketing situation, however, may preclude direct selling through sales offices or subsidiaries because of limited demand or governmental restrictions against foreign control.

A manufacturer attempting to reach overseas markets may deal with: (1) export firms (located in the home country of the producer) who may act either as agents (not taking title to the goods, and perhaps not taking possession either) or as merchants (who take title and usually possession); and/or (2) import agents or merchants located in the foreign countries. Many international middlemen act variously as importers and exporters, and as agents and merchant middlemen, and in a number of markets. Some have even grown into international trading companies: the four largest trading companies in Japan had sales totaling over $84 billion (U. S. dollars) in 1973.[20]

A marketer attempting to shorten the channel in some countries

[20] "Annual Survey of International Corporate Performance: 1973," *Business Week,* July 6, 1974, p. 82.

may run into difficulties because of ingrained customs and the political power of existing intermediaries. In some such cases the existing structure must suffice, cumbersome and inefficient though it
may be, but in others, the environmental factors can be altered as
Sears did in South America.

Physical Distribution

The need for fast, reliable shipping and availability of goods is as
great as in domestic marketing if a firm is to be competitive. However, in less developed countries there are, of course, less practical
transportation and storage alternatives—the choices may be limited,
sometimes mostly to air, or perhaps to navigable waterways. The
need for additional packing or crating, the use of specialized agents
such as freight forwarders, and the complex documentation requirements, make the foreign distribution process relatively more costly
than domestically. And in less developed countries, geographic and
climatic conditions, such as high humidity, and problems of pilferage and careless handling add to the complications and costs.

Distribution problems have held up marketing efforts in underdeveloped
countries, but in western Europe distribution is similar to that in the
United States; only the language is different. *Courtesy Pepsi Cola Company.*

Containerization, described in the last chapter, seems likely to bring major changes to the physical aspects of international commerce, and even to trade patterns. Not all problems are solved yet, but a great expansion of containerization is taking place and hundreds of millions of dollars are being spent for large container ships and for new dock facilities around the world.

Promotion

Three aspects of advertising in foreign markets present problems different from those found in the United States: (1) the degree of standardization of advertising that can be done in the various markets, (2) the difference in media availability, and (3) governmental restraints on certain advertising practices.

Standardization. Sometimes a firm can use the same promotional theme in all markets, and do so effectively. Thus Esso successfully extended its U. S. "tiger in your tank" campaign to most of the world. International soap and detergent manufacturers have been able to use essentially the same ads in differing markets (even though the product might have to be adjusted to meet different water conditions and washing equipment). It can be argued that, at least in Europe, advertising campaigns tailored to a single nation, a single market, should be abandoned in favor of more commonality of theme, slogan, copy, and layout. Under the Common Market, national traits and traditional characteristics are merging with "millions of Europeans living under largely similar conditions, although they read and speak different languages."[21]

But there is disagreement about the effectiveness of such striving for homogeneity in international advertising. Even the Common Market countries have diverse local customs, regulations, and cultures, and especially of media structure. And Esso's "tiger" required some modification in France and was not successful in all countries. For example, in most of Southeast Asia the tiger is a symbol of power and luck and this was good, but in Thailand the tiger is not a symbol of strength and the campaign fizzled.[22]

In some European countries, the philosophy of hard work and devotion to domestic duties is part of the social code. In these, such time-saving products as instant coffee, cake mixes, and the like are not effectively promoted if emphasis is on their convenience aspects; a dishwasher, however, was successfully promoted with an appeal to sanitation, pointing out the greater sterilization possible with high temperatures used by dishwashers.[23] In non-European

[21] Erik Elinder, "How International Can European Advertising Be?" *Journal of Marketing,* April 1965, pp. 7–11.

[22] "Admen in Thailand, Singapore, Find Unusual Problems," *Advertising Age,* November 27, 1967, p. 50.

[23] Fayerweather, p. 88.

countries, cultural influences may be more pronounced. For example:

> In India, illustrations or suggestions of kissing would be offensive. For religious reasons, a Sikh sees no value in a razorblade. A Hindu, however, prizes soap highly and considers that the European who takes a bath only once a day is a very dirty fellow indeed. African women want straight hair. The Japanese would like theirs wavy. In China red is lucky, white is for mourning. In many other territories, white signifies purity.[24]

Language sometimes presents difficulty. Literal translations sometimes are not enough because of nuances and idiomatic differences in language. This may even pose problems where the same language is used in different countries: for example, the word *napkin* means "diaper" to the English. And then there was the Matador of American Motors. Research had found that this name meant virility and excitement to consumers. However, when the Matador was introduced in Puerto Rico, it immediately ran into language problems: matador, it turns out, is the Spanish word for killer, hardly a good selling point in Puerto Rico, which has an unusually high traffic fatality rate.[25]

Therefore, at the present time any generalization about the possible homogeneity of advertising is probably too simplistic. However, the future may find national differences lessening and life styles homogenizing.

Media Considerations. Some media, such as *Time* and *Reader's Digest,* circulate in more than one country and can be considered international media. Certain radio and television stations also are becoming international, especially where located near national borders.

Availability of suitable media varies widely in foreign markets. Level of literacy may limit the practical use of print media in some countries, although the literate and affluent consumers may well represent the prime target market. Where illiteracy is a problem, radio and TV are significant media.

Substantial differences in media patterns occur even with the Common Market countries. In France, most advertising money has been spent in magazines and newspapers; commercial advertising on TV was not permitted until recently. In Belgium, magazines are less prominent, with direct mail widely used. A further factor complicating advertising in this small country is that advertisements need to be run in two languages—Flemish and French—to reach maximum coverage. In West Germany, national newspapers reach

---

[24] R. R. Walker, "Marketing Opportunities in the Developing Countries of Africa and Asia," in S. Watson Dunn, ed., *International Handbook of Advertising* (New York: McGraw-Hill, 1964), p. 563.

[25] *Time,* October 26, 1970, p. 110.

broad markets. In Italy, a daily newspaper is purchased by only one out of ten people, but half of the Italian women buy women's magazines. Luxembourg has a powerful advertising vehicle in Radio Luxembourg which reaches deeply into other European countries with a 200,000-watt transmission (the most powerful U. S. stations are limited to 50,000 watts).[26]

The cinema represents an important advertising medium in some countries, especially where print and broadcast facilities are marginal. Cinema offers the opportunity for visual presentation and demonstrations; the audience is captive; and in some countries, such as Spain, Greece, and Iraq, the theater is the major source of entertainment for the urban population. Furthermore, since theaters attract different clientele, markets can be segmented.

Governmental Restrictions on Promotion. Many countries impose restrictions of various kinds on advertising. Sometimes these affect the message or type of illustration to be used; media are frequently prohibited from some or all commercial messages; and taxation may be imposed as an added burden. These generally reflect national prejudices against hard selling as being an economic waste and in bad taste. In many European countries and those British-oriented such as Canada and Australia, radio and television programming is under public rather than private control. Therefore, advertising can be tightly regulated.

Let us look at a sample of some of the restrictions. Italy controls drug advertising, while prohibiting TV advertising of deodorants, laxatives, toilet tissues, and similar personal items. In West Germany, no TV commercials are permitted on Sundays or holidays; on other days only about 20 minutes a day are available for commercials. Pharmaceutical advertising is also under government control. Advertisers in Germany may not make comparisons between their products and competing products. Even references to noncompeting products may be banned. For example, Goodyear demonstrated the strength of its "3T" tire cord in the United States by showing a steel chain breaking. In Germany, such a visualization was not permitted: it was considered disparaging to the steel-chain manufacturers.[27]

The practice of grouping commercials is common in Europe. Holland, which first allowed TV commercials in 1967, permits only 15 minutes a day, as does Switzerland. Italy allows 26 minutes. Britain has two BBC channels—government-owned—and these remain noncommercial; a third channel, which is independent, can have 7 minutes of commercials per hour. France in 1968 loosened TV restraints and now permits 20 minutes of commercial time just before the 8 PM newscast. Advertisers in France are not allowed to

---

[26] C. Laury Botthof, "One Common Market or Six Markets?" *Journal of Marketing,* April 1966, pp. 16–18.

[27] *Advertising Age,* May 9, 1966, p. 75.

repeat one commercial more than three times "to avoid saturation like in the United States."[28]

Advertising has been subject to taxation in many countries. France has a service tax of 9.29 percent on all advertising operations. Italy taxes newspaper advertising 4 percent, radio and TV commercials 15 percent, cinema and prizes 10 percent, and outdoor advertising 10–12 percent. Most other countries taxing have rates ranging from 1 percent to as much as 30 percent for certain media.

It is obvious, when considering the restrictions of other countries, that advertising often is not viewed as tolerantly and permitted the freedom which exists in the United States. For U. S. firms seeking to do business in other countries, restrictions must be recognized and the marketing mix adjusted accordingly.

Personal selling. U. S. firms, in trying to adapt successful personal selling techniques in America to the overseas market, sometimes encounter difficulties. And when a firm is heavily dependent on this strategy in its promotion mix, the results can be disheartening.

---

[28] "French Get An Important Message," *Business Week*, May 11, 1968, pp. 103–06.

**MARKETING
IN
ACTION**

Personal Selling Difficulties in Overseas Marketing—Avon Products
Avon has between 80 and 90 percent of the domestic direct sales market in beauty products, with no significant competition. In the decade of the 1960s and early 1970s, Avon was one of the foremost growth stocks and the darling of Wall Street. Its salesladies made door-to-door selling respectable and were welcomed by many "fettered housewives" in middle-class suburban communities. But the company found there is no infinite room for growth in so specialized a market. Aware of approaching saturation, Avon hoped to gain abroad what might be slowing at home.

There are more representatives overseas (325,000) than in the U. S. and Canada (275,000), yet sales volume is less than half as much. Europe especially shows abysmal sales productivity: while U. S. "Avon ladies" average $2,200 in orders, England representatives average only $600 and those in Germany $700. Cultural problems probably account for this. European women are more reluctant to sell door-to-door to strangers than are American women, and are also more hesitant at selling to friends at a profit.

Avon has attempted to enter the Japanese market, but also with little success: cultural problems again seem to be slowing down progress. Consequently, Avon has had difficulty both in recruiting and in retaining sales representatives.

For thought and discussion:
Do you see any way to overcome these "cultural problems" in the near future?
What would you recommend for Avon regarding its overseas marketing strategy?

CHALLENGES IN INTERNATIONAL MARKETING

The very diversity of foreign markets creates challenges and often necessitates unique and specially designed marketing programs and strategies. There are other challenges inherent in international marketing that lie beyond the profit and loss statement, namely the contributions that marketers can make to: (1) world friendship, (2) economic development in underdeveloped countries, and (3) improvement of the standard of living in all countries.

World Friendship. J. Paul Austin, president of the Coca-Cola Company, has advanced the thesis that world trade, rather than being dependent on world peace as in times past, may actually influence a reality of peace through the growing dependence of the countries of the world on each other. He sees the "walls of nationalism and trade protectionism falling under the new attitudes and methods of marketing, which include licensing, granting franchises, formation of joint ventures, and financing local business representatives in overseas areas."[29] This must remain one of the idealistic challenges of marketers, to better meet the needs and serve the aspirations of world customers, and to do so fairly, diplomatically, and efficiently.

Economic Development. While the immediate sales and profit potential of doing business in underdeveloped markets may not be as favorable as in more developed countries, there need not be a basic incompatibility with the profit motive.

Responsive marketing is needed internationally, as well as domestically. Sears practiced it in Latin America, and did make a profit. The success of U. S. soft-drink firms in achieving worldwide distribution of their products also suggests that marketers can solve the distribution problems inherent in many underdeveloped markets. And in the process, native aspirations may be raised, accepted ways of doing things may be challenged, and economic development stimulated.

Failure to close the imbalance between the "have" and the

[29] J. Paul Austin, "World Marketing as a New Force for Peace," *Journal of Marketing,* January 1966, p. 3.

"have not" people could lead to unrest, subversion, and revolution —certainly a climate unhealthy for overseas business operations. On the other hand, the potential that some U. S. marketers have to help less advantaged people—for mutual benefit—is probably best exemplified by the success of Pier I Imports, which was described in chapter 1.

Standard of Living. A host of new products and expanded consumption choice characterizes most parts of the world today. As profit-oriented firms seek other markets for their expanded production, customs change and aspirations increase. Goods, such as automobiles, appliances, and television sets, become symbols of success in increasingly achievement-minded societies (much as they have been in this country, at least until recently).

However, not all people can use the sophisticated innovations pouring from the more advanced countries. As we observed earlier in this chapter, the powered washing machine is out of reach for vast numbers in South America and elsewhere. The need to "invent backwards," to strive for products and improvements geared to less advanced societies, can make a significant contribution to standards of living in many parts of the world. The inexpensive, entirely practical, and labor-saving hand washing machine developed by Colgate serves a hitherto unfilled need. Are there other such needs unheeded in our quest for greater technological sophistication? Of course there are. They are there for creative marketers to tap, and in the process, not only improve standards of living, but profits too.

QUESTIONS AND PROBLEMS

1. What are incentives for overseas marketing? How do these vary by type and size of firm?
2. Compare the opportunities for market segmentation in an advanced economy with those in an undeveloped economy.
3. In the various foreign markets, it is not uncommon to find the paradox of some countries placing severe impediments on foreign marketers, while other countries at about the same level of economic development are making maximum efforts to encourage foreign investment and marketing. How do you explain this paradox?
4. How does a high illiteracy rate affect a company's marketing program? Does this preclude effective promotion?
5. There are serious impediments in doing marketing research in some foreign countries. Discuss these and suggest ways that some market information might be obtained. In the absence of such information, what marketing adjustments may be needed?
6. Discuss the thesis of J. Paul Austin, president of Coca-Cola, that world trade is a new force for world peace and amity.

7. Elinder, a Swedish advertising executive, argues that, at least in Europe, national characteristics are homogenizing so that common advertising themes and campaigns may now be substituted for those tailored to individual nations. Evaluate his position, considering forces acting for and against the "homogenizing."

8. What is "dumping"? Why are most countries strongly opposed to this on the part of foreign marketers? What benefits does dumping offer (a) to the marketer, (b) to the consumer in the market where this is occurring?

Project

In your community, identify as many sources of information about doing business in foreign markets as you can. Some possibilities are banks, government agencies, libraries, foreign trade offices, and consulates. Prepare a brief report on the type of information provided and its general usefulness to a small- or medium-sized American firm interested in exporting.

Exercise in Creativity

Review again the Pier I Imports example in chapter 1 of how a U. S. firm is profitably aiding economic development in foreign countries. What opportunities can you think of for other U. S. firms profitably to aid economic development in foreign countries?

What ideas can you come up with for doing something similar for certain sectors of U. S. society?

Role-playing Case

Skol's beer was advertised as a standardized product being sold in 36 countries of the world, although not yet in the United States.

Place yourself in the role of management consultant with Skol's as one of your clients. They have told you that they want to invade the U. S. market. Discuss the pros and cons of various alternative marketing strategies for doing this. Select the strategy you think is best and defend it.

CHAPTER 17

EVALUATING

MARKETING

PERFORMANCE

Evaluating performance is commonplace. We receive grades evaluating our academic efforts, and scores measure our performance in sports. Our salaries to an extent measure our worth to an employer.

Most firms periodically evaluate marketing performance. In many cases this is systematic, and a variety of analytical devices may be used to determine how well the job is being done and/or to catch any potential weaknesses. But there still are firms (usually the smaller ones) that use no systematic measures of performance. Even larger firms may be content with surface data and miss early symptoms of ills, as well as marketing opportunities.

In this chapter then we look at the tools for evaluating marketing performance and also pose some cautions in the use of performance evaluations. Key terms are:

market-share analysis	sales analysis
iceberg principle	customer satisfaction measures
distribution cost analysis	marketing audit
80–20 principle	profiteering
customer attitude surveys	social audit

OBJECTIVES OF EVALUATING MARKETING PERFORMANCE

Evaluating performance provides feedback on how well something is being done. Without such feedback it is impossible to judge whether improvement is possible, where it should occur, how much is needed, and how quickly it must be accomplished. Without feedback, a situation can deteriorate until it is too late for corrective action. The control or measurement tools that provide the feedback must, however, furnish relevant information promptly or the usefulness is seriously dissipated. For example, if a major product is facing serious customer resistance, feedback must be prompt; a six-month delay in discovering a problem and its causes might place the viability of the firm in jeopardy.

As firms become larger, the necessity for better controls increases because top management can no longer personally monitor all aspects of the operation. The trend toward diversification and mergers, which often results in loosely controlled decentralized operations, also makes timely feedback on marketing performance crucial.

MARKETING MISTAKES: WOULD BETTER MARKETING EVALUATIONS HAVE HELPED?

Marketing mistakes are probably inevitable given the state of marketing knowledge and the dynamic environment in which uncontrollable and sometimes unpredictable factors are often introduced. Increasingly adding to marketing worries (and challenges) is a multi-faceted competition, not only intraindustry, but interindustry; foreign firms as well have invaded the domestic market and sometimes carved surprising niches as we saw with motorcycles, and as has occurred with electronic equipment and small automobiles, where domestic-company market shares have been reduced substantially. Even firms entrenched in stable industries are vulnerable in innovative competition.

Granted that mistakes of omission or commission will occur, alert and aggressive management is characterized by certain actions or reactions:

1. There should be a quick recognition of looming problems or present mistakes, and the causes.
2. There should be a quick response or reaction to take corrective action (and sometimes this action may require a ruthless axing of the product or the promotional approach).
3. There should be some learning experience coming from such mistakes; the same mistakes should not be repeated; the total operation should be improved as a result.

When a long-established company (for example, the A. C. Gilbert Company, described in the Marketing Mistake box) finds itself in a deteriorating situation for a number of years, and the response is late in coming and ill conceived, then criticism is in order. Controls were either inadequate or ignored; marketing evaluation was superficial or biased; actions were finally taken without careful diagnosis of the problems and the causes.

A. C. Gilbert Company

For two generations this company successfully marketed its Erector sets, American Flyer trains, chemistry sets, and microscopes. Then beginning in 1962 were five straight years of losses, rising from $300,000 in 1962 to $9,000,000 in 1966, and the company went out of business with liabilities exceeding assets by more than $12,000,000.

An initial sales drop in 1961 was attributed to an insufficient number of new products and an insufficient advertising budget. To spur volume, the sales staff was increased 50 percent and executive changes made, but sales again dropped and the initial loss incurred. For the 1963 Christmas selling season, more than 50 new toys were added, including toys for preschool children and for girls. But sales again declined, and a whopping $5,700,000 loss was posted, stemming mostly from huge returns of low-priced toys shipped on a guaranteed-sale basis to supermarkets. In the next year a strong economy drive was initiated, with the salesmen replaced by manufacturers' representatives (manufacturers' representatives are independent salesmen, usually handling products of several manufacturers, and charging a straight commission on sales; by using these the manufacturer sacrifices control for a reduced selling expense); administrative and operating expenses were cut from $10,000,000 to $4,700,000. For the 1964 Christmas season, 20 new toys were added, and although sales increased, losses were still almost $2,000,000.

Most of the stakes were placed on the 1965 Christmas selling season, with a $2,000,000 TV campaign for Saturday morning cartoon shows and a $1,000,000 point-of-purchase program consisting of 65,000 animated displays furnished free to dealers. Sales increased almost 30 percent, but losses totaled nearly $3,000,000 and the company's doom was effectively sealed, although it faltered for another year to the $9,000,000 loss.

What went wrong? Failure to recognize a changing environment was an initial error: toy promotion was changing from in-store displays and comic books to TV; low-priced, highly advertised toys were now sold in discount stores and supermarkets more than in the traditional toy shops and department stores; table-top slot-car auto racing was beginning to outsell toy trains; sales of fad items hit record peaks in frantic spurts of short-lived popularity. The traditional conservative toy maker was ill-fitted to thrive in the new fast-moving, competitive volume toy market—but it tried.

The tremendous expansion of the product line resulted in lack of quality in the new toys and the deterioration in quality of the standard items; the company lost its image as a reliable producer of high-quality toys. Tremendous returns of unsold toys by the aggressive, high-volume toy retailers reflected both the deterioration of quality and lack of good timing in entering the market with fad-type items. Timing in some instances was incredibly bad. For example, spy figures (Man from U.N.C.L.E., James Bond, Honey West) were introduced on Christmas Day in 1965, too late for the selling season in which spy items were especially popular. The manufacturers'-representative system, while it reduced selling costs somewhat, alienated dealers who were used to the service of company salesmen.

SOURCE: Adapted from "A. C. Gilbert: A Victim of Poor Quality, Timing, Product Planning," *Marketing Insights,* March 6, 1967, pp. 10–11.

For thought and discussion:
How might Gilbert have more quickly detected a changing environment?
When should it have begun adjusting to such changes?
How might it better have reacted (be as specific as possible)?

Now let us look at another example of a long-established company that permitted itself to bask in the luxury of complacency a little too long. Reaction and adjustment came quickly, although not before substantial competitive inroads were made.

MARKETING MISTAKE

Gillette Company
In the early 1960s the Gillette Super Blue Blade had firmly grasped 90 percent of the double-edge razor blade market (which accounts for about 75 percent of all blades sold), and the company was enjoying a 16 percent after-tax profit. But early in 1962, long-lasting stainless blades from Britain's Wilkinson Sword Ltd. began infiltrating, and shortly after, Gillette's two old competitors—Schick and American Safety Razor—also introduced stainless blades.

Gillette finally realized that its market share was ebbing badly—it dropped to as low as 70 percent—and rushed its own stainless blade to market by the fall of 1963. But the delay was crucial and long-lasting damage had been done; today Gillette's share of the total maket has apparently stabilized at about 75 percent, with profitability dropping to 12 percent. In an attempt to counteract the damage caused by the lost blade business, Gillette turned to diversifications. But the Toni and Paper Mate Divisions also began faltering: the vogue for straight hair styles was affecting home permanent kit sales, while Paper Mate was severely pinched by a flood of low-price ballpoint pens.

A carefully conceived diversification in another direction was clearly necessary. Even if competition is disregarded, growth in shaving business is limited to increases in the shaving population. A market study was undertaken to find out what types of products the public associated with Gillette. Surprisingly, consumers thought of the company in terms of grooming products, even though Foamy shaving cream was its only such product at that time; cutlery and related products were low on the list.

Right Guard, a deodorant in an aerosol can, was introduced as a man's deodorant and was a striking success, not only with men but with their wives and daughters too. Other men's toiletries, such as hair spray, have been developed and in this area, and in overseas business, Gillette faces growth possibilities.

SOURCE: Adapted from "How Gillette Has Put on a New Face," *Business Week*, April 1, 1967, pp. 58–66.

For thought and discussion:
Compare and contrast the reactions of Gillette and Gilbert when faced with a changing competitive environment.

TYPES OF MARKETING PERFORMANCE ANALYSIS

Tools for evaluating marketing performance may be classified as follows:

1. Measures of specific performance, i.e., measures of individuals or specific marketing functions:
  (a) Criteria for measuring performance of salespeople (pages 361–62).
  (b) Measures of advertising effectiveness. (Table 12–5)
2. Measures of overall marketing results:
  (a) Total sales and profits.
  (b) Market share analysis.
  (c) Sales analysis.
  (d) Distribution cost analysis.
  (e) Measures of customer satisfaction.
  (f) Marketing audit.
  (g) Social responsiveness.

In this chapter we will devote most of our attention to the measures of overall marketing results since the specific performance measures have been briefly described in chapter 12 on advertising and chapter 13 on personal selling.

In the tools for evaluating marketing performance, a key point is that these need to be used on a *current* and *continuing basis* if they are to provide the feedback on how an enterprise is really doing and if they are to provide an early warning of a worsening situation. A one-time analysis, perhaps of sales and of market-share coverage in various territories, may do almost more harm than good. Without comparative figures for determining if performance is better or worse than past periods, problem areas may go undiscovered and any fears allayed. Sales and market-share analysis could be done every month; others such as a distribution cost analysis perhaps only once a year. The complete marketing audit also lends itself to periodic use, although many firms view it more as a "crisis" analysis than one that can be used to tap new potential or prevent crises from occurring.

In some firms the measure of the success is couched in total sales and profit figures. As long as a firm is making a profit—as much or more than the preceding year, everything is assumed to be satisfactory. In some cases net profit results tend to be subordinated to steadily increasing gross sales. Often as firms become larger, concern for measuring the effectiveness of the efforts becomes centered on market-share performance. Here the true measure of success is perceived to be not absolute sales performance but relative sales performance—that is, sales relative to those of competitors.

Market Share Analysis

The desire to better competition is a very human tendency, whether in sports or in business. A measurement of performance relative to competitors fulfills the competitive urge and can be a highly motivating device for management, salesmen, and other company employees. Furthermore, data on market share usually avoids the contaminating effects of noncontrollable exogenous factors. For example, if sales decline over the preceding year, but market share remains constant or even improves, this suggests that the firm is doing a good job and while certain factors adversely affected the industry for that particular period, weakness in the company's marketing program could hardly be blamed.

For certain consumer goods manufacturers, there are several syndicated services which provide a measurement of competitive brand position and a basis for projecting total market size, as well as other helpful statistics. The two major services are the A. C. Nielsen Company, which conducts store audits in the grocery, drug, and certain other fields, and the Market Research Corporation of America (MRCA), which gathers information on consumer expenditures through a panel of consumers maintaining a record of purchases in diaries. Speedata, Inc. furnishes an intermediate step in measuring product flow by recording shipments of grocery products through 100 major warehouses servicing over 30,000 retail outlets in all sections of the United States. The diagram below shows the point of data collection by the Nielsen, MRCA, and Speedata services:

Speedata ⟶ Nielsen ⟶ MRCA

Manufacturer ⟶ Wholesaler ⟶ Retailer ⟶ Consumer

These services are expensive—frequently costing $35,000 a year and more for the minimum—but some manufacturers subscribe to several since they furnish somewhat different information. While both major services provide data on size of total market by product class, brand share, relative importance of types and sizes of containers, and trends, Nielsen also tells about retailer inventories, out-of-stock conditions, retail prices, and point-of-purchase displays. MRCA, on the other hand, can furnish data on customer characteristics and brand loyalty. These services can be faulted as being based on sampling outlets and consumers having questionable representativeness; however, their use for several decades reflects the value in providing information badly needed in a competitive environment. Another major reason for using these services is the time lag of sales to consumers; since the manufacturer does not sell directly to consumers, but rather through middlemen, the current invoices reflecting sales may not reveal the latest information on consumer purchases, since sales to wholesalers and retailers may merely indicate building up or replacing inventories due to past sales. With conditions changing rapidly, past sales may not typify the present situation.

Market-share performance rightly should be a key indicator of how well a firm is doing. It is of most value in spotting emerging problems; a decline in market share should induce strenuous efforts to ascertain the cause and to take corrective action. The complacency of A. C. Gilbert Company faced with a declining market share at least partly accounted for the eventual failure to overcome its marketing problems. Gillette, while aroused to strenuous efforts after market share of razor blades had declined substantially, apparently did not get this feedback promptly or did not react with the initial decline, waiting until erosion became more serious.

Although market-share information is a valuable management tool, it should not be used as the primary or sole measure of marketing performance. A major flaw in its use is that it ignores profitability. An overcommitment to increasing market share—and some executives are motivated in this direction since their prestige is bound up with company size and growth relative to other firms in the industry —can lead to rash sales growth at the expense of profits. Heavy doses of advertising, or concern for short-term sales results at the expense of more satisfied customers and dealers, will undoubtedly increase market share. The massive $3,000,000 promotional expenditure of Gilbert in 1965 increased sales almost 30 percent, but losses skyrocketed and directly led to bankruptcy. A firm more concerned with profitable business, and with the necessary weeding out of unprofitable products and customers, may find market share declining while profits are rising.

The important thing to remember about market-share measurements is that they should signal areas needing further research and investigation. Perhaps there is a satisfactory explanation for an initial decline in market share: for example, it might be accounted for by a large sale occurring in an adjacent period; or perhaps a new firm has entered the market and is taking some market share from every existing firm. On the other hand, a declining market share may indicate a serious lapse in performance.

Sales Analysis

In every company there tend to be wide variations in sales performance between sales territories, products, salesmen, and customers. These differences are disguised and mitigated when gross sales performance and/or gross market-share performance is analyzed. A systematic and periodic analysis of the details of sales, comparing actual results with planned figures to determine what variation occurred, and to note the extent and cause of the variation, is an important measurement tool; this can lead to increased sales performance as well as catch problems before they can affect total market-share performance.

It is not uncommon for outstanding performance in certain territories, or by certain salesmen, to cover up weaknesses in other areas. This is commonly known as the *iceberg principle*. Just as an iceberg has most of its mass submerged below the surface, so is important data hidden when only gross figures are used.

A decision has to be made as to how finely sales are to be broken down. Some of the more common subdivisions for reporting and analyzing sales are:

1. Geographical regions, such as states, cities, and sales territories.
2. Salespeople, and sometimes by method of sale, such as mail order, telephone, or direct sale.
3. Customers, and this may be done by size, by type or class of trade, and perhaps by key or major customers.
4. Product, and this may be by dollars and/or physical units, for various sizes, colors, styles, etc.

The extent and the particular data to be gathered should be tailored to the needs of the firm. Additional information may sometimes be desired, such as analysis by size of order, by terms of sale, by date sold, and so on. This information may be reported monthly, quarterly, or for some other period of time.

With today's electronic data processing equipment, the gathering of such data is not as formidable as it once was. But usually special provision must be made for processing this information from sales invoices and other sources; otherwise it tends to be buried in files after the normal accounting and billing has been performed. A caveat is in order here. The data to be gathered and analyzed are worthless unless they are used. An overabundance of sales reports and analyses may be disregarded by busy executives unless provision is made to flag significant deviations from plans or quotas or other standards.

Tracking Down a Major Problem Through Analysis of Sales Data

A major carpeting manufacturer in the late 1950s was experiencing steady sales growth. It sold rather high quality goods with a well-established and reputable brand to department stores, furniture stores, smaller carpet shops, and some institutional customers. However, for the first six months of this particular year, the sales manager of the company found that the eastern region was $80,000 below quota, slightly more than ½ of 1 percent. The other regions were at or above quota. An analysis was made of the districts of the eastern region and this showed the following results:

**Sales Performance, Eastern Region—Six Months
(thousands of dollars)**

	Quota	Actual	Sales Differential	Quota Performance, Percent
Total Eastern Region	$ 15,300	$ 15,220	−$ 80	99.5
Philadelphia	4,400	4,472	+ 72	102.
Pittsburgh	4,200	4,248	+ 48	101.
Baltimore	3,600	3,560	− 40	99.
Richmond	3,100	2,940	− 160	95.

Obviously the Richmond district was having serious difficulties. In fact the difficulties were more serious than first indicated by the under-quota attainment of the eastern region, the entire region being $80,000 under plan, while the Richmond district was $160,000 under. This not unusual situation illustrates the iceberg principle and shows how more serious problems may not be evident from gross figures.

A more in-depth probe of the situation at Richmond was advised. The breakdown of the Richmond figures by salesmen is shown below.

**Sales Performance, Richmond Salesmen—Six Months
(thousands of dollars)**

	Quota	Actual	Sales Differential	Quota Performance, Percent
Kelly	$ 800	$ 820	+$ 20	103
Schmidt	720	760	+ 40	106
Andersen	480	500	+ 20	104
Cameron	1,100	860	− 240	78
	$ 3,100	$ 2,940	−$ 160	95

The analysis of Richmond sales showed only one trouble spot, but a most serious one, again far more serious than the $80,000 gross regional figures would have led one to suspect. The more detailed analysis of sales does not provide the answer of why sales results are under plan; but it does flag the problem area, one which needs further investigation to ascertain causes.

SOURCE: This case was brought to the author's attention by E. H. Lewis of the University of Minnesota.

For thought and discussion:

How do you account for the high quota of Cameron?

What are possible explanations for the Cameron performance?

What would you as sales manager do at this point?

Distribution Cost Analysis[1]

While sales analysis delves into sales variations from plans or quotas so that these can be explained and possible corrective action taken, the distribution cost analysis seeks to determine the relative profitability of the present ways of doing business. A substantial part of the efforts of most companies does not yield commensurate profits; efforts could better be directed to those areas that can make the biggest contribution to profit.

The 80–20 Principle. The 80–20 principle describes the not uncommon situation in which 20 percent of the customers account for 80 percent of the volume or profit. The same principle also typically characterizes products and salesmen with, for example, 20 percent of a company's products and 20 percent of the salesmen contributing most of the profitability. Of course exact percentages will vary, but even well-managed firms have imbalances. For example, one study found that the top one third of products and customers accounted for 74 percent of profits, the top third of salesmen, 58 percent, and of territories, 61 percent.[2]

A certain unevenness of profit contribution is inevitable. Some products are easier to sell and yield a higher markup; some salesmen are star producers; some customers buy in bigger quantities and require less "push" and less service. Unfortunately, the emphasis on sales in most firms—commissions are usually paid to salesmen and to their supervisors on sales volume, not on profit contribution—results in reluctance to eliminate unprofitable smaller customers

[1] For more detailed treatment of marketing or distribution cost analysis, see Donald R. Longman and Michael Schiff, *Practical Distribution Cost Analysis* (Homewood, Ill.: Irwin, 1955); Charles H. Sevin, *Marketing Productivity Analysis* (New York: McGraw-Hill, 1965).

[2] Harry D. Wolfe and Gerald Albaum, "Inequality in Products, Orders, Customers, Salesmen, and Sales Territories," *Journal of Business,* July 1962, pp. 298–301.

and a natural inclination to push the easier-to-sell products, rather than those which might yield the most profit. We have noted in an earlier chapter the natural difficulty most firms have in weeding out weak products. Sales force turnover usually brings with it salesmen in varying degrees of training, experience, and motivation; even were there no turnover, salesmen would differ in motivation, effective energy, and competence. Although some disparity cannot be prevented, where it becomes excessive, efficiency is diminished and marketing costs soar. This disparity of profit contribution tends to grow unless periodic analyses are made of the profitability of territories and salesmen, products, customers, and similar analysis units.

Problems Involved in Analyzing Marketing Costs. Unlike production costs involving material, factory wages, equipment maintenance, and the like, which can be apportioned fairly accurately to the various products and processes, marketing costs frequently are difficult to measure and to apportion, and therefore control. Any allocation has to be somewhat arbitrary, and the effect of various marketing efforts on the final order cannot be determined as can the inputs of material and labor on production costs.

The accounting systems of most companies do not permit pulling marketing cost information directly from ledger accounts. Most accounting records are maintained by so-called natural accounts, such as salaries, supplies, advertising, and so on, the names of their expense categories. Therefore, for a distribution cost analysis, the items in these natural accounts have to be reclassified by functions— i.e., the purpose for which the expenditures are made—such as for products, customers, or territories. This reorganizing and reclassifying is costly and time-consuming and often not done.

Procedure for Analyzing Marketing Costs. There are two basic methods of developing the distribution cost analysis: the full-cost approach, and the contribution-to-margin approach. In the *full-cost* method, all indirect expenses are allocated among the items being analyzed. For example, marketing administrative expenses—those of the chief marketing executive and the staff—are indirect expenses which under the full-cost approach would be charged to territories, products, and customers on the basis of some measurable characteristics, such as number of salesmen, amount of sales, number of invoices, and the like.[3] Table 17-1 shows some recommended bases for allocating certain direct and indirect costs.

The difficulty in allocating costs is accentuated when the full-cost approach is used. For example, in attempting to allocate the administrative (indirect) expenses of the sales manager to territories, products, and customers, the common basis is that of sales: the territory with the largest sales volume is charged with the largest pro-

[3] Michael S. Morton and Andrew M. McCosh, "Terminal Costing for Better Decisions," *Harvard Business Review,* May–June, 1968, pp. 147–56.

Table 17-1.

Bases for Allocating Selective Functional Cost Groups to Sales Territories, Products, and Customers

Functional Cost Groups	Bases of Allocation		
	To Territories	To Products	To Customers
Selling—direct costs Salaries, commissions, travel, etc.	Direct	Time studies	Number of sales calls
Selling—indirect costs Field office expense, training, etc.	Equal charge for each salesperson	In proportion to direct selling time	Number of sales calls
Advertising	Direct; or analysis of media circulation	Cost of space for specific products	Cost of space of specific customer advertising
Transportation, storage, and shipping	Weight	Weight	Weight
Billing	Number of order lines	Number of order lines	Number of order lines
Accounts receivable	Number of invoices posted	Number of invoices posted	Number of invoices posted

Sources: Adapted from Charles H. Sevin, *Marketing Productivity Analysis* (New York: McGraw-Hill, 1965), pp. 13–15; Charles H. Sevin, "Analyzing Your Cost of Marketing," *Management Aids for Small Manufacturers* (Washington, D.C.: Small Business Administration, June 1957), p. 3.

portion of these expenses. This admits to the underlying philosophy that the burden should be applied where it can best be borne. However, this allocation disregards the very real probability that the problem territories, products, and customers take up disproportionately more administrative time than those functioning smoothly. Consequently, the results may be misleading and patently unfair.

Because of the difficulty in assigning such indirect expenses other than on an arbitrary and not entirely defensible basis, there are many advocates of the *contribution-to-margin* approach. This considers only those measurable costs definitely related to the market segment, and thus focuses attention and responsibility on variable costs rather than on total costs. The controversies that can accompany arbitrary assignment of indirect costs that favorably or unfavorably affect certain measures of relative performance are then avoided. The contribution-to-margin method purports to show only what has actually been contributed to the general overhead and profit.

Yet even this poses some allocation problems. For example, consider the direct expenses of a salesman: his base salary and travel expenses. Breaking these down and distributing to products and to customers may not always be equitable: the common allocation in proportion to volume sold disregards the fact that all products and customers are not equally easy to sell. To make exhaustive time studies may be impractical and still produce questionable results. However, these allocation difficulties should not obscure the benefits that can come from a systematic analysis of marketing costs, albeit some inequities.[4]

Corrective Action Considerations. The payoff of doing a somewhat tedious and relatively expensive distribution cost analysis comes in the corrective actions that should follow. The flagging of unprofitable segments of business should normally result in efforts to improve the profitability of these segments, or perhaps to eliminate them entirely. Since the complete analysis will cover territories, products, and customers (or customer categories), any desirable corrective action would concern these. However, the distribution cost analysis, as the sales analysis, seldom spells out what corrective action is needed—it only identifies relative problem areas deserving further attention and investigation. For example, a poor sales territory relative to others may be found to need to be expanded to realize sufficient potential, to need greater infusions of advertising and sales promotion, or to need greater supervision and motivation.

In chapter 10 we discussed possible actions regarding weak products, those not contributing their share to profits. Sometimes these weak products should be eliminated or phased out; in other cases there may be sound reasons for keeping them despite continued weakness. If needed to round out a line, to meet competition, to create a good image, or simply to maintain customer goodwill, then they should be retained. Usually a company finds, however, that there are far more weak products in the line that are contributing little, while absorbing a disproportionate amount of attention and expense, than there are ones whose continued presence is desirable.

Unprofitable customers are a problem for many firms. Often the smaller accounts are not really worth the expense of contacting and of handling the small orders. The firm would be more profitable without such accounts, even though sales would be somewhat less at first. Often such a manufacturer would be wiser to seek more selective distribution (with fewer dealer outlets) and give distributors

---

[4] More specifics on distribution cost analysis can be found in R. D. Buzzell et al., *Product Profitability Measurement and Merchandising Decisions* (Boston: Division of Research, Graduate School of Business Administration, Harvard University, 1965); *Cost Analysis for Product Line Decisions*, Management Services Technical Study No. 1 (New York: American Institute of Certified Public Accountants, 1965); J. L. Goldstucker, "Allocating Costs in International Operations," *Business Horizons*, Winter 1965, pp. 75–84.

more attention and service, than to continue with a more intensive type of distribution. However, eliminating small, relatively unprofitable accounts should hardly be undertaken in wholesale fashion. Some accounts may be growing to a profitable size.

A more practical alternative to eliminating unprofitable accounts is to create incentives for increasing the average order size. Two experts offer some suggestions for doing so:

1. The customer who is buying from several different suppliers may be induced to concentrate his purchases; it is to the advantage of both buyer and seller to have more concentration of sales transactions.
2. The customer buying on a hand-to-mouth basis with many small orders may be persuaded to buy less frequently, and thereby save himself some handling and billing expenses.
3. The sales compensation plan may need to be changed to discourage acceptance of smaller orders or to offer a bonus to large orders.
4. Direct mail or telephone selling may be substituted for salesmen's calls on unprofitable accounts.
5. An account may be shifted altogether to a wholesaler rather than have the manufacturer deal directly.
6. A seller may establish a minimum order.
7. The pricing structure may be changed in order to pass part of the extra costs on to the buyer in the form of a minimum dollar charge or a service charge.
8. The cost of handling orders can be reduced by such things as more efficient packaging and net pricing. For example, instead of packing in lots of a dozen or gross, a firm may switch to decimal packaging, where the units are packed in boxes of 10, 100, or 1000, thus simplifying the accounting and record keeping.[5]

A Needed Evaluation Tool: Measure of Customer Satisfaction

Methods for evaluating customer satisfaction are not as well established as those for evaluating profit.

One study surveyed 128 major firms asking, "How do you determine the degree to which you are satisfying your customers?" Fifty-two useful replies were received, as shown in Table 17-2. (It would be expected that the 40 percent of firms that responded would represent those making the more positive efforts in this area.)

Most of these reported factors for measuring consumer satisfaction are flawed. For example, sales and market-share results are certainly very indirect measures and lack sensitivity since many

---

[5] Adapted from William J. Stanton and Richard H. Buskirk, *Management of the Sales Force*, 3d ed. (Homewood, Ill.: Irwin, 1969), pp. 612–13.

Table 17-2.
Reported Measurement Factors for Consumer Satisfaction

Measurement Factor	Number of Companies* Using Factor	Percent of Companies* Using Factor
Consumer research studies	34	65.2
Unsolicited consumer responses	34	65.2
Sales volume/trends	29	56.0
Share of market	22	42.0
Opinions of middlemen and salespeople	20	40.0
Market test results	7	13.0
Profit	1	2.0

* Some companies reported using more than one measurement factor.

Source: James U. McNeal, "Consumer Satisfaction: The Measure of Marketing Effectiveness," *MSU Business Topics,* Summer 1969, p. 33.

other determinants, such as environmental elements, quality of competition, and so on, affect sales and market share. This data gives no indication of the degree of satisfaction: Are customers strongly pleased, or merely tolerant of the product but buy it because of the effort involved in switching? And sales results probably lag behind changes in consumer satisfaction.

Soliciting opinions of middlemen and salesmen tends to give biased results since the tendencies are for salesmen to be optimistic and dealers pessimistic. While market tests may give fairly definitive results of consumer satisfaction with the new product or package or whatever is being tested, follow-up measures would seem logically necessary.[6]

Most direct feedback from customers that reaches the ears of responsible executives comes from occasional letters of complaint directed to the president. Such feedback is fragmented at best; it very likely is not representative of most customer attitudes, being the product of a vocal minority of customers most difficult to satisfy (or most desperate to have their product or service deficiency corrected). Other dissatisfied customers simply take future business elsewhere. With most firms the gaining of new customers offsets the loss of old customers and this can disguise the full seriousness of this erosion of business.

A more positive approach can be taken to ascertain the existence and sources of customer dissatisfaction and to provide feedback on their views about the policies and actions of the firm. The opportunity exists both to win new customers and to cement the loyalty of present customers. *Customer attitude surveys* can be effective here.

[6] James U. McNeal, "Consumer Satisfaction: The Measure of Marketing Effectiveness," *MSU Business Topics,* Summer 1969, pp. 31–35.

Customer Attitude Surveys

For a retail firm, attitude surveys can be made by interviewing customers leaving the store or department, perhaps those without a package, under the assumption that such people did not find what they wanted or were in some other way not satisfied. Brief questionnaires inviting customer opinions may be inserted in packages or in monthly statements. The samples need not be large. They should, however, be systematic and continuous; otherwise trends in attitudes go unnoticed and danger areas not spotted until serious erosion of old customers occurs.

More ingenuity may be required by manufacturers to obtain feedback on customer attitudes, but this is not usually difficult, since customers can be invited to express their opinions and their satisfaction or lack of it. And the assumption can be made that the more serious complaints or the strongest customer feelings will be brought to light.

Direct measures of customer satisfaction have these particular advantages: (1) trends can be established for customer attitudes and problem areas detected early before they become serious, (2) goodwill can be fostered by continuing efforts of this kind, and the reputation gained of "the firm that cares," (3) time and expense need not be great, and (4) unfilled customer needs and wants may be revealed and these may suggest opportunities to be tapped by innovation.

For thought and discussion:

How would you answer the objection that customer attitude surveys are a waste of time and an imposition on customers?

How would you assure that a customer attitude survey is as representative of customers as possible?

What arguments can you give for urging that customer attitude surveys be done regularly rather than sporadically?

Consumer panels may be used to advantage to obtain clues for various facets of consumer satisfaction. Where the panel is used periodically, the firm may detect changes in its customer-satisfaction effectiveness before they become serious. However, these panels of consumers suffer from the flaws of not always being representative of consumers in general in their method of being selected, as well as their quickly becoming "experts."

Marketers need today more than ever before to develop and more systematically use their sensors of customer satisfaction. This should be done periodically in order to detect changes. And direct measures of customer attitudes are far superior to any indirect purported measures, such as profit, sales, market share, etc.

The Marketing Audit

The total evaluation of marketing efforts can be termed a marketing audit. Inherent in any type of audit is objectivity and a critical review. The accounting audits are best known and these are periodically carried out by outsiders, usually public accountants, for the protection of stockholders and creditors.

Oxenfeldt sees the total marketing audit as appraising six separate aspects of marketing activities: (1) objectives, (2) policies, (3) organization, (4) methods, (5) procedures, and (6) personnel.[7] A thorough marketing audit would examine the whole picture, the whole marketing program, the interrelationships and their optimality in view of the objectives of the organization.

To insure objectivity, a separate department in the company, or preferably outside consultants, should conduct the audit. The sales analysis, distribution cost analysis, the various measures of advertising effectiveness and performance of salesmen, are essentially management tools, control devices, that permit marketing management to adjust as needed in order to perform the marketing operation better. The marketing audit is a measure, an evaluation, of top marketing management itself. To gain the possible benefits that can come from a comprehensive audit, management must face the possibility that their efforts could be improved, that performance is not as good as it might be. No one likes to be exposed to criticism, and to having others learn of it. Perhaps for this reason more than any other, marketing audits are performed infrequently, and then more in situations where the marketing function, and even the entire firm, is faltering. Here the audit falls into the realm of "fire fighting," a last desperate device to save a company or a division. For example, the Gilbert Company badly needed such an audit.

But this is not the way the audit can best be used. One writer points out that an audit is intended for "prognosis as well as diagnosis. . . . It is the practice of preventive as well as curative marketing medicine."[8] It can be used as an aid to decision making, such as evaluating various alternatives before a decision is reached. It can be used to single out strong points so that these can be capitalized on. If certain parts of the operation are weak, an informed management is better able to take corrective action. If used to its fullest potential a marketing audit could lead to new vistas and to innovative thinking.

Despite over a decade of attention given to the marketing audit,

---

[7] Alfred R. Oxenfeldt, *Executive Action in Marketing* (Belmont, Calif.: Wadsworth, 1966), p. 746.

[8] Abe Shuchman, "The Marketing Audit: Its Nature, Purposes, and Problems," *Analyzing and Improving Marketing Performance,* Report No. 32 (New York: American Management Association, 1959), p. 14.

its use is still limited. To be a viable part of the evaluation process, to be more than simply a desperation measure when company life is in jeopardy and time and money are too short to do more than take short-term remedial action, the marketing audit must be made more palatable to marketing executives. Its use as a tool for grading performance and placing some executive futures in perceived jeopardy must be changed. The potential value of periodic audits will hardly be realized until these become tools of management rather than criticisms of management. Despite the growing number of marketing scholars and practitioners who advocate the comprehensive approach of a marketing audit, it needs to be better sold to top management as well as to marketing executives. Marketing efficiency may thereby be improved.

Social Responsiveness

As more laws and regulations are effected—many times obfuscating because of fuzzy language and varying possible interpretations—another marketing evaluation employed is: "Is it legal?" Tentative actions which might be legally questionable, then, must be reviewed and passed by the legal department.

Unfortunately, attention often is inordinately riveted to this criterion. If the particular proposed action is judged to pass the legal hurdle, its way is clear. And perhaps this is mistaken, sometimes, and in some ways.

Would another criterion be more suitable to today's business environment? Perhaps a better basis for action is: "Is it desirable from the consumers' viewpoint?" or, "Is it in the public interest?" With such measures or criteria conscientiously used for evaluating potential decisions and actions, as well as those that have already been taken, perhaps a better marketing milieu would result. Perhaps less dissatisfaction would occur.

The very fact that many firms refuse to take corrective or remedial actions until forced to by law tends to accentuate legalistic remedies for whatever ails. This pendulum of proliferating laws and regulations may well swing too far. The preoccupation with observing what is legal rather than what might be desirable or in the public interest may eventually place business in an untenable position.

Policies and decisions affecting the public sector should be reviewed and evaluated in a systematic and objective way. If they have detracted from the firm's role as a responsible citizen, they may need to be rescinded or modified. While subjective judgment would have to be applied here, a checklist of relevant criteria could be developed, such as:

Is the promotional message free of deception and distortion?
Is the product one we can be proud to stand behind?

Is it free of environmental problems?

Does the price give the customer an honest value?

The very fact that there is a review and post facto evaluation by concerned executives could be a healthful and progressive step of marketing leadership.

CAUTIONS IN THE USE OF MARKETING PERFORMANCE EVALUATIONS

In the interest of more efficient marketing, the various evaluative tools that have been described are needed. Otherwise, operations are uncontrolled and of uneven efficiency levels, with the tendency toward widening disparity. But certain cautions should be considered in the use of these tools. Too much emphasis on them and on the performance which they purport to measure may lead to certain undesirable actions. Where promotions and compensation are completely tied to the gods of sales and profit production, with strong top management pressure for performance, responsive marketing may suffer. We will briefly discuss some of the gray and darker areas where overconcern with sales and profit performance at any cost may lead.

Profiteering

There is little agreement over the meaning of "profiteering." It may be defined as "charging more than a fair price." And this is not a very satisfactory definition, since "fair" is subject to all kinds of opinions and disagreements. Many executives and economists believe that a firm should charge all it can get: this acts as an incentive for innovation, and is a basic tenet to the mechanics of the economic system. However, others tacitly accept the idea that a point can be reached where profits are excessive and not in the best interests of society. Especially is this true in a time of strong inflationary pressures.

One example of what may be called profiteering or irresponsible management concerns the tire and rubber companies. In April and May 1970, the unions won a 7 to 8 percent hourly increase in wages. Productivity, a measure of labor efficiency, had been rising 5 percent. This means that a tire worker could achieve a 5 percent pay increase without prices being raised. Therefore, since the pay raise was more than this, unit labor costs were being boosted by 2 to 3 percent. But labor compensation represents only 30 percent of the value of the tires; therefore, the wage hike translates into only 1 percent increase in production costs.

And what did the companies do? They announced in June and July a 5% hike in replacement tire prices.[9]

Seeking maximum profits in all circumstances can be detrimental. High unit prices attract competitors and may even leave a firm and industry vulnerable to foreign competition, as the U. S. steel and auto industries have found. Then governmental reaction is always a possibility: high oil company and sugar producer profits in 1974 brought serious threats of governmental investigations and restrictive measures.

Less than Scrupulous Practices

Heavy emphasis on sales and profit performance can motivate employees toward less-than-honest marketing practices, such as false claims, deceptive packaging, exaggerated price comparisons. While approval of top management for such practices may not be explicit, it may be implied in the demands on subordinates for performance at all costs.

Illegal Actions

Sometimes pressure for performance becomes so extreme that lower and middle executives may actually break laws in order to meet performance goals and expectations. The most famous example of this was the "electrical conspiracy" which we described in chapter 5. There, you may recall, some fifty corporation executives were indicted for price-fixing in violation of the Sherman Act and seven actually received jail sentences.

Disregard for Social Issues and Consequences

It is most difficult for an executive, when faced with heavy demands for sales and profits, to give attention to social and environmental needs and consequences of his actions because to devote time and effort to social and environmental matters means time and effort taken away from profit production. Furthermore, most actions taken regarding social and environmental matters tend to impose a cost; this is hardly compatible with producing greater profits, at least in the short run.

A *social audit* or social accounting has been proposed to evaluate the social impact—good and bad—of a firm's operation. This would measure actions not in profit-and-loss performance, but in the arithmetic of quality. Such social accounting does not presently exist except in theory, but the need for it is becoming apparent. Some

---

[9] Hobart Rowen, "Inflation 'Alert' is Fine as a Start," *Washington Post*, August 11, 1970, p. A16.

businessmen themselves are anxious to demonstrate objectively that their enterprises do indeed benefit society. Although this is more an accounting challenge than a marketing one, and it will be difficult to standardize social contributions objectively, doing so would give marketers more incentive to heed social and environmental needs.[10]

QUESTIONS AND PROBLEMS

1. Market-share analysis requires data on total industry sales, or at least the sales of major competitors. How is this information to be obtained? Is there a lag in getting such information which may prevent action until too late?

2. The need has been mentioned to develop other evaluation measures to supplement the common sales and profit ones. Can you develop some objective criteria to measure an executive's contribution to (a) public relations, (b) community involvement, (c) employee development?

3. As the president of a large company manufacturing industrial goods, explain how you would evaluate the marketing performance of your firm.

4. What is the "iceberg principle"? Why is it important to the marketing manager?

5. What is the "80–20" rule? What is its importance in performance appraisal?

6. Why might a marketing audit be desirable even in a well-run company? What are major obstacles to its wider use? How would you overcome these obstacles?

7. During the 1950s many department stores were oblivious to the drain that discount stores were beginning to make on their market share. Their long delay in adjusting to this major threat enabled discounters to extend their beachheads until they were unassailable. How could department stores have made a much earlier assessment and reaction to such a changing environment?

8. Discuss the desirability of obtaining objective measures of customer satisfaction. What are the difficulties in getting such information? What would you recommend?

Project

Levitz Furniture initiated warehouse furniture showrooms, in which customers could obtain instant delivery of furniture at discount prices instead of waiting weeks for an order to arrive, as was often the case at conven-

---

[10] For an expanded discussion of the issue and the problem of social accounting see Frederick Andrews, "Puzzled Businessmen Ponder New Methods of Measuring Success," *Wall Street Journal,* December 9, 1971, pp. 1 and 25.

tional furniture dealers. For a while it seemed that Levitz would revolutionize furniture retailing. But then by 1972 sales and profits began falling, and the firm barely struggled on trying to save itself from bankruptcy. Using library research, determine the factors that led to Levitz's problems. Could Levitz have detected its emerging problems before they became so serious?

Exercise in Creativity

Describe as many ways as you can how customer satisfaction with a firm can be measured.

Role-playing Case

Your company has just conducted a study of its distribution costs. As a result of the study, a conference has been called.

Mr. Bullock, the controller, is saying, "The study indicates clearly that it is not profitable for us to handle orders under $150. I'm recommending that all customer orders must total at least $150 from now on."

Your boss, Mike Faricy, the marketing vice president, shuffles the pages of the report. "I know it looks like this should be our stated policy. But first I'd like to hear my sales manager's thoughts on this." He turns to you. "Stan, what other factors should we consider before making this decision?"

What would you say? Defend your position.

PART IV

SOCIAL
AND
ENVIRONMENTAL
ISSUES

CHAPTER 18

CONSUMERISM AND ENVIRONMENTAL PROBLEMS

Society is in the process of change, not only in needs and wants, but in tolerance and expectations. The result is that issues are being raised concerning a number of our social, business, and political institutions today, marketing among them. In this chapter we confront the major issues involving marketing: the factors that led to consumerism, and its implications; problems of marketing in the ghetto; and marketing's involvement with the environment. Important terms are:

consumer sovereignty

Consumer Reports

product testing

consumerism

the ghetto market

solid waste

recycling

THE QUESTION OF CONSUMER SOVEREIGNTY

The idea that the consumer is sovereign in our economy is appealing. It has long been the byword of advocates of the American business enterprise system. Statements such as "the customer is always right" are frequently displayed in prominent places in business offices and retail stores.

Consumer sovereignty signifies that the consumer is in fact the ultimate king with a right to buy or not to buy, that production is ultimately oriented toward meeting the wants of consumers (remember the marketing concept?), and that marketing performance is responsive to consumer demands.

Contrary to the view that our purchase decisions dictate to the marketplace, some social critics view consumers more as pawns who can be shrewdly manipulated by the unscrupulous huckster (as

Vance Packard has argued). But, as with most controversies, the answer apparently lies somewhere in between.

Up to the limits of our income (and the credit available to us), we can freely choose the kind and amount of goods and services to purchase. These choices and decisions made in the marketplace affect the fortunes of products, brands, and companies (and of the executives involved). And many firms today try to direct their efforts first to determine what consumers want and will buy, and second, to produce and market accordingly.

But in reality there are limitations to consumer sovereignty. Efforts of special interest groups such as farmers, labor, and business may lessen the influence of consumers, by limiting choice and raising prices. The value of many products is difficult for consumers to determine. Furthermore, consumers are relatively unorganized; some are apathetic; many others are ill-informed. If a firm overprices its product, fails to live up to the glowing descriptions in its advertisements, gives poor service, or is reluctant to stand behind the product, the notion of consumer sovereignty predicts that consumers refusing to purchase will force the firm to improve or go out of business. But this does not always happen. Some people may continue to buy out of ignorance or apathy, and thus the less-than-ideal marketing practices may be maintained. Although most consumers are influenced to some extent by promotional practices, price claims, displays, and salespeople, few, if any, are swayed to buy against their will. Yet some may be confused by conflicting or incomplete information. At times, consumers must stand up for their rights just as the businessman must stand up for his if consumers make unreasonable demands.

EFFECTIVENESS OF CONSUMER INFORMATION SOURCES

What means are available to the consumer to lessen confusion and aid buying effectiveness?

Considerable information is usually imparted by salespeople, advertisements, and the package. Unfortunately this information may be biased and incomplete—since persuasion to buy is the objective —with disadvantages or shortcomings seldom mentioned.

A more objective evaluation may be gained from past experience with a product by the consumer and his acquaintances. But past experience may be unreliable: one person's experience with a product is too small a sample, since the particular item may have been better or worse than the average. This is particularly likely to be true with automobiles and other complex products. Probably you can recall a friend who had good experience with a particular make of car, and another acquaintance who did not. And past experience in a rapidly changing technology may not be of much help, since few products and brands remain unchanged year after year.

Many consumers are unaware of product information disseminated by various government agencies and objective product-testing organizations such as Consumers Union in its *Consumer Reports*. Some 2,000 models in 70 product categories are tested by CU every year.[1] These published reports have some impact on sales, particularly with certain "buff industries," such as stereo components and cameras. Furthermore, these objective tests create an incentive for improving product quality, especially if a particular model tests poorly.

However, the product information provided by Consumers Union has two major limitations: (1) Only one item of a particular brand or style is usually tested. While it may be rigorously evaluated and compared with similar products, the particular item may not be representative; another random selection of the same brand might have yielded different results. (2) Some items are tested only once every several years; therefore, the items being currently produced may be far different from those that were tested.

Although progress has been made in recent years, both the amount and quality of product information available to consumers fall short of the ideal. However, a lot of evidence suggests that relatively few consumers make any effort to take advantage of the available information. Those who do take advantage of product information sources appear to be those who would seem to need help the least, the relatively highly educated and affluent consumer.[2] While obtaining more and better product information for consumers is a worthy goal for consumer organizations, they might be well advised to give an even higher priority to educating consumers to make use of the information currently available to them. Also, it would seem clearly to the advantage of the manufacturer who stresses quality in his products to participate in the education of consumers with respect to the use of product information. This is yet another example of how the responsive marketer can contribute to the improvement of consumer welfare while increasing his competitive advantage in the marketplace.

CONSUMER MILITANCE: CONSUMERISM

Consumer protests have intensified in the last decade. The term given to this new militance of consumers is *consumerism*.

[1] "Consumers Union Puts on Muscle," *Business Week*, December 23, 1967, pp. 84–86.
[2] Hans B. Thorelli, "Concentration of Information Power Among Consumers," *Journal of Marketing Research*, November 1971, pp. 427–32.

Consumer agitation or militancy is not new. Three such periods have occurred in recent U. S. history.

Early 1900s. The first major consumer protection law, the Pure Food and Drug Act of 1906, was primarily attributable to Harvey W. Wiley, Chief of the Chemistry Division of the Department of Agriculture. Beginning in 1889, pure food and drug proposals had been continuously introduced into Congress without success. But Wiley persisted in publicizing the dangers of preservatives then being used in food. His most successful tactic was a "poison squad" of 12 healthy young men who were fed adulterants daily. The marked effect of the additives on the health of these men led to widespread clamor for a food law. The resulting law forbade adulteration and misbranding of foods and drugs sold in interstate commerce.

The Meat Inspection Act of 1906 was signed into law on the same day. Its enactment stemmed from the book *The Jungle* by Upton Sinclair. Sinclair wanted to expose the inhuman exploitation of workers by the Chicago meat-packing houses. His description of the lack of sanitary conditions in the plants aroused the public and resulted in this law providing for federal inspection of slaughtering, packing, and canning plants that shipped meat across state lines.

In the 1930s. The drug elixir sulfanilamide was introduced without adequate safety testing. Over 100 persons died as a result. A shocked public got the Food, Drug, and Cosmetic Act of 1936.

In the mid-1960s. During the early 1960s prices rose gradually at about 1 percent per year. Then in 1966 there was a 5 percent increase in food prices, with the increases affecting some of the most frequently purchased items, such as beef, pork, and eggs.[3] Many consumers consequently faced a decline in purchasing power. And a wave of supermarket picketing began in Denver late in 1966.

Other factors fed the latest rise of consumer militance. Unemployment was low during most of the late 1960s, resulting in employment of marginal workers who contributed to a lessening of quality. At the same time, products were becoming technologically more complex, making for reliability and servicing problems.[4]

Undoubtedly a major influence, and possibly the precipitator of the current consumer movement, was Ralph Nader. His book *Unsafe at Any Speed,* and the clumsy efforts to discredit him by General Motors, led to a new perception of the auto industry—and the rest

[3] Robert O. Herrmann, "Consumerism: Its Goals, Organizations and Future," *Journal of Marketing,* October 1970, p. 56.

[4] Richard H. Buskirk and James T. Rothe, "Consumerism—An Interpretation," *Journal of Marketing,* October 1970, p. 63.

of business as well—one of indifference to the needs and even the safety of the public. Nader and his assistants (called "Nader's Raiders") subsequently turned their attention to many other areas affecting the general public.

Whereas the two earlier periods of consumer agitation flared up and as quickly subsided, the current period of consumerism shows few signs of doing this. It has already lasted a decade; inflation and serious recession have exacerbated the situation. The consumer today remains wary of companies and products.

Harvard sociologist David Riesman expresses it this way: "People are not as easily sold or satisfied, and they are more prone to litigation." Riesman points to the great rise in the number of malpractice suits, and the more than "100,000 people in law school, one quarter of our current legal population." To Riesman this suggests far more litigation and consumer resistance to come.[5] Philip Kotler notes that consumerism first focused mainly on product durability and integrity, but that now it is getting into the effect of products and services on our quality of life: "If you smoke, then I want you to go to another part of the theater, bus, plane, or train. Or if you drive a big car, that means you are polluting my air, and I may not like that."[6]

Support for the belief that modern consumerism will remain important comes from a recent survey in which four fifths of consumers and two thirds of businessmen believed that consumerism is here to stay and will even grow in strength in the future. The survey also found that consumerism is understood as encompassing a wide variety of issues—information, health and safety, repair and servicing, pricing issues, pollution, product quality, and consumer representation in government—and is broadening its domain.[7]

Industry Reaction to Consumerism

In the past apathy and unconcern were typical attitudes toward consumer complaints. Some executives maintained that protests were characteristic of a small minority of "chronic complainers," and therefore not worthy of any attention.

It was, moreover, easy to blame small marginal firms (such as used car dealers, car and home repair businesses, and recreational land developers) for abuses. However, even large firms have sometimes refused to stand behind defective products such as automo-

[5] "Marketing When the Growth Slows," *Business Week*, April 14, 1975, p. 45.

[6] "A Marketing Man Takes Marketers to Task," *Business Week*, July 28, 1975, p. 43.

[7] Norman Kangun, Keith K. Cox, James Higginbotham, and John Burton, "Consumerism and Marketing Management," *Journal of Marketing*, April 1975, pp. 3–10.

biles, appliances, and furniture. And "puffing" or exaggerating a product's attributes was common and sometimes deceptive.

Some marketers have opposed legislation aimed at requiring the provision of more information. For example, the Truth-in-Lending Law was finally enacted in 1968, after eight years of struggle to get it through Congress. Retailers, banks, and small loan companies opposed laws requiring them to reveal the true annual interest rate of credit buying. Likewise the posting of octane ratings at gasoline pumps has been resisted by major oil companies.

Other firms made constructive efforts to cater to consumer desires for better information and treatment. Giant Food is a notable example.

MARKETING
IN
ACTION

Responsiveness to Consumerism—Giant Food, Inc.

Giant is a regional supermarket chain that is developing a reputation as an innovative business ally of the consumerist movement. With considerable fanfare, it became one of the first major supermarket chains to adopt unit pricing, open-dating of perishables, and ingredient labeling of private-brand foods, cosmetics, toiletries, and over-the-counter drugs.

In 1970 the firm hired Esther Peterson, the former consumer adviser to Presidents Kennedy and Johnson. This militant consumer advocate was employed as the "consumer's representative at Giant." Since then she has engineered Giant's major reforms. Giant has pushed for recycled paper products and low- and no-phosphate household detergents, and for a major toy-safety campaign. Further efforts directed to product safety have included packaging its own brand of soft drinks in shatter-proof bottles, and dropping all references to food flavors, such as "lemon-fresh," from its private label household products in an attempt to prevent children from taking them to be food.

Results? In 1968 before the consumerism campaign, Giant's share of the competitive Washington, D.C., market was 26 percent, and its major competitor, Safeway, had 31 percent. By 1974 Giant had gained 30 percent of the total Washington market, while Safeway struggled to maintain its 31 percent.

SOURCE: "The Shoppers' Friend at Giant Supermarkets," *Business Week*, April 6, 1974, p. 38.

For thought and discussion:

As an executive of Giant, how would you counter the criticism that these actions are strictly public relations gestures and are really superficial?

Would you credit the gain in market share entirely to the consumerism emphasis? Why or why not?

Giant's example is by no means unique today. More than 300 corporations, with large companies leading the way, now have established consumer relations departments or ombudsmen (as we described in chapter 4) in order to be more responsive to customer complaints. It is true that most companies entered the consumer affairs area under duress as the consumer movement became so heated in the late 1960s that such departments seemed a necessity. But they are solidly established now.

Many firms are finding that the information flowing into their consumer relations departments is yielding valuable data that can be sent to marketing, sales, and quality-control departments. For example, complaints from consumers that paper napkins emitted a strange odor resulted in Scott Paper Company finding a concealed valve that had worked open and was causing the smell. Seven regional consumer boards for Pantry Pride, made up of a cross-section of supermarket shoppers, have led it to nutritional labeling and better satisfied customers; minutes of the board meetings are channeled to all Pantry Pride officers.[8] Responsive marketers are finding that profit and sales opportunities exist when they can develop and communicate broad consumer programs and that a competitive advantage can be gained over those firms slower to deal with consumer frustrations.[9] Furthermore, as more individual firms react positively to the challenges posed by consumerism, the more chance there is that pressures for government action will be reduced and burdensome regulations can be avoided.[10]

GHETTO MARKETS: THEIR PARTICULAR MARKETING PROBLEMS

Ghetto markets are not limited solely to ethnic minorities such as blacks, Indians, Puerto Ricans, and Mexican-Americans. Many native-born white Americans live under ghetto conditions. However, the extensive black ghettos in major U. S. cities represent the extreme examples of concentrations of underprivileged segments of the population. Ghetto markets offer challenges and opportunities for responsive marketing. Unfortunately, abuses also take place in these markets, of which the following is an example of some of the worst.

[8] "Disgruntled Customers Finally Get a Hearing," *Business Week*, April 21, 1975, pp. 138–42.
[9] Esther Peterson, "Consumerism as a Retailer's Asset," *Harvard Business Review*, May–June 1974, pp. 19–101.
[10] Kangun, Cox, Higginbotham, and Burton, pp. 8–9.

Abuses on the Reservation:

The Federal Trade Commission has taken action against the operators of 19 trading posts on Navajo and Hopi Indian reservations in Arizona and New Mexico. The operators of the posts—often the only places to shop within many miles of the Indians' homes—agreed to stop such tactics as:

> Refusing to cash checks in currency, issuing instead credit slips good only at the trading post.
>
> Giving only credit slips, no cash, in exchange for the Indians' handi-craft or livestock.
>
> Not marking prices on goods for sale, nor giving the Indians itemized statements of their purchases, so that they are misled about actual prices and amount owed.
>
> Selling pawned items before the legal redemption period is over.
>
> Failure to disclose true interest charges in credit transactions as required by the Truth in Lending Act.

It was charged that the practices of some trading posts kept the Navajo in a vicious circle of economic bondage, in which they repeatedly paid exorbitant prices for inferior goods.

SOURCE: "19 Trading Posts Agree to Stop Bilking Indians," *Cleveland Plain Dealer,* August 3, 1974, p. 5-C.

For thought and discussion:

What factors do you think led to such abusive practices?

Do these factors differ in the big-city ghetto?

Dimensions and Characteristics of the Ghetto Market

The original meaning of the word *ghetto* comes from the Italian *borghetto,* denoting the quarters in Italian towns to which Jews were restricted in the seventeenth century.[11] The term is more commonly used today to refer to certain areas of large cities where various low-income ethnic groups are "restricted," generally because of economic factors, but intensified by social factors.

Per capita income is low in the ghetto, although the total purchasing power in U.S. ghettos is estimated at about $50 billion. Undoubtedly this is growing rapidly, as more blacks increase their income, the growth rate being significantly higher than for whites, and as more funds are distributed in ghetto development programs.[12]

[11] *Oxford Universal Dictionary* (Oxford: Clarendon Press, 1964), p. 790.

[12] John W. Gould, Normal B. Sigband, and Cyril E. Zoener, Jr., "Black Consumer Reactions to Integrated Advertising," *Journal of Marketing,* July 1970, p. 20.

The individual ghetto dweller usually has insufficient cash because of low-paying jobs and small welfare checks for the jobless. Low and irregular pay requires a "hand to mouth" existence, with goods and services tailored to this requirement. Furthermore, there appears to be a general inability to manage money in ghetto households. Credit is often unavailable because of a poor record or lack of steady employment or perhaps because the person is new to the city.

A lack of mobility characterizes the ghetto consumer: no car, poor bus service, inability to afford taxis. But more than the lack of physical mobility, there often is a psychological immobility: even if the physical means of transportation were available, there may be a reluctance to brave the unfamiliarity of the world outside the ghetto. This plays a major role in perpetuating less than desirable marketing practices in the ghetto.

Marketing Practices in the Ghetto

The ghetto environment makes doing business difficult, as well as more costly than elsewhere. Extremely high rates of shoplifting, vandalism, and armed robbery are characteristic. But there are other drawbacks that dissuade large reputable firms from entering the ghetto. Donald Perkins, president of Jewel Companies, which operates supermarkets, cites some reasons behind a reluctance to open stores in the inner city:

1. Rents are higher—as much as 50 percent higher than land costs in the suburbs.
2. Operating costs are higher—because the per capita sale averages only one half the typical sale in a suburban store, twice the traffic is needed to produce the same sales; this results in more help required, and more wear and tear.
3. Pilferage and security costs are higher—several times as high in the ghetto as in suburban stores.
4. Experienced and successful supermarket management, whether white or black, wears down from the increased pressures of lawlessness and militancy which characterize large parts of the ghetto.[13]

To these costs must be added higher insurance costs for operating in the ghetto; in some cases insurance cannot even be obtained.

Consequently the ghetto is usually left to small independent merchants who manage a precarious—and even fearful—existence. Typically the ghetto store is drab and run-down. The owner does not

[13] Donald S. Perkins, "The Low-Income Consumer—a Human Problem and a Selling Problem," Executive Lecture Series, March 2, 1970, University of Notre Dame.

have to invest capital in order to compete. Merchandise is of inferior quality and high-priced. Stores handling major durables are plentiful since cultural pressures are such that the consumer attempts to improve low social standing through *compensatory consumption*—success being measured by what one is able to buy.

Special adaptations of credit are used. Credit is offered in spite of high risk; it is tailored to the particular needs of low-income consumers, such as "no money down" and "a dollar down and a dollar a week." And of course the credit charges are all that the law allows, and sometimes more. A special form of credit is the *balloon note*, which prescribes small payments until the end, when a high final payment is required, one often beyond the means of the debtor; thereby, repossessions are facilitated and some of this merchandise may be sold over and over again.

Formal controls over credit consumers include liens against property and wages, repossession of merchandise, and discounting paper (selling the note or the sales contract to a third party, such as a finance company). In the latter case (unless specifically voided by recent legislation), this third party becomes the "innocent" holder in due course and is entitled to full recompense regardless of the condition of the merchandise or service sold—even if the appliance falls apart in a few weeks. Informal controls are frequently used. These include flexible credit which allows for an occasional missed payment, and small weekly payments which the customer brings to the store. The latter provides an opportunity for the merchant to sell additional goods and to know the customer better (rather like being in debt to the company store).

There are no laws that regulate maximum markups, and these may be two or three times the original price. Some stores might be termed *multiprice stores:* there is an absence of price tags, and the sales personnel vary the price according to whether the customer looks like a poor risk, or whether he appears naive. *Bait advertising* may be used to attract customers, with items offered at unusually low prices; in reality these are not available, or else are shopworn or broken, so that the customer is switched, perhaps with high-pressure tactics, to more expensive items.

Price sometimes may be deliberately misrepresented; a sales contract may have the price and terms left blank, to be filled in by the merchant after the customer has signed it and left; terms of a contract may not be explained and may be far different from what the customer thought. Often the customer has no privilege to return goods which are purchased in good faith as being new, even if they turn out to be defective or used.[14]

[14] For more specifics of the ghetto marketing situation, see Frederick D. Sturdivant, "Better Deal for Ghetto Shoppers," *Harvard Business Review,* March–April 1968, pp. 30–39; also Michael Drosnin, "Spanish Harlem Furniture Seller Provides Credit, plus High Prices and Hard Dunning," *Wall Street Journal,* August 28, 1970; Donald E. Sexton, Jr., "Comparing the Cost of Food to Blacks and to Whites—A Survey," *Journal of Marketing,* July 1971, pp. 40–46.

Profitability in the Ghetto

With the practices which can occur in the ghetto where there often is a captive and naive consumer, the question naturally arises as to the relative profitability of ghetto and nonghetto stores. An indication of this is a 1966 survey of District of Columbia appliance and furniture stores which was conducted under the auspices of the Federal Trade Commission.[15] This not only provided information on relative selling prices of ghetto and nonghetto stores, but of expense and profitability measures as well. Table 18-1 shows this comparison.

Several things are obvious from this table. Undoubtedly the low-income market is a very expensive place to buy durable goods. Not only is the average retail price for the particular product category, such as television sets, from 40 to 80 percent higher than that of nonghetto retailers, but the direct product and brand comparisons show an even more striking disparity. The indication is that low-income market retailers carry lower-quality items than other retailers, but charge so much more that the average retail price is considerably higher.

The product gross margin comparisons also bear out the much higher prices charged in the ghetto stores. The total gross margin as a percent of sales reflects the overall high markups. Not all of this high markup translates into net profits, since the net profit figures, while higher than for the other categories of retailers, are not unusually high. However, a key indicator of relative profitability is the comparison of *return on investment*. Here the ghetto stores show up very poorly indeed, compared to the other retailers. Evidently the high prices charged have been accompanied by substantially higher costs of doing business. High credit losses, greater chances of being robbed, and difficulty in getting insurance probably account for some of these greater costs; and some probably are due to a generally inefficient operation. Despite a high profit per item, lack of volume selling also does not lead to high return on investment profits.

Therefore, it can hardly be concluded that low-income market retailers make profits substantially higher on the average than retailers in general.

Opportunities for Improving Marketing in the Ghetto

Per capita income is low in the ghetto, but total purchasing power is large and growing. Competition in the inner city is vulnerable to chains and other responsible retailers offering bigger, cleaner stores,

[15] Federal Trade Commission survey, "Economic Report on Installment Credit and Retail Sales Practices of District of Columbia Retailers," as reported in Frederick D. Sturdivant, *The Ghetto Marketplace* (New York: Free Press, 1969), pp. 76–107.

Table 18-1.

Comparative Statistics of Low-Income and General-Market
Appliance and Furniture Retailers in the District of Columbia, 1966

	Low-Income Market Retailers	General Market Retailers	
		Appliance Stores	Furniture Stores
Number of companies	18	22	22
Gross margin as percent of sales	60.8	30.2	41.2
Average gross margins (as percent of sales) on best-selling items			
Television sets	46.4	23.7	28.4
Refrigerators	50.6	24.5	24.9
Stereo phonographs	52.7	33.0	36.8
Vacuum cleaners	57.9	26.3	30.2
Radios	60.0	23.4	38.0
Average "retail prices"			
Television set	$ 187	$ 131	$ 140
Refrigerator	202	132	133
Stereo phonograph	211	149	157
Vacuum cleaner	237	136	143
Radio	250	130	161
Specific product and brand comparisons of retail prices			
Motorola portable TV	$ 219.95	$ 129.95	
Admiral portable TV	249.95	129.95	
Norge automatic washer	299.95	155.00	
Norge dryer	249.95	102.45	
Hoover upright vacuum cleaner	79.95	59.95	
Net Profit (after taxes) as			
Percent of sales	4.7	2.1	3.9
Return on investment	10.1	20.3	17.6

Source: Adapted from Federal Trade Commission survey, "Economic Report on Installment Credit and Retail Sales Practices of District of Columbia Retailers," as reported in Frederick D. Sturdivant, *The Ghetto Marketplace* (New York: Free Press, 1969) pp. 76–107.

honest values, and improved services. As supermarket, drug, variety, and other chains enter or remodel in ghetto locations, they can play a major role in beautifying the inner city and in giving a new sense of pride to people tired of dilapidated and dirty buildings.

However, companies that view this as a potential new market face challenges and problems they may never have faced before. A firm's marketing strategy can engender hostile attitudes, or strong support and cooperation. Ghetto consumers are particularly sensitive to a company's employment practices, its advertising posture, and its perceived attitudes toward minority consumers. "Tokenism" in hiring, advertising, and other aspects of company operations may arouse hostility as black communities tend to be extremely suspicious of perceived nongenuine efforts.[16]

Successfully tapping the ghetto market, then, requires a changed and specially tailored marketing program, such as the following box describes. This is especially true with credit. The established ghetto merchants who have shoddy goods at exorbitant prices do provide relatively liberal credit. If ghetto consumers are not to remain chained to these merchants, other retailers must provide easier credit.

**MARKETING
IN
ACTION**

Tapping the Ghetto Market
Retail outlets that face doing business in the ghetto, either from choice or because the ghetto expanded and grew around an existing store, need to adjust merchandising and operating policies if they are to be successful in this environment. Small details such as the following are vitally important:

Use of black manikins in windows and displays

Extra large sizes in skirts, blouses, sweaters, and dresses (since a poor diet results in a greater proportion of overweight women among blacks)

Christmas cards with black angels or a black Santa dressed in an African dashiki; black dolls

Use of black salespeople (in Spanish-speaking neighborhoods, using salespeople who speak the language, and advertising through local Spanish-speaking radio stations)

As an example of how a retailer may successfully direct a marketing strategy to the ghetto consumer, McBride's discount chain in Washington, D.C., has four major stores, all deep in ghetto neighborhoods. Managed and staffed by blacks (although under white ownership), McBride's offers reasonable prices and a big assortment of merchandise, all geared to the black community. Newspaper ads and local TV commercials feature blacks exclusively.

For thought and discussion:
Do you think white managers would necessarily be a drawback to a ghetto store, as long as most of the salespeople were black? How about white owners?

---

[16] H. Naylor Fitzhugh, "The Ethnic Challenge to Marketing Management," *University of Washington Business Review,* Spring 1969, p. 31.

Ecological issues relevant to marketing for the most part concern problems of packaging and problems of certain product and land use. The convenience of nonreturnable containers has contributed to the littering of our landscape. An automobile culture has led to an insatiable demand for construction of highways, to air pollution, to a plethora of billboards and honky tonks, and to piles of discarded autos and other junk. An ever growing consumption of land resulting from urban sprawl and recreational land development has raised ecological and esthetic concerns.

In truth, consumers themselves have exhibited a selfish disregard for what ecologists have called the creeping destruction of the environment. For example, the litter of throwaway containers reflects public demand for the convenience of this type of packaging. Human litter cannot be ignored as part of the pollution problems: careless picnickers deface and dump refuse, and the beer can at the side of the road was thrown there by someone.

Our *solid wastes* proliferate:
Solid wastes accumulated in the U. S. total 4.3 billion tons annually.
Americans collect over 200 million tons of household solid waste annually—over five pounds a day for every man, woman, and child in the nation. By 1977 the figure will reach six pounds a day.
We spend some $4.5 billion to dispose of refuse.
We throw away annually 48 billion cans, 26 billion bottles and jars, 4 million tons of plastic, and 30 million tons of paper.[17]

Some states are beginning to take action to reduce solid waste. Oregon in 1972 was the first state to enact legislation to reduce litter. Its widely acclaimed "bottle law" required deposits on all beverage containers and banned detachable-tab "pop-top" cans; other provisions aimed at encouraging reuse of containers. South Dakota and Vermont followed quickly and passed similar laws.

There is the possibility that one of the most popular methods of packaging and dispensing hair spray, deodorant, insect repellant, and other products that require a fine spray—aerosol containers—may be threatening the ozone layer in the stratosphere. Nearly 3 billion cans of aerosol products are sold annually in the U. S., and some scientists contend that the fluorocarbons, the chemical propellants, could deplete the ozone layer by 16 percent within 25 years, resulting in increased skin cancer and serious alterations of the world's

[17] David Pinto, *How to Make Ecology Work for You* (New York: Chain Store Age Books, 1972), pp. 123–24.

weather. Should the evidence against aerosols prove so conclusive that they are banned, Du Pont officials note: ". . . we're in the chemistry business, and we have the capability of inventing something new—if we have to."[18]

In addition to problems being posed by solid waste disposal and aerosols, marketers are being challenged in their use of land:

> In Hastings-on-Hudson, N. Y., people tried to block a $50 million shopping center in adjacent Yonkers. They feared increased air pollution, noise pollution, and big traffic jams.

> In Rutland, Vermont, a developer finally won state approval for a shopping center after a 16-month delay, during which he had to improve the drainage system and provide more open space.[19]

> Helter-skelter land development is being curbed in some states: Colorado has acted to prevent overbuilding on its slopes; California declared a moratorium on all development within 1,000 ft. of its entire Pacific coastline; New York passed a bill to control land use on 3,700,000 acres of the Adirondacks; Vermont enacted legislation to control land development and speculation.[20]

The firm that ignores or is not responsive to environmental pressures is vulnerable. In 1971, Boise Cascade Corporation, at that time the nation's largest recreational land developer, decided to get out of the business and wrote off $300 million of assets in doing so. It had been plagued with lawsuits stemming from high-pressure selling methods, false promises to customers, and demands for more ecological safeguards in its developments, such as better sewage facilities.

We need to recognize the complexity of solving some environmental problems. While the legislation to control the use of nonreturnable containers is effective—Oregon reported reductions in beverage-container litter of 75 to 85 percent[21]—the effect of reduced use of bottles and cans nationwide would be drastic on the canmaking industry and cause some unemployment. Similarly, when a plant is closed because its air pollution controls do not meet certain standards the resulting unemployment makes it a harsh remedy.

[18] "Why Aerosols are under Attack," *Business Week,* February 17, 1975, pp. 50–51.

[19] "Environmental Clashes Held Up Construction of Shopping Centers," *Wall Street Journal,* September 25, 1973, pp. 1 and 19.

[20] "Saving the Land," *Time,* May 28, 1973.

[21] Ibid.

What Marketers Can Do

Marketers can take at least four approaches toward easing our environmental problems. The growing burden of solid-waste disposal is making apparent the need to eliminate throwaways and indestructible containers, even at the sacrifice of some jobs and of some consumer convenience. But eliminating throwaway containers may not be easy, competitively, unless all firms in a given industry do likewise (perhaps through government bans).

Marketers can provide for waste disposal in their marketing programs. For durable goods of limited life expectancy, consumers can be offered incentives for systematic disposal of worn-out products, perhaps through trade-ins or scrap rebates.

Advertising can be used to impress consumers with the importance of pollution control and waste abatement. They may have to be persuaded to accept some sacrifice of convenience and perhaps some increase in prices. Yet the need to do a powerful selling job for environmental control may be as great as it is for soap and toothpaste and cars.

Finally, some marketers may have to sacrifice potential market opportunity and profits. A firm concerned with the environment may have to refuse to market certain products that would cause disposal or pollution problems for which no solution apparently is possible. This then becomes a real test of *responsive marketing.*

There are examples of marketers who are making positive

Reynolds, among other firms, sponsors recycling programs for aluminum cans. *Courtesy Reynolds Metals Company.*

efforts to combat ecological problems. The efforts of Giant Food in promoting *recycled* (that is, reprocessed and reused) paper products, such as toilet paper, towels, and napkins, as well as low phosphate detergents was mentioned earlier in this chapter. Another supermarket chain in the Denver area has vigorously promoted ecology.

**MARKETING
IN
ACTION**

Promoting Environmental Involvement—King Soopers

King Soopers is a small regional supermarket chain (thirty-one stores) that has gained a national reputation as a leader among retail ecologists. Much of its efforts are aimed at arousing public awareness of environmental problems and motivating positive efforts to lessen these problems. Brochures and booklets are distributed urging citizens to get involved in ecology. Ads are run urging Boy Scouts and similar groups to help fight pollution, and suggestions made as to what can be done. Certain products are recommended at the expense of others—such as low-phosphate detergents, vinegar to cut soap film, fly paper and fly swatters rather than pesticides. Milk is sold in bottles, soft drinks in returnable containers. The chain has even gone so far as to distribute trees during Earth Week to local students.

SOURCE: David Pinto, *How to Make Ecology Work for You* (New York: Chain Store Age Books, 1972), pp. 84–86.

For thought and discussion:

If one retailer refuses to stock canned beverages and throwaway containers and insists on returnable bottles, but competitive merchants do not, what is likely to be the consequence? Is there a solution to this for the ecologically concerned marketer?

Recycling or reusing paper products has been cited for its ecological benefits in saving our trees. Unfortunately, the cost of recycling paper products makes them as expensive as new products. How would you as a retailer promote the use of recycled toilet paper and paper towels (these goods are neither as durable nor as soft as nonrecycled products)? Would you expect to be successful?

There can be a compatibility between profits and ecology-mindedness. Giant Food and King Soopers both realized sales and profit gains from their vigorous promotion of ecology. As another example, First National Bank of Denver, in a two-month savings promotion, offered to plant one tree along Denver's South Platte River for each $200 deposit. Result: it planted 4,205 new trees, and gained $8 million in new deposits.[22]

[22] "Marketing Observer," *Business Week*, June 9, 1975, p. 64.

An attuning to emerging environmental problems can influence a firm to change its whole long-range strategy and company objectives. Rohr Industries, in plotting population curves and the life of the world's known mineral deposits, is transforming its direction. Formerly it drew 100 percent of its sales from aerospace. Now it is shifting its marketing emphasis toward mass transit and other energy-conserving transportation systems: "We foresaw the day when it would no longer be economic to put 4,000 pounds of irreplaceable resources into an automobile and then pump 5,000 gallons of gasoline through the car to run it."[23]

QUESTIONS AND PROBLEMS

1. What do you think are the fundamental causes of the abusive marketing practices in the ghetto?

2. Comment on the following statement:
   "Freedom of shopping decision is a fundamental prerogative—even the freedom to be wrong, to make a wrong choice. No one has to buy anything, at any price, at any time . . . Some degree of responsibility must rest on and with the consumer. He cannot be regarded as a pitiable imbecile. He cannot be wholly protected in every move and every purchase he makes, every day of his life."[24]

3. In your shopping, are you concerned with getting the best value for your money? How do you approach this problem?

4. What are limitations of the product-testing information furnished by such organizations as Consumers Union and its *Consumer Reports*? Do you think these limitations can be overcome? How?

5. It is estimated that if the U. S. soft-drink and beer producers would switch entirely to returnable containers—thereby eliminating a major source of solid waste—the glass container and can-manufacturing industries would have their sales cut from one half to two thirds, with the consequent mass layoff of workers. How would you resolve the dilemma between an improved environment and unemployment? What should our priorities be?

6. Have you encountered any "bait advertising"? Was this on the part of a large reputable firm, or small marginal ones? What was your reaction?

7. In our quest for better information in making our buying decisions, what do we still need? Can you suggest priorities for furnishing such information?

8. In your judgment, can consumerism and government reaction go too far? What criteria would you use in making such a determination?

[23] "Marketing When the Growth Slows," *Business Week*, August 14, 1975, pp. 44–46.

[24] As quoted in E. B. Weiss, "Marketers Fiddle While Consumers Burn," *Harvard Business Review*, July–August 1968.

Project

Check for consumer-help organizations in your community. Ascertain how long they have been in operation, their specific function or objectives, and how many consumers they have benefited. Evaluate their effectiveness. How could they be more effective?

Exercise in Creativity

A supermarket chain has decided to push ecology. The president is sincerely concerned with environmental problems, but he also sees some benefits to the firm in developing a public image of an environmental protector. How many ideas can you come up with for such a firm to develop an ecology public-relations campaign?

Role Playing Case

You are the district sales manager for an encyclopedia firm. Your salesmen sell door-to-door; they are paid on a straight commission. Consequently the poorer ones are quickly weeded out and the nucleus of your sales force are very effective producers.

However, you have been troubled that some of these effective producers are "high-pressure artists" who have been most successful in low-income neighborhoods. One day a particularly indignant woman calls you complaining that her husband had just been pressured into buying a set of encyclopedias for which their children would have no earthly use for years since the oldest was still a toddler. Finally you decide to talk to your boss, the vice-president of sales, about this and similar situations.

You explain to him how you know a considerable proportion of sales are being made to rather unsophisticated customers who are pressured to sign a sales contract, and then regret it. "Mr. Rankin," you tell him, "I would like to recommend a new policy to give our customers three days, in case they change their minds, to cancel the sale."

Mr. Rankin silently appraises you, all the while steadily puffing on his pipe. Finally he says mildly, "John, what do you think such a policy would do to sales? Once the salesman is gone, won't we have quite a few customers changing their minds?"

How would you answer this objection? (Assume that your state has no law allowing for a "cooling-off period" in which consumers may change their minds.)

CHAPTER 19

EVALUATING

MARKETING

PRACTICES

The over-all objective of this book is to provide the basic knowledge and understanding of marketing needed as a foundation for understanding the general process of business administration, whatever specialty in business one might wish to follow. The theme, or special flavor, of this book is its emphasis on *responsive* management. The responsive manager is one who is always aware of conditions in the environment and who constantly searches for ways to respond with positive actions that better serve the needs of the consumer while giving the firm an advantage over competitors who are less sensitive to the signals from the environment.

Throughout the book we have stressed that marketing is by its very nature the most visible of the business functions and therefore tends to receive a lion's share of public attention and criticism. The responsive manager can turn criticism to advantage by accepting it with an open mind and trying to maintain an objective viewpoint. If criticisms result from misinformation or misunderstanding, the responsive marketing manager may be able to provide information in advertisements or on the product itself to overcome the criticisms. If criticisms have substantive grounds, the responsive marketer seeks to modify the product or marketing practices to overcome the criticisms. The responsive marketer meets criticisms head on and tries to deal with them rather than ignoring or dismissing them.

Throughout the text a number of criticisms of marketing have been discussed. In this final chapter we will consolidate and review a wide variety of criticisms and attempt to evaluate their validity and to consider ways in which marketers can deal with them responsively. Key terms are:

distribution costs	**dependence effect**
planned obsolescence	**resource misallocation**
proliferation of brands	**behavior manipulation**
inefficient channels	**taste manipulation**

Criticisms that have been directed at marketing range from complaints about specific instances of minor flaws in products to sweeping indictments of the marketing system under the following major categories:

1. Inefficiencies in the marketing system
2. Marketing malpractices
3. Marketing omissions
4. Influence on morals

Some of the more common criticisms in each of these categories are listed in Table 19-1.

CRITICISMS OF MARKETING EFFICIENCY

Costs of Marketing

Various researchers have placed distribution costs at between 42 and 59 cents for every dollar the ultimate consumer pays.[1] The amount varies depending primarily on whether marketing activities of manufacturers and transportation agencies are included. The figure seems large under any estimate. And the implication drawn by critics of marketing is that marketing is inefficient and wasteful.

Nowhere is marketing subjected to more criticism of its efficiency than with food products: the farmer decries the small amount he receives for his goods, while the same goods when processed and on grocers' shelves sell for several times as much. For example, in 1972 farmers received about 55 cents per gallon for Grade A milk. That same milk, after being moved through the marketing system to retailers' shelves, cost the consumer an average of $1.29 a gallon.

Yet while the jump in price from farmer to consumer more than doubled, and might seem excessive for a product that is not substantially changed en route to final consumption, an analysis of the steps or processes shows none that could be eliminated:

STEPS IN DISTRIBUTING MILK FROM FARM TO TABLE[2]

1. Handling and transporting to county station where production from many farmers is accumulated each day;

---

[1] Reavis Cox, *Distribution in a High-Level Economy* (Englewood Cliffs, N.J.: Prentice-Hall, 1965), p. 149; Paul W. Stewart and J. Frederic Dewhurst, *Does Distribution Cost Too Much?* (New York: Twentieth Century Fund, 1939), pp. 117–18; and W. F. Malenbaum, "The Cost of Distribution," *Quarterly Journal of Economics*, February 1941, pp. 255–70.

[2] For a breakdown of costs for each of the stages in the distribution of milk, compiled in 1966, see Robert E. Dallos, "Milk: Case History of a Rising Price," *New York Times*, August 7, 1966.

Table 19-1.
Classification of Marketing Criticisms*

Marketing Inefficiency—"Marketing Costs Too Much"
  Too many middlemen; distribution is too complex.
  Too many inefficient firms, especially small retailers.
  Too many kinds of goods.
  Too much advertising.
  Service to customers is decreasing, and costs are increasing.
Marketing Malpractices
  Poor-quality products.
  Murky and deceptive warranties.
  Poor service on defective goods.
  Deceptive packaging.
  Deceptive pricing.
  Prices are too high.
  Deceptive advertising and promotional practices.
  Planned product obsolescence.
Marketing Omissions
  Unconcern with effects on environment, pollution, congestion, etc.
  Unconcern with health and safety of consumers.
  Unconcern with problems and needs of minority groups.
  Indifference to ethics, aesthetics, and social responsibilities.
Marketing's Influence on Morals
  Marketing manipulates us.
  Dependence effect of Galbraith.
  Fosters hedonism in the masses; false values; materialism.
  Marketing is in bad taste.

---

* Some of these do not fit neatly in any one category; for ease of discussion, however, this has arbitrarily been done.

2. Handling and transporting to city: milk is inspected, tested, cooled, and shipped in tank trucks to city;
3. Processing: milk is sampled, pasteurized, and homogenized;
4. Packaging: handled and placed in milk containers;
5. Local delivery to retailer;
6. Handling by retailer.

Substantial costs are incurred at each of these stages. These costs—of processing, transportation, packaging, and merchandising—all involve substantial wage payments to workers and the use of expensive facilities. The initial impression of rank exploitation of the dairy farmer hardly seems warranted when one examines the complete process of marketing milk.

Growing Labor Force in Marketing

Attention became focused on the size of marketing, as indicated by the number of persons employed in it, as the result of a monumental study by Harold Barger. In tracing the growth of marketing, he found that the percentage of the total labor force engaged in marketing was 8 percent in 1870; in 1950 it was 25 percent. Stated another way, this is a twelvefold increase in the number of retail and wholesale workers, and only a threefold increase in the number of production workers.[3] Thus is posed the question: Does this indicate a growing waste and inefficiency in marketing as suggested by the critics of marketing?

In appraising the relative increase of marketing employment, one must consider whether marketing is performing a bigger task now than in 1870. Even a critic must concede that:

1. Demands for services, such as credit, more attractive stores, faster transportation, and the like, have increased.
2. Consumers are demanding, and marketing is providing, a greater choice of goods, more convenient packaging, and smaller units—more assortment and more convenience.
3. As the total market increases, there is a greater lapse of time and distance between producers and consumers, and it is marketing's task to fill this gap. While production facilities may be centralized, marketing facilities must be near consumers.

It is true that marketing has not become as automated, as mechanized, as scientifically planned, as much of production. But most aspects of marketing do not permit such automation, nor would consumers tolerate it. How can personal selling and other service activities be mechanized? The totally mechanized retail store, or the use of closed-circuit TV to enable the customer to see goods at home and order through a computer system with billing and delivery arranged automatically, seems still far in the future, despite some optimists.[4] There is very real doubt if enough consumers would support these innovations even if the costs could be made competitive.

There are solid examples of increasing marketing efficiency. Particularly is this true in food distribution, and since food is such a vital part of our well-being, improving efficiencies here assumes greater importance relative to other consumption areas. The large food chains have progressively reached for the new technologies in the physical handling of their bulky products. One result has been a median increase in inventory turnover by supermarkets of nearly 28 percent in the period 1954 and 1965.[5] This means that less inventory

[3] Harold Barger, *Distribution's Place in the American Economy Since 1869* (Princeton, N.J.: Princeton University Press, 1955), chap. 1.

[4] E. B. Weiss, "What Will Retailing Be Like in 1975?" *Marketing Insights,* November 7, 1966, pp. 14–16; A. F. Doody and W. R. Davidson, "Next Revolution in Retailing," *Harvard Business Review,* June 1967, pp. 4–21.

[5] National Commission on Food Marketing, *Organization and Competition in Food Retailing, Technical Study No. 7,* June 1966, p. 227.

Table 19-2.
Tons Handled per Man-hour in
Retail-Chain Warehouses

	Annual Average Tons Handled per Man-hour
1954	1.85
1956	1.87
1958	2.02
1960	2.11
1962	2.12
1964	2.26

Source: National Commission on Food Marketing, *Organization and Competition in Food Retailing, Technical Study No. 7,* June 1966, p. 229.

has to be maintained—through a more efficient operation—to support a given amount of sales. Another measure of increasing efficiency is the tons handled per man-hour in retail-chain warehouses. Table 19-2 shows this steady upward trend.

Are There Too Many Middlemen?

It is commonly believed that the more middlemen involved in the process of distribution, the more costly it is and the more inefficient. This overlooks the economies of scale in transportation, storage, and merchandise handling available to large middlemen. Also, the point is missed that certain functions have to be performed after an item is produced before it can reach the final consumer in acceptable form. Usually one or more stages of processing, assembling, packaging, and distribution must be provided. The functions and tasks must be done; it matters not whether independent middlemen perform the functions, or whether some or most are provided by either the manufacturer or the retailer. Regardless of who provides the functions, there is a cost involved; it cannot be escaped.

The often highly specialized intermediaries that have evolved in the channel of distribution may represent the most efficient form of operation. An example here is the food broker who has become extremely important in grocery distribution, accounting for more than half of the processed goods sold in grocery stores. Representing food manufacturers, food brokers call predominantly on grocery wholesalers and chains, and for the usual commission of 5 percent of sales handle the entire selling function for both large and small clients. Their growth in the food marketing channel indicates their greater efficiency in performing a specific function than is possible with other alternatives.

Perhaps other costs can be reduced, at least in some cases. It is sometimes possible to distribute goods both more cheaply and also more quickly, by a fresh approach, one which uses the latest advances in technology, in systems analysis, in equipment handling, and warehouse operation. One need only observe the number of outmoded, multistory warehouse and wholesale facilities that continue to exist in our central cities, to realize the efficiencies possible just in changing physical facilities.

MARKETING
IN
ACTION

Streamlining Distribution: Rebirth of Farmers' Markets

In the past five years, old fashioned farmers' markets have opened in the downtown areas of more than 60 cities. In Louisville, Kentucky, for example, the weekly farmers' market in an inner-city parking lot found four of its 18 farmers sold out of turnips, green peppers, squash and other fresh produce in just 2½ hours after opening, while hundreds of shoppers crowded around the laden tables.

Typically a farmers' market is a group of stands that local farmers rent to sell their produce one or two days a week, from spring to fall. At one time farmers' markets were a key part of the agricultural distribution system, but improved transportation and refrigeration, and the spead of suburban shopping centers drove most of them to extinction. Now they are coming back because fruits and vegetables often cost one-third less than at supermarkets. The personalized, friendly atmosphere is also appealing to many consumers turned off by the impersonality of supermarkets. Many shoppers are rebelling against mass marketing of plastic-wrapped and processed foods; they prefer buying freshly picked produce from those who grow it.

While some established retailers have complained about certain city organizations, such as chambers of commerce and urban renewal agencies, sponsoring the farmers' markets, many downtown merchants have turned into boosters as customer traffic and sales increase on market days.

SOURCE: "Farmers' Markets Sprout Inside the Cities as Buyers Like Low Prices, Friendly Aura," *Wall Street Journal*, August 25, 1975, p. 20.

For thought and discussion:
In what ways are the farmers' markets a more efficient way of marketing? A less efficient way?
Can you think of other examples where marketing might be streamlined?

Are There Too Many Inefficient Firms?

This criticism is difficult to refute. As discussed in chapter 3, the easy entry into retailing, the fact that the untrained, the under-financed, even the totally incompetent can open a retail store and exist for a while makes this part of marketing less efficient than it might be were entry restricted to only large, professionally managed firms. The high rate of business failure of small firms—especially small retailers—adds both a marketing cost and a social cost when viewed as isolated events.

Would we be content with our society were business entry restricted only to the able and the wealthy? Probably not. One of the options available to us—to go into business for ourselves—would be denied to most. Even though only a small proportion take the option of self-employment, its loss, in the interest of an impersonal greater efficiency, might make us all psychologically poorer. Most of today's large and efficient retailing organizations began as small individually owned stores.

Are There Too Many Goods and High Product Failure?

Our economy today is characterized by a proliferation of goods, of brands, models, and styles. This results in shorter product life cycles, more product failures. It causes inventory problems, results in broken sizes and colors, overstocks in marginal goods, a lack of display space and stock space. It results in almost desperate efforts by manufacturers to grasp at some semblance of differentiation, however trivial, in order to gain a measure of distinction and thereby have some competitive advantage. This adds to marketing costs: bookkeeping, inventory, physical handling, and product development costs, promotional costs (in order to constantly introduce another differentiated product), and the costs of product failure. The multiplicity of brands, of conflicting claims, and of thinly differentiated products confuses the customer and makes nearly impossible the search for the best value.

But at the other extreme, of limited brands and assortments, consumer choice would be thwarted and our needs less well satisfied. It is doubtful that we would be content with this situation, despite the fact that marketing efficiency in a mechanical, impersonal sense might thereby be substantially improved.

Is There Too Much Advertising?

Some of the loudest criticisms of marketing concern advertising. Even people in the advertising industry admit concern:

> The believability of advertising is being seriously jeopardized by the attempt to create "psychological differences," psychological superiorities, in products where no such

differences or superiorities exist. . . . [T]he sheer volume of advertising . . . there is too much of it.[6]

With advertising expenditures at over $25 billion, and the average family exposed to 1,500 advertisements per day, it is likely that many firms are advertising in ineffective ways. But until the effectiveness of advertising can be far better measured than it is today, the chances are that expenditures will continue to mount, since few firms dare risk cutting back on advertising when its power is a relatively unknown factor. With the marketplace becoming ever more competitive and a spate of new and quasi-new products continuing to enter, advertising is not likely to diminish in importance. But we may be approaching an upper limit; indeed, as Eldridge suggests, we may already have passed the point of diminishing returns.

Few of us would advocate doing away with advertising (although there are such advocates, one being the historian Arnold Toynbee).[7] Even the Soviet Union, with its planned economy, has found the need to advertise. Some firms that have a policy of heavy use of advertising have been markedly successful. Bristol-Myers has been advertising at the rate of 15–20 percent of sales and showed a sales growth rate of 13 percent a year between 1960 and 1969, while profits rose even faster, expanding at a 23 percent yearly pace.[8] Undoubtedly with some products, advertising, by opening up mass consumption markets, has resulted in lowering prices. In other cases, advertising may only be adding to marketing costs. The problem is that we do not know how much is too much and what the extent of the waste might be.

Is Customer Service Decreasing?

Despite inflationary pressures that seem to result in steadily increasing prices, consumers complain of finding not only fewer salespeople, but also fewer knowledgeable and courteous ones. Self-service has progressed from supermarkets not only to discount stores but to variety stores and even certain departments in department stores, without any obvious beneficial effects on prices. Consumer credit—especially installment credit—has been revealed to be not so much a customer service as a money-making operation for many retailers. Other customer services, such as delivery and gift wrapping, are often discouraged and are no longer included in the price. And ser-

[6] From a speech given by Clarence Eldridge before the National Retail Merchants Association, as reported in *Progressive Grocer*, July 1964, New York, pp. 1–2. Mr. Eldridge has been a vice-president at Young & Rubicam advertising agency, and marketing vice-president at both Campbell Soup Company and General Foods in his 50 years of marketing experience.

[7] "Is It Immoral To Stimulate Buying?" *Printers' Ink*, May 11, 1962, p. 43; "The Real Enemy?" *Time*, September 22, 1961, p. 112.

[8] *Barron's*, August 10, 1970, p. 19.

vicing of products continues to be a sore spot for many consumers, with little improvement in sight.

All of these criticisms have some validity. One contributing factor is that the service industries and retailing often are the last refuge of the marginal worker, and productivity, service, and selling effectiveness reflect this. Despite the trend to self-service, costs continue to rise; a decrease in services offered may slow this trend, but hardly stop it. The provision of high-quality services for those who are willing to pay for them may provide an opportunity for responsive marketing management.

As we have explored in this section, there is considerable evidence that certain aspects of marketing are wasteful of resources and reflect less than optimum efficiency. The role of marketing in an advanced economy which has a great amount of discretionary income and many wants is important and complex. No system is perfect: imbalances are continually arising which need to be corrected and efficiencies are yet to be gained.

Marketing efficiency will continue to improve. More sophisticated tools and more professional management are leading in this direction; these are replacing family ownership and decision by intuition, which have characterized many marketing firms, especially retailers and wholesalers. Certain aspects of marketing have been criticized as costing too much. These include the presence and the opportunity for entry of small, relatively inefficient enterprises, the proliferation of products, the abundance of advertising. These are interwoven into our marketing system and are not likely to be changed by any one marketing manager or any firm. But there are other costs and inefficiencies which can and should be approached by individual marketers. A successful quest for a more efficient marketing operation can give a firm a competitive advantage. This tends to be contagious. It forces other firms to emulate and find a higher efficiency. And society thereby benefits.

CRITICISMS OF MARKETING PRACTICES

Certain marketing practices have been the focus of consumer ire and have even resulted in major legislation. Unfortunately, when a firm or industry engages in these practices, criticism tends to be overdone or exaggerated.

Poor Quality Products?

The difficulty the average consumer has with a new car confounds many of us. Defects may be encountered with any product having moving parts, and problems are exacerbated by complexity of products today and a decline in repair-service capability.[9]

A controversy erupted in the public press and in Congress concerning the nutritional value of the cereals that have long had their health benefits extolled. Puffed rice was noted by one nutritionist as being five times as expensive as ordinary rice and yet providing smaller amounts of most nutrients. Another nutritionist pointed out that it would be fairly easy for the companies to add more vitamins and minerals to cereals.[10] Still another critic, in analyzing and ranking cereals by their nutrients, found such old standbys as General Mills' Cheerios and Wheaties, Kellogg's Sugar Frosted Flakes, and Nabisco Shredded Wheat to be near the bottom of the list, providing "empty calories" and little else.[11]

The basic issue of product quality is how much quality and quality control can be given a product and still keep the price competitive and attractive? Manufacturers are groping with this issue, but are faced with the trade-off between providing more durable goods and keeping costs within the limits of acceptable demand. No one can doubt that putting heavier bumpers and fenders on cars will add to the cost. But perhaps the consumer should have this option available, and savings in insurance premiums may help offset the higher price for the car.

There is widespread public demand for manufacturers to design products that are simpler to repair. And there have been some significant moves in this direction. For example, Motorola has a color TV with "works in a drawer," which usually eliminates hauling the set to the repair shop. The subcompacts of Ford and General Motors, the Pinto and the Vega, were designed to be adjusted easily by the ordinary driver and had far fewer parts than standard-size cars. The Vega was originally designed with only 1,231 parts, compared to 3,500 for a standard Impala and 9,000 parts for a Lincoln Continental.[12]

Vague Warranties and Poor Compliance?

Dissatisfaction resulting from the failure of the manufacturer or seller to replace or repair defective or otherwise unsatisfactory merchandise or services is probably the greatest source of consumer complaints.[13] The legal and ethical issues are far too technical and

[9] "America the Inefficient," *Time*, March 2, 1970, pp. 75–76.

[10] "Not by Cereal Alone," *Time*, August 17, 1970, p. 57.

[11] "A Package of Trouble for Cereal Makers," *Business Week*, August 1, 1970, p. 24.

[12] "A Fix-It-Yourself Approach," *Time*, August 17, 1970, pp. 57–58.

[13] "She Leads the Fight for Consumerism," *Washington Post*, February 22, 1970, p. L8.

complex to be discussed in detail here; however, one can identify three basic situations leading to consumer dissatisfaction: (1) failure of the seller and/or manufacturer to live up to his obligations (implicit or explicit) under the warranty agreement; (2) disappointment by the consumer upon learning after purchase the limited nature of the warranty service the seller is obligated to provide; and, (3) disappointment by the buyer resulting from his own unrealistic expectations of product performance rather than any failure to live up to the warranty or other claims by the seller.

When the seller refuses to live up to his legal obligations, one can seek legal redress through a small claims court or regular legal channels. In the event the injured consumer does not feel the remedy obtained in the courts will be worth the effort, he can complain to the local Better Business Bureau or consumer protection agency in an effort to bring public pressures to bear on the seller. In addition, he can boycott the seller himself and tell his friends and acquaintances about his experience.

Dissatisfaction of the second and third kind mentioned above usually can be avoided if the buyer makes an effort to understand completely the nature and extent of the warranty before purchase and makes an effort to be sure that his expectations about the performance of the item are realistic. However, warranties are often very difficult to read and interpret and even those that are prepared in the best of faith by the manufacturer are often confusing to consumers, not to mention the case when an unscrupulous firm might try to make them misleading (remember the Dispoz-a-Lamp "guarantee" described in chapter 4). Recently enacted federal legislation should provide some help to both the consumer and the manufacturer. The Federal Trade Commission has issued detailed rules and requirements for the preparation of warranties which are intended to ensure that warranties are clear and understandable by consumers.[14]

Many firms today are trying to improve their handling of service adjustments and customer complaints. A number of firms, including the major auto manufacturers, have set up a special office to handle complaints and customer queries. Sometimes a toll-free telephone line is provided so that customers can call free of charge to register complaints or ask for advice. Whirlpool, the appliance manufacturer, was perhaps the first major firm to institute such a procedure; they called it the "cool line," and it was available for customer calls 24 hours a day. Firms have liberalized their warranties, given them more meaningful language, and instituted special efforts to assure their being backed by dealers and representatives. So positive efforts

[14] "The Guesswork on Warranties," *Business Week*, July 14, 1975, pp. 51–52.

are being made to handle complaints; more, of course, remains to be done.

Deceptive Packaging?

As the consumerism movement gained strength in the 1960s, a favorite target of criticism was the package. In particular, it was argued that many packaging practices of manufacturers confused and misled consumers. Sizes and shapes of boxes sometimes did not represent the quantity contained within and pictures and descriptions on packages might constitute "false and misleading advertising." Critics also alleged that the lack of standardization in package sizes among manufacturers made it very difficult for the consumer to make comparative evaluations and choose the best buy. Manufacturers for the most part defended their practices and took the position that the package was a major instrument of competition and that they were merely taking advantage of it as such.

Consumerists argued and lobbied for much more stringent and restrictive government regulation of packaging practices. Manufacturers argued and lobbied against increased government regulation of competitive activities. The resulting legislation, the Fair Packaging and Labeling Act of 1966, imposed stricted requirements on manufacturers with regard to the nature of the information provided on packages but fell short of the sweeping restrictions proposed by consumerists. Consumerists regarded the law as a victory for special interests while manufacturers regarded it as a step toward increased government control of business but one that was not as bad as it could have been. As a result of the debate and discussion about packaging, many manufacturers and retailers have made changes in addition to those required by law so that packages are now generally more informative and useful to the consumer in making choices.

Deceptive Advertising and Promotional Practices?

Not many decades ago truth in advertising was the exception rather than the rule: cures were promised for incurable diseases, fortunes assured from certain investments, wild claims made and deception practiced as a matter of course. Today this has changed. Outright falsehoods are rare and generally not long tolerated.

While the vast majority of advertising cannot be faulted in this respect, enough instances occur to still cast advertising in a bad light. Moderate "puffing" or exaggeration is permitted by law as part of normal selling activities. But the boundaries become hazy between what is moderate puffing and what is downright deceptive. The Federal Trade Commission, the main governmental watchdog of advertising practices, is taking a harder look at commercials, and in some cases insisting that claims be proved. As an example of

FTC challenges to claims, the contention of Sterling Drugs' Lysol that one can use it to kill influenza virus and other germs and thereby prevent or reduce the spread of colds and influenza, was challenged, and Sterling accepted the order to stop such advertising.[15]

However, companies can delay adjudication of complaints brought against them. The Geritol case is perhaps the classic example of this. Geritol advertising had claimed it was a "generally effective remedy for tiredness" when in fact it was not.

> After more than eight years of investigations, hearings, and court appeals, the FTC in 1967 issued a cease and desist order against continued deceptive advertising of the product . . . The deceptive advertising was not stopped, according to the Justice Department, which filed a suit against Geritol's maker, J. B. Williams Co., and its ad agency for violating the FTC order . . . This action came 11 years after the FTC opened the Geritol case and more than two years after the commission issued its order banning the deceptive advertising.[16]

Deceptive selling methods sometimes occur in the door-to-door selling of magazine subscriptions and encyclopedias. Entry is often gained under the guise of conducting a market research study. One such firm even used the name American Marketing Associates, Inc., with its close similarity with the American Marketing Association, as a door opener for its salesmen to peddle encyclopedias under the pretext of taking a "marketing survey." Such practices not only cast marketing in general in a bad light, but jeopardize legitimate market research efforts by causing consumers to be suspicious of anyone claiming to be a researcher.

Sometimes shady operators go beyond minor deceptions to blatantly fraudulent practices as seen in the following examples:

> "Congratulations! Your lucky telephone number was selected at random from all the people in your area to receive a new deluxe zigzag sewing machine . . . AT NO CHARGE!!" . . . To get the free machine, however, one had to sign a hocus-pocus 10-year service contract at $7.95 a year, or double the wholesale price of the machine.[17]

> . . . the notorious food-freezer racket. In that instance, thousands of New Yorkers signed up for a food plan, thinking they were getting a giant food freezer absolutely free. In fact,

---

[15] Case is summarized in "Legal Developments in Marketing," *Journal of Marketing,* January 1975, p. 103.

[16] David Vienna, "FTC Establishes Council to Alter Rules, Speed Cases," *Washington Post,* June 1, 1970, p. D9.

[17] "New York Leads the Consumer Crusade," *Business Week,* January 31, 1970, p. 50.

the customer signed an installment contract to pay an exorbitant $1,200 for his new appliance. When the food was delivered in smaller quantity or poorer quality than expected, the horrified customers found they could cancel the plan but were stuck with paying off the freezer.[18]

There are crooks who operate in every aspect of human endeavor; marketing is hardly unique in this respect although crooks in marketing tend to be more visible than other kinds. Outright fraud is certainly the exception to marketing practices. But it is more likely to occur with products and services where there is *no repeat business* and no need to cultivate customer loyalty. It is also more likely when the consumer is poorly educated and uninformed.

Prices Too High?

The factors that influence the prices charged by business firms are complex and difficult to understand. Generally a firm's freedom to set prices is constrained by the presence or threat of competition, or by a limited demand at higher prices. But occasionally there may be wide pricing discretion. In a private enterprise economy firms have the right to charge the most profitable price. But in a time of burgeoning inflation, restraint in raising prices would appear to be socially desirable. And for products essential to health and welfare, such as some drugs, many would question the propriety of firms that charge all that the market will bear.

A simplistic answer to the problem of high prices would be to call for government regulation of prices in socially or economically sensitive areas such as ethical drugs and steel. However, past efforts to control prices selectively have been both ineffective and dysfunctional. Price regulation tends to work only if the total operations of the firms are also tightly regulated by the government. Any dramatic extension of government price regulation is likely to move us rapidly to a government-planned national economy similar to those of Russia and China. Unless one wishes to advocate the abandonment of the private enterprise economy, an alternative to extensive government price regulation seems necessary. The present policy of our federal government appears to be to: (1) actively prosecute those who engage in deceptive or misleading pricing practices; (2) actively prosecute firms who collude or conspire to restrict the competitive determination of prices; and (3) seek to overturn any barriers to the free dissemination of price information (such as state laws against the posting or advertising of ethical drug prices). The Bureau of Consumer Protection of the Federal Trade Commission and other federal agencies are charged with carrying out these policies.

[18] Ibid.

Planned Product Obsolescence?

Planned product obsolescence in the sense of annual model changes has long characterized the auto industry and the household appliance industry. While scattered criticisms are heard about the economic undesirability of continuous model changes, more damaging criticisms contend that manufacturers are purposely downgrading quality and shortening the useful life of their products, in order to force constant rebuying. These latter criticisms are for the most part unjustified. In today's competition, few manufacturers would dare risk marketing a purposely inferior product. On the other hand, the increased costs of manufacturing parts with noticeably longer service lives may raise prices beyond levels consumers are willing to pay so that a price/quality trade-off is necessary.

Betty Furness, then the Special Assistant to the President for Consumer Affairs, made a plea to an annual conference of the American Marketing Association that manufacturers or marketers give the consumer the basic facts about the *design life* of a product:

> Why shouldn't the housewife know that there are "X" number of hours of service in her washing machine or that the life expectancy of a toaster falls short of a golden wedding anniversary? . . . The manufacturer knows, and the marketer knows, what the design life of their product is. Shouldn't the consumer also know? Wouldn't that make him a more satisfied and regular customer? Doesn't he have a right to know?[19]

There have been difficulties in implementing such a suggestion, since customers differ in their usage of appliances and there are bound to be variations in life of products even under similar patterns of use. Now, however, a new device has been introduced by North American Philips Corp. which enables manufacturers to base their warranties on actual appliance operating time rather than on length of ownership.[20] With such a device the feasibility of revealing design life and basing warranties on it is made more practical.

MARKETING OMISSIONS

Society is beginning to look at things that business, and the marketing part of business, should do to improve our quality of life, both as regards social relations and the environment.

---

[19] Betty Furness, "Responsibility in Marketing," in Reed Moyer (ed.), *Changing Marketing Systems*, 1967 Winter Conference Proceedings (Chicago: American Marketing Association, 1968), p. 26.

[20] "Not How Long but How Much," *Forbes*, September 1, 1974, p. 12.

Unconcern with Effects on Environment?

The most serious offenders in polluting our air and water are heavy industries: paper mills, steel, chemical plants, and the utilities. Admittedly, the successful marketing of air conditioners and other appliances of our affluent age has resulted in vastly increased power needs; the marketing of automobiles has increased demands for steel and further spawned the growth of heavy industry and its consequent pollutants. But manufacturing cost miserliness in the installation of antipollution devices is more directly to blame.

Some environmental ills have been directly attributed to marketing. It is blamed for the phosphate detergents which may be injurious to wildlife in streams and lakes and the air pollution caused by millions of auto exhausts. Marketing is also blamed for its products that cause litter: no-return bottles, aluminum cans, junked cars and appliances.

But why should marketing be blamed for the choice of ingredients by manufacturers or for the behavior of litterers? There is no product made that cannot be used to produce litter or used in an abusive way. To blame marketing for litter with packaging materials makes no more sense than to blame marketers for drug abuse or for hit-and-run deaths.

Disregard for Consumer Health and Safety?

Criticisms have been leveled at manufacturers regarding the safety of their products. Examples of unsafe products include:

Floor furnaces with grilles that burn toddlers
Toys that cut children
Electric steam vaporizers that scald infants
Appliances, toys, hospital diagnostic equipment, and charcoal igniters that electrocute
Fabrics that "explode" into flames
Lemon furniture oil (poisonous) that smells like soda pop
Unsanitary processing of meat, poultry, and fish
Color TVs that leak excessive radiation

The alleged lack of safety of General Motors' Corvair, which Ralph Nader highlighted in his book *Unsafe at Any Speed,* played a key role in stimulating the consumer movement. The argument advanced by auto executives that safety did not sell, hardly absolves them from the responsibility to lead in the quest for greater highway safety.

Public outcry has resulted in governmental action in many areas of product safety. A Wholesome Meat Act now brings small, intrastate meat-packing plants under federal interstate jurisdiction; auto safety standards have been improved; there are now laws concerning flammable fabrics, the wholesomeness of fish and fish products, and of poultry; radiation control, natural-gas pipeline safety, coal mine health and safety, are other areas of recent legislation. And the Consumer Product Safety Act of 1972 created an independent commission with powers to prescribe safety standards for virtually all consumer products not already covered by existing safety legislation. Consumers are much better protected today from unsa: products than they were even a decade ago.

Indifference to Ethics, Aesthetics, and Social Responsibilities?

Marketers are often accused of indifference to anything that does not help them sell products. We have discussed marketing practices which, while not illegal, would certainly shade into questionable ethics. One has only to look at unregulated sectors of our highways where billboards, junk dealers, used car lots, and "honky-tonks" proliferate to witness the disregard for aesthetic considerations.

The issue of social responsibility brings unresolved questions, such as:

Should a firm commit stockholders' money to projects which promise little or no earnings, such as low-rent ghetto housing?

If, as often happens, the hiring of poorly educated workers results in shoddy goods and sloppy service, so that the customer is penalized, who should be favored?

The answer to these and similar questions depends on one's values. There is yet little agreement as to the priority of values that should exist in our pluralistic society. But some thoughtful businessmen are beginning to ponder whether social programs should not be considered rather as an investment in survival—for our capitalistic system as well as for the individual company—than as an expense which should be shunted aside.

MORAL ISSUES IN MARKETING

Criticisms of the lack of marketing concern with social and environmental matters are of rather recent vintage, but marketing has long been assailed on moralistic grounds. Many of these criticisms, however, should be levied at our entire economic and social system, rather than the marketing aspect of it.

Does Marketing Manipulate Us Against Our Will?

The charge that consumers are being swayed by powerful advertising efforts, their defenses probed and penetrated by the mystique of motivation research, is a familiar one.[21]

Despite the fact that some consumers do buy irrationally and often on emotional and impulsive grounds, the designation of such powers to advertising and promotional efforts gives far too much credit to the abilities of marketers. The number of contradictory and confusing claims, the sheer number of promotional messages which confront us, the very real evidence that only a small minority of such messages are even perceived, refutes the argument that we are helplessly swayed. Even the feared and quickly prohibited appeal to subliminal perception (see chapter 6) was found to be relatively ineffectual upon closer, more objective investigation.

Undoubtedly advertising, and especially massive doses of it, exerts some influence on buying behavior (it at least brought people to Edsel showrooms, although they did not buy)—otherwise, why advertise? But advertisers know it is far easier to "swim with the tide" than against it; in other words, to try to buck established preferences, customs, and mores is an uneconomic use of advertising dollars. Far better to adapt products to consumer preferences, and then use advertising to inform how well such products satisfy existing needs.

Related to this issue and to the criticisms concerning misallocation of resources is the "dependence effect" propounded by Galbraith in *The Affluent Society*. He argues that marketing does not serve the needs and wants of society—that supply does not follow demand, but instead *creates* demand. Galbraith sees the welfare of our society as no longer greater at higher levels of production than at lower levels. The reason is that consumer wants have come to depend on the technology rather than on actual needs. Therefore industry will sell whatever it can successfully produce, advertise, and sell, rather than what the consumer needs.[22]

This then suggests some kind of artificial or created allocation of resources according to the whim (and expediency) of influential marketers. It suggests a lack of responsiveness to the marketplace, the "dictates" of which have been circumvented or defused.

Whether or not we can accept the Dependence Effect premise of Galbraith in toto, there are elements of validity to it, if advertising is to be credited with any effectiveness where consumer needs are hazily defined or not definitive (as is often the case). However, an increasing public awareness, typified by consumerism and mounting consumer legislation, is evidence that society is beginning to "dictate" its needs and wants, is not satisfied with the social attuning of

[21] Vance Packard in his best-seller, *The Hidden Persuaders* (New York: Pocketbooks, Inc., 1958), stressed this theme.
[22] John Kenneth Galbraith, *The Affluent Society* (New York: Mentor Books, 1964), p. 128.

industry, and is finding some flaws in the allocation of resources encouraged by industry.

Is There Misallocation of Resources?

Certain social critics, notably Arnold Toynbee and Galbraith (again), decry the production and distribution of luxury goods and other products of an affluent society, when vast portions of the world, and indeed, part of our own country, suffer deprivation of even basic wants. Yet while admitting inequities in our society and great environmental and social needs, is the way to correct this by regulating and restricting the private sector, by denying us as consumers freedom of choice, and taking away the incentive of our individual desires? Who is to assume the power position of deciding what we are to have or are not to have? The second car, or the vacation second home, might be considered an unacceptable luxury; yet to the suburban housewife the second car may be a virtual necessity, while to the growing family in the confines of the city, a second house on the lake or in the mountains may be worth other sacrifices.

Does Marketing Foster Hedonism, False Values, and Materialism?

The criticisms concerning materialism relate to the preceding about misallocation of resources. To some extent our society is attuned to the puritan ethic—the goodness of hard work, of sacrifice—and it is difficult to adjust gracefully to an economy of abundance, of relative leisure and the elimination of drudgery. William Lazer suggests, however, that rather than feeling guilty about living in a materialistic, abundant society, that this should be recognized as one of the major accomplishments of our age, and not the indication of a sick, failing, or decaying society.[23]

A comfortable life, one of abundant leisure, can foster a wider perspective, a reaching out instead of within, and may actually be the most conducive climate for stimulating curative actions both at home and abroad. With our own immediate needs satisfied, priorities can change; an aura of social responsibility rather than narrow parochial interests may then be on the threshhold.

Is Marketing in Bad Taste?

Certain aspects of marketing are criticized for their "bad taste"; the "wasteland of TV," banal advertising, intrusions on privacy through commercials, salesmen, and market researchers. There is no doubt that many aspects of marketing could stand improvement and it is clear that objectionable advertising is harmful not only to consum-

[23] William Lazer, "Marketing's Changing Social Relationships," *Journal of Marketing,* January 1969, p. 5.

ers, but to marketers as well. The results of uncreative and trite advertising usually have no positive effect on sales.

Door-to-door and telephone selling are a nuisance to some people and a godsend to others. Marketing research, while growing in importance, affects most of us as respondents only minimally, except for certain overused test market cities. Anyone unwilling to put up with the minor inconveniences of sales solicitations or interviews can quickly terminate the contact.

On balance, most of us are willing to tolerate some boring and tasteless commercials in order to enjoy the entertainment, which is largely supplied through advertising dollars.

COMMENTS ON MARKETING CRITICISMS

We have examined a wide range of criticisms. Some are clearly justified, others are debatable, and many are unjustified. All marketing suffers from the action of a few; the focus of blame usually rests only with a minority of firms. However, not all of these are small, marginal operations, as some would claim. Efforts to conceal, confuse, and otherwise prevent consumers from making knowledgeable buying decisions have often come from the largest firms. Executives of these firms have sometimes stubbornly opposed legislation which would force better information in the marketplace, such as the Truth-in-Packaging and Truth-in-Lending acts.

But many of the criticisms we have described lack real validity. Marketing is being unjustly blamed for things beyond its control (such as the behavior of those who would litter), or else naively accused of power it does not possess (such as the power to manipulate us).

Now let us turn our attention to the positive side of marketing.

CONTRIBUTIONS OF MARKETING

One writer sees marketing as making major contributions to our society in these areas:

1. Consumer sovereignty
2. Resource allocation in accordance with demand
3. Employment to provide purchasing power
4. Freedom to compete and to choose an occupation
5. Cultural diffusion of innovation[24]

We will examine these contributions next.

[24] George Fisk, *Marketing Systems* (New York: Harper and Row, 1967), chap. 22.

Consumer sovereignty was explored in the preceding chapter. While allegedly the "consumer is king," there are serious obstacles in the path of such kingship, not the least being the lack of perfect information in the marketplace. But consumer acceptance of a product or of a marketing practice is essential for the viability of a firm. The need to estimate this acceptance constantly confronts marketers and results in millions spent for marketing and advertising research in order to obtain the still imperfect appraisals of consumer attitudes and preferences. The more choice presented consumers and the better information provided them, the greater becomes their sovereignty. In today's marketplace we generally are provided more than ample product choices; what is not well provided is information—despite advertising and product claims.

It might be argued that consumer sovereignty is not such a desirable thing. Consumers cannot always be depended upon to exercise their choice in the optimum way, from society's viewpoint. (A current example of this, at a time when the condition of the environment is looming ever more important, is the reluctance of many consumers to refrain from buying the nondisposable containers, even though they may condemn the encroachments of business and marketing on the environment.) There are those who would say that the choice, the options, should be taken from the rank and file consumer, that someone else or some agency should decide what is in their best interest. Yet although we make mistakes, few of us would wish to abdicate this prerogative to someone else.

One of the strongest arguments for the contribution of the marketing system is the *allocation of resources according to demand;* the alternative embodied in wartime rationing makes us shudder with its imperfection. The complexities, the abuses, the development of massive black markets, attribute to the general unworkableness of such regulations vis-à-vis the self-adjusting competitive market system, except under conditions of extreme national emergency.

While totalitarian countries, such as the Soviet Union and her satellites, have achieved satisfactory growth rates under planned economies, the growth rates have been many times greater for those countries which ascribe to a market economy: Japan, West Germany, Italy, France, Holland. This empirical evidence suggests that market or demand-directed economies lead to the flexibility needed to stimulate the best allocation of resources, as well as providing the most incentive for both workers and entrepreneurs.

Fisk notes that *marketing provides purchasing power* in two ways: (1) in providing direct employment—and we have seen that the labor force engaged in marketing has grown substantially in the last century; and (2) in expanding employment in nonmarketing occupations, by raising aspiration levels and stimulating demand.[25]

[25] Ibid., p. 687.

One of the seldom heralded accomplishments of the persuasive communications of marketing is the stimulation of aspirations. The rather deprecated idea of "keeping up with the Joneses" has a solid basis in real life, even though we may be reluctant to admit it. The material possessions and attainments of our neighbors influence us, even though we may want to go our own distinct way. With mass media, and exposure to a myriad of "Joneses," we are stimulated to want more, to work harder to get it, and thereby to have a reasonable probability that most of our expectations will be realized. Such stimulation thereby expands employment in nonmarketing and service occupations.

The *freedom to compete and to choose an occupation* we take for granted. Sometimes competition may lead to excesses—of claims or of selling efforts. Generally, as consumers, we benefit from a high degree of competition and from the expanded choice it offers us. As workers, we also have more choice, not only in type of work but in employers; usually we can move to better things if the urge strikes or discontent occurs. And despite the resources of the large firms and their influence through millions of dollars expended in the mass media, there is still room for the innovator to enter successfully.

It has been said that marketing is the delivery of a standard of living. Fisk calls this the *cultural diffusion of innovation*. There is little doubt that marketing has affected the quality of life by making available to most segments of our society many and improved products. Mass communication has permitted a rapid dissemination of information on products and styles. Our life style, even in the ghetto, is measurably better than twenty years ago. And this diffusion of innovation is spreading to other countries. Especially in the underdeveloped countries the acquiring of new wants for the material products made available by marketing is mitigating lethargy.

**MARKETING
IN
ACTION**

**Diffusion of Innovation—Eastman Kodak and
The Spreading of Popular Photography**
A stream of products has come from the research labs of Eastman
Kodak in the last 50 years, each more simple to use than the last. In the
process, from a highly esoteric, cumbersome, technical pursuit, photography
has become readily accessible and usable by all.

In 1963 the Kodak Instamatic camera was introduced, designed to
be practically "idiot proof." So successful was it that over 10 million
were sold in 26 months. Its introduction was an impressive example of
well-executed marketing: on one day, February 28, 1963, in 147 countries

around the world, the Instamatic camera was introduced with complete warehousing, complete availability of the product to 75,000 retailers, and major advertising in eight languages.

The convenience of the camera and the high probability it afforded of taking good pictures encouraged people to buy more expensive film. For example, over 90 percent of film purchases were color film versus less than 50 percent before. And where the older Brownie camera users bought three to four rolls of film a year, Instamatic users bought eight. Furthermore, women found photography more intriguing, and from less than 40 percent, now 60 percent of pictures were taken by women. And film found its way onto supermarket shelves.

In 1972 when the even more convenient pocket Instamatic was introduced, 10 million were sold in less than 18 months, and film usage again moved up.

SOURCE: "The Blurry Picture at Eastman Kodak," *Forbes*, September 15, 1974, pp. 83–96.

For thought and discussion:
How would you measure the social contribution of photography made popular, against the criticisms that marketing fosters false values, is in bad taste, and misallocates resources? In other words, how would you weight these pros and cons of marketing?

CONCLUSIONS ON VALUE OF MARKETING

In this chapter, the space devoted to the criticisms of marketing has far surpassed the pages discussing its contributions. We must not infer from this that the criticisms far outweigh the contributions— that marketing on balance must be condemned.

Each of us in his own value judgment must assign weights to the various pros and cons of marketing. Whatever weights are assigned, however, one can hardly give equal importance to the contribution of marketing in making possible a high standard of living, and to the negative feature of banal advertising, too much advertising, and confusing product claims. The one aspect is generally a trivial annoyance; the other, the key contributor to our society.

Marketing is an imperfect institution. So are all of our institutions: our government, our churches, our schools, even our families. If the criticisms of marketing are accepted for what they should be, that is, designated areas where efforts at improvement should be directed, then they are of value and are constructive. There is a need for marketers to take cognizance of these criticisms. Individual marketers need to work harder to make the system better: less inner (firm) directed, and more outer (society) directed—to be better attuned to the exogenous factors of society and the environment.

1. Which of the criticisms of marketing do you think are the most valid? the most serious? Why?

2. Some marketing critics think there are too many gasoline stations in their communities. What criteria would you use to determine this? What method would you use to reduce the number of stations?

3. What proposals do you have for regulating advertising?

4. How would you reduce the costs of marketing?

5. Do you think the government (perhaps local or state) should exercise control over those who wish to start their own businesses, restricting this to those financially able and with adequate education and/or business experience? By so doing, many marginal and inefficient firms could be eliminated and the trauma of bankruptcy could be reduced.

6. In your judgment, are there too many products and brands in the marketplace? If there are too many, how would you reduce the proliferation? If you think we should have more variety, how would you encourage a greater proliferation?

7. What is the "Dependence Effect" of Galbraith? How valid is this?

8. What do you see as the responsibility of marketers in regard to the disposal of cans, bottles, paper cartons and wrappers, and other litter caused by the products of marketing? Should this be a responsibility of business, or is it really a responsibility of the consumers who use —and discard—these items?

9. Do you see any difficulties on the part of manufacturers in implementing the plea of Betty Furness to give the consumer the design-life of the product he purchases?

10. How do you account for the presence of deceptive selling methods on the part of some large and presumably reputable firms? Do such practices hurt the public image of these firms? Should they be concerned with their public image? Why or why not?

Project

(a) Collect several ads which seem to you to be questionable: that are deceptive, in bad taste, or just downright insulting to intelligence. State and support your criticisms of these advertisements.

(b) Collect several ads that are excellent examples of effective marketing communication. State their good points and contrast them with the ads chosen in (a).

Exercise in Creativity

You are the sales manager of a recreational land development project located about 100 miles from a major eastern city. The land has a stream which plans call for damming up into a small lake; it also has a hill which plans call for developing for skiing. In order to accumulate sufficient funds for these promised amenities, it is necessary that half of the 5,000 lots be sold. Prices range from $7,500 to $15,000. Develop a detailed plan for selling these lots, a plan which will be scrupulously honest—that is, no high pressure, no deception. What do you estimate is likely to be the sales effectiveness of your proposal?

Role-playing Case

A newspaper in your city has just published an article critici ; the safety features of the football helmets you are promoting heavily : your toy department:

> The helmets do not prevent brain co~cussions. They are dangerous
> to our youngsters and should be banı d from sale. Furthermore,
> the Morris Department Store should be required to check on the
> safety of the products they sell.

"But I cannot check every item in the store," you respond to some complaining mothers.
What policy recommendations would you make regarding product safety of the merchandise you carry?

CASES

GUIDE TO USING CASES

These cases present a wide range of practical marketing problems, many of which require a creative approach to solve. Usually there is no one "right" solution, but certain alternatives will be found to be more practical than others. In some of these cases the firm faces a real crisis (in one case, we are even too late to save the company, but may gain from analyzing the mistakes); in other instances, an already good operation might possibly be improved. This is the challenge for your creative evaluation and judgment.

The arrangement of the cases follows that of the book. However, most are broad in scope or are multifaceted, so that a different sequence is possible if desired; also, some cases can be treated several times, for example, once under the discussion of ethical or ecological perspectives, and perhaps again under promotional considerations or marketing strategy approaches.

The ideas and the research for some of these cases have come from my students; some are rewritten or edited versions. In some cases names of firms and people have been purposely disguised to maintain confidentiality. I wish to thank the following students for their research efforts: H. B. Aldrich III, John T. Anderson, Robert Anderson, David M. Benson, James W. Boyd, Peter Breese, Russell E. Corey, Elizabeth L. Fellows, Lance R. Goldberg, Richard L. Gruber, Ferdinand A. Hauslein, Jr., Edward R. Herbert, Robert Jackson, John Lukianowicz, Scott McFadden, Michael Milchiker, J. Allan Mitchell, Joseph S. Musial, James H. Nachod, Paul O'Donoghue, Phillip L. Potts, Thomas D. Reese, Jr., Charles G. Stevens, Jerry E. Stevens, Deborah J. Stone, Daniel J. Sullivan, Warren E. Trumble, Jr., Thomas L. Vannaman, and Samuel C. Work.

PART I

Overview
of
Marketing

Case 1
Noble Jewelry—
Small Store
Seeking a
New Location

Noble Jewelry is a small neighborhood store located in Cleveland Heights, Ohio. Since it began operations in its present location, sales have climbed only slightly:

1968	$19,273
1969	22,154
1970	23,051
1971	24,150
1972	24,859
1973	25,397
1974	25,876

In the last two years the neighborhood has begun to change. A number of robberies have taken place nearby, and the Noble store itself has been broken into twice. Many of the better customers are moving away from the area, and this in turn has hurt sales further. Faced with this dismal situation, the owner, Mr. Milchiker, is considering whether or not to relocate his jewelry store.

Mr. Milchiker was born and raised in Poland and learned his watch repair skills from his uncle. Shortly after World War II he immigrated to the U. S. Soon after arriving in Cleveland, Ohio, Mr. Milchiker opened his first jewelry store on Euclid Avenue, a main street, and about two miles from downtown. Over the years he built up a large following of loyal customers and a very successful business. His success could be traced to two things: (1) the personal service he gave his customers, and (2) the excellent watch repair work he did. However, in the early 1960s the neighborhood began deteriorating, culminating in his being robbed and injured so badly that he spent several months recovering. After that he closed his store and relocated in Cleveland Heights, an older middle-class suburb. Although he practiced the same business philosophy in his new store, he was never able to build up as large a clientele of loyal customers as he had previously.

The stagnant sales of the Cleveland Heights store can be attributed partly to changes in the retail jewelry business itself. Competition from discount stores, department stores, variety stores, and catalog showrooms is such that many smaller retailers are being forced out of business.

Mr. Milchiker is seriously considering locating in a suburban shopping center. He finds that the rent for a 20-foot by 40-foot store in one such center would be $550 per month. This does not include the following additional estimated expenses: (1) $25 per month maintenance, (2) $60 per month for utilities, (3) $60 per month for comprehensive insurance, (4) $25 per month for miscellaneous expenses. Furthermore, a five-year lease is required, and 4 percent of gross sales over $100,000 is collected by the lessors. He also considered locating in a larger and more prestigious shopping center. But there the rent alone would be $800.

In recent years a unique concept in shopping centers has developed: an "Enclosed Shopping Village." Existing vacated buildings—usually abandoned discount department stores—are subdivided into as many as 155 individualized stores, within the one large building. Two of these "villages" had recently opened in the Cleveland area. These were leased on the following basis: the landlord paid all utilities, maintenance, and security costs. The shopkeeper signed a one-year lease with a two-year option, and he received three paneled walls, eight feet high, and three electrical outlets. The front of the shop was left open and the shopkeeper was required to close it at his own expense using his own taste. The hours that the "village" was open were 6:00–10:00 PM on Thursday and Friday, 12:00–10:00 PM on Saturday, and 12:00–6:00 PM on Sunday, for a total of 24 hours per week.

Rents in a new third center, called Grand Central Station, range from $149 a month for a 10-foot by 10-foot unit, to $450 a month for 15 by 20 feet. Furthermore, the units are leased with no percentage of sales involved. The only additional cost to the shop owner is a $25 monthly advertising charge, and this goes toward a $100,000 a year overall shopping center advertising and promotional budget. The surrounding population within 3.7 miles of Grand Central Station is 487,000, and the developer estimates that customer turnout will range between 14,000 and 22,000 per week.

QUESTIONS

1. What sales volume would Mr. Milchiker have to achieve to make a profit in the first shopping center he is considering, if his gross profit (before expenses) is 40 percent of sales, and his expenses other than occupancy costs are $10,000 which includes his salary or draw?

2. What sales volume does he have to reach to break even at Grand Central Station in the 10-foot by 10-foot shop?

3. What disadvantages do you see in locating in Grand Central Station?

4. On balance, what is your recommendation to Mr. Milchiker? Why?

Case 2
The Southern Motel—
Changing Competition

The Southern Motel was located in a small agricultural town in southeastern Georgia. It originally had been a tourist camp, and at that time (in the late 1920s) was the only tourist camp or motel in the town, and one of the first such operations in that part of the state. However, the town's location on the main highway leading from the Midwest to the East Coast of Florida looked promising for such an enterprise. Furthermore, the town was a central marketplace for the tobacco, cotton, and truck farmers of the surrounding area, and a considerable number of buyers and sellers for the farm trade and various tobacco auctions gave further potential.

Billboard advertising was used heavily, and business increased most satisfactorily. New units were added to the camp; a gas station and a restaurant were also established, thereby permitting a transient to satisfy all his needs at one stop.

However, the depression and the end of the Florida land boom adversely affected business, with tourism coming to a virtual standstill. The camp survived due to the sporadic use of those attending the tobacco auctions and other agricultural market activities.

World War II brought an upsurge of business, not from tourists, due to gasoline rationing, but from an air force base near town. The camp provided housing for the construction workers at the base and later for the families of those stationed there. During this period, a trailer court was also added to the facilities. With the ending of the war, tourist trade accentuated and more units were constructed. Several other motels were built in the town but their competition did not seem a serious problem. The Korean War and increased activity at the base benefited the entire business community.

By the middle 1960s Southern had been a profitable operation for almost forty years, and it had changed its name—reflecting the changing times—to Southern Motel. But the situation was worsening. Three major problems were threatening the viability of the whole enterprise.

1. The interstate highway program called for bypassing the town, thereby reducing the number of transients and the exposure of the motel to through traffic.

2. The motel business itself was in the throes of major changes as motel chains and franchise operations, such as Holiday Inn and Howard Johnson, opened near the town. These motels offered modern decor and other amenities such as television, air conditioning, swimming pools, atmosphere restaurants, and—very important—reservation service. The latter, for a motel chain, was a

powerful influence in keeping tourist patronage within the chain: many travelers find the convenience of having a night's lodging assured at a destination a day's journey away much to be preferred over the need to "shop" for a motel at the end of a long, tiring day on the highway.

3. Southern Motel was also encountering problems with its gas station and restaurant operations. Both of these had been operated by leasees for a number of years. These leasees, however, had permitted the physical facilities to deteriorate, management and service was a continuing problem, and in light of increased competition, neither the gas station nor the restaurant was any longer profitable.

The first problem—the loss of transient traffic to the town—proved to be relatively easy to solve. Travelers had to leave the interstate highway in order to reach motels, gas stations, restaurants, and other services. All such businesses in the town faced the same problem and they agreed to sponsor standard signs on the highway announcing the availability of "Gas–Food–Lodging." Total transient business in the town subsequently even increased, due of course to the stimulation to travel that the interstate highway provided.

The increased competition was a much more difficult problem. To be competitive in terms of facilities would require a major investment in rebuilding and modernizing. Such an investment could not even assure that the competitive problem would be solved, since these chain motels had engendered brand loyalty on a national scale, and heavily promoted their reservation service (whereby, free of charge, one motel would teletype another at the desired subsequent destination for availability of rooms and placement of reservations.

In defense against the chain motels, some independent motel operators were joining motel associations, such as Quality Courts and Western Motels. These permitted the member firms to benefit from joint advertising expenditures, a recognized national or regional sign and motif, a uniform and carefully maintained reputation for quality and service, some interaction with other motel operators and their problems and solutions, as well as certain managerial and accounting aids. Furthermore, as the memberships in these associations became larger, they were able to make available a somewhat similar reservation service to that of the motel chains.

However, to join such an association would also require a considerable investment in remodeling an older motel and bringing it up to the standards required for membership. And joining would still not give Southern Motel any distinct advantage over its present competitors, and would certainly add to the cost burden to be met before any profits would be forthcoming: not only franchise and association costs, but the fixed expense due to the financing of the new construction needed. This would require a higher occupancy rate to break even.

The unprofitability of the gas station and restaurant operations also defied easy solution. Considerable investment would be needed here in modernizing and the problem still remained of finding good management for these ancillary operations. The owner of the Southern Motel was unwilling to assume active management of these in addition to managing the faltering motel.

QUESTIONS

1. Evaluate the major problems facing Southern Motel as to duration and possible solutions.
2. Would you attempt to join a motel association at this point?
3. What sort of image do you think is most feasible for Southern Motel?
4. What marketing approach would you recommend to maintain the viability of Southern Motel?
5. What would you do about the gas and restaurant operations?

Case 3
Virginia Camera Shop—
Small Independent Store
versus Discount
Store Competition

The Virginia Camera Shop is a small retail photographic equipment store in a suburb about 25 miles from Washington, D.C. It is located about one hundred feet from the main street and consequently lacks the proximity to other stores which would be offered by a shopping center location. It is graced by a small, unimpressive sign. The shop has three employees, one of whom is an expert photographer, as is also the owner, Mr. Daniels. In recent years Mr. Daniels has become increasingly aware of the competition from other camera stores and especially from discount stores such as Gem, Memco, Zayre, and the like. Some of these stores quote prices from one third to one half of Mr. Daniels's prices.

Eighty percent of the store's sales comes from high-quality foreign and domestic cameras and other accessory equipment, and photographic materials such as film, paper, and flashbulbs. The shop is franchised for such popular camera brands as Kodak, Yashica, Minolta, Nikon, Miranda, Polaroid, and the like. Cameras range in price from $7.95 to over $500. Used cameras are sold for customers for a 10 percent commission fee, and it has been necessary to take trade-ins to sell more expensive equipment. The store carries a complete line of darkroom and developing equipment, as well as specialty items such Viewmasters, Lucite picture cubes, photo albums, etc. A camera repair service is also offered. Over half the sales are on short credit terms, usually thirty days. Customers are allowed to use charge accounts, but there is no installment plan because Mr. Daniels believes that the high cost of such a plan would be prohibitive. Cameras and equipment are rarely discounted at the store since it is felt that the franchise might be revoked if one of the items is sold for less than the manufacturer's list prices. One of the salesmen noted: "Mr. Daniels has a real phobia against selling anything below the list price." Service and film developing contribute to the remaining 20 percent of the store's sales volume.

In addition to discount stores, several supermarkets and drugstores also offer price competition. Some of these carry limited lines of cameras and film, and because they offer no service other than film developing and have no large inventories of photographic equipment, these outlets are able to operate with a lower profit margin. The discount stores buy in large quantities at better prices and frequently stock discontinued models. They do not offer the personal service, such as demonstration and operating instruction, that Mr. Daniels's store provides. Their lower overhead expenses and better buying terms permits them to offer substantially lower selling prices.

To compete against these price cutters, Mr. Daniels has tried to make the Virginia Camera Shop service-oriented. Customers are encouraged to come to him or one of his salesmen for constructive criticism about their pictures. Demonstrations are given on photography and development techniques. Equipment is shown to a customer with details on operation and mechanical construction carefully presented. Some service-oriented advertising has been done in local community newspapers but much of the advertising efforts seem to be ineffective.

Several courses of action have been considered, among them dropping camera brands that are drastically price cut by the discounters: such as Kodak, Bell & Howell, and Polaroid. Mr. Daniels believes he has lost many customers who are now purchasing such lines elsewhere at lower prices. He could also discount certain brands and attempt to compete pricewise, instead of on the basis of quality and service. Service and operating costs might be decreased to some extent so that he could better compete on a price basis.

However, Mr. Daniels doubts that he could ever match the discount operations with their much larger sales volume and purchasing power. He feels that his best marketing strategy is still to offer a high degree of expertise, considerable service, and complete lines of cameras and accessories. Discount stores primarily stock less expensive items, and a much smaller variety of goods; for the advanced amateur photographer interested in the high-priced, more complex cameras, the wider variety of goods and the assistance of a specialist is usually desired. Mr. Daniels consequently sees his market as being much different from that of the discount stores.

However, sales continue to erode, and a heavy investment in inventory is placing the viability of the Virginia Camera Shop in jeopardy.

QUESTIONS

1. Do you think this store can fill a niche in the market and thereby compete against the large discount and other mass-volume retailers?

2. What marketing strategy changes do you think need to be made at this point?

Case 4
The Crossroads Delicatessen— Small Business Firm in a Changing Environment

In 1963 two brothers, Antonio and Ricardo Taliafero, purchased a small delicatessen-grocery store, the Crossroads Delicatessen. It was located at the intersection of two main roads in Kimberly, then a small rural township in New Jersey, thirty-three miles from New York City. The previous owner had had a small but prosperous business due largely to his low overhead, since the store was old and few improvements had been made. There was little competition, and higher prices reflected this. The store was divided into a lunch counter, a packaged-grocery section, a meat and produce counter, and a liquor and wine section.

The Taliaferos paid $70,000, of which $50,000 was used to purchase the liquor license. After purchasing the store they made another $50,000 worth of improvements, expanding and paving the parking lot, purchasing new signs, and rebuilding the interior, adding new fixtures and lighting. Both the meat counter and the lunch counter were expanded and modernized by moving into a part of the storage room. As a result of these efforts the appearance of the store was transformed from a dingy "mom and pop" store into a small but modern supermarket-liquor-luncheon store.

Because of the small size—2,200 square feet—the Taliaferos managed to keep a personal touch. They were able to continue the friendly atmosphere built up by the previous owner, a long-time resident of the community.

Business almost doubled within the first six months. New customers were attracted in addition to the regular customers of the previous owner. The Crossroads Delicatessen enjoyed a prosperous and growing business.

By 1969 however, business had stopped growing despite the growth of Kimberly. Although the town was zoned mostly for residential units, the neighboring communities permitted light industry and many businesses were relocating in the area. Large corporations such as insurance companies and scientific laboratories were also moving in, largely because of the cheaper land prices combined with the advantages of being near New York City. The whole area began to develop and Kimberly became an attractive area for commuters to New York and Newark, partly because the area was nicely wooded, with a wildlife preserve nearby. Not only were more people moving in, but they were different from the rural population of 1963. Most were upper middle class, and the woods near the store were soon filled with $60,000 and $70,000 houses. Most families were very mobile, with at least two cars. In addition, better roads were built that joined Kimberly with large shopping centers.

Now, instead of being the only store in the area, the Taliaferos were faced with competition from larger stores in neighboring communities offering large selections at generally lower prices. Instead of buying everything he needed from the Taliaferos a customer now stopped in and bought only one or two items in between trips to one of the shopping centers.

As a result, business in grocery products declined. The brothers managed to keep sales at the same level despite this because their other departments picked up the slack. The liquor department in particular grew, occupying a whole row of shelves that had previously been stocked with groceries. Meat and delicatessen sales also picked up, because high-quality products were offered, and the prosperous new residents were willing to pay the higher prices for better quality than was obtainable in the supermarkets. Even the lunch-counter business improved as more workmen were in town servicing and building new houses. Thus the Crossroads Delicatessen was a prosperous if stagnant business in a growing community.

In October 1972 a new shopping center opened on the other side of town in one of the few commercially zoned areas in Kimberly. While it contained a supermarket, drugstore, dry cleaners, and similar stores, it brought no discernible impact to the Taliafero business.

In December a group of businessmen applied to the township committee for a liquor license to operate a liquor store in the new shopping center. The current town plan provided for only three liquor licenses in Kimberly, and all three were already owned, one by the Taliaferos. The only way to get a liquor license was to buy one of the existing ones. The other two were not for sale, but Antonio had developed a personal need for a large sum of money. Accordingly, theirs was sold to the shopping center concern for $120,000 with assurances from the township committee that when the new master plan was drawn up in late 1974, they would be able to purchase another license for considerably less than they had sold theirs for.

As the situation stood in early 1973, more than a quarter of the Crossroads Delicatessen was virtually empty since the liquor license was sold. Sales are declining as are profits. While some of the $120,000 had to go to repay money that Antonio had borrowed, more than half of this is left to invest. The question now is how to use the money to best advantage, and what to do with the present business.

"We want to stay here if we can," Antonio is quick to say. "But what can we do with our business? How can we beef it up? I'm not sure that pouring more money into it is what is needed. Some new idea, a new approach, perhaps, that is what we need. The township has assured us we can buy a new liquor license a year and a half from now. Should we wait for this? And how good is this going to be for us now that another bigger liquor store has been started?"

1. Evaluate the present marketing efforts of Crossroads Delicatessen.
2. How would you make this business more viable today?

Case 5
A Ghetto Marketing Endeavor— Problems of Black Entrepreneurship

Ned Brown had long wanted to go into business for himself. It took him fifteen years to amass the $5,000 he hoped would be enough to get him started. Unfortunately, his troubles began when he opened for business.

Brown was born in a small, rural southern town, and like many blacks in the South, he did not receive much formal education. His mother had sent him to a dilapidated one-room school located within the black sector, but when he was eleven his father disappeared and the boy was needed to contribute to the family income. He did odd jobs for the wealthier white farmers, and perhaps his motivation to own a business dated from this period.

At sixteen he decided to move north, having heard of the wonderful opportunities available to blacks there. He settled into a one-room tenement apartment in Washington, D.C., and learned that conditions in northern cities were no better than in the South, and in some ways much worse. By the time he was seventeen, frustrated and disillusioned, he enlisted in the army. When he was discharged three years later he had accumulated $800, and the possibility of someday owning his own business became more clear.

He knew it would take more than $800 to get started and took a job as a mechanic in a Washington garage, having received such training in the service. Although the pay was not high, he tried to save a small amount from every check (although marriage temporarily set him back). Finally in 1968, after 15 years, he had $5,000 and was ready to make his move.

With his experience in mechanics, he wanted to open a repair shop for small appliances and machines. But finding a good location presented problems: either the price was too high or the location was downright bad. He was not particularly happy with what was finally settled on, but he used $3,000 of his $5,000 for a down payment and signed a 20-year, $15,000 mortgage for a small lot and building on a narrow side street with little traffic. With his remaining money he bought the necessary tools and furniture and made needed repairs to the premises; some as substantial as a rebuilt furnace.

Brown opened for business in February 1969 with no fanfare or advertising. For the first two weeks he had three customers and sales of $16. He discovered that the people in the immediate neighborhood were for the most part too poor to own any mechanized appliances, much less be able to afford repairs.

And unfortunately, the payment dates for Brown's bills—especially the large mortgage payment—marched inexorably on. He had to return to the garage job (temporarily, he hoped) until the business could be built up. For 15 years he had been careful about paying bills and usually managed to save a small amount each pay; now he was slipping into debt. And the shop was being vandalized during the hours when he was working in the garage. In desperation, Brown decided to move his family above the shop, in this way being able to spend more time there and also leave it less vulnerable to vandals. Also, this gave him only one "rental" payment.

At this time he attempted to make the shop more of a going thing (although still working at the garage). A young boy was hired on a part-time basis to be in the repair shop when he was not. And a small advertisement was placed in a neighborhood weekly shoppers' newspaper. These two moves made a dramatic improvement in his business and sales in the next few months, and his optimism grew. Unfortunately, expenses still continued to exceed receipts.

Then Brown discovered that his employee had been stealing from him. When customers came in to make payments and the boy was alone, he pocketed the money and never recorded the receipts. Consequently, when Brown notified customers that payment was due, they became very indignant; some threatened never to come back. He was forced to look for someone else to be a part-time helper and found this extremely difficult, needing as he did someone trustworthy who was also willing to work for the small amount he could pay.

Brown also was finding out that he was too lenient in giving credit. He had been extending it to friends and neighbors if they did not have cash at the time to pay for the work done. And while many of these kept promising to pay the next week, they seldom did, but continually procrastinated. And Brown was unable to force them to pay.

The business struggled on. By October 1970 Brown was convinced that it would have to close. He calculated that about $100 a month was being lost on the venture, and only through working overtime at the garage could this drain be met. However, the more overtime, the less time available to spend on the business. The future was bleak indeed; his dream of self-employment was dissolving into nothingness (along with the $5,000 so carefully and patiently accumulated).

QUESTIONS

1. What were Brown's marketing mistakes?
2. What, if anything, can be done at this late point?
3. Does the example of this case suggest the impracticality of encouraging minority entrepreneurship in the ghetto? Why or why not?

Case 6
Davis Investment Company— Business Ethics

Daniel Davis was convinced that the key to success in the real estate business was honesty in dealing with the customer. He and his partner, Joseph Rasmussen, had built the Davis Investment Company to over $5 million in assets by the early 1960s. The company was successful both with commercial properties and with luxury homes. Sometimes the firm sold sites as is, and in other instances it engaged contractors to build the desired buildings and either lease them to the commercial user, or sell them outright, as was done with the luxury homes.

The opportunities and profits existing in the executive and luxury home market seemed so appealing and there was such a shortage of such properties that Davis and Rasmussen decided to concentrate on this aspect of the market and sell off and not replace the commercial holdings. And the Davis Company became the best-known and most sought-after brokerage firm for luxury homes in the Washington, D.C., area.

However, the profit picture began deteriorating as the commercial part of the business was relinquished. In 1965 the firm showed a net loss of $75,000, and half the sales staff was cut. In 1966 the net loss was $110,000, and the branch office was closed and the sales staff again halved, with only five salesmen remaining. Davis and Rasmussen agreed that a new approach would have to be devised if they were to have success in the luxury home market. The biggest problem seemed to be that the supply of homes was not sufficient to meet the inquiries of prospective buyers and to generate the amount of business needed.

Accordingly, it was decided that the firm should develop its own luxury home project. It already possessed a suitable tract of land, and by mid-1968, plans were completed for "Executive Estates," a luxury home development of 500 units. The firm committed itself to the limit of its financial capabilities.

The new development was highly publicized. A notable addition to the promotional efforts was the offer by Davis to join two other real estate firms in donating some acres of land adjoining the development to the community for use as a nature park.

The first units were completed in early 1970, and sales at first were excellent. However, the economic situation in the Washington area found government departments and bureaus in an economy drive, resulting in their reducing their strength and culminating in a rise in unemployment. In addition, efforts to curb the ever-increasing inflationary trend in the nation's economy produced a progressively worsening tight money situation, with higher interest rates and a drying up of funds for home mortgages. Sales in Executive Estates fell too low to cover expenses. The Davis Investment Company again had to retrench: the downtown office was closed, and the staff reduced to one secretary and the two principals, Mr. Davis and Mr. Rasmussen.

Mr. Davis was becoming incapacitated due to advancing age. Mr. Rasmussen, who also was old and unwilling or unable to cope with the demands of creditors and related difficulties, in desperation urged Mr. Davis's son, Robert, to return to Washington and assume leadership of the troubled firm.

Robert seemed well fitted to such a rescue role. He was a Harvard MBA, had worked in the real estate business in California for some ten years, and was experienced in residential as well as industrial and commercial sales and property development.

Robert was somewhat shocked at the desperate straits of the Davis Investment Company (he had assumed that when his father retired he would come into top management of a growing, viable firm). Quick action now seemed needed if the business were even to be salvaged. After a week's study of the situation, Robert came to some conclusions which he proposed to implement immediately. Hasty research indicated that the most potential existed in homes in the $25,000–$30,000 category. He consequently suggested that the remainder of the lots in Executive Estates be committed to these lower-priced homes. At that time, 87 of the planned 500 lots for luxury homes had been sold and the houses built. The owners of these lots had been told that the entire 500 in the development would consist of homes costing $50,000 and up. However, there was nothing in their sales contracts that guaranteed this.

Since the less expensive houses would offer reduced profits per unit, Robert further suggested that additional lots be developed in the acreage that his father had set aside as a donation to the nature park. No actual transfer of the land had taken place, and since he planned to use the creek that flowed through the acreage as the exit point for the development's storm drains, he felt that it would hardly be suitable for a nature park in any case.

QUESTIONS

1. Evaluate Robert's proposed marketing plans. Are they ethical?
2. What changes would you make?
3. How do you view the question of the nature park and the proposed water pollution of the creek?

PART II

Understanding and Analyzing the Market

Case 7
**Jericho Dry Cleaners—
Consumer Characteristics
Affecting Marketing**

Jed Jericho had owned and operated dry cleaning establishments in several small towns for over twenty years. In 1972 he had an opportunity to sell out the present interests for a good profit. He decided to do so, and then to relocate in Baltimore and go into this business again.

He opened two stores rather quickly. One was located in a small local shopping center situated along a moderately traveled street in a working-class suburb of Baltimore: we will call this the Glen Burnie store. The second store was located in a regional shopping center adjacent to a heavily traveled thoroughfare in a middle-class suburb: this is his Route 40 store. In addition to containing dry cleaning equipment similar to that in the Glen Burnie store, the Route 40 location also contained customer-operated coin laundromat equipment.

When evaluating the potential of the Glen Burnie location, Mr. Jericho noted that it had good accessibility, adequate and adjacent parking facilities, was located in a thriving local shopping center, and it was a comfortable distance from the nearest competitor. However, Jericho failed to consider the importance of researching the consumers in this area. It is important that a dry cleaner be close to the target market, since generally people will not travel out of their way to patronize one.

He later learned that this part of Glen Burnie was a well-established area composed of lower-class, blue-collar workers While the majority of these people had an income that would permit using a dry cleaner's service, in many cases they had few dry cleaning needs; some were even furnished with uniforms and coveralls for their jobs by their employers. In addition, since this was an old, well-established community of home owners, almost everyone had a washer and dryer. This factor also reduced dry cleaning needs.

The people living around the Route 40 store were mostly white-collar with above average incomes. They had a large and consistent need for the services offered by a dry cleaner. In addition, the area was dominated by garden-style apartments. Jericho noted that this was significant since many of the customers told him they disliked going into dark and secluded basement laundry rooms. Many of these apartment dwellers used the dry cleaners and the coin-operated laundromats as a means to escape unpleasant laundry facilities. This contrasted sharply with the Glen Burnie community where most people had laundry equipment in their homes. These basic differences in the two locations had major effects on the viability of the two outlets:

"I rushed into these ventures rather quickly before I really knew the city of Baltimore," Mr. Jericho said. "I guess I was overconfident—after all, I had been in the dry cleaning business for twenty years. I was more concerned with a good traffic location, enough parking, a clean rentable location. I completely ignored checking into the type of people who lived around these locations." Mr. Jericho pondered his mistakes in retrospect.

Aside from the work requirements of the two categories of consumers, their life styles varied considerably and also had an impact on demand for dry cleaning at the two locations. The upper-lower-class and lower-middle-class blue-collar inhabitants of the Glen Burnie area did not do the type of entertaining and other related social activities that required clothing to be dry cleaned. Conversely, the Route 40 community was an extremely active social neighborhood. These people were accustomed to buying clothes that must be dry cleaned and they regarded the dry cleaner as more a necessity than a luxury.

Even economic factors affected business for the two stores. Glen Burnie had recently had many of its people laid off or given reduced work weeks by such companies as Martin-Marietta, Bendix, Bethlehem Steel, and Westinghouse. With the Route 40 people being mostly white-collar workers employed in a variety of businesses and professions, they did not experience similar layoffs and were much less affected by the economic slowdown of 1974.

Jericho even experienced difficulty in obtaining good employees. The people in the Glen Burnie area did not want to work in the cleaning plant. He was not sure exactly why there was this unwillingness, although he thought it was the result of racial prejudices because in this area blacks customarily staffed cleaning plants. Few blacks lived there and, consequently, such employees had to be obtained from more distant areas. Absenteeism was a constant problem. This lack of dependable personnel was a great concern to Jericho for he had always prided himself on quality and flexible operations, responsive to customer needs. The situation eventually became so bad that cleaning operations at the Glen Burnie store were discontinued; it was made a branch store with all cleaning handled by the other store. As a result of increased strains being put on the Route 40 store, Jericho's full-time presence was usually required there. With absentee management in the Glen Burnie store, thievery became a problem.

Jericho had established the prices in his two stores somewhat higher than competition. He did this because he believed that people were less concerned with price and more concerned with quality service. He hoped by these somewhat higher prices to establish his reputation as a quality cleaner whose higher prices reflected this: "People usually take their nicest clothes to an expensive, quality cleaner where they think they are paying for better work."

Price reductions were offered occasionally. For example, two-piece suits sometimes were cleaned at 15 percent below the regular price. At the Glen Burnie location this special had no appreciable impact on sales. However, significant sales increases occurred at the Route 40 store for some of these specials. Tim Davis, manager of the Route 40 store, noted, "While Mr. Jericho runs a few specials, he is very reluctant to do so. Other dry cleaners I've worked for have done this much more. Also, we don't run any seasonal specials—such as cleaning heavy suits in the winter or lightweight suits in the summer. I think Mr. Jericho is too gung-ho with his quality image, and it may be costing him business."

Promotional activities were practically nonexistent. Price specials were occasionally advertised in the storefront windows of both stores. Advertisements with coupons offering discounts that would be redeemed at the store were placed in the local Glen Burnie newspaper for several weeks. Only three coupons were redeemed in this period, so the idea was abandoned. Ads were never placed in the large newspapers such as the *Baltimore Sun,* because of the great expense involved.

Service was an important part of the marketing efforts. Jericho frequently inspected work in process to insure quality cleaning, "I will never knowingly give out a poor job." If a stain cannot be removed, a tag is affixed to the garment informing the customer that the stain was not neglected but simply could not be removed. If a garment is ever damaged or lost while in the possession of the cleaner, immediate monetary restitution is made to the customer. As a result of having all the cleaning done by the Route 40 store, it is possible to have one-day service there, but it takes two to three days to have the same service done through the Glen Burnie store.

As of early 1975, the Glen Burnie store is operating at a loss. The Route 40 store is moderately successful, although sales seem to be on a plateau, with little growth.

QUESTIONS

1. Evaluate the location research efforts of Mr. Jericho.
2. Evaluate the marketing approach being used.
3. What actions would you take to improve the present operations?
4. What location research would you advise for any additional outlets that might be opened?

Case 8
**Soft-Shell Structures—
Market Potential
for an Imported
Innovation**

Askura Company, Ltd., is a Japanese firm which manufactures and sells a wide range of canvas products including many kinds of tents ranging from small camping tents to "supersize" tents for various purposes. The latter are called "soft-shell structures," which refers to a canvas, tentlike structure which is dome-shaped and supported by air. Askura's principal sales have been in Japan. It has also exported in a small way to South America and southern Asia. It would like to market its soft-shell structures in the United States.

There are a wide range of potential applications. One use would be an accompaniment for urban renewal projects. Here an entire city block could be covered, thereby providing the many displaced businesses with a sheltered area so that they could continue as viable enterprises during the renewal process. At the present time approximately fifty cities have planned urban renewal programs. In Japan, Askura has used its structures for exhibition pavilions, restaurants, open air theaters, and other applications, ranging from covering swimming pools and football fields, to use as offices, warehouses, and greenhouses. Soft-shell structures also have considerable potential for carnivals. And in 1976, each of the fifty states plans to participate in the U.S. Bicentennial celebration.

A major advantage of the soft-shell structure is low cost: from $1.50 to $3.50 a square foot compared to $15 to $20 a square foot for regular buildings. The structures are aesthetically pleasing. Other advantages are:

1. They are inexpensive to heat—only air has to be heated, not such mass as walls and floors.
2. They can provide an unobstructed clear span, which is especially important for athletic events.
3. They are easily cleaned and require little maintenance.
4. They are completely dependable and can be properly engineered with respect to air pressure, fan location, anchorage, drainage, electricity and lights, etc.
5. They are safe, are well able to withstand strong winds, are fire-resistant as well as vandal-resistant.

These structures combine strength and economy as well as flexibility. It must be noted, of course, that they are not permanent buildings. The life of a soft-shell structure is 5–7 years, although the shell can be replaced for a semi-permanent arrangement.

These characteristics give them many potential uses. However, the Askura Company felt that initial efforts would best be concentrated on gaining acceptance with a single market rather than diffusing their efforts and using a shotgun approach. Accordingly, it was thought that the educational market might represent the initial direction of U.S. market entry.

Several factors which they had ascertained from architects and some educators encouraged them in this direction:

1. There is often a need for a shorter time period between the beginning and the completion of school construction projects.
2. Many school districts are experiencing a shortage of funds and increasing taxpayer reluctance so that they face tighter budget constraints.
3. Construction costs are constantly increasing.
4. Educators and architects are recognizing a need to develop new and better techniques to meet different educational demands and innovations.
5. The trend in enrollments is beginning to flatten in some areas, indicating that the burgeoning needs of some school districts today may eventually represent overcapacity—especially if conventional, permanent structures are built.

Several universities are already using soft-shell structures, and these prototypal users are enthusiastic about them. For example, Princeton University used a "bubble dorm" to house between 55 and 70 students, and this cost less than half as much as standard dormitories per student. It offers more space per inhabitant than any known dormitory and furnishes the utmost flexibility: the one large space is divided into three distinct areas by partitions, one area for recreational activities such as concerts and medium-sized assemblies, a social area allows for dining, cooking, studying, and lounging, while another area provides sleeping quarters for the inhabitants. Antioch University, on its Columbia, Maryland, campus, set up a one-acre air-supported structure to house campus needs.

While the potential undoubtedly exists for these structures, the Askura executives were understandably concerned with how easily this could be tapped, what competitors might be entering the market, and what the best marketing approach might be. They were also concerned about psychological resistance that architects, educators, builders, as well as the public who would utilize and pay for such structures, might have in regard to a product that was so radically different from the existing.

Some of the diversity of attitudes concerning soft-shell structures which came out of informal interviews with various educators and architects are reflected in these statements:

> It is not fair to "experiment" with taxpayers' money on this type of venture.
>
> Some company should enclose a swimming pool with a soft-shell structure as part of a pilot project at no cost to the recreation department. If the structure's performance was satisfactory and the community felt that a year-round pool enriched its recreation program, then the rest of the pools could be enclosed.
>
> There is no way for us to escape the traditional brick and mortar construction concept. The voters would not permit it.
>
> Because of an uneven growth rate in our country, we have had

to rely heavily on temporary classrooms, since permanent buildings have not always been available to accommodate the growing number of students. We have even had to use 150 trailers as temporary classrooms. These air structures might be an answer to our needs.

QUESTIONS

1. Develop a research plan to determine the market potential for soft-shell structures in the educational and recreational markets.
2. Develop a plan to market these structures in the United States.
3. What major difficulties do you see in marketing these, and how would you counter or overcome them?
4. Do you think Askura is best advised to give first attention to the educational market, or do you think some other sectors would offer better feasibility for market entry?
5. Do you think this Japanese firm would have serious problems in "invading" the United States market and gaining acceptance, since it is a foreign firm?

Case 9
Computer Center Security— Market Potential for a New Service

The computer center is a vulnerable part of modern organization. Besides the investment in equipment and facilities, the computer has resulted in the centralization of record keeping. In many cases it has resulted in the elimination of bookkeeping procedures that used to act as a double check and provide backup records. Bookkeeping personnel have been eliminated so that a firm no longer has the capability to revert to manual accounting procedures as a substitute for computer accounting.

Both the equipment and the records face hazards. Magnetic tape, for example, is highly vulnerable to destruction by fire or sabotage, and this data requires only a small fraction of the storage space that other documents once required, which suggests that its destruction could be easier and more complete. In many organizations the loss of these records—of accounts receivable, of creditors, and the like—could seriously jeopardize the viability of the enterprise.

There have been some recent examples of EDP records losses: a Pentagon fire destroyed 7,000 reels of tape, estimated at $10 million; rioting students at Sir George Williams University in Montreal completely destroyed computer equipment and files valued at $1.6 million (fortunately, the school had duplicate files in a remote location, but it took eight months to restore normal operations).

Table A-1.

Relationship Between Fire Damage and Business Failure

Disaster	Percentage of Firms
Business struck by fire that suffered a one-third reduction in credit rating	14
Firms struck by fire that previously furnished financial statements and no longer did so	17
Firms struck by fire that had their credit ratings unaffected	26
Firms struck by fire that did not resume business or were out of business within six months	43
Total	100

Source: R. J. Healy, *Design for Security* (New York: Wiley, 1968), p. 174.

The potential loss from fire alone would seem a persuasive justification for sound protection of vital records and assets. There is a correlation between fire damage and business failure as Table A-1 shows.

Nathan and Associates is a small consulting firm experienced in computer technology and management information systems. On the basis of an informal investigation by the principals of the firm, a vast untapped market seemed to exist for better security for computer equipment and data. Mr. Nathan noted, "Management has in the past paid little attention to computer security problems. Although natural or human engineered disasters could happen despite all reasonable precautions and countermeasures, many victims place the blame on company or institutional management for its failure to recognize potential hazards and to adopt countermeasures. Institutional management can no longer ignore the risk involved in operating computer centers."

There are three broad groups of computer users, and hence potential markets for computer security systems: industrial and commercial firms, universities, and the government. Nathan and Associates saw the university sector as offering a more manageable market for a small consulting firm. Several recent surveys of the use of computers on campuses had indicated that a majority had computers or would be using computers in the next few years. For example, Table A–2 shows the result of a survey by the American Association of Collegiate Registrars and Admissions Officers regarding the use of computers for administrative purposes relating to registrar and admissions records-processing and other applications. This survey found 61 percent of the respondents reporting using the computer, compared with 41 percent so reporting in a similar survey three years earlier. With some 2,500 institutions of higher education in the United States, the number of such computer users makes this an attractive market segment.

Table A-2.
Relationship Between Institutional
Enrollment and Computer Use

Enrollment	Percentage Using Computer
Below 1,000	28.4
1,000–4,999	69.3
5,000–9,999	93.3
10,000–14,999	97.6
15,000–19,999	100.0
20,000–Over	100.0
Total, all schools	61.0

Source: *Survey of the Management and Utilization of Electronics Data Processing Systems in Admissions Records and Registration* (Washington, D.C.: Report prepared by the American Association of Collegiate Registrars and Admissions Officers, 1970), pp. 1–30.

Nathan and Associates envisioned developing a computer-center security checkup program which would survey a school's existing situation, point out security weaknesses, estimate costs to reconstruct lost or destroyed data, and recommend security procedures and equipment. At first it was not anticipated that the firm would provide or install any of this equipment; it would simply act in the role of an objective adviser. However, it was thought that some common security devices might subsequently be handled. Also, Nathan and Associates did not plan to provide a continuing supervision of operations for clients, although this might also be a possible expansion of the firm's activities. Eventually as the university market was more completely tapped and as the size, the resources, and the experience of the firm became greater, the other two major sectors— the industrial/commercial, and the governmental—might be more actively sought.

Several problems of course confront Nathan and Associates. While the need undoubtedly exists for better security, and the risk seems real, it is doubtful if either security-consulting services or the major investment of security equipment is likely to be marketable. There is not only the requirement for expertise in the technical aspects of computer security, but a strong and persuasive selling job also is needed. And competition can by no means be ignored. It is entirely likely that a spate of such firms as Nathan and Associates will be emerging, since entry will be easy, requiring only one or more "experts," and one or more good salesmen. Therefore, it must be anticipated that, though the market and the potential is large, there will be more than enough firms vying for this market.

Before committing the firm to full efforts toward computer security, Nathan wanted to find out whether officials felt they needed computer security. If there was little perceived need, the selling job would of course be much more difficult and prolonged.

QUESTIONS

1. Design a research plan to help ascertain the perceived need of college administrators for computer security.
2. How would you plan your marketing approach to these people?
3. Discuss the advisability of Nathan diversifying into the stocking and installation of security equipment (rather than consulting alone).
4. Do you think the easy entry possible for competitors into this area makes this an inadvisable activity for Nathan?
5. Do you think it is wise to limit efforts to the educational market at this point?

Case 10
Marriott Corporation— Research for Increasing Hotel Occupancy

The Marriott Corporation is a family-controlled, diversified company operating in the lodging–food service industry. Founded in 1927, it has grown from a single root-beer stand. J. W. Marriott, Jr., the son of the founder, became president in 1964; sales climbed from $85 million to $538 million by 1973, the number of facilities in restaurant operations, lodging, and airline catering rose from 120 to 570, and the number of employees grew from 9,600 to 38,700.

Food operations account for 41 percent of corporate sales; these activities are primarily in the fast-food area. These include Big Boy Coffee Shops, Hot Shoppes Restaurants and Cafeterias, Roy Rogers Family Restaurants, Farrell's Ice Cream Parlours, Tollroad Restaurants, Fairfield Farm Kitchens Commissary, and a Food Service Management group in the specialized and institutional market. Some of these are franchised units while others are company-operated.

Marriott In-Flight Services furnish food service for airlines around the world, as well as airline terminal restaurants, and catering for various other organizations. This operation represented 28 percent of corporate sales in 1973.

Marriott is developing three major theme park complexes (rides, live entertainment, restaurants, specialty shops, etc.). These will be somewhat similar to Disney World, and the first will open in Santa Clara, California, in 1975. The firm has also diversified into a cruise ship line operating in the Aegean and Caribbean seas.

The Hotel System accounted for 31 percent of 1973 sales. Some twenty hotels were owned by Marriott in 1973, while another ten were franchised; rooms totaled over 10,000. In this case we will be concerned with the problems of one unit of this hotel division, the Washington, D.C., Crystal City unit, which opened in 1970 with 301 rooms. The uneven occupancy problems of this unit are by no means unique; many hotels experience similar problems, although any solutions may require special tailoring.

Marriott Hotels offer facilities and service at the top of the scale for transient hotels and have set their rates accordingly. They attempt to spread demand equally between group business, individual commercial business, and family travel. The rationale for this attempted equal proportionate trade is to spread the risk of a serious lag in the particular segment.

A profile of the typical Marriott Hotel customer showed him to be earning over $20,000, traveling by air for business, employed by one of the largest 500 corporations, a repeat customer, and a guest at a Marriott Hotel while traveling with his family by automobile.

Occupancy rate is important for any hotel, and the Marriott hotels average above 80 percent, which is well above the industry's 61 percent. To meet the anticipated needs of its selected customers, Marriott attempts to locate near airports and in high-traffic areas. This puts Marriot near the customer's arrival point and at a location convenient for him to do business. Food and beverage services contribute substantially to the net profits of the hotels and this also is well above industry average.

Despite the superior performance of Marriott hotels, low weekend occupancy is a persistent and frustrating problem to hotel management. It represents a considerable investment virtually left idle for eight or more days per month. The fixed investment is far larger than the operating expense of keeping a property going at half speed or less, and constitutes a drain when occupancy rate is down. A considerable number of employees over the weekend are underutilized, yet hotel services have to be maintained. Consequently, a hotel can afford to accept less than its normal fee during the weekend, and still do better than having these facilities remain idle. There is a need to find some untapped market to fill this gap in occupancy and increase the net profits of the hotel.

The Crystal City Marriott, like other hotels, is trying to solve this problem. It sees a possibility of additional weekend sales by offering the right mixture of programs to attract visitors from the outer suburbs and from towns and cities up to 200 miles distant from Washington. By developing and promoting what these people would respond to, the Crystal City Marriott believes it could significantly increase its weekend occupancy.

QUESTIONS

1. What types or segments of consumers can you hypothesize might constitute such a "weekender" market for the Crystal City Marriott?

2. Design a research project to establish the extent and composition of such a weekender market.

3. How would you appeal to this market? What promotional efforts would you use? What programs? How about prices?

4. Do you have any other practical recommendations for increasing occupancy on weekends? How would you test them?

5. How would you design a research study to determine the market potential for a "theme" park? for a cruise ship acquisition?

PART III

Programming the Marketing Strategy

Case 11
Hawaiian Candy Company—
Marketing Planning
and Diversification

For a number of years the Hawaiian Candy Company in Honolulu had been operated as a family enterprise. The Japanese-American owner and his wife handled the management of the company and had six women employees who were candy dippers. Although the company was small, its candy was well accepted within its small market, and it had a deservedly good reputation for quality. Partly this was due to the good ingredients used; partly it reflected the expert work of the women dippers who were dedicated workers despite their relatively low salaries.

Honolulu had a number of other candy manufacturers, but most specialized in candy types other than chocolates, such as coconut, macadamia nuts, and passion fruit. Two other firms specialized in chocolate candies: Ed and Don's Candies and Ice Cream Company, and Kay's Candies. Ed and Don's sold high-quality chocolates both by the box and as wrapped bars. They distributed partly through their own stores and partly through hotels, department stores, and drugstores. This company was the market leader in Hawaii. Kay's Candies was a small operation of no competitive significance. The market share and competitive efforts of all three companies, up until 1969, were static with none attempting to step up production or promotional efforts to obtain a larger market share.

The death in 1969 of John Say, owner of the Hawaiian Candy Company, brought changes. His widow tried to continue operating the company but found it beyond her capability. She was persuaded by a friend of her husband to hire David Meyer, a young college graduate who had majored in business administration and marketing and who was aggressive and ambitious.

"A business cannot long exist without growing," he told Mrs. Say. "You have to develop some new ideas, perhaps put in some more money, and be prepared to grow, if it is to survive. Otherwise, your competitors will take over the market, or perhaps some new firms from the mainland will find this an attractive market." Mrs. Say hired him as manager, and with his forceful manner, he soon took over the entire operation of the company. He was determined to make it the industry leader in Hawaii. Accordingly, he set out to learn all he could about the candy industry and candy production. He visited candy producers on the West Coast and inspected their processes and equipment. He learned that one of the major companies was using flash freezing to maintain freshness in storage. Freshness could be maintained thereby for more than a year without loss of quality.

Meyer's analysis of his current production facilities showed that under peak production periods, 135 pounds of hand-dipped chocolates could be produced by the work force. This was far below the capacity of Ed and Don's larger and more modern machinery. Since training hand dippers was a lengthy process and there were few seeking such employment, the transition from hand dipping to machine production or a combination of the two seemed the best course of action.

Based on his analysis and study, he presented Mrs. Say the following plan of action: (1) lease a larger facility; (2) install new equipment to expand production; (3) market the candy under a new name, "Aloha Candies," packaged in a striking new box with the cover designed by him. Mrs. Say gave her consent to this expansion and drew out some money from her savings to help finance it.

A former roller skating rink was leased to provide more floor space for the new production layout. While waiting for the new machinery to arrive, production at the old facilities was kept at a peak level. Workers were given a pay raise, the first in a long time, and this proved an excellent incentive and spurred them on to greater efforts. Meyer started keeping production records for each worker, and each tried to outdo the others.

As a promotional technique, Meyer employed an attractive young lady to pass out candy samples in shopping centers. This resulted in the largest discount chain taking on the products. An experienced salesman was also hired and paid 10 percent on all sales he produced, and orders began rolling in. As a further move to increase market share, especially at the expense of Ed and Don's, prices were reduced. All of these actions were based on anticipated increased production which would come from the new machinery soon to arrive.

Meyer also saw a bonus potential in the flash-freezing process. He thought it could well be used to process fish and tropical fruit for shipment to the Mainland. As it was, certain tropical fruit and fish could not be shipped fresh because of perishability.

Another possible project also seemed to have promise. Macadamia nuts were used in much of the candy. It appeared that the company's expanded nut requirement could be more cheaply met from company-owned groves. Therefore negotiations were undertaken to acquire 450 acres of nut trees on the island of Hawaii.

Since both the nuts and the fish (to be flash-frozen) would have to be transported from the island of Hawaii to the island of Oahu, it appeared logical to acquire one or two cargo aircraft for this purpose. Negotiations were therefore begun to acquire two used cargo planes.

With so many projects developing, Meyer found the demands on his time almost overwhelming. He had no one to take on any of the planning or supervision, since Mrs. Say had retreated to an uneasy retirement. Machinery began to arrive for installation in the new facilities. The flash-freezing project reached the stage of development where increased cash investment was required. The nut grove negotiations also firmed up to the need for commitment of more funds, and all that was needed to finalize purchase of the two aircraft was cash to complete payment.

"The stage is all set for us to become a million-dollar business," he told Mrs. Say, as he approached her for additional money.

But Mrs. Say neither had available the quantity of cash needed nor was she willing to release any more that she did have. Not only did the flash-freezing, nut grove, and airplane negotiations terminate, but also enough money was not available to install the machinery which had arrived. Without warning, the Hawaiian Candy Company closed its doors in April 1971, and ceased operations.

QUESTIONS

1. Discuss in detail the mistakes that were made.

2. Were any aspects of Meyer's performance praiseworthy?

Case 12
Boneshaker, Inc.—
Product Innovation
via Nostalgia Theme

In September 1973, twenty-one-year old Joseph LoConti had an idea. He thought that a high-priced, high-wheeler bicycle—such as was popular in the late 1890s "when gents with handlebar moustaches, polo caps, and knickerbockers pedaled about frightening horses"[1]—might again be salable due to the nostalgia boom.

He took the specifications for such a bicycle to five different bicycle manufacturers, trying to interest them in doing the subcontracting fabrication for a prototype. But all five turned down the idea, stating that in order to consider tooling, a start-up order of 250 bicycles at a cost of $200 each was needed. LoConti finally found a small metal fabricator who was willing to custom make the bicycles, one at a time, and four prototypes were made, one of them chrome for "publicity" purposes, and a smaller version as a female model. It was decided to call the cycles "boneshakers" since the tires were solid rubber and every bump "rattled your eyes and shook your bones."

The question now was: Would anybody be willing to pay upward of $300 for such a novelty item? How could this be researched? The National Bike Show was being held in Miami Beach. The firm rented a booth there

[1] Quoted from *Wall Street Journal*, "High Wheeler Bikes Dandy for Nostalgia but Awful for Riding," December 17, 1974, p. 1.

and displayed its prototypes. "It was unreal. People went crazy over them. Why in three days we had orders for almost 300 bikes." The following month at the New York Trade Show they got another 300 firm orders. At that point, not a single bicycle had yet been delivered to a customer, nor was the retail price definitely finalized.

It seemed that demand would be rather inelastic for this product; therefore a low price and modest markup would probably not yield much more volume than a high price and a larger per-unit profit. The retail price was finally established at $279, which gave dealers a 32 percent markup, while yielding Boneshaker, Inc., $75 profit on each cycle. Since the fabricator was using idle plant capacity, manufacturing costs were moderate although production capability was limited. It appeared that the firm had nothing to gain costwise by trying to take over the manufacturing function itself. Furthermore, the fabricator agreed to guarantee the quality and provide free repairs in case of any defect

The product seemed to promote itself; wherever one appeared, a crowd gathered, and even the news media was interested. By mid-1975, the Boneshaker had appeared in 35 front pages as a novelty story, humor caption with pictures, or small business success story. Even the *Wall Street Journal* gave it a front page article on December 17, 1974. Three New York Jets football players rode the product on St. Patrick's Day through Manhattan. The Mike Douglas Show presented it with the host riding a Boneshaker through Philadelphia. Boneshakers were ridden on racetracks, used to promote Bikethons for retarded children, and ridden for publicity by 10 mayors and 5 Congressmen. All this promotion was free and worth thousands of dollars. The firm continued to limit its efforts to trade shows and brochures distributed from its booth at such shows. By 1974, Boneshaker had received 6,000 orders.

But Jim Krivanik, the general manager, worried:

"If new orders next spring hit 500 units monthly, we will again fall behind in filling them. The demand is there, yet it seems we can't keep it at a smooth level. In the winter months, orders trickle to one or two a week, and expand to fantastic proportions just before spring and summer. We're assembling them by hand at a maximum of 3 units per day. We can only work so fast, and Boneshaker, Inc., would hate to be forced to look for another fabricator just to meet peak demand, and then lose money during the slow months. We still would like to increase sales, if just to keep production at an even level through the year. What do we do?"

QUESTIONS

1. What do you suggest Boneshaker do at this point?
2. Do you think they should change their marketing strategy, and if so, how?
3. Do you see any other markets for Boneshaker?

Case 13
**Skippy Nuts—
Push and Pull
Strategies in
Gaining Distribution**

C.P.C. International is a large corporation with sales in 1974 of over $2.5 billion. Among its many products is Skippy, a quality peanut butter known throughout the nation and in many foreign countries. Having acquired the Kelling Nut Company, a producer of nuts sold by drug stores, variety stores, and nut shops, it seemed a natural to enter the dry roasted nut market using the "Skippy" name, and direct efforts to grocery stores where the Skippy name had been traditionally associated.

The major competitor was Planters, which controlled about 70 percent of this market. There were also several strong regional brands, such as Flavor House in the central region and Franklin Nut in the south. But C.P.C. felt that this competition could be overcome so that a significant share of the market could be captured.

It was decided to offer only the more popular types of nuts: peanuts, cashews, and mixed nuts. These were to be bottled in two sizes, 8 ounces and 12 ounces. A flavor coating of sugar and spices was applied to the nuts to give them a distinctive flavor and a rich brown color.

The new product was test marketed in small towns in the South, North, Midwest, and West. As a result, the flavor coating was made lighter, although it was still felt that this flavor coating would be an important factor in selling the product.

C.P.C. decided to pull the product onto the market with heavy consumer advertising in all media, particularly radio and TV. The advertising basically emphasized two points: the Skippy name, and the special flavor coating. The price was about the same as Planters.

But despite the advertising, Skippy captured only a small percentage of the market, although results were somewhat better in the New York-New Jersey area where the Skippy name helped considerably. A large second wave of advertising was launched the following summer in hopes of bolstering sales. The amount of flavor coating was also reduced again. The results continued disappointing.

In efforts to save the product, a management change was made and new plans drawn up for the following year. First, all TV and radio advertising was cut off except for "tags"—i.e., two- or three-second plugs for Skippy Nuts tagged onto the end of Skippy Peanut Butter commercials. Emphasis instead was directed to getting shelf space in supermarkets, and this had proven surprisingly difficult before. Special deals including free goods were given stores that took the product; extra discounts were provided those who displayed it prominently; point-of-purchase display material was furnished dealers. The idea of the special flavor coating was not emphasized, but rather that Skippy was a quality nut. And the product supported this claim. In an average bottle of Skippy Nuts, 75 percent were whole nuts as opposed to Planters, which had 50 percent pieces or split nuts. There was less residue on the bottom of a bottle of Skippy. Furthermore, Skippy used nuts that were slightly larger.

In attempting to push the product, major efforts were directed to the larger food chains. These chains usually have one central buying office, and Skippy attempted to influence these buyers with large discounts. The small corner grocery stores were ignored as it was not felt they could generate sufficient sales volume to be worth the expense of contacting.

While these various strategies brought some increase in sales, Skippy still failed to capture any significant portion of the market. Where it gained market share it was at the expense of the regional brands and private labels, not from Planters, its formidable national competitor.

In view of the lack of success of Skippy Nuts, the company faced the decision of whether to drop the product, change its marketing strategy again, or simply continue the same way in hopes that sales eventually would improve.

QUESTIONS

1. What do you advise, and why?

Case 14
Allied Division—
Marketing Strategy
for a Sonic
Toothbrush

Quality Products, Inc., was organized in 1960, and steadily grew to sales of $28 million by 1974. In January of 1974, three mechanical engineers of its

Allied Division developed a new type of electric toothbrush, and the company obtained a patent on it.

The toothbrush was significantly different from any currently on the market in that sonic vibratory energy was transmitted to the bristles from the handle. These vibrations caused the bristle head to move, thus creating a sound field that produced acoustic streaming in the liquid medium surrounding the tooth surface to be cleaned. Conventional automatic toothbrushes do little more than clean and polish exposed tooth surfaces, even to the extent of sometimes causing abrasion of the tooth enamel; they are relatively ineffective in cleaning spaces between teeth. Allied contracted with a dental school to test the clinical effectiveness of the sonic toothbrush. The results indicated its definite superiority, even to the extent of potentially bringing periodontally afflicted patients back to a state of improved periodontal health. The university research concluded that the Allied sonic toothbrush was a potentially outstanding oral hygiene system.

Allied performed a cost evaluation to determine the feasibility of marketing the toothbrush. The unit contribution to manufacturing overhead and other fixed expenses was determined to be:

Unit price to wholesaler		$11.00
Less: Variable manufacturing costs	$3.50	
Allowance to wholesalers and dealers for local advertising	1.00	4.50
Contribution per unit		6.50

The total costs to be recovered by the variable contribution per unit would be:

Fixed manufacturing overhead	$150,000
Selling expenses	150,000
Advertising costs	125,000
Total	425,000

Accordingly, the breakeven point at which costs would be recovered was determined to be 65,385 units (i.e., $425,000 fixed costs divided by the $6.50 contribution per unit). The total market was estimated at 100,000 units annually.

The proposed distribution system involved selling the toothbrush to wholesalers who in turn would sell to dealers at 30 percent above the cost to them, or $14.30 per unit. The dealers' suggested retail price was $24.95. Price competition was to be avoided, and Allied was determined to refuse to sell to dealers who tried price-cutting. The $24.95 suggested retail price was considerably higher than the price being paid for competitors' electric toothbrushes. However, the sonic toothbrush was considered to be revolutionarily different and superior, and the higher retail price was deemed justified.

Despite the favorable test results obtained from the university study and the estimated market potential of 100,000 units, only 27,000 Allied brushes were sold in 1974. This was considerably below the breakeven volume of 65,385 units, and a loss of $270,200 was incurred.

QUESTIONS

1. Calculate the breakeven point if the firm should reduce its unit price to wholesalers by $2.
2. What do you recommend the company do at this time? Support your recommendations.

Case 15
Arden-Mayfair, Inc.—
Promoting a
Company Image

Arden-Mayfair, Inc., is a medium-sized, Los Angeles-based company principally engaged in producing, processing, manufacturing, and distributing food products. Operations are concentrated in the Western states, with major efforts in California.

The company began operations as Western Dairies, then changed the name to Arden Farms in 1940. The present name came as a result of a merger with Mayfair Markets in 1964. The company is diversified into various supermarket and discount food divisions; a complete line of dairy products distributed to food stores, restaurants, hotels, and vending operations; swimming pool chemicals and equipment; printing and lithography; and ice cream shops. Mayfair Markets is the major division, with 1969 sales of $448,000,000, or 76 percent of consolidated sales. However, while the smaller divisions are doing relatively well profitwise, this division is not.

Pretax profit margins for the company as a whole decreased from 2.0 percent in 1965 to 0.5 percent in 1969, even though sales increased from $506.9 million to $588.1 million. Net income went from $5.4 million in 1965 to $1.7 million in 1969. This, along with the inconsistent management, caused the stock to go from $28 to a low of 6½ in 1970.

There has been a history of inconsistent leadership, with management turning over six times since the present company was formed in 1964. This has tended to generate a lack of continuity in the philosophy of the company and in its operation. Many of the executives who came in had little or no previous experience in grocery retailing. The present president, Albert Crosson, was formerly with Chicken-of-the-Sea and Hunt-Wesson, which is a more relevant experience.

At least part of the company's problems can be laid to overzealous diversification efforts in 1964–65 at a time when the beginning of an inflationary period was putting a squeeze on profit margins of the grocery industry. Even though costs of labor, money, new stores, etc., were moving sharply higher, the competitive climate—especially in California and the

West where many aggressive supermarket chains were based—did not allow for fully offsetting retail price increases. And Arden-Mayfair suddenly had 224 supermarkets and assimilation problems.

Efforts were made to increase efficiency. In-store data transmitters were introduced to speed up the merchandise ordering process and the delivery cycle, thereby reducing both the number of out-of-stock items and the investment in inventory. Many Mayfair Markets went to a 24-hour day, a not uncommon practice in the West. However, there were no figures on the profitability of a 24-hour operation versus stores open more regular hours. Near the Mexican border many people come over the border to shop at night; further north the plan may not be worthwhile. Some experimentation was done with low-margin discount markets which have achieved considerable public acceptance on the West Coast. These discount markets are open shorter hours, offer a modified service level, and do not issue trading stamps or engage in extensive promotional activities. Additional existing locations may be converted if it is determined that greater long-term profitability can be expected from such a change.

An intangible obstacle to the profitable growth of the company may be the lack of a strong company or brand image with the consumer, other than the Arden Dairy Products which are marketed outside of Mayfair Markets as well. A private label, Mayfresh, is used for canned goods although the use of this varies from store to store. A wide variety of nationally known brands are offered—perhaps too many, so that the company is now trying to eliminate the less popular brands and sizes and to rely on fewer suppliers, thereby reducing inventory and handling costs. The private or house brands are given no special promotion and generally face limited demand.

The company appears to lack "showmanship." The signs used at store locations are not attention-getting or distinctive; radio advertising is not memorable or attention-getting. Ads are customarily run in the food section of newspapers along with those of other chains. With profit margins so scanty, the practicality of a vast image-building campaign would seem remote. But the fact remains that the lack of a distinctive character or image has resulted in most customers shopping at Mayfair stores because of their proximity and not because of reputation or products.

At the present time, the company is attempting to consolidate operations and even sell stores in some areas in order to get down to a number that can be handled profitably, before expanding further. The program calls for giving more careful attention to boosting the volume in existing stores, remodeling older stores, and for better-defined and -developed marketing plans for each store.

QUESTIONS

1. How would you develop a more distinctive image?
2. How would you improve "showmanship"?
3. Develop a five-year program to increase sales and profits. Be as specific as you can.

Case 16
The Odds 'n Ends Shop—
Promoting and
Stocking
a Small Store

Miss Katherine Travis conceived the "Odds 'n Ends Shop" in the summer of 1972, while vacationing in a small Maine resort town. The town had been a prosperous family resort area before World War II, but had been going downhill ever since: it was located near the tip of a small peninsula and off the main stream of tourist traffic, and there was no longer any public transportation into the town (at the height of its popularity, trains carried many vacationers into town for the resorts located in proximity of it). Miss Travis, a teacher, had spent her summers in the town for a number of years and had become attached to it and rather saddened by its decay. By 1972, there were eight empty storefronts on the main street and the dilemma of this small hinterland town was not atypical of hundreds elsewhere.

Miss Travis thought that a new business might provide some spur to the economy of the town and decided to open a small gift store which would appeal both to the small band of faithful summer visitors and to the year-round inhabitants as well. She also envisioned the town reviving in subsequent years as more people sought to escape the congestion of major vacation areas and looked for quieter surroundings. She rented and renovated an old but picturesque building, and she created a rather distinctive "character" sign to highlight the building and the new shop.

Fall and winter of 1972 was spent in shopping for goods to stock the store. New York City, where Miss Travis taught, of course provided ample sources of goods, but she did look elsewhere as well. She prided herself in being a knowledgeable shopper and had years of experience in collecting various artifacts and antiques for her own use. Acquiring merchandise for the store was therefore no particular problem, but rather a source of real enjoyment and challenge. The shop was to carry toys, provincial artifacts, local effort (such as hand-knitted items and carvings), costume jewelry, belts and ties, and some antiques and reproductions. Most of the items were bought to sell for under $25, although some antiques were relatively expensive.

The shop opened in June 1973, and several local girls were hired to help out. Miss Travis held an open house for the town's other retail merchants to convince them that she was not carrying any items that might compete with any of theirs, and to elicit their support and encourage them to recommend her store to their customers. This goodwill gesture, the fact that local girls were being hired, and Miss Travis's long support of the town, easily gained the cooperation of the other merchants.

However, sales the first year did not come up to expectations (or else the sales forecast had been too optimistic), and a loss of $1,700 resulted. Miss Travis, in retrospect, was inclined to think her promotional efforts had been ineffective. She had shunned billboards, thinking these should be banned from highways as detracting from the scenery. She had used brochures and flyers (distributed rather aimlessly), and some local newspaper ads. She had attempted to change window displays every few weeks. No price reductions or sales were announced until a final "20 percent off' September clearance. The store was closed down for the winter months—as the tourists for the most part departed by Labor Day, and Miss Travis had to leave for her school term—by the middle of September.

A few changes were instituted the following year. One major change was to remain open longer hours. Other stores along Main Street were open until 9:00 PM and catered to many browsers during the long summer evenings. Miss Travis hoped this next year that by following suit some of these customers would find their way to the Odds 'n Ends. An optimistic omen for future business was a growing percentage of customers who had come from a distance upon the recommendation of their friends and acquaintances: word-of-mouth publicity was beginning to be effective.

By the end of the 1974 season, a 30 percent sales increase had been recorded, and the store had earned a small profit.

		1973		1974
Sales		$14,800		$19,600
Beginning inventory .	8,500		3,000	
Purchases	2,000		9,800	
Less ending inventory	−3,000		−5,000	
Cost of goods sold		7,500		7,800
Gross margin		7,300		11,800
Expenses		9,000		9,600
Net Profit (loss)		(1,700)		2,200

Miss Travis could still at this point not afford to give up her teaching and devote full time to the store (although if the store could have been operated as a year-round business, this might have been more feasible). However, she seemed to be approaching a crossroads: whether to devote aggressive efforts to making the store a major success (and perhaps even expanding it, or opening another store), or to be content with a summertime profitable "hobby." She recognized that she lacked an adequate business acumen, especially in budgeting and keeping records, and also in controlling her inventories. For example, the first year she had carried $3,000 worth of inventory through the winter months when the shop was closed; and by the end of the 1974 selling season, she had about $5,000 worth of such unsold goods.

However, she believed her buying ability for this type of merchandise was excellent. She was especially enthusiastic about her ability to renovate "junk." For example, a chair had been purchased for $9 and after refurbishing, sold for $70; similarly, an old desk which she acquired for $10 she had sold for almost $100.

1. Should Miss Travis attempt to expand the operations of the Odds 'n Ends?

2. How should the marketing mix be designated to be more effective? In particular, should promotional and pricing efforts be changed?

3. What problems do you see in this particular operation?

Case 17
Falstaff Brewing Company— Promotional and Pricing Problems of a Regional Brewer

A decade ago there were 171 companies brewing beer in the United States; only 80 remain today. In 1970 total beer sales rose 4 percent, but the nine largest regional brewers eked out only a 1.4 percent sales gain. Falstaff was among those regional brewers that slipped badly, with sales off 10 percent (in Texas, sales dropped 30 percent). The big three of the brewing industry —Anheuser-Busch, Schlitz, and Pabst—increased their collective market share from 21.5 percent to 39.7 percent in the last decade.

Falstaff markets in the Midwest and in California. Its sales in 1970 were $144 million, which makes it a large regional brewer. However, brewing is a classic economies-of-scale industry, and the large-size national companies with their ability to pour out several million or more barrels annually definitely have the advantage. Advertising and promotion also favors the very large at the expense of the small and medium-size firms. One would think that the smaller brewer could develop a unique taste, or a special quality to its beer—a distinctive, differentiated product—to insulate it from the devastating competition of the national brewers. However, this is usually not the case. The differences in taste are so subtle as to be more psychologically created by advertising, than tangible and objectively evident.

The national beers usually are able to command a premium price in most areas vis-à-vis the local or regional beers, since they have developed an aura of quality, enhanced by heavy image-building promotional efforts. In recent years these national brewers have used price as an effective tool to establish large market-share inroads against the regional and local brands. In some markets, the national brands were being promoted at prices under those of the locals. In order not to dissipate their quality image by lowering prices across the board, more selective price cutting was often being used effectively: for example, the price of a "six pack" might be reduced on the national brand, while keeping up the premium prices on the other quantities and sizes. The regional and local brewers were therefore disadvantaged in two ways: they did not have the quality or prestige image of the national brand, and they could not match the distribution and production costs since they did not have the same economy of scale.

Blue-collar workers have been one of the major market segments for beer. Their rising affluence has made them likely candidates for premium beers at premium prices. In many cases they have tended to disdain the "old, local standby" for the prestige brand with its more solid manifestation of their higher income.

The youth market comprises the other major market for beer. The twenty-one to thirty-four age bracket is the fastest-growing segment of the market. However, this group is less wedded to traditional brands and often is attracted by the new and the nonlocal. This group also has greater affluence and is more swayed by the particular image that a beer marketer is able to engender. Some smaller brewers are attempting to cater to this youth market. Ballantine's, for example, sponsored a series of rock concerts in college towns up and down the Eastern seaboard. Another brewer appealed to youth's proclivity to try new products by introducing a new malt liquor called "Hop 'N Gator." Schmidt's released an advertising campaign for "One Beautiful Beer."

A handful of regional brewers have bucked the downward trend. Coors of Colorado greatly increased its market penetration, rising from twelfth place in 1965 to fourth place in 1970. Heileman Brewing of LaCrosse, Wisconsin, bought a nationally known name, Blatz, formerly a subsidiary of Pabst that the Justice Department had pressured Pabst into relinquishing, and sales have risen 260 percent since 1965. New York's Rheingold Corporation also found the last half of the decade most pleasing. However, its beer sales did not so much contribute to the prosperity, as its diversification: it diversified into soft drinks—is the world's largest franchised Pepsi-Cola bottler—and vigorously expanded this operation into Southern California, Mexico, and Puerto Rico (these areas all have "year-round" thirsts, without any cold-weather slackening).

Falstaff attempted to be aggressive. It improved its can-making facilities; it introduced the "Tapper," a 2¼-gallon keg for home consumption; it attempted to selectively increase its prices (in order to seek more of a quality image). It extensively promoted Falstaff beer, mostly through TV advertising, including year-round sponsorship of some sports-events programs. Current (1970) executive thinking is that Falstaff may have overspent on TV and underspent on local merchandising. The brewer cut back sharply on TV advertising in an economy move.

QUESTIONS

1. Evaluate Falstaff's efforts up to 1970.
2. What marketing approach would you use at this time (1970)?
3. In the next five years, what efforts can Falstaff undertake to blunt the marketing power of the national brands? How successful do you think these efforts are likely to be?

Case 18
Adam Cigarettes—
Introducing a
New Brand Under
Promotional Constraints[1]

In August 1971, Liggettt & Myers began testing a new cigarette, Adam, "for men only." It had been designed to convey a strong appeal for rugged males in the twenty-one to forty-nine age bracket.

This was the second "specialized" cigarette by L & M, the first being Eve, a moderately successful female-oriented cigarette introduced in January 1971. Adam had borrowed the masculine look of a small cigar, such as General Cigar's Tijuana Smalls, but was positioned as a cigarette with brown cigarette paper and a cream-colored filter tip. The introductory ads read, "The first cigarette for men—Adam, the man's cigarette . . . the cigarette with a man's taste and a man's look. Filtered mild to give you real tobacco taste. Tailored in brown to stand out from all the others. Adam. It won't make you more of a man. But then, you don't need to be."

Mr. Pippert, director of brand management for L & M, was keenly aware of the effects of the ban on TV cigarette advertising imposed as of January 2, 1971, but believed that packaging would now play the important role. Adam's packaging showed a contemporary male portrait in three tones of brown. The cigarette was ringed with a band of brown and two bands of gold.

It was decided to test market the new product in three small, relatively isolated towns: Salinas, California; Galesburg, Illinois; and Pittsfield, Massachusetts. Advertising consisted of newspaper and outdoor billboards, as well as heavy point-of-sale displays.

However, results were discouraging and Liggett & Myers stopped testing Adam in April 1972. The test marketing suggested that both packaging and advertising needed improvement. Subsequent package tests indicated that the original Adam pack placed dead last in competing with three new designs; a package resembling a leather cigarette case with gold studs in the corners was judged most effective.

Liggett & Myers changed advertising agencies and reintroduced Adam in September 1972 with a new theme, "the brown cigarette getting back to taste." It was decided that test marketing would be expanded to take place in 25 percent of L & M's sales territories.

The "new" Adam now being marketed in Los Angeles, San Diego, Boston, Chicago, Atlanta, and Washington, D.C., in its new leatherlike package, was distinctly different from the Adam that faltered in the early test markets. For one thing, the cigarette introduced in 1971 as "the first cigarette for men," was repositioned as a flavor cigarette designed to appeal to the Marlboro or Winston smoker. The cigarette's brown appear-

---

[1] Adapted from "L & M Test Adam Cigaret," *Advertising Age*, August 16, 1971, p. 59; "C & W, Norman, Craig to Split $15,000,000 L & M Ad Account," *Advertising Age*, March 12, 1973, pp. 2, 8.

ance originally was meant to strengthen its appeal to "new conformists—guys who were first to adopt new clothing styles or hair styles." The "new" Adam's appearance was now linked to taste, "Brown makes the difference. The special brown wrapper actually adds to Adam's natural mellow flavor." Current advertising was also intended to underline the fact that Adam was a cigarette. This was to prevent consumers from classifying it as a little cigar, something that past advertising had failed to accomplish.

Adam was again promoted with color spreads in general interest, special interest, and men's magazines. Newspaper supplements, regional magazines, and outdoor advertising were also used. L & M spent $476,956 on magazine advertising alone for Adam in 1972. And company executives conceded that it would take longer to generate impact for a new brand through the print media than would have been the case with TV.

But in September 1973 their patience ran out. L & M decided to quit testing Adam, and drop it. Eve found herself a widow. It was generally concluded that part of the reason for the market failure was the ban on TV, which resulted in a lower consumer awareness of the new product.

QUESTIONS

1. With the ban on TV advertising of cigarettes, do you think Liggett & Myers should have attempted to introduce a new cigarette brand?
2. What mistake did they make with Adam?
3. How do you think Adam might have been introduced successfully? Are there other advertising appeals or promotional approaches that might have led to more success?
4. Does this failure suggest that new brands of cigarettes cannot be successfully introduced since they cannot be given the massive impact of TV advertising?

Case 19
A & P's WEO—
A Price-Cutting
Strategy

William Kane took over as chief executive of the Great Atlantic & Pacific Tea Co. in 1971 at a time when the nation's largest supermarket chain was finding its sales leveling and its profits shrinking. In early 1972 he made the decision to convert the chain to superdiscount stores. "We have to start the growth factor in this company right now," Kane was quoted by *Business Week*. "This is a business based strictly on volume, with sales measured in tonnage."[1]

[1] "A & P's Ploy: Cutting Prices to Turn a Profit," *Business Week*, May 20, 1972, p. 76.

Overnight in various cities across the country, stores were converted to something called "Where Economy Originates" or WEO's for short. Two major changes were made in the stores:

1. Prices were lowered on 90 percent of the merchandise.
2. Variety of goods was reduced so that there were fewer sizes and kinds of certain items.

How much were prices really reduced in the WEO stores? The impact is best seen in the effect on margins. Margins or markup percentages for most supermarkets including the regular A & Ps are around 20–22 percent; the WEO margins were estimated to run between 9 percent and 13 percent. This translated into a can of beef stew being reduced from 67¢ to 59¢, for example, while plastic sandwich bags went from 53¢ to 49¢.

New signs and banners were used to acquaint customers with the new policies. Furthermore, heavy advertising was used, not only in the traditional newspaper, but also on radio and TV. However, even if sales volume were to increase dramatically, the question in the fall of 1972 was whether volume would rise fast enough to yield profits at the low margins. But Kane expressed his basic food merchandising philosophy:

> I want to get us back to good, sound, basic fundamentals.
> This company was built on quality foods sold at low prices.[2]

The background for the decision to seek a larger market share by means of drastically reducing prices was the worsening competitive situation of A & P especially compared to its closest competitor in size, Safeway. The comparative statistics for the two chains at the eve of the WEO decision are shown in Table A-3.

The price-cutting strategy of A & P fostered strong competitive reactions as other firms tried to match prices. Profits for most of the supermarket industry dropped. For example, Kroger reported a 36 percent profit drop for 1972, and Food Fair had profits down 50 percent in two quarters of 1972.

And what did A & P accomplish? It increased its market share by

Table A-3.

	A & P Sales (000,000)	Income	Market Share	Safeway Sales (000,000)	Income	Market Share
1965	$5,119	$52.3	19.0%	$2,939	$48.2	10.9%
1967	5,458	55.9	17.6	3,361	50.9	10.8
1969	5,753	53.3	15.4	4,100	51.3	11.0
1971	5,508	14.6	12.1	5,359	80.2	11.8

Sources: U. S. Dept. of Commerce reports, and Moody's.

[2] Ibid.

1 percent for 1972; in the process it incurred a deficit of $51,280,000. While its sales slightly topped those of Safeway for the year, Safeway also gained market share, and increased its profits as well, as shown below:

	1972 Sales	Income	Market Share
A & P	$ 6,307,000,000	def. $ 51,280,000	13.1%
Safeway	6,058,000,000	91,060,000	12.5

Early in 1973, A & P eased its price-cutting tactics. The major question facing the firm in 1973 was whether the hard-won gains would be lasting. Would customers who had been wooed by A & P because of supposed lower prices, to the tune of an $800 million sales increase, stay with A & P? Or would they quickly shift when they discover that WEO prices are comparable to those of other stores?

QUESTIONS

1. What other strategies might have been used by A & P instead of price-cutting in the early 1970s?

2. What would you advise the company to do at this point?

3. What conclusions can you draw—as regards applicability for future decisions—from the WEO campaign?

Case 20
TeleMart Enterprises[1]— A Marketing Logistical Innovation

Most marketing changes are rather minor: a changed package, a different product feature, a new ad campaign, and so on. Once in a great while a substantial marketing change is offered. Sometimes these major innovations have a sweeping effect on the marketplace—as did discount stores and TV. Sometimes, however, a major innovation may be too different, and wither for lack of consumer acceptance.

TeleMart Enterprises, Inc., located in San Diego, California, offers a major innovation in food retailing. TeleMart, which is an acronym for "telephone market," proposes to abandon the concept of self-service food stores. It will receive a housewife's grocery order by telephone and then deliver her order several hours later. It is planned to operate on a membership basis, with a $2 initial membership fee.

The housewife makes out her grocery list from over 3,000 items, all of which have unique code numbers. From 7:00 AM until 11:00 PM calls are received by up to 90 TeleMart operators, who then hook the calls into an

---

[1] This material has partially been adapted from "Dialing for the Groceries," *Business Week,* March 28, 1970, pp. 110–16.

audio-response computer. The computer receives the order, verifies it item by item, and quotes prices for various quantities. Delivery is promised within four hours, and is also pinpointed as to which two-hour period it will occur (thereby freeing the housewife for other errands, without fear of not being home when the delivery is attempted). A $1 service charge is placed on each order; the customer can either pay the delivery man or she can be billed monthly.

A former advertising executive, A. G. Bailey, originated the idea after about a year in research and development of the system. The company's first operation is expected to cost $1.1 million, and will have a distribution center with a capacity of ten large supermarkets. Bailey anticipates that personnel expenses will be much greater than those of an average supermarket, but he expects to realize cost advantages in other aspects of the operation, so that the total expense picture will be somewhat less than for the typical supermarket. For example, the distribution center will essentially be a large warehouse located on industrial land; there is no need for huge customer parking areas and the only parking spaces would be those for the delivery trucks. Accordingly, large operational and investment savings should be realized in the land and building.

Other savings are expected to be realized in purchasing, shipping, and handling costs through buying in quantity. Some 40,000 members are expected by opening day, and estimates are that 3,000 customers will use the facilities each day. The company will use 75 leased trucks for the delivery part of the operation, with a computer determining optimum distribution routes and order priorities. The computer will also print out an order sheet for the warehouse shipping clerks. Thus only with a computer could a logistic effort of this magnitude be handled.

One of the early criticisms of TeleMart was that the 3,000 items it anticipated carrying would not be enough for profitable operations and would force the customer to do considerable shopping elsewhere, thus mitigating the convenience advantage of TeleMart. While it is true that the average supermarket carries upward of 9,000 items, Bailey points out that his limited list accounts for 80 percent of all the food dollars spent in San Diego. It is anticipated that the shopping guide will be changed quarterly and the number of items somewhat expanded in the future.

Another possible limiting aspect of TeleMart's operations is that women will no longer be able to shop personally for items such as meat and produce. But Bailey points out that a customer can return any unsatisfactory merchandise at the time it is delivered. He also believes that the customer will more than make up the dollar delivery charge by savings realized from quantity orders. Since the merchandise is delivered to her door, the housewife may be more inclined to buy by the case or in the jumbo economy size.

In entering the market initially in San Diego—plans are to rapidly expand nationwide—Bailey spoke to women's groups, offered potential customers a month's free trial membership, and spent about $30,000 a month for television spot announcements.

Bailey realizes that although TeleMart is in the retail food business,

CASE 20 / TELEMART ENTERPRISES

in reality a convenience service is being sold. "Our main challenge," he says, "is a marketing one. Our Wheaties are no different than anyone else's. What we've got to sell is service."

QUESTIONS

1. What disadvantages do you see in TeleMart from the consumers' viewpoint?
2. What advantages? How would you evaluate TeleMart's proposed operation, on balance, from the consumers' perspective?
3. Would you make any changes in the proposed operation?
4. Do you agree with the promotional efforts, or would you change them?
5. What is your estimate of the viability and potential for this marketing innovation?

Case 21
The Red Fox—
Breakeven Study
of a Restaurant
Venture[1]

Douglas Robinson was a respected black businessman who had owned a restaurant, The Red Fox, since 1947 in a black neighborhood not far from the downtown area. Through the years, largely due to his friendliness and good food at reasonable prices, the business had prospered, and he had expanded facilities several times.

However, by 1971 sales were declining. Partly this reflected deterioration of the neighborhood. About half of the business came from the surrounding area, and Mr. Robinson thought that this part of the business had probably reached its full potential since the low income of the black families living there precluded their frequent eating out. Heretofore, an important part of the business of the Red Fox was luncheon business by downtown businessmen attracted by the good food and reasonable prices. But the progressive deterioration of the neighborhood was resulting in less and less of this business.

Mr. Robinson recognized that his restaurant was at a critical point, and he was seeking new ways to revitalize the business. A move to another location seemed desirable, but there was the problem of building up a clientele all over again, plus considerable new investment in facilities that would be required. However, he could think of no way to rejuvenate the faltering business in its present location. The alternative was to accept stagnation and decline, and eventually, dissolution of the business.

[1] Case adapted from one prepared by Professor Donald W. Scotton, Cleveland State University.

Then an opportunity presented itself to relocate in a large and modern apartment complex being built near the center of the business district. The buildings would contain some 1100 apartments when finished; these would be luxury apartments renting from $150 to $500 per month, appealing to young business and professional singles, married couples generally without children, and well-to-do retirees. A shopping mall was located between two 20-story tower buildings, and here the new restaurant could be located. (Mr. Robinson planned to continue to use the name Red Fox.)

Based on the number of residents, plus the noon business which he hoped to reestablish, Mr. Robinson estimated that he should realize $200,000 sales annually. He would have to sign a 10-year lease, the terms as follows:

Base rent, $900 a month for the first 3 years;
$1,000 a month after the first 3 years.

Other expenses—for maintainence, utilities, and joint advertising of the mall—were expected to add $100 a month.

A considerable investment would have to be put into the proposed restaurant. Estimated decorating, fixtures, and equipment came to $190,000. This seemed no problem although interest charges would run $22,000 a year. The investment would depreciate at 10 percent per year. Based on his past experience, Mr. Robinson calculated that he should be able to maintain a 50 percent margin on sales (that is, the cost of the food would be about half what it is sold for). Variable expenses for the restaurant and kitchen should amount to 30 percent, which would mean that 20 percent of sales should be available for overhead and any profits.

QUESTIONS

1. Compute a breakeven point in dollar sales.
2. Based on Mr. Robinson's estimate of sales, should he open the new restaurant?
3. Are there other factors which bear on this decision?
4. What do you think of his decision to use the same name for the proposed new restaurant?

PART IV

Social and Environmental Issues

Case 22
Cuyahoga Sheltered Industries, Inc.— Marketing a Service

Dr. White, director of Cuyahoga Sheltered Industries, Inc. (CSI) is concerned about the present and future situation of his four sheltered workshops. A sheltered workshop is a nonprofit establishment providing employment to persons who, because of their physical, mental, social, or emotional handicaps, are unable to find employment in competitive industry. CSI performs subcontract work (that is, work done in a sheltered workshop to the specifications of a contractor) on a competitive bidding basis for businesses in the Cleveland area. CSI is funded by the Cuyahoga County Board of Mental Retardation (CCBMR).

Lately the four workshop managers have been reporting to Dr. White that they have not been receiving as much work from their steady customers as usual, and that they have received only a few new contracts. Although the basic goal of CSI is rehabilitation, subcontract work is the means by which the workshops accomplish their objectives, and the inability to provide continuous and meaningful employment defeats the very purpose of their existence.

CSI presently employs one full-time contract procurement person, Bill Rice, to seek contracts for all four workshops. Rice is fifty-four years old and had worked in sales in the garment industry for twenty years before joining CSI five years ago. In addition, one of the workshops has a nonprofit board of directors, composed of members of the business community, that aids the shop in procuring contracts.

Rice makes from twenty to forty blind calls per day to local businesses, and these produce an average of two leads. He then follows these leads up with visits to the firms and bids on the work to be done. Regarding these contacts, Rice says, "But nine out of ten times, CSI can't get the job. Sometimes this is because we can't offer a low enough price, but more often it's because we can't do the work due to lack of proper machinery, lack of adequate personnel skill, inability to meet production demands, or quality control requirements. CSI needs to purchase more equipment and thus be able to offer more than just manual labor. For example, packaging has been a good source of work for the retarded, but fewer products are being hand packaged now. Machines that could handle large volume operations would help us get more jobs."

Rice also feels that CSI doesn't do enough advertising and public relations work: "I have to spend too much time explaining the CSI program to potential customers and trying to convince them that the mentally retarded can perform skillfully enough to handle their contracts."

CSI has never done any advertising or sales promotion. The CCBMR has a one-person public relations department that has public relations responsibility for all phases of the county program for the retarded. Most of the efforts are directed to publicizing the schools. However, a brochure was produced four years before which presented all the preliminary information a prospective customer might need to know about what CSI does and how it can help the businessman. Bill Rice distributes these to potential customers he calls upon. Occasionally an article about CSI has appeared in the newspapers.

There is some competition in the sheltered industry market from such organizations as Goodwill, Society for the Blind, and United Cerebral Palsy Workshop. However, it is generally agreed that there should be enough work for all.

The workshop managers state that they are willing to take on a wide variety of jobs and would be willing to invest in specialized machinery—such as packaging equipment—if they could be assured of even a moderate return on the investment. They do not think Bill Rice is bringing in the right type of work for their shops, and state that he is only producing 25 percent to 50 percent of the contracts they have. Many of the best contracts are obtained through efforts of the workshop managers themselves (they claim that sometimes these contacts are made on their own time), and also by the board of directors of the one workshop. All the managers say they would like to do more to promote their program, but time just doesn't allow.

QUESTIONS

1. Dr. White has scheduled a meeting to discuss the problem of dwindling contracts and to consider what might be done in the future to increase contract procurement. What suggestions do you have?

Case 23
Stanley's Furniture and Appliance Store— Marketing Practices in the Ghetto

Steve Stanley graduated with a degree in business administration from a prominent university. His father had long been trying to persuade him to come into the family business, which was a furniture and appliance store in New York's Harlem. With the father nearing sixty, he wanted to slow down from the six-day a week job and be able to gradually turn responsibility over to the son. Despite the very real fact that the profits from this store gave the Stanley family a comfortable living in an affluent suburb and had enabled Steve to graduate from a prestigious university, certain aspects of his father's operation troubled him badly. "This is the only way that business can be done in the ghetto," his father had always dogmatically maintained.

The Stanley Store occupies a prestige location on a corner. Consequently, it has a double exposure of windows: two windows facing each of the two moderately busy intersecting streets. Mr. Stanley believes this permits him to almost double his sales over what he would have with a noncorner location. And he uses his windows to advantage. One window on each side of the corner entrance usually features a complete room of brightly colored furniture—perhaps a $77 bedroom suite, or a complete living room for "only $99." The other two windows often do not carry price tags, but display color TV sets and other appliances, along with big signs, "Friendly, Easy Credit!" Sale streamers are pasted on all four windows and on the doors as well. "Our customers want to shop where they feel welcome, where there is always a 'sale,' and, of course, where they can buy on time."

Inside the store most merchandise does not carry a price tag. "I find it better to be somewhat flexible in my pricing," Mr. Stanley acknowledges. "Some people can't afford as much as some others, so I try to adjust to what I think they can afford—within limits." Steve knows that his father charges high prices—sometimes he is appalled at the customary $100 to $200 difference over what a downtown department store might charge. For example, a black-and-white TV set was sold one day while he was in the store for $349; he recalled having seen the same brand and model displayed for $169 in one of the larger downtown stores. "I have to charge more," his father explained. "I only buy these one at a time and so pay a lot more. Then my credit losses—most customers buy on credit—run up to 25 percent. My insurance charges are higher. I have to worry about being robbed. All these add to my costs of doing business."

The customers are mostly black, with a scattering of Puerto Rican. Most of them have low-paying jobs and are or have been on welfare. They do not have cash, and if they are to buy any furniture or appliances, it must be done on credit. Yet they are poor credit risks; the bigger downtown stores refuse to take the risk. But Stanley's is willing to take this risk, for a fee (as are most other stores in the ghetto).

Mr. Stanley pushes his installment sales, even though he doesn't believe the 18 percent annual interest rate—the maximum allowed by law—yields much if any profit, since most of this is eaten up by collection costs, attorney's fees, and uncollectable account losses. "We push this because every installment customer is a future customer. He has to come into the store to make his weekly or monthly payments. Often, he sees something else to add to his account." The office is on the second floor; thereby, the customer has to go all through the store to make his payment.

While bad debt losses run fairly high (20–25 percent), considering the type of customer and the low income, this is probably quite moderate. Stanley does not discount his installment contracts to a finance company, preferring to make his own collections. He is reluctant to grant credit to those who do not have wages that can be attached in the event of non-payment, although he will consider doing business with welfare recipients and employees of the federal government and others who cannot be garnished, if they have a large downpayment. He attempts to be firm but flexible in his collection methods. If a customer occasionally misses a payment, he will not immediately repossess, but will use a polite reminder letter. In this way he hopes to not lose a customer, and to even be sympathetic to any unusual problems of the customer. However, dunning can become much harsher. Threatening letters will be used, as well as phone calls (if the customer has a phone). The employer may also be contacted, and be reminded of the extra bookkeeping involved if a garnishment is required, and the suggestion made that the employer use some persuasion to get his delinquent employee to pay up. There are no qualms about taking a case to court. Mr. Stanley wins most of these cases by default since the customers are generally unfamiliar with legal procedures.

Another aspect of the operation troubled Steve Stanley. The four salesmen his father employs are masters of the "bait and switch," in which the customer coming in for the $99 living room set (displayed in the window) will be adroitly "switched" to a higher-priced, better-profit set. "I would not keep these men if they could not use the hard sell. Our customers need a push. They appreciate having their decisions made for them. If we don't do it here, they'll go to some other store, and someone else will give them the hard sell," as Mr. Stanley responds.

Steve observed that if one salesman was not able to provide the necessary sales-culmination impetus with a particularly difficult customer, then a wink to another salesman—or sometimes to Mr. Stanley—would result in turning the customer over to someone else to prevent a "hasty" departure. This "tossover" technique often is effective in crumbling a customer's defenses. As Steve's father says, "We only get 10 to 12 customers a normal day in here; we can't let any of them get away. Competition is too keen. There are 40 or more stores like us in this area."

Steve's father does very little advertising. Most of the promotional efforts are done through window displays that emphasize 50 percent discounts and other price-appealing "bargains." Mr. Stanley explains that most of the Puerto Rican customers cannot read English (some cannot even speak it), while many of the blacks are not able to read, or else seldom buy a newspaper.

Steve pondered the decision of whether to join his father. He felt ashamed of some of the practices his father and other ghetto merchants were using—"there must be a better way." At the same time, the low turnover, the high costs of insurance, the need to furnish credit, yet the substantial credit risks, all these were obstacles in using more "legitimate" methods of operation. There was always the danger of rioting and looting —although this seemed to be lessening in the last few years; however, robberies and muggings were increasing. And there was a social onus in being a ghetto merchant: you were criticized by your neighbors, and often hated by your customers for selling shoddy goods and forcing the ever-lasting monthly payment.

QUESTIONS

1. What do you think Steve's decision should be? Why?

2. Would you change the Stanley operation? How?

3. Where would you draw the line regarding ethical conduct in this case?

4. How can more "legitimate" marketing practices be viable in the ghetto environment?

Case 24
Indian Springs Lakes— Environmental Problems of a Land Developer

Indian Springs Lakes (ISL) was started by a land developer in early 1960 at a time when interest in vacation lots—second homes—was becoming apparent. A typical ISL project had a lake, a country club with a golf course and "Olympic" swimming pool, as well as certain other amenities, such as skiing at certain sites. The price for an average one-third to one-half acre lot was $9,000, although this varied according to lot size and location, with waterfront property and lots on the golf course being considerably higher. The average project was developed to yield 3,000 to 4,000 lots.

By 1970 there were 26 projects under way from the East Coast to Hawaii. However, the rate of expansion had slowed: only two new projects were begun in 1970, instead of six which had been planned. In most cases ecological concerns by the interested public were the causes of this deviation from plans.

For example, ISL had planned a recreational community on the shore of Lake Lionel, a small lake a hundred miles from Portland, Oregon. But Lake Lionel was the water supply for a nearby town; the threat of 2,000 new septic tanks draining into their lake aroused vigorous opposition on the part of these townspeople. ISL, discouraged by the consequent need to install a sewage system, abandoned the project entirely although it had already spent $500,000 in land options and planning studies.

Other projects encountered similar difficulties. A planned project in Maine was dropped upon the advice of a consulting ecologist anticipating the reaction of area residents. A project in New York was delayed at least until 1972 in another squabble over sewage treatment. In other projects, local and state authorities insisted on certain environmental features being preserved, thereby raising costs sharply. Thus to compensate for the ecological effects of a project near Seattle, more than $200,000 had to be spent to provide fish spawning beds.

A 9,000-acre site on Lake Tahoe, acquired in 1968, was stalled as planning agencies repeatedly increased environmental safeguard requirements. As a result, development costs rose to more than 50 percent of the project's market value; development costs in a normal situation should be no more than one-third of market value. A Massachusetts project also encountered serious additional development costs in converting from septic tank sewage disposal to a chemical and filtration means of sewage treatment. As a result of this additional $3-million expenditure, no profits were anticipated from this project.

Because of these experiences, understandably, the executives of ISL are upset and off balance: "We are being plagued by this environmental thing. It's costing us a lot of money. We hope that the environmentalists will get tired after a while. Until then, we'll just have to avoid ecologically sensitive areas even though choice property locations may have to be ignored. The future seems unsure." Not only were development and land acquisition costs steadily rising, but there were indications that demand may also be tapering off (or at least being more satiated as more developers enter the market). Evident of a slowing demand, in the state of California only 3 percent of all recreational lots sold in recent years have had houses built on them.

ISL's promotional efforts usually consist of mailing brochures or "invitation to visit" letters, or telephone contacts to affluent middle class and upper middle class persons. A favorite device is to offer free dinners to these prospective clients, followed by a sales "pitch" complete with movies of other successful projects. Once a prospect has been induced to visit the particular project site (often trading stamps or free gifts are offered to encourage this), hard sell is utilized. A strong attempt is made to create a sense of "urgency," that any presently available lot is imminently in danger of being sold by another salesman to someone else. Accordingly, the salesmen's cars are equipped with two-way radios by which they can radio the central "communications" office to tensely ask whether such and such a lot is still "available."

Sales for 1970 decreased almost 20 percent from the $160-million level set in 1969. At the beginning of the year, the company had aimed for $200 million in sales for 1970.

QUESTIONS

1. Evaluate the marketing strategy.
2. Evaluate the marketing research.
3. What social and ethical considerations are involved here?
4. What direction should the company take at this point?

McCabe Chemical Company—
Ecological Problems
Facing a Small Manufacturer

Malcolm McCabe, an industrial chemist, founded the McCabe Chemical Company in 1952. In the early 1950s plastics was one of the fastest-growing industries in the nation. McCabe had developed several relatively inexpensive processes for producing vinyl stabilizers and plasticizers which are essential in the production of vinyl plastics and certain other plastic compounds. Since he had some available capital and had patent protection, he decided to start his own company and market the products to producers of finished plastic products.

The company grew fast; by the late 1950s it had several hundred factory and office personnel in its main plant in New York City. By the early 1960s it had opened branches in Japan, France, England, and Canada. A wholly owned subsidiary had been established and this specialized in producing peroxide products and certain specialty products. In 1968, Mr. McCabe decided to sell the company to Standard Chemicals, a major chemical firm, for approximately $25 million. He was appointed a vice-president of Standard and a member of its board of directors. While some management shifts occurred, the McCabe Division continued to operate rather autonomously from the rest of Standard Chemical Company.

From its inception, McCabe had experienced few marketing problems. It had a product line which was in considerable demand and, since it sold only to other manufacturers, no lengthy marketing channel was required. A full-time staff of twelve salesmen and a sales manager—all of whom were chemists—was used to contact other manufacturers directly. Since the firm's products did not reach the retail market, and since they were of interest only to certain specialized manufacturers, little advertising was needed. The company did use some "image" advertising in selected trade journals: "We believe in a soft-sell approach, both on the part of our sales representatives, and in what advertising we do. We occasionally like to run a short series of ads to put forth the McCabe name and some of the products we have—we think this makes the salesmens' job a little easier."

McCabe relied on large customers and did 70 percent of its business with three large accounts, such as Monsanto Chemical. However, it continually sought to expand its market. A staff of 20 chemists and chemical engineers was engaged in finding new products and in research and development. The company found an effective way to introduce its new products was to ship samples to present and potential customers. The recipients were then free to experiment with these products and to run tests of their own on them, thereby not having to rely on the producer's performance specifications.

Up until 1970 the McCabe Chemical Company had carved out a niche which seemed comfortable and enduring. But then a problem arose with its roots in ecology and which now threatened the viability of McCabe.

McCabe's main plant was in New York City, and several aspects of the operation came under the close scrutiny of New York's Department of Air Resources. It was found to be in violation of several of the newly established regulations concerning smoke and particulate emissions. While the company had previously equipped some of the reactors and vents with various emission control devices, apparently these were not sufficient. Exacerbating the problem was the site of this plant: while located in an industrial area, it was close enough to residential developments to affect them. Some of the main problem areas cited by the Department of Air Resources were

1. Vacuum drying of stabilizers—even though gas treatment devices had been installed, some octyl alcohol was still being emitted.
2. Stripping of hydrocarbons—even though condenser and scrubber types of treatment apparatus were being used, hydrocarbons were still being emitted into the air.
3. Oxidation of hydrocarbons—these emissions were also occurring, despite condenser and demister control devices being used.
4. Air oxidation of cadmium—cadmium oxide was being emitted even though a dust-collector device had been installed.

After lengthy discussions and some research, the McCabe executives believed that the first three of the above problem areas could be brought within the city regulations fairly easily and without prohibitive costs. But the cadmium operations were another matter entirely.

The City of New York was planning to enact a regulation banning all cadmium emissions. This was a consequence of recent findings that cadmium was a very dangerous element to have present in the air or water. A particularly dangerous property of cadmium is its accumulating in the body over a long period of time and displacing materials vital to the life process. In Japan cadmium poisoning had reached the point that a series of deaths occurred, and these were traced to the metal-contaminating water coming from a mining plant. In the United States, toxic cadmium metal in concentrations some federal health officials felt was well above safe levels had been found in oysters taken along the Atlantic Coast from Maine to North Carolina.

In early 1971 when this problem initially confronted McCabe, it was uncertain just when the regulation banning cadmium emission would come into effect. The probability was that it would not for a year or more; but this could come sooner and the McCabe executives felt that they should be prepared for this eventuality.

This poses the problem facing McCabe: cadmium is essential in the production of about 25 percent of McCabe's products; there is no known substitute for cadmium at this time.

QUESTIONS

1. Faced with this situation, what alternatives do you see McCabe Chemical Division as having?
2. What should be management's response to this situation?
3. Do you think the company is being unfairly victimized?

INDEXES

NAME INDEX

A

Aamco, 107, 108
Adams, J. K., 141
Adler, Lee, 176, 264, 265, 277
Alexander, Ralph S., 149, 173, 253
Allvine, Fred C., 51, 71, 338, 340
Ambrose, David M., 157
Andersen, R. Clifton, 272
Andrews, Frederick, 469
Andrus, Roman R., 31
Anthony, Robert N., 386
Appel, David L., 51
Arm & Hammer, 30
Armstrong, Gary M., 127
Armstrong, J. Scott, 212
Arndt, Johan, 130, 196
Asch, Solomon E., 129
Ash, Roy L., 82
Audubon Magazine, 307
Austin, J. Paul, 446
Auto-Train, 31
Avon Products, 445, 446

B

Baker, Henry G., 206, 207
Ballou, Ronald H., 412
Banks, Seymour, 180, 189
Barger, Harold, 495
Barksdale, Hiram C., 40
Bauer, R. A., 258
Bayton, James A., 137
Beckman, M. D., 124
Belasco, J. A., 356
Beldo, Leslie A., 194
Bell, Martin L., 40
Bell Telephone, 92, 93
Bellows, Roger, 354
Berelson, B. R., 140, 141
Berenson, Conrad, 176

Bishop, James, Jr., 14
Blackwell, Roger D., 145, 146, 147, 293
Blankenship, Albert B., 154, 311
Blankertz, Donald F., 173
Bogart, Leo, 136, 294, 295
Borden, Neil H., 220, 287, 300
Boring, R. A., 383
Botthof, C. Laury, 444
Bourne Francis, S., 125
Bowen, Howard R., 77
Bowersox, D. J., 288, 399
Boyd, Harper W., Jr., 170, 171, 435
Bratt E. C., 159
Brehm, J. W., 145
Bridges, S. Powell, 283
Brien, Richard H., 176
Bright, James, 157
Bristol-Myers Co., 108, 296, 297
Britt, Steuart Henderson, 136
Brody, Robert P., 212
Brooks, J., 141
Bruce, Grady D., 124
Bucklin, Louis P., 270
Burnett, Leo, 30
Burton, John, 477, 479
Burton, Philip Ward, 312
Buskirk, Richard H., 354, 462, 476
Buzzell, R. D., 461
Bybee, H. Malcolm, 234

C

Campbell, Roy H., 320, 322
Campbell Soup Co., 12, 13
Cannell, C. F., 140
Carmone, Frank J., 200
Carper, Jean, 14, 76
Carter, R. F., 140
Chambers, John C., 160

573

Grant Co., W. T., 209, 210
Green, Robert, 82, 124
Green, Paul E., 200
Greenberg, Herbert M., 347, 353, 355
Gross, Walter, 149
Grown, James K., 320
Gulf Oil Co., 19
Guttman, I., 145

H

Haire, Mason, 196
Hall, Edward T., 122
Hamm, B. Curtis, 137
Handel, Gerald, 258
Hanna, Missim, 219
Haring, Albert, 360
Hart, Philip A., 335
Hartley, Robert F., 216, 354
Haskins, J. B., 300
Hattwick, Melvin S., 302
Hawkins, Del I., 146
Hawkins, Edward R., 382
Heidingsfield, M. S., 311
Hendon, Donald W., 250
Herrmann, Robert O., 476
Hershey Foods, 332, 426
Heskett, J. L., 417
Higginbotham, James, 477, 479
Hill, Richard M., 149
Hinkle, Charles L., 342
Hise, Richard T., 40
Hoffman-La Roche Co., 439, 440
Hollander, Sidney, Jr., 173
Hollander, Stanley C., 344
Hollingsworth, H. L., 354
Honda Co., 227, 228
Hoover Co., 273
Houston, Michael J., 394
Howard, John A., 322
Howard, Marshall C., 111
Hubbard, Henry, 14
Huegy, H. W., 382, 400
Hughes, Jonathan, 34
Hugli, W. C., Jr., 300
Hunt, Shelby D., 283
Hyman, G., 140

I

International Telephone & Telegraph, 431
Isakson, Hans R., 394

J

Jahoda, Marie, 191
Jain, S. C., 133
Jensen, Walter, Jr., 239
Jolson, Marvin A., 347

K

Kaish, Stanley, 242
Kangun, Norman, 477, 479
Kanter, Donald, 294
Kaplan, A. D. H., 372, 373
Kassarjian, Harold W., 129, 131, 139
Katona, George, 14
Keegan, Warren J., 436, 437, 438
Kelley, Eugene J., 200, 208
Kendall, C. L., 94
Kentucky Fried Chicken, 37
King, Charles W., 128
King, William R., 176
Kizalbash, A. H., 219
Kleimenhagen, Arno K., 242
Kollat, David T., 145, 146, 147
Korvette Co., 35, 36
Kotler, Philip, 213, 219, 229, 232, 233, 244, 274, 358
Kriesberg, Martin, 398
Krieser, Gene, 394
Kuehl, Philip G., 325
Kuehn, Alfred A., 196, 197, 318

L

Lamont, Douglas F., 435
Lansillotti, Robert F., 372, 373
Lavidge, Robert J., 41
Lazarsfeld, P. F., 140
Lazer, William, 5, 510,
Lazo, Hector, 40
Leavitt, Harold J., 234
Lele, Uma J., 39
Lestoil, 284
Lever Bros., 261, 262
Levitt, Theodore, 83, 350
Levy, Sidney J., 132, 219, 229, 232, 233
Lewis, Edwin H., 271, 287, 299, 300, 458
Lichtenstein, Stanley, 432
Lipson, Harry A., 435
Literary Digest, 155
Little, Robert W., 287, 288
Lockley, Lawrence C., 154
Loen, R. O., 364
Lopata, Richard S., 62

LoSciuto, Leonard A., 146
Loudenback, Lynn J., 240
Louis, Arthur M., 81
Luck, David J., 234, 318

M

MacDonald, J. C., 140
Magnuson, Warren G., 14, 76
Mahoney, Tom, 24
Malenbaum, W. F., 493
Mandell, Maurice I., 312
Manischewitz, D. Beryl, 85
Margolius, Sidney, 14, 85
Market Research Corporation of
    America, 454, 455
Marshall, Kenneth, 412
Martineau, Pierre, 131, 132
Maslow, A. H., 137
Mason, Joseph B., 104
Mathews, H. Lee, 132, 133
Maurizi, Alex R., 394
Mayer, David, 347, 353, 355
Mayer, Morris L., 104
Maytag Co., 214, 215
Mazis, Michael, 82
Mazze, Edward M., 239
McCarthy, E. Jerome, 220, 288
McClelland, W. G., 40
McConnell, J. Douglas, 383
McConnell, J. V., 141
McCosh, Andrew M., 459
McFall, John, 137
McGarry, Edmund D., 290
McGuire, Joseph W., 83
McNeal, E. B., 141
McNeal, James U., 463
McPhee, W. N., 140
Mead, Richard R., 153, 154
Meeker, Marcia, 131
Mertes, John E., 242
Merton, R. K., 128
Midas Muffler Co., 59
Millar, Frank I., 38
Miller, Clyde R., 298
Miller, J. Robert, 312
Mindak, William A., 192, 234
Mitchell, R. V., 382, 400
Miyashita, Sally, 394
Monroe, Kent B., 383
Montgomery, David B., 318
Morrill, John E., 322
Morris, Malcolm L., 360
Mortimer, Charles G., 38

Morton, Michael S., 459
Moyer, Reed, 149, 435
Mullick, Satinder K., 160
Myers, James H., 125, 131, 153, 154

N

Nader, Ralph, 239, 476, 477, 507
Namias, Jean, 158
Neuschel, R. P., 417
Nevin, John H., 283
Newman, Joseph W., 141, 147
Newman, William H., 171
Newton, Derek A., 363
Nielsen, A. C. Co., 454, 455
Nielsen, A. C., Jr., 315, 341

O

O'Connor, Neal W., 322
Orbeck, E. A., 104
Osborn, Alex F., 32
Osgood, Charles E., 192
Oshikawa, S., 146
Oxenfeldt, Alfred R., 87, 88, 91, 92, 352,
    391, 465

P

Packard, Vance, 509
Parks, Henry G., 72, 73
Patterson, James M., 86
Pechmann, Frederick Von, 196
Penney, J. C., 35, 36
Perdue, Frank, 4
Perkins, Donald S., 482
Perloff, Robert, 146
Peters, William H., 133
Peterson, Esther, 479
Pier I Imports, 19, 20
Pinto, David, 487, 489
Plummer, Joseph T., 212
Porter, Sylvia, 113
Postal Service, U. S., 230, 231
Prasad, V. Kanti, 132
Procter & Gamble Co., 105, 261, 262,
    296, 297

R

Rados, David J., 240
Rainwater, Lee, 258
Ray, M., 136
Reynolds, Fred D., 138
Reynolds, William H., 125, 131

SUBJECT INDEX

caveat emptor, 14, 78
Celler-Kefauver Antimerger Act, 99,
    104–105
chains, 48
  chain store taxes, 110
  voluntary chains, 62, 68–69
channel
  conflicts, 286–87
  deficiencies, 290–91
  factors affecting choice of, 280–85
  importance of decisions, 273–75
  in foreign markets, 440–41
  leadership, 287–88
  problems of new producers, 283–85
  pushing and pulling policies, 285–86
  trends, 288–89
channels of distribution, 44–45, 269–73
class, social, 131–33
class rates, 408
Clayton Act, 99, 101, 105
cluster sample, 182
coercive power of federal government,
    115–16
cognitive dissonance, 144–46
coincidental surveys, 319
collusion, 370
commissary stores, 48
commission merchants, 61
commodity rates, 408–409
common carriers, 408
comparative advertising, 326
component parts, 241
computers, 199–200
conditioning, 134–35
conflicts in distribution channels, 286–
    87
conformity, 128–29
conglomerate merger, 104–105
consignment selling, 283
consumer clinic, 168–69, 189
consumer goods, 241–42, 278
consumer jury, 189
consumer panel, 168–69, 464
Consumer Product Safety Act, 239
consumer protection laws, 105–10
consumer sovereignty, 473–74, 512
consumer use tests, 168–69
consumerism, 14, 32–33, 475–79
containerization, 404–406
contract carriers, 408
contribution to margin, 460–61
controllable factors, 220–22
convenience goods, 241–42

convenience sample, 183
coops, 101–102
corporate identity programs, 223–24
corrective advertising, 325
costs
  average, 385
  fixed, 385
  marginal, 385
  sunk, 386
  variable, 385
counter-commercials, 325
cultural influences, 122–23
cumulative discounts, 377
customer attitude surveys, 463–64
customer satisfaction, measures of,
    462–64
customer service, 86–95, 499–500
  overtones, 81–92
customer or consumer orientation, 38–39

D

data
  primary, 184–89
  secondary, 184–85
dealer brands, 255–58
deceptive advertising, 503–505
deceptive packaging, 503
delivered pricing, 375
Delphi technique, 157
demand
  derived, 279
  elasticity, 386–87
demand-backward pricing, 387
demarketing, 219
department stores, 49
dependence effect, 509
derived demand, 279
desk jobber, 60
detail men, 348
differentiation, 4, 217–18
diffusion of innovation, 513–14
discount catalog showrooms, 49
discount stores, 49, 56, 274–75
discounts, 376–77
dissociative reference groups, 125
dissonance, 144–46
distribution-center concept, 412–13
distribution cost analysis, 458–62
diversion in transit, 402–403
drop-shipper, 60
dumping, 438
durable goods, 241

E

early adopters, 126–28
ecological issues, 486–90
econometric models, 159
economic man, 121
economic motives, and patronage, 138
economic shoppers, 138
"80–20" principle, 458–59
electrical-equipment manufacturers
   conspiracy, 100
environmental interface of marketing,
   486–90
equilibrium price, 371
ethical shoppers, 138
ethics, 76–77
   codes of, 80–81
ethnic influence, 122–23
European Economic Community
   (Common Market), 433
evaluating performance
   measuring customer satisfaction,
      462–64
   objectives, 449–50
   social audit, 468–69
   types of analyses, 453
exception rates, 409
exchange controls, 430
exchange process, 46
exclusive distribution, 276–78, 282–83
experimentation, 184, 187–89
export subsidies, 432

F

factors, 61
fad, 251
Fair Packaging and Labeling Act, 106
fair trade, 110–11, 380–81
family brand, 258
family influence, 124
farmers' markets, 497
fashion, 128–29, 251
fashion goods, 251–53
fast freight, 402
federal consumer-protection laws,
   105–109
Federal Trade Commission (FTC), 100–
   101, 107–108, 112–14, 324–26
Federal Trade Commission Act, 99–100
fishyback, 402
F.O.B., 375
Food, Drug, and Cosmetic Act, 106
food brokers, 64

forecasting sales, 156–60
franchise operations, 48, 68–70
freight absorption pricing, 375
freight forwarders, 407
full-cost approach, 459
functional cost accounts, 459–60
functional discounts, 376
functions, marketing, 45–46
Fur Products Labeling Act, 106

G

gamesmanship, 340–41
general-specific-general cycle, 54–55
generic brand name, 255
geographic pricing, 375
ghetto markets, 479–86
good-faith defense, 103
Green River ordinances, 110

H

habit, 135, 147
hierarchy of needs, 137
horizontal integration, 104–105

I

iceberg principle, 456
impulse buying, 142–43
indirect action advertising, 302
industrial buying, 147–50
industrial goods, 240–41, 278–80
information systems, 175–76
innovative-thinking, 30–32
innovators, 33–37
   in new product adoption, 126–28
installations, 240
institutional advertising, 301
institutional convenience, 24–25
integration
   horizontal, 104–105
   vertical, 104–105
intensive distribution, 276–78
intermediate customers, 147–50
international marketing
   challenges, 446–47
   channels of distribution, 440–41
   incentives, 424–25
   marketing research, 435
   organization, 433–35
   physical distribution, 441–42
   pricing, 438–40
   product planning, 436–38
   promotion, 442–46
   scope, 423–24

N

national brand, 255–58
nationalism, 429–30
needs, 136–37
  hierarchy of, 137
new products
  dangers and rewards, 258–62
  development, 262–65
Nielsen audimeter, 170–71, 185, 319
noncumulative discounts, 377
nondurable goods, 242
nonprice competition, 371–72
nonprobability sample, 182–83
nonproduct marketing, 228–35
nonsigner's clause, 104
nonstore retailers, 50
nostalgia, effect of, 250–51

O

objective and task method, 315
objectives of the firm, 208–10
observation method, 185
obsolescence, product, 252–53
odd pricing, 382
oligopoly, 369–71
ombudsman, 95
one-price policy, 374
operations research (OR), 196–99
opinion leaders, 129–31
optimization, 226–27
order-call ratio, 361–62
outdoor advertising, 309–10

P

packaging, 333–36
panels, 168–69, 464
passive dictation, 124
patent protection, 249, 254–55
patronage factors, 52
payoff, of research, 173–74
penetration pricing, 389–90
perception
  selective, 139–41
  subliminal, 141
performance analysis, marketing,
  453–65
personal interview surveys, 186
personalizing shoppers, 138
personal selling
  challenges, 345–47
  compensation, 357–58

importance, 344–45
limitations, 352–53
measuring effectiveness, 360–62
motivation of salespeople, 359–60
selecting salesforce, 353–56
supervision, 358–59
training, 356–57
types of sales jobs, 347–50
persuasion, 298
petroleum bulk plants and terminals, 61
physical distribution, 397–422
  in international markets, 441–42
physical distribution manager, 420–21
piggyback service, 402
pioneering advertising, 302–303
pipelines, 406
place utility, 400
planned obsolescence, 506
planning, 205–207
point-of-purchase displays, 142–44,
  330–32
pool cars, 402
population, in sampling, 183–84
positioning advertising, 312–13
post exchange (PX), 48
postage stamp pricing, 375
prestige pricing, 382–83
price
  determination
    cost-oriented, 385–86
    demand-oriented, 386–87
  discrimination, 102–103
  fixing, 99–100
  guarantees, 379
  leadership, 370–71
  lining, 381
  maintenance policies, 380–81
  unit, 85, 394–95
pricing
  administered, 368–69
  bait and switch, 381
  basing point, 375–76
  demand-backward, 387
  discounts and promotional, 376–77
  F.O.B., 375
  in foreign markets, 438–40
  freight absorption, 375
  geographic, 375
  government-controlled, 369
  inverted, 368
  market pricing, 367–68
  negotiated, 391–92
  objectives, 372–73

services, 242
Sherman Act, 98–101, 111
shopping goods, 241–42
simple random sample, 181
skimming pricing, 289–90
small business
   competitive advantages, 65–66
   competitive disadvantages, 66–67
   minority enterprises, 71–73
   opportunities, 67–71
   public concern, 65
Small Business Administration (SBA), 65, 72
social audit, 468–69
social class, 131–33
   and store patronage, 132
social influences, 124–33
social responsibility, 81–84
social responsiveness (defined), 84–86
Spanish-speaking market, 123
specialty goods, 241–42
specialty stores, 49
stamps, trading 337–40
Standard Industrial Classification System (SIC), 1865–67
status quo objectives, 210
storage, 409–12
stratified sample, 182
style, 251
supermarkets, 49
supplies, 241
survey
   mail, 186–87
   methods, 186
   personal interview, 186
   telephone, 186
"Survey of Buying Power," 161–65
symbiotic relationship, 277, 286

T

target market, 210
target return, 372–73
tariffs, 429
tastemakers, 126–27
technical specialists, 348
telephone survey, 186
test marketing, 167–68
testimonial advertising, 124–25
time utility, 409

total cost approach to physical distribution, 417–19
total-package-procurement (TPP), 393
trade association, 67–68
trade discounts, 376–77
trademark, 255
trading stamps, 337–40
transfer pricing, 439–40
transit privilege, 403
transloading privilege, 403
transportation, 400–401
trend extension, 158
trickle across hypothesis, 128
trickle down hypothesis, 128
trucks, 403–404
truth-in-lending, 85, 106
two-step communication flow, 129–30

U

uncontrollable factors, 224–26
unfair practices acts, 110–11
unit pricing, 85, 394–95
utility, 45–46

V

variable price policy, 374
variety stores, 49
vending machines, 50
vertical integration, 104–105, 288–89
vice-president of consumerism, 94–95
voluntary chains, 62, 68–69

W

warehouses, 411
warranties, 88–90, 501–503
waterways, 404–406
wheel of retailing, 53–54
Wheeler-Lea Amendment, 99–100, 107
wholesalers, 45, 59
   classification, 60–61
   costs, 63–64
   services performed, 59–61
   trend, 61–63

Z

Zip codes, 213
zone pricing, 375
zoning laws, 110